# MATHEMATICS 381

## UNIVERSITY OF NORTH CAROLINA AT CHAPEL HILL

# DISCRETE MATHEMATICS AND ITS APPLICATIONS

## SEVENTH EDITION

### KENNETH H. ROSEN

*Monmouth University*
*(and formerly AT&T Laboratories)*

Mc Graw Hill Education

8 9 0  BRP BRP  17

ISBN-13:  978-1-259-23181-0
ISBN-10:  1-259-23181-X

*Learning Solutions Consultant: Lauren Langley*
*Project Manager: Lynn Nagel*
*Photo Credits: 143026.tif © Digital Vision / Getty Images; 143026a.tif © Digital Vision / Getty Images;*
*19302502.tif © Hemera Technologies*

# Contents

# About the Author

**K**enneth H. Rosen has had a long career as a Distinguished Member of the Technical Staff at AT&T Laboratories in Monmouth County, New Jersey. He currently holds the position of Visiting Research Professor at Monmouth University, where he teaches graduate courses in computer science.

Dr. Rosen received his B.S. in Mathematics from the University of Michigan, Ann Arbor (1972), and his Ph.D. in Mathematics from M.I.T. (1976), where he wrote his thesis in the area of number theory under the direction of Harold Stark. Before joining Bell Laboratories in 1982, he held positions at the University of Colorado, Boulder; The Ohio State University, Columbus; and the University of Maine, Orono, where he was an associate professor of mathematics. While working at AT&T Labs, he taught at Monmouth University, teaching courses in discrete mathematics, coding theory, and data security. He currently teaches courses in algorithm design and in computer security and cryptography.

Dr. Rosen has published numerous articles in professional journals in number theory and in mathematical modeling. He is the author of the widely used *Elementary Number Theory and Its Applications*, published by Pearson, currently in its sixth edition, which has been translated into Chinese. He is also the author of *Discrete Mathematics and Its Applications*, published by McGraw-Hill, currently in its seventh edition. *Discrete Mathematics and Its Applications* has sold more than 350,000 copies in North America during its lifetime, and hundreds of thousands of copies throughout the rest of the world. This book has also been translated into Spanish, French, Greek, Chinese, Vietnamese, and Korean. He is also co-author of *UNIX: The Complete Reference*; *UNIX System V Release 4: An Introduction*; and *Best UNIX Tips Ever*, all published by Osborne McGraw-Hill. These books have sold more than 150,000 copies, with translations into Chinese, German, Spanish, and Italian. Dr. Rosen is also the editor of the *Handbook of Discrete and Combinatorial Mathematics*, published by CRC Press, and he is the advisory editor of the CRC series of books in discrete mathematics, consisting of more than 55 volumes on different aspects of discrete mathematics, most of which are introduced in this book. Dr. Rosen serves as an Associate Editor for the journal *Discrete Mathematics*, where he works with submitted papers in several areas of discrete mathematics, including graph theory, enumeration, and number theory. He is also interested in integrating mathematical software into the educational and professional environments, and worked on several projects with Waterloo Maple Inc.'s Maple$^{TM}$ software in both these areas. Dr. Rosen has also worked with several publishing companies on their homework delivery platforms.

At Bell Laboratories and AT&T Laboratories, Dr. Rosen worked on a wide range of projects, including operations research studies, product line planning for computers and data communications equipment, and technology assessment. He helped plan AT&T's products and services in the area of multimedia, including video communications, speech recognition, speech synthesis, and image networking. He evaluated new technology for use by AT&T and did standards work in the area of image networking. He also invented many new services, and holds more than 55 patents. One of his more interesting projects involved helping evaluate technology for the AT&T attraction that was part of EPCOT Center.

# Preface

In writing this book, I was guided by my long-standing experience and interest in teaching discrete mathematics. For the student, my purpose was to present material in a precise, readable manner, with the concepts and techniques of discrete mathematics clearly presented and demonstrated. My goal was to show the relevance and practicality of discrete mathematics to students, who are often skeptical. I wanted to give students studying computer science all of the mathematical foundations they need for their future studies. I wanted to give mathematics students an understanding of important mathematical concepts together with a sense of why these concepts are important for applications. And most importantly, I wanted to accomplish these goals without watering down the material.

For the instructor, my purpose was to design a flexible, comprehensive teaching tool using proven pedagogical techniques in mathematics. I wanted to provide instructors with a package of materials that they could use to teach discrete mathematics effectively and efficiently in the most appropriate manner for their particular set of students. I hope that I have achieved these goals.

I have been extremely gratified by the tremendous success of this text. The many improvements in the seventh edition have been made possible by the feedback and suggestions of a large number of instructors and students at many of the more than 600 North American schools, and at any many universities in parts of the world, where this book has been successfully used.

This text is designed for a one- or two-term introductory discrete mathematics course taken by students in a wide variety of majors, including mathematics, computer science, and engineering. College algebra is the only explicit prerequisite, although a certain degree of mathematical maturity is needed to study discrete mathematics in a meaningful way. This book has been designed to meet the needs of almost all types of introductory discrete mathematics courses. It is highly flexible and extremely comprehensive. The book is designed not only to be a successful textbook, but also to serve as valuable resource students can consult throughout their studies and professional life.

## Goals of a Discrete Mathematics Course

A discrete mathematics course has more than one purpose. Students should learn a particular set of mathematical facts and how to apply them; more importantly, such a course should teach students how to think logically and mathematically. To achieve these goals, this text stresses mathematical reasoning and the different ways problems are solved. Five important themes are interwoven in this text: mathematical reasoning, combinatorial analysis, discrete structures, algorithmic thinking, and applications and modeling. A successful discrete mathematics course should carefully blend and balance all five themes.

1. *Mathematical Reasoning:* Students must understand mathematical reasoning in order to read, comprehend, and construct mathematical arguments. This text starts with a discussion of mathematical logic, which serves as the foundation for the subsequent discussions of methods of proof. Both the science and the art of constructing proofs are addressed. The technique of mathematical induction is stressed through many different types of examples of such proofs and a careful explanation of why mathematical induction is a valid proof technique.

2. *Combinatorial Analysis:* An important problem-solving skill is the ability to count or enumerate objects. The discussion of enumeration in this book begins with the basic techniques of counting. The stress is on performing combinatorial analysis to solve counting problems and analyze algorithms, not on applying formulae.

3. *Discrete Structures:* A course in discrete mathematics should teach students how to work with discrete structures, which are the abstract mathematical structures used to represent discrete objects and relationships between these objects. These discrete structures include sets, permutations, relations, graphs, trees, and finite-state machines.

4. *Algorithmic Thinking:* Certain classes of problems are solved by the specification of an algorithm. After an algorithm has been described, a computer program can be constructed implementing it. The mathematical portions of this activity, which include the specification of the algorithm, the verification that it works properly, and the analysis of the computer memory and time required to perform it, are all covered in this text. Algorithms are described using both English and an easily understood form of pseudocode.

5. *Applications and Modeling:* Discrete mathematics has applications to almost every conceivable area of study. There are many applications to computer science and data networking in this text, as well as applications to such diverse areas as chemistry, biology, linguistics, geography, business, and the Internet. These applications are natural and important uses of discrete mathematics and are not contrived. Modeling with discrete mathematics is an extremely important problem-solving skill, which students have the opportunity to develop by constructing their own models in some of the exercises.

# Changes in the Seventh Edition

Although the sixth edition has been an extremely effective text, many instructors, including longtime users, have requested changes designed to make this book more effective. I have devoted a significant amount of time and energy to satisfy their requests and I have worked hard to find my own ways to make the book more effective and more compelling to students.

The seventh edition is a major revision, with changes based on input from more than 40 formal reviewers, feedback from students and instructors, and author insights. The result is a new edition that offers an improved organization of topics making the book a more effective teaching tool. Substantial enhancements to the material devoted to logic, algorithms, number theory, and graph theory make this book more flexible and comprehensive. Numerous changes in the seventh edition have been designed to help students more easily learn the material. Additional explanations and examples have been added to clarify material where students often have difficulty. New exercises, both routine and challenging, have been added. Highly relevant applications, including many related to the Internet, to computer science, and to mathematical biology, have been added. The companion website has benefited from extensive development activity and now provides tools students can use to master key concepts and explore the world of discrete mathematics, and many new tools under development will be released in the year following publication of this book.

I hope that instructors will closely examine this new edition to discover how it might meet their needs. Although it is impractical to list all the changes in this edition, a brief list that highlights some key changes, listed by the benefits they provide, may be useful.

## More Flexible Organization

- Applications of propositional logic are found in a new dedicated section, which briefly introduces logic circuits.
- Recurrence relations are now covered in Chapter 2.
- Expanded coverage of countability is now found in a dedicated section in Chapter 2.

- Separate chapters now provide expanded coverage of algorithms (Chapter 3) and number theory and cryptography (Chapter 4).
- More second and third level heads have been used to break sections into smaller coherent parts.

## Tools for Easier Learning

- Difficult discussions and proofs have been marked with the famous Bourbaki "dangerous bend" symbol in the margin.
- New marginal notes make connections, add interesting notes, and provide advice to students.
- More details and added explanations, in both proofs and exposition, make it easier for students to read the book.
- Many new exercises, both routine and challenging, have been added, while many existing exercises have been improved.

## Enhanced Coverage of Logic, Sets, and Proof

- The satisfiability problem is addressed in greater depth, with Sudoku modeled in terms of satisfiability.
- Hilbert's Grand Hotel is used to help explain uncountability.
- Proofs throughout the book have been made more accessible by adding steps and reasons behind these steps.
- A template for proofs by mathematical induction has been added.
- The step that applies the inductive hypothesis in mathematical induction proof is now explicitly noted.

## Algorithms

- The pseudocode used in the book has been updated.
- Explicit coverage of algorithmic paradigms, including brute force, greedy algorithms, and dynamic programing, is now provided.
- Useful rules for big-$O$ estimates of logarithms, powers, and exponential functions have been added.

## Number Theory and Cryptography

- Expanded coverage allows instructors to include just a little or a lot of number theory in their courses.
- The relationship between the **mod** function and congruences has been explained more fully.
- The sieve of Eratosthenes is now introduced earlier in the book.
- Linear congruences and modular inverses are now covered in more detail.
- Applications of number theory, including check digits and hash functions, are covered in great depth.
- A new section on cryptography integrates previous coverage, and the notion of a cryptosystem has been introduced.
- Cryptographic protocols, including digital signatures and key sharing, are now covered.

### Graph Theory

- A structured introduction to graph theory applications has been added.
- More coverage has been devoted to the notion of social networks.
- Applications to the biological sciences and motivating applications for graph isomorphism and planarity have been added.
- Matchings in bipartite graphs are now covered, including Hall's theorem and its proof.
- Coverage of vertex connectivity, edge connectivity, and $n$-connectedness has been added, providing more insight into the connectedness of graphs.

### Enrichment Material

- Many biographies have been expanded and updated, and new biographies of Bellman, Bézout Bienyamé, Cardano, Catalan, Cocks, Cook, Dirac, Hall, Hilbert, Ore, and Tao have been added.
- Historical information has been added throughout the text.
- Numerous updates for latest discoveries have been made.

### Expanded Media

- Extensive effort has been devoted to producing valuable web resources for this book.
- Extra examples in key parts of the text have been provided on companion website.
- Interactive algorithms have been developed, with tools for using them to explore topics and for classroom use.
- A new online ancillary, *The Virtual Discrete Mathematics Tutor*, available in fall 2012, will help students overcome problems learning discrete mathematics.
- A new homework delivery system, available in fall 2012, will provide automated homework for both numerical and conceptual exercises.
- Student assessment modules are available for key concepts.
- Powerpoint transparencies for instructor use have been developed.
- A supplement *Exploring Discrete Mathematics* has been developed, providing extensive support for using Maple™ or Mathematica™ in conjunction with the book.
- An extensive collection of external web links is provided.

## Features of the Book

**ACCESSIBILITY**   This text has proved to be easily read and understood by beginning students. There are no mathematical prerequisites beyond college algebra for almost all the content of the text. Students needing extra help will find tools on the companion website for bringing their mathematical maturity up to the level of the text. The few places in the book where calculus is referred to are explicitly noted. Most students should easily understand the pseudocode used in the text to express algorithms, regardless of whether they have formally studied programming languages. There is no formal computer science prerequisite.

Each chapter begins at an easily understood and accessible level. Once basic mathematical concepts have been carefully developed, more difficult material and applications to other areas of study are presented.

**FLEXIBILITY**    This text has been carefully designed for flexible use. The dependence of chapters on previous material has been minimized. Each chapter is divided into sections of approximately the same length, and each section is divided into subsections that form natural blocks of material for teaching. Instructors can easily pace their lectures using these blocks.

**WRITING STYLE**    The writing style in this book is direct and pragmatic. Precise mathematical language is used without excessive formalism and abstraction. Care has been taken to balance the mix of notation and words in mathematical statements.

**MATHEMATICAL RIGOR AND PRECISION**    All definitions and theorems in this text are stated extremely carefully so that students will appreciate the precision of language and rigor needed in mathematics. Proofs are motivated and developed slowly; their steps are all carefully justified. The axioms used in proofs and the basic properties that follow from them are explicitly described in an appendix, giving students a clear idea of what they can assume in a proof. Recursive definitions are explained and used extensively.

**WORKED EXAMPLES**    Over 800 examples are used to illustrate concepts, relate different topics, and introduce applications. In most examples, a question is first posed, then its solution is presented with the appropriate amount of detail.

**APPLICATIONS**    The applications included in this text demonstrate the utility of discrete mathematics in the solution of real-world problems. This text includes applications to a wide variety of areas, including computer science, data networking, psychology, chemistry, engineering, linguistics, biology, business, and the Internet.

**ALGORITHMS**    Results in discrete mathematics are often expressed in terms of algorithms; hence, key algorithms are introduced in each chapter of the book. These algorithms are expressed in words and in an easily understood form of structured pseudocode, which is described and specified in Appendix 3. The computational complexity of the algorithms in the text is also analyzed at an elementary level.

**HISTORICAL INFORMATION**    The background of many topics is succinctly described in the text. Brief biographies of 83 mathematicians and computer scientists are included as footnotes. These biographies include information about the lives, careers, and accomplishments of these important contributors to discrete mathematics and images, when available, are displayed.

In addition, numerous historical footnotes are included that supplement the historical information in the main body of the text. Efforts have been made to keep the book up-to-date by reflecting the latest discoveries.

**KEY TERMS AND RESULTS**    A list of key terms and results follows each chapter. The key terms include only the most important that students should learn, and not every term defined in the chapter.

**EXERCISES**    There are over 4000 exercises in the text, with many different types of questions posed. There is an ample supply of straightforward exercises that develop basic skills, a large number of intermediate exercises, and many challenging exercises. Exercises are stated clearly and unambiguously, and all are carefully graded for level of difficulty. Exercise sets contain special discussions that develop new concepts not covered in the text, enabling students to discover new ideas through their own work.

Exercises that are somewhat more difficult than average are marked with a single star *; those that are much more challenging are marked with two stars **. Exercises whose solutions require calculus are explicitly noted. Exercises that develop results used in the text are clearly identified with the right pointing hand symbol ☞. Answers or outlined solutions to all odd-numbered exercises are provided at the back of the text. The solutions include proofs in which most of the steps are clearly spelled out.

**REVIEW QUESTIONS**     A set of review questions is provided at the end of each chapter. These questions are designed to help students focus their study on the most important concepts and techniques of that chapter. To answer these questions students need to write long answers, rather than just perform calculations or give short replies.

**SUPPLEMENTARY EXERCISE SETS**     Each chapter is followed by a rich and varied set of supplementary exercises. These exercises are generally more difficult than those in the exercise sets following the sections. The supplementary exercises reinforce the concepts of the chapter and integrate different topics more effectively.

**COMPUTER PROJECTS**     Each chapter is followed by a set of computer projects. The approximately 150 computer projects tie together what students may have learned in computing and in discrete mathematics. Computer projects that are more difficult than average, from both a mathematical and a programming point of view, are marked with a star, and those that are extremely challenging are marked with two stars.

**COMPUTATIONS AND EXPLORATIONS**     A set of computations and explorations is included at the conclusion of each chapter. These exercises (approximately 120 in total) are designed to be completed using existing software tools, such as programs that students or instructors have written or mathematical computation packages such as Maple$^{TM}$ or Mathematica$^{TM}$. Many of these exercises give students the opportunity to uncover new facts and ideas through computation. (Some of these exercises are discussed in the *Exploring Discrete Mathematics* companion workbooks available online.)

**WRITING PROJECTS**     Each chapter is followed by a set of writing projects. To do these projects students need to consult the mathematical literature. Some of these projects are historical in nature and may involve looking up original sources. Others are designed to serve as gateways to new topics and ideas. All are designed to expose students to ideas not covered in depth in the text. These projects tie mathematical concepts together with the writing process and help expose students to possible areas for future study. (Suggested references for these projects can be found online or in the printed *Student's Solutions Guide*.)

**APPENDIXES**     There are three appendixes to the text. The first introduces axioms for real numbers and the positive integers, and illustrates how facts are proved directly from these axioms. The second covers exponential and logarithmic functions, reviewing some basic material used heavily in the course. The third specifies the pseudocode used to describe algorithms in this text.

**SUGGESTED READINGS**     A list of suggested readings for the overall book and for each chapter is provided after the appendices. These suggested readings include books at or below the level of this text, more difficult books, expository articles, and articles in which discoveries in discrete mathematics were originally published. Some of these publications are classics, published many years ago, while others have been published in the last few years.

## How to Use This Book

This text has been carefully written and constructed to support discrete mathematics courses at several levels and with differing foci. The following table identifies the core and optional sections. An introductory one-term course in discrete mathematics at the sophomore level can be based on the core sections of the text, with other sections covered at the discretion of the instructor. A two-term introductory course can include all the optional mathematics sections in addition to the core sections. A course with a strong computer science emphasis can be taught by covering some or all of the optional computer science sections. Instructors can find sample syllabi for a wide range of discrete mathematics courses and teaching suggestions for using each section of the text can be found in the *Instructor's Resource Guide* available on the website for this book.

| Chapter | Core | Optional CS | Optional Math |
|---------|------|-------------|---------------|
| 1 | 1.1–1.8 (as needed) | | |
| 2 | 2.1–2.4, 2.6 (as needed) | | 2.5 |
| 3 | | 3.1–3.3 (as needed) | |
| 4 | 4.1–4.4 (as needed) | 4.5, 4.6 | |
| 5 | 5.1–5.3 | 5.4, 5.5 | |
| 6 | 6.1–6.3 | 6.6 | 6.4, 6.5 |
| 7 | 7.1 | 7.4 | 7.2, 7.3 |
| 8 | 8.1, 8.5 | 8.3 | 8.2, 8.4, 8.6 |
| 9 | 9.1, 9.3, 9.5 | 9.2 | 9.4, 9.6 |
| 10 | 10.1–10.5 | | 10.6–10.8 |
| 11 | 11.1 | 11.2, 11.3 | 11.4, 11.5 |
| 12 | | 12.1–12.4 | |
| 13 | | 13.1–13.5 | |

Instructors using this book can adjust the level of difficulty of their course by choosing either to cover or to omit the more challenging examples at the end of sections, as well as the more challenging exercises. The chapter dependency chart shown here displays the strong dependencies. A star indicates that only relevant sections of the chapter are needed for study of a later chapter. Weak dependencies have been ignored. More details can be found in the Instructor Resource Guide.

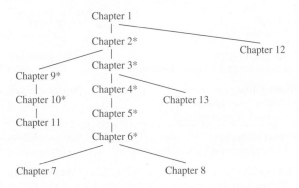

# Ancillaries

**STUDENT'S SOLUTIONS GUIDE**     This student manual, available separately, contains full solutions to all odd-numbered problems in the exercise sets. These solutions explain why a particular method is used and why it works. For some exercises, one or two other possible approaches are described to show that a problem can be solved in several different ways. Suggested references for the writing projects found at the end of each chapter are also included in this volume. Also included are a guide to writing proofs and an extensive description of common mistakes students make in discrete mathematics, plus sample tests and a sample crib sheet for each chapter designed to help students prepare for exams.

*(ISBN-10: 0-07-735350-1)*     *(ISBN-13: 978-0-07-735350-6)*

**INSTRUCTOR'S RESOURCE GUIDE**     This manual, available on the website and in printed form by request for instructors, contains full solutions to even-numbered exercises in the text. Suggestions on how to teach the material in each chapter of the book are provided, including the points to stress in each section and how to put the material into perspective. It also offers sample tests for each chapter and a test bank containing over 1500 exam questions to choose from. Answers to all sample tests and test bank questions are included. Finally, several sample syllabi are presented for courses with differing emphases and student ability levels.

*(ISBN-10: 0-07-735349-8)*     *(ISBN-13: 978-0-07-735349-0)*

# Acknowledgments

I would like to thank the many instructors and students at a variety of schools who have used this book and provided me with their valuable feedback and helpful suggestions. Their input has made this a much better book than it would have been otherwise. I especially want to thank Jerrold Grossman, Jean-Claude Evard, and Georgia Mederer for their technical reviews of the seventh edition and their "eagle eyes," which have helped ensure the accuracy of this book. I also appreciate the help provided by all those who have submitted comments via the website.

I thank the reviewers of this seventh and the six previous editions. These reviewers have provided much helpful criticism and encouragement to me. I hope this edition lives up to their high expectations.

## Reviewers for the Seventh Edition

Philip Barry
*University of Minnesota, Minneapolis*

Miklos Bona
*University of Florida*

Kirby Brown
*Queens College*

John Carter
*University of Toronto*

Narendra Chaudhari
*Nanyang Technological University*

Allan Cochran
*University of Arkansas*

Daniel Cunningham
*Buffalo State College*

George Davis
*Georgia State University*

Andrzej Derdzinski
*The Ohio State University*

Ronald Dotzel
*University of Missouri-St. Louis*

T.J. Duda
*Columbus State Community College*

Bruce Elenbogen
*University of Michigan, Dearborn*

Norma Elias
*Purdue University, Calumet-Hammond*

Herbert Enderton
*University of California, Los Angeles*

Anthony Evans
*Wright State University*

Kim Factor
*Marquette University*

Margaret Fleck
*University of Illinois, Champaign*

Peter Gillespie
*Fayetteville State University*

Johannes Hattingh
*Georgia State University*

Ken Holladay
*University of New Orleans*

Jerry Ianni
*LaGuardia Community College*

Ravi Janardan
*University of Minnesota, Minneapolis*

Norliza Katuk
*University of Utara Malaysia*

William Klostermeyer
*University of North Florida*

Przemo Kranz
*University of Mississippi*

Jaromy Kuhl
*University of West Florida*

Loredana Lanzani
*University of Arkansas, Fayetteville*

Steven Leonhardi
*Winona State University*

Xu Liutong
*Beijing University of Posts and Telecommunications*

Vladimir Logvinenko
*De Anza Community College*

Darrell Minor
*Columbus State Community College*

Keith Olson
*Utah Valley University*

Yongyuth Permpoontanalarp
*King Mongkut's University of
Technology, Thonburi*

Galin Piatniskaia
*University of Missouri, St. Louis*

Stefan Robila
*Montclair State University*

Chris Rodger
*Auburn University*

Sukhit Singh
*Texas State University, San Marcos*

David Snyder
*Texas State University, San Marcos*

Wasin So
*San Jose State University*

Bogdan Suceava
*California State University, Fullerton*

Christopher Swanson
*Ashland University*

Bon Sy
*Queens College*

Matthew Walsh
*Indiana-Purdue University, Fort
Wayne*

Gideon Weinstein
*Western Governors University*

David Wilczynski
*University of Southern California*

I would like to thank Bill Stenquist, Executive Editor, for his advocacy, enthusiasm, and support. His assistance with this edition has been essential. I would also like to thank the original editor, Wayne Yuhasz, whose insights and skills helped ensure the book's success, as well as all the many other previous editors of this book.

I want to express my appreciation to the staff of RPK Editorial Services for their valuable work on this edition, including Rose Kernan, who served as both the developmental editor and the production editor, and the other members of the RPK team, Fred Dahl, Martha McMaster, Erin Wagner, Harlan James, and Shelly Gerger-Knecthl. I thank Paul Mailhot of PreTeX, Inc., the compositor, for the tremendous amount to work he devoted to producing this edition, and for his intimate knowledge of LaTeX. Thanks also to Danny Meldung of Photo Affairs, Inc., who was resourceful obtaining images for the new biographical footnotes.

The accuracy and quality of this new edition owe much to Jerry Grossman and Jean-Claude Evard, who checked the entire manuscript for technical accuracy and Georgia Mederer, who checked the accuracy of the answers at the end of the book and the solutions in the *Student's Solutions Guide* and *Instructor's Resource Guide*. As usual, I cannot thank Jerry Grossman enough for all his work authoring these two essential ancillaries.

I would also express my appreciation the Science, Engineering, and Mathematics (SEM) Division of McGraw-Hill Higher Education for their valuable support for this new edition and the associated media content. In particular, thanks go to Kurt Strand: President, SEM, McGraw-Hill Higher Education, Marty Lange: Editor-in-Chief, SEM, Michael Lange: Editorial Director, Raghothaman Srinivasan: Global Publisher, Bill Stenquist: Executive Editor, Curt Reynolds: Executive Marketing Manager, Robin A. Reed: Project Manager, Sandy Ludovissey: Buyer, Lorraine Buczek: In-house Developmental Editor, Brenda Rowles: Design Coordinator, Carrie K. Burger: Lead Photo Research Coordinator, and Tammy Juran: Media Project Manager.

*Kenneth H. Rosen*

# The Companion Website

The extensive companion website accompanying this text has been substantially enhanced for the seventh edition This website is accessible at *www.mhhe.com/rosen*. The homepage shows the *Information Center*, and contains login links for the site's *Student Site* and *Instructor Site*. Key features of each area are described below:

## THE INFORMATION CENTER

The Information Center contains basic information about the book including the expanded table of contents (including subsection heads), the preface, descriptions of the ancillaries, and a sample chapter. It also provides a link that can be used to submit errata reports and other feedback about the book.

## STUDENT SITE

The Student site contains a wealth of resources available for student use, including the following, tied into the text wherever the special icons displayed below are found in the text:

- **Extra Examples**    You can find a large number of additional examples on the site, covering all chapters of the book. These examples are concentrated in areas where students often ask for additional material. Although most of these examples amplify the basic concepts, more-challenging examples can also be found here.

- **Interactive Demonstration Applets**    These applets enable you to interactively explore how important algorithms work, and are tied directly to material in the text with linkages to examples and exercises. Additional resources are provided on how to use and apply these applets.

- **Self Assessments**    These interactive guides help you assess your understanding of 14 key concepts, providing a question bank where each question includes a brief tutorial followed by a multiple-choice question. If you select an incorrect answer, advice is provided to help you understand your error. Using these Self Assessments, you should be able to diagnose your problems and find appropriate help.

- **Web Resources Guide**    This guide provides annotated links to hundreds of external websites containing relevant material such as historical and biographical information, puzzles and problems, discussions, applets, programs, and more. These links are keyed to the text by page number.

Additional resources in the Student site include:

- **Exploring Discrete Mathematics**    This ancillary provides help for using a computer algebra system to do a wide range of computations in discrete mathematics. Each chapter provides a description of relevant functions in the computer algebra system and how they are used, programs to carry out computations in discrete mathematics, examples, and exercises that can be worked using this computer algebra system. Two versions, *Exploring Discrete Mathematics with Maple*$^{\text{TM}}$ and *Exploring Discrete Mathematics with Mathematica*$^{\text{TM}}$ will be available.

- **Applications of Discrete Mathematics**    This ancillary contains 24 chapters—each with its own set of exercises—presenting a wide variety of interesting and important applications covering three general areas in discrete mathematics: discrete structures, combinatorics, and graph theory. These applications are ideal for supplementing the text or for independent study.

- *A Guide to Proof-Writing*   This guide provides additional help for writing proofs, a skill that many students find difficult to master. By reading this guide at the beginning of the course and periodically thereafter when proof writing is required, you will be rewarded as your proof-writing ability grows. (Also available in the *Student's Solutions Guide*.)

- *Common Mistakes in Discrete Mathematics*   This guide includes a detailed list of common misconceptions that students of discrete mathematics often have and the kinds of errors they tend to make. You are encouraged to review this list from time to time to help avoid these common traps. (Also available in the *Student's Solutions Guide*.)

- *Advice on Writing Projects*   This guide offers helpful hints and suggestions for the Writing Projects in the text, including an extensive bibliography of helpful books and articles for research; discussion of various resources available in print and online; tips on doing library research; and suggestions on how to write well. (Also available in the *Student's Solutions Guide*.)

## INSTRUCTOR SITE

This part of the website provides access to all of the resources on the Student Site, as well as these resources for instructors:

- *Suggested Syllabi*   Detailed course outlines are shown, offering suggestions for courses with different emphases and different student backgrounds and ability levels.

- *Teaching Suggestions*   This guide contains detailed teaching suggestions for instructors, including chapter overviews for the entire text, detailed remarks on each section, and comments on the exercise sets.

- *Printable Tests*   Printable tests are offered in TeX and Word format for every chapter, and can be customized by instructors.

- *PowerPoints Lecture Slides and PowerPoint Figures and Tables*   An extensive collection of PowerPoint slides for Chapters 1–10 of the text are provided for instructor use. In addition, images of all figures and tables from the text are provided as PowerPoint slides.

- *Homework Delivery System*   An extensive homework delivery system, under development for availability in fall 2012, will provide questions tied directly to the text, so that students will be able to do assignments on-line. Moreover, they will be able to use this system in a tutorial mode. This system will be able to automatically grade assignments, and deliver free-form student input to instructors for their own analysis. Course management capabilities will be provided that will allow instructors to create assignments, automatically assign and grade homework, quiz, and test questions from a bank of questions tied directly to the text, create and edit their own questions, manage course announcements and due dates, and track student progress.

# To the Student

**W**hat is discrete mathematics? Discrete mathematics is the part of mathematics devoted to the study of discrete objects. (Here *discrete* means consisting of distinct or unconnected elements.) The kinds of problems solved using discrete mathematics include:

- How many ways are there to choose a valid password on a computer system?
- What is the probability of winning a lottery?
- Is there a link between two computers in a network?
- How can I identify spam e-mail messages?
- How can I encrypt a message so that no unintended recipient can read it?
- What is the shortest path between two cities using a transportation system?
- How can a list of integers be sorted so that the integers are in increasing order?
- How many steps are required to do such a sorting?
- How can it be proved that a sorting algorithm correctly sorts a list?
- How can a circuit that adds two integers be designed?
- How many valid Internet addresses are there?

You will learn the discrete structures and techniques needed to solve problems such as these.

More generally, discrete mathematics is used whenever objects are counted, when relationships between finite (or countable) sets are studied, and when processes involving a finite number of steps are analyzed. A key reason for the growth in the importance of discrete mathematics is that information is stored and manipulated by computing machines in a discrete fashion.

**WHY STUDY DISCRETE MATHEMATICS?**    There are several important reasons for studying discrete mathematics. First, through this course you can develop your mathematical maturity: that is, your ability to understand and create mathematical arguments. You will not get very far in your studies in the mathematical sciences without these skills.

Second, discrete mathematics is the gateway to more advanced courses in all parts of the mathematical sciences. Discrete mathematics provides the mathematical foundations for many computer science courses including data structures, algorithms, database theory, automata theory, formal languages, compiler theory, computer security, and operating systems. Students find these courses much more difficult when they have not had the appropriate mathematical foundations from discrete math. One student has sent me an e-mail message saying that she used the contents of this book in every computer science course she took!

Math courses based on the material studied in discrete mathematics include logic, set theory, number theory, linear algebra, abstract algebra, combinatorics, graph theory, and probability theory (the discrete part of the subject).

Also, discrete mathematics contains the necessary mathematical background for solving problems in operations research (including many discrete optimization techniques), chemistry, engineering, biology, and so on. In the text, we will study applications to some of these areas.

Many students find their introductory discrete mathematics course to be significantly more challenging than courses they have previously taken. One reason for this is that one of the primary goals of this course is to teach mathematical reasoning and problem solving, rather than a discrete set of skills. The exercises in this book are designed to reflect this goal. Although there are plenty of exercises in this text similar to those addressed in the examples, a large percentage of the exercises require original thought. This is intentional. The material discussed in the text provides the tools needed to solve these exercises, but your job is to successfully apply these tools using your own creativity. One of the primary goals of this course is to learn how to attack problems that may be somewhat different from any you may have previously seen. Unfortunately, learning how to solve only particular types of exercises is not sufficient for success in developing the problem-solving skills needed in subsequent courses and professional work. This text addresses many different topics, but discrete mathematics is an extremely diverse and large area of study. One of my goals as an author is to help you develop the skills needed to master the additional material you will need in your own future pursuits.

**THE EXERCISES**     I would like to offer some advice about how you can best learn discrete mathematics (and other subjects in the mathematical and computing sciences). You will learn the most by actively working exercises. I suggest that you solve as many as you possibly can. After working the exercises your instructor has assigned, I encourage you to solve additional exercises such as those in the exercise sets following each section of the text and in the supplementary exercises at the end of each chapter. (Note the key explaining the markings preceding exercises.)

**Key to the Exercises**

| | |
|---|---|
| no marking | A routine exercise |
| * | A difficult exercise |
| ** | An extremely challenging exercise |
| ☞ | An exercise containing a result used in the book (Table 1 on the following page shows where these exercises are used.) |
| (*Requires calculus*) | An exercise whose solution requires the use of limits or concepts from differential or integral calculus |

The best approach is to try exercises yourself before you consult the answer section at the end of this book. Note that the odd-numbered exercise answers provided in the text are answers only and not full solutions; in particular, the reasoning required to obtain answers is omitted in these answers. The *Student's Solutions Guide*, available separately, provides complete, worked solutions to all odd-numbered exercises in this text. When you hit an impasse trying to solve an odd-numbered exercise, I suggest you consult the *Student's Solutions Guide* and look for some guidance as to how to solve the problem. The more work you do yourself rather than passively reading or copying solutions, the more you will learn. The answers and solutions to the even-numbered exercises are intentionally not available from the publisher; ask your instructor if you have trouble with these.

**WEB RESOURCES**     You are ***strongly*** encouraged to take advantage of additional resources available on the Web, especially those on the companion website for this book found at *www.mhhe.com/rosen*. You will find many Extra Examples designed to clarify key concepts; Self Assessments for gauging how well you understand core topics; Interactive Demonstration Applets exploring key algorithms and other concepts; a Web Resources Guide containing an extensive selection of links to external sites relevant to the world of discrete mathematics; extra explanations and practice to help you master core concepts; added instruction on writing proofs and on avoiding common mistakes in discrete mathematics; in-depth discussions of important applications; and guidance on utilizing Maple™ software to explore the computational aspects of discrete mathematics. Places in the text where these additional online resources are available are identified in the margins by special icons. For more details on these and other online resources, see the description of the companion website immediately preceding this "To the Student" message.

| TABLE 1  Hand-Icon Exercises and Where They Are Used | | | |
|:---:|:---:|:---:|:---:|
| *Section* | *Exercise* | *Section Where Used* | *Pages Where Used* |
| 1.1 | 40 | 1.3 | 31 |
| 1.1 | 41 | 1.3 | 31 |
| 1.3 | 9 | 1.6 | 71 |
| 1.3 | 10 | 1.6 | 70, 71 |
| 1.3 | 15 | 1.6 | 71 |
| 1.3 | 30 | 1.6 | 71, 74 |
| 1.3 | 42 | 12.2 | 820 |
| 1.7 | 16 | 1.7 | 86 |
| 2.3 | 72 | 2.3 | 144 |
| 2.3 | 79 | 2.5 | 170 |
| 2.5 | 15 | 2.5 | 174 |
| 2.5 | 16 | 2.5 | 173 |
| 3.1 | 43 | 3.1 | 197 |
| 3.2 | 72 | 11.2 | 761 |
| 4.2 | 36 | 4.2 | 270 |
| 4.3 | 37 | 4.1 | 239 |
| 4.4 | 2 | 4.6 | 301 |
| 4.4 | 44 | 7.2 | 464 |
| 6.4 | 17 | 7.2 | 466 |
| 6.4 | 21 | 7.4 | 480 |
| 7.2 | 15 | 7.2 | 466 |
| 9.1 | 26 | 9.4 | 598 |
| 10.4 | 59 | 11.1 | 747 |
| 11.1 | 15 | 11.1 | 750 |
| 11.1 | 30 | 11.1 | 755 |
| 11.1 | 48 | 11.2 | 762 |
| 12.1 | 12 | 12.3 | 825 |
| A.2 | 4 | 8.3 | 531 |

**THE VALUE OF THIS BOOK**    My intention is to make your substantial investment in this text an excellent value. The book, the associated ancillaries, and companion website have taken many years of effort to develop and refine. I am confident that most of you will find that the text and associated materials will help you master discrete mathematics, just as so many previous students have. Even though it is likely that you will not cover some chapters in your current course, you should find it helpful—as many other students have—to read the relevant sections of the book as you take additional courses. Most of you will return to this book as a useful tool throughout your future studies, especially for those of you who continue in computer science, mathematics, and engineering. I have designed this book to be a gateway for future studies and explorations, and to be comprehensive reference, and I wish you luck as you begin your journey.

*Kenneth H. Rosen*

# 1

# The Foundations: Logic and Proofs

The rules of logic specify the meaning of mathematical statements. For instance, these rules help us understand and reason with statements such as "There exists an integer that is not the sum of two squares" and "For every positive integer $n$, the sum of the positive integers not exceeding $n$ is $n(n + 1)/2$." Logic is the basis of all mathematical reasoning, and of all automated reasoning. It has practical applications to the design of computing machines, to the specification of systems, to artificial intelligence, to computer programming, to programming languages, and to other areas of computer science, as well as to many other fields of study.

To understand mathematics, we must understand what makes up a correct mathematical argument, that is, a proof. Once we prove a mathematical statement is true, we call it a theorem. A collection of theorems on a topic organize what we know about this topic. To learn a mathematical topic, a person needs to actively construct mathematical arguments on this topic, and not just read exposition. Moreover, knowing the proof of a theorem often makes it possible to modify the result to fit new situations.

Everyone knows that proofs are important throughout mathematics, but many people find it surprising how important proofs are in computer science. In fact, proofs are used to verify that computer programs produce the correct output for all possible input values, to show that algorithms always produce the correct result, to establish the security of a system, and to create artificial intelligence. Furthermore, automated reasoning systems have been created to allow computers to construct their own proofs.

In this chapter, we will explain what makes up a correct mathematical argument and introduce tools to construct these arguments. We will develop an arsenal of different proof methods that will enable us to prove many different types of results. After introducing many different methods of proof, we will introduce several strategies for constructing proofs. We will introduce the notion of a conjecture and explain the process of developing mathematics by studying conjectures.

## 1.1 Propositional Logic

### Introduction

The rules of logic give precise meaning to mathematical statements. These rules are used to distinguish between valid and invalid mathematical arguments. Because a major goal of this book is to teach the reader how to understand and how to construct correct mathematical arguments, we begin our study of discrete mathematics with an introduction to logic.

Besides the importance of logic in understanding mathematical reasoning, logic has numerous applications to computer science. These rules are used in the design of computer circuits, the construction of computer programs, the verification of the correctness of programs, and in many other ways. Furthermore, software systems have been developed for constructing some, but not all, types of proofs automatically. We will discuss these applications of logic in this and later chapters.

# Propositions

Our discussion begins with an introduction to the basic building blocks of logic—propositions. A **proposition** is a declarative sentence (that is, a sentence that declares a fact) that is either true or false, but not both.

**EXAMPLE 1**    All the following declarative sentences are propositions.

Extra Examples

    1. Washington, D.C., is the capital of the United States of America.
    2. Toronto is the capital of Canada.
    3. $1 + 1 = 2$.
    4. $2 + 2 = 3$.

Propositions 1 and 3 are true, whereas 2 and 4 are false.    ◄

Some sentences that are not propositions are given in Example 2.

**EXAMPLE 2**    Consider the following sentences.

    1. What time is it?
    2. Read this carefully.
    3. $x + 1 = 2$.
    4. $x + y = z$.

Sentences 1 and 2 are not propositions because they are not declarative sentences. Sentences 3 and 4 are not propositions because they are neither true nor false. Note that each of sentences 3 and 4 can be turned into a proposition if we assign values to the variables. We will also discuss other ways to turn sentences such as these into propositions in Section 1.4.    ◄

We use letters to denote **propositional variables** (or **statement variables**), that is, variables that represent propositions, just as letters are used to denote numerical variables. The

Links

---

ARISTOTLE (384 B.C.E.–322 B.C.E.)    Aristotle was born in Stagirus (Stagira) in northern Greece. His father was the personal physician of the King of Macedonia. Because his father died when Aristotle was young, Aristotle could not follow the custom of following his father's profession. Aristotle became an orphan at a young age when his mother also died. His guardian who raised him taught him poetry, rhetoric, and Greek. At the age of 17, his guardian sent him to Athens to further his education. Aristotle joined Plato's Academy, where for 20 years he attended Plato's lectures, later presenting his own lectures on rhetoric. When Plato died in 347 B.C.E., Aristotle was not chosen to succeed him because his views differed too much from those of Plato. Instead, Aristotle joined the court of King Hermeas where he remained for three years, and married the niece of the King. When the Persians defeated Hermeas, Aristotle moved to Mytilene and, at the invitation of King Philip of Macedonia, he tutored Alexander, Philip's son, who later became Alexander the Great. Aristotle tutored Alexander for five years and after the death of King Philip, he returned to Athens and set up his own school, called the Lyceum.

Aristotle's followers were called the peripatetics, which means "to walk about," because Aristotle often walked around as he discussed philosophical questions. Aristotle taught at the Lyceum for 13 years where he lectured to his advanced students in the morning and gave popular lectures to a broad audience in the evening. When Alexander the Great died in 323 B.C.E., a backlash against anything related to Alexander led to trumped-up charges of impiety against Aristotle. Aristotle fled to Chalcis to avoid prosecution. He only lived one year in Chalcis, dying of a stomach ailment in 322 B.C.E.

Aristotle wrote three types of works: those written for a popular audience, compilations of scientific facts, and systematic treatises. The systematic treatises included works on logic, philosophy, psychology, physics, and natural history. Aristotle's writings were preserved by a student and were hidden in a vault where a wealthy book collector discovered them about 200 years later. They were taken to Rome, where they were studied by scholars and issued in new editions, preserving them for posterity.

conventional letters used for propositional variables are $p, q, r, s, \ldots$. The **truth value** of a proposition is true, denoted by T, if it is a true proposition, and the truth value of a proposition is false, denoted by F, if it is a false proposition.

The area of logic that deals with propositions is called the **propositional calculus** or **propositional logic**. It was first developed systematically by the Greek philosopher Aristotle more than 2300 years ago.

**Links**

We now turn our attention to methods for producing new propositions from those that we already have. These methods were discussed by the English mathematician George Boole in 1854 in his book *The Laws of Thought*. Many mathematical statements are constructed by combining one or more propositions. New propositions, called **compound propositions**, are formed from existing propositions using logical operators.

**DEFINITION 1**

Let $p$ be a proposition. The *negation of $p$*, denoted by $\neg p$ (also denoted by $\overline{p}$), is the statement

"It is not the case that $p$."

The proposition $\neg p$ is read "not $p$." The truth value of the negation of $p$, $\neg p$, is the opposite of the truth value of $p$.

**EXAMPLE 3**

Find the negation of the proposition

"Michael's PC runs Linux"

**Extra Examples**

and express this in simple English.

*Solution:* The negation is

"It is not the case that Michael's PC runs Linux."

This negation can be more simply expressed as

"Michael's PC does not run Linux."

◄

**EXAMPLE 4**

Find the negation of the proposition

"Vandana's smartphone has at least 32GB of memory"

and express this in simple English.

*Solution:* The negation is

"It is not the case that Vandana's smartphone has at least 32GB of memory."

This negation can also be expressed as

"Vandana's smartphone does not have at least 32GB of memory"

or even more simply as

"Vandana's smartphone has less than 32GB of memory."

◄

| TABLE 1 The Truth Table for the Negation of a Proposition. | |
|:---:|:---:|
| $p$ | $\neg p$ |
| T | F |
| F | T |

Table 1 displays the **truth table** for the negation of a proposition $p$. This table has a row for each of the two possible truth values of a proposition $p$. Each row shows the truth value of $\neg p$ corresponding to the truth value of $p$ for this row.

The negation of a proposition can also be considered the result of the operation of the **negation operator** on a proposition. The negation operator constructs a new proposition from a single existing proposition. We will now introduce the logical operators that are used to form new propositions from two or more existing propositions. These logical operators are also called **connectives**.

**DEFINITION 2**    Let $p$ and $q$ be propositions. The *conjunction* of $p$ and $q$, denoted by $p \wedge q$, is the proposition "$p$ and $q$." The conjunction $p \wedge q$ is true when both $p$ and $q$ are true and is false otherwise.

Table 2 displays the truth table of $p \wedge q$. This table has a row for each of the four possible combinations of truth values of $p$ and $q$. The four rows correspond to the pairs of truth values TT, TF, FT, and FF, where the first truth value in the pair is the truth value of $p$ and the second truth value is the truth value of $q$.

Note that in logic the word "but" sometimes is used instead of "and" in a conjunction. For example, the statement "The sun is shining, but it is raining" is another way of saying "The sun is shining and it is raining." (In natural language, there is a subtle difference in meaning between "and" and "but"; we will not be concerned with this nuance here.)

**EXAMPLE 5**    Find the conjunction of the propositions $p$ and $q$ where $p$ is the proposition "Rebecca's PC has more than 16 GB free hard disk space" and $q$ is the proposition "The processor in Rebecca's PC runs faster than 1 GHz."

*Solution:* The conjunction of these propositions, $p \wedge q$, is the proposition "Rebecca's PC has more than 16 GB free hard disk space, and the processor in Rebecca's PC runs faster than 1 GHz." This conjunction can be expressed more simply as "Rebecca's PC has more than 16 GB free hard disk space, and its processor runs faster than 1 GHz." For this conjunction to be true, both conditions given must be true. It is false, when one or both of these conditions are false.◀

**DEFINITION 3**    Let $p$ and $q$ be propositions. The *disjunction* of $p$ and $q$, denoted by $p \vee q$, is the proposition "$p$ or $q$." The disjunction $p \vee q$ is false when both $p$ and $q$ are false and is true otherwise.

Table 3 displays the truth table for $p \vee q$.

| TABLE 2 The Truth Table for the Conjunction of Two Propositions. | | |
|:---:|:---:|:---:|
| $p$ | $q$ | $p \wedge q$ |
| T | T | T |
| T | F | F |
| F | T | F |
| F | F | F |

| TABLE 3 The Truth Table for the Disjunction of Two Propositions. | | |
|:---:|:---:|:---:|
| $p$ | $q$ | $p \vee q$ |
| T | T | T |
| T | F | T |
| F | T | T |
| F | F | F |

The use of the connective *or* in a disjunction corresponds to one of the two ways the word *or* is used in English, namely, as an **inclusive or**. A disjunction is true when at least one of the two propositions is true. For instance, the inclusive or is being used in the statement

"Students who have taken calculus or computer science can take this class."

Here, we mean that students who have taken both calculus and computer science can take the class, as well as the students who have taken only one of the two subjects. On the other hand, we are using the **exclusive or** when we say

"Students who have taken calculus or computer science, but not both, can enroll in this class."

Here, we mean that students who have taken both calculus and a computer science course cannot take the class. Only those who have taken exactly one of the two courses can take the class.

Similarly, when a menu at a restaurant states, "Soup or salad comes with an entrée," the restaurant almost always means that customers can have either soup or salad, but not both. Hence, this is an exclusive, rather than an inclusive, or.

**EXAMPLE 6** What is the disjunction of the propositions $p$ and $q$ where $p$ and $q$ are the same propositions as in Example 5?

Extra Examples

*Solution:* The disjunction of $p$ and $q$, $p \lor q$, is the proposition

"Rebecca's PC has at least 16 GB free hard disk space, or the processor in Rebecca's PC runs faster than 1 GHz."

This proposition is true when Rebecca's PC has at least 16 GB free hard disk space, when the PC's processor runs faster than 1 GHz, and when both conditions are true. It is false when both of these conditions are false, that is, when Rebecca's PC has less than 16 GB free hard disk space and the processor in her PC runs at 1 GHz or slower. ◀

As was previously remarked, the use of the connective *or* in a disjunction corresponds to one of the two ways the word *or* is used in English, namely, in an inclusive way. Thus, a disjunction is true when at least one of the two propositions in it is true. Sometimes, we use *or* in an exclusive sense. When the exclusive or is used to connect the propositions $p$ and $q$, the proposition "$p$ or $q$ (but not both)" is obtained. This proposition is true when $p$ is true and $q$ is false, and when $p$ is false and $q$ is true. It is false when both $p$ and $q$ are false and when both are true.

Links

GEORGE BOOLE (1815–1864)    George Boole,  the son of a cobbler, was born in Lincoln, England, in November 1815. Because of his family's difficult financial situation, Boole struggled to educate himself while supporting his family. Nevertheless, he became one of the most important mathematicians of the 1800s. Although he considered a career as a clergyman, he decided instead to go into teaching, and soon afterward opened a school of his own. In his preparation for teaching mathematics, Boole—unsatisfied with textbooks of his day—decided to read the works of the great mathematicians. While reading papers of the great French mathematician Lagrange, Boole made discoveries in the calculus of variations, the branch of analysis dealing with finding curves and surfaces by optimizing certain parameters.

In 1848 Boole published *The Mathematical Analysis of Logic*, the first of his contributions to symbolic logic. In 1849 he was appointed professor of mathematics at Queen's College in Cork, Ireland. In 1854 he published *The Laws of Thought*, his most famous work. In this book, Boole introduced what is now called *Boolean algebra* in his honor. Boole wrote textbooks on differential equations and on difference equations that were used in Great Britain until the end of the nineteenth century. Boole married in 1855; his wife was the niece of the professor of Greek at Queen's College. In 1864 Boole died from pneumonia, which he contracted as a result of keeping a lecture engagement even though he was soaking wet from a rainstorm.

| TABLE 4 The Truth Table for the Exclusive Or of Two Propositions. | | |
|:---:|:---:|:---:|
| $p$ | $q$ | $p \oplus q$ |
| T | T | F |
| T | F | T |
| F | T | T |
| F | F | F |

| TABLE 5 The Truth Table for the Conditional Statement $p \to q$. | | |
|:---:|:---:|:---:|
| $p$ | $q$ | $p \to q$ |
| T | T | T |
| T | F | F |
| F | T | T |
| F | F | T |

**DEFINITION 4**   Let $p$ and $q$ be propositions. The *exclusive or* of $p$ and $q$, denoted by $p \oplus q$, is the proposition that is true when exactly one of $p$ and $q$ is true and is false otherwise.

The truth table for the exclusive or of two propositions is displayed in Table 4.

## Conditional Statements

We will discuss several other important ways in which propositions can be combined.

**DEFINITION 5**   Let $p$ and $q$ be propositions. The *conditional statement* $p \to q$ is the proposition "if $p$, then $q$." The conditional statement $p \to q$ is false when $p$ is true and $q$ is false, and true otherwise. In the conditional statement $p \to q$, $p$ is called the *hypothesis* (or *antecedent* or *premise*) and $q$ is called the *conclusion* (or *consequence*).

**Assessment**

The statement $p \to q$ is called a conditional statement because $p \to q$ asserts that $q$ is true on the condition that $p$ holds. A conditional statement is also called an **implication**.

The truth table for the conditional statement $p \to q$ is shown in Table 5. Note that the statement $p \to q$ is true when both $p$ and $q$ are true and when $p$ is false (no matter what truth value $q$ has).

Because conditional statements play such an essential role in mathematical reasoning, a variety of terminology is used to express $p \to q$. You will encounter most if not all of the following ways to express this conditional statement:

"if $p$, then $q$"              "$p$ implies $q$"
"if $p$, $q$"                   "$p$ only if $q$"
"$p$ is sufficient for $q$"     "a sufficient condition for $q$ is $p$"
"$q$ if $p$"                    "$q$ whenever $p$"
"$q$ when $p$"                  "$q$ is necessary for $p$"
"a necessary condition for $p$ is $q$"   "$q$ follows from $p$"
"$q$ unless $\neg p$"

A useful way to understand the truth value of a conditional statement is to think of an obligation or a contract. For example, the pledge many politicians make when running for office is

"If I am elected, then I will lower taxes."

If the politician is elected, voters would expect this politician to lower taxes. Furthermore, if the politician is not elected, then voters will not have any expectation that this person will lower taxes, although the person may have sufficient influence to cause those in power to lower taxes. It is only when the politician is elected but does not lower taxes that voters can say that the politician has broken the campaign pledge. This last scenario corresponds to the case when $p$ is true but $q$ is false in $p \to q$.

Similarly, consider a statement that a professor might make:

"If you get 100% on the final, then you will get an A."

If you manage to get a 100% on the final, then you would expect to receive an A. If you do not get 100% you may or may not receive an A depending on other factors. However, if you do get 100%, but the professor does not give you an A, you will feel cheated.

Of the various ways to express the conditional statement $p \to q$, the two that seem to cause the most confusion are "$p$ only if $q$" and "$q$ unless $\neg p$." Consequently, we will provide some guidance for clearing up this confusion.

To remember that "$p$ only if $q$" expresses the same thing as "if $p$, then $q$," note that "$p$ only if $q$" says that $p$ cannot be true when $q$ is not true. That is, the statement is false if $p$ is true, but $q$ is false. When $p$ is false, $q$ may be either true or false, because the statement says nothing about the truth value of $q$. Be careful not to use "$q$ only if $p$" to express $p \to q$ because this is incorrect. To see this, note that the true values of "$q$ only if $p$" and $p \to q$ are different when $p$ and $q$ have different truth values.

To remember that "$q$ unless $\neg p$" expresses the same conditional statement as "if $p$, then $q$," note that "$q$ unless $\neg p$" means that if $\neg p$ is false, then $q$ must be true. That is, the statement "$q$ unless $\neg p$" is false when $p$ is true but $q$ is false, but it is true otherwise. Consequently, "$q$ unless $\neg p$" and $p \to q$ always have the same truth value.

We illustrate the translation between conditional statements and English statements in Example 7.

*You might have trouble understanding how "unless" is used in conditional statements unless you read this paragraph carefully.*

**EXAMPLE 7**  Let $p$ be the statement "Maria learns discrete mathematics" and $q$ the statement "Maria will find a good job." Express the statement $p \to q$ as a statement in English.

**Extra Examples**

*Solution:* From the definition of conditional statements, we see that when $p$ is the statement "Maria learns discrete mathematics" and $q$ is the statement "Maria will find a good job," $p \to q$ represents the statement

"If Maria learns discrete mathematics, then she will find a good job."

There are many other ways to express this conditional statement in English. Among the most natural of these are:

"Maria will find a good job when she learns discrete mathematics."

"For Maria to get a good job, it is sufficient for her to learn discrete mathematics."

and

"Maria will find a good job unless she does not learn discrete mathematics."    ◀

Note that the way we have defined conditional statements is more general than the meaning attached to such statements in the English language. For instance, the conditional statement in Example 7 and the statement

"If it is sunny, then we will go to the beach."

are statements used in normal language where there is a relationship between the hypothesis and the conclusion. Further, the first of these statements is true unless Maria learns discrete mathematics, but she does not get a good job, and the second is true unless it is indeed sunny, but we do not go to the beach. On the other hand, the statement

"If Juan has a smartphone, then $2 + 3 = 5$"

is true from the definition of a conditional statement, because its conclusion is true. (The truth value of the hypothesis does not matter then.) The conditional statement

"If Juan has a smartphone, then $2 + 3 = 6$"

is true if Juan does not have a smartphone, even though $2 + 3 = 6$ is false. We would not use these last two conditional statements in natural language (except perhaps in sarcasm), because there is no relationship between the hypothesis and the conclusion in either statement. In mathematical reasoning, we consider conditional statements of a more general sort than we use in English. The mathematical concept of a conditional statement is independent of a cause-and-effect relationship between hypothesis and conclusion. Our definition of a conditional statement specifies its truth values; it is not based on English usage. Propositional language is an artificial language; we only parallel English usage to make it easy to use and remember.

The if-then construction used in many programming languages is different from that used in logic. Most programming languages contain statements such as **if** $p$ **then** $S$, where $p$ is a proposition and $S$ is a program segment (one or more statements to be executed). When execution of a program encounters such a statement, $S$ is executed if $p$ is true, but $S$ is not executed if $p$ is false, as illustrated in Example 8.

**EXAMPLE 8**    What is the value of the variable $x$ after the statement

**if** $2 + 2 = 4$ **then** $x := x + 1$

if $x = 0$ before this statement is encountered? (The symbol := stands for assignment. The statement $x := x + 1$ means the assignment of the value of $x + 1$ to $x$.)

*Solution:* Because $2 + 2 = 4$ is true, the assignment statement $x := x + 1$ is executed. Hence, $x$ has the value $0 + 1 = 1$ after this statement is encountered.    ◀

CONVERSE, CONTRAPOSITIVE, AND INVERSE    We can form some new conditional statements starting with a conditional statement $p \rightarrow q$. In particular, there are three related conditional statements that occur so often that they have special names. The proposition $q \rightarrow p$ is called the **converse** of $p \rightarrow q$. The **contrapositive** of $p \rightarrow q$ is the proposition $\neg q \rightarrow \neg p$. The proposition $\neg p \rightarrow \neg q$ is called the **inverse** of $p \rightarrow q$. We will see that of these three conditional statements formed from $p \rightarrow q$, only the contrapositive always has the same truth value as $p \rightarrow q$.

We first show that the contrapositive, $\neg q \rightarrow \neg p$, of a conditional statement $p \rightarrow q$ always has the same truth value as $p \rightarrow q$. To see this, note that the contrapositive is false only when $\neg p$ is false and $\neg q$ is true, that is, only when $p$ is true and $q$ is false. We now show that neither the converse, $q \rightarrow p$, nor the inverse, $\neg p \rightarrow \neg q$, has the same truth value as $p \rightarrow q$ for all possible truth values of $p$ and $q$. Note that when $p$ is true and $q$ is false, the original conditional statement is false, but the converse and the inverse are both true.

Remember that the contrapositive, but neither the converse or inverse, of a conditional statement is equivalent to it.

When two compound propositions always have the same truth value we call them **equivalent**, so that a conditional statement and its contrapositive are equivalent. The converse and the inverse of a conditional statement are also equivalent, as the reader can verify, but neither is equivalent to the original conditional statement. (We will study equivalent propositions in Section 1.3.) Take note that one of the most common logical errors is to assume that the converse or the inverse of a conditional statement is equivalent to this conditional statement.

We illustrate the use of conditional statements in Example 9.

**EXAMPLE 9**   What are the contrapositive, the converse, and the inverse of the conditional statement

"The home team wins whenever it is raining?"

*Solution:* Because "*q* whenever *p*" is one of the ways to express the conditional statement $p \rightarrow q$, the original statement can be rewritten as

"If it is raining, then the home team wins."

Consequently, the contrapositive of this conditional statement is

"If the home team does not win, then it is not raining."

The converse is

"If the home team wins, then it is raining."

The inverse is

"If it is not raining, then the home team does not win."

Only the contrapositive is equivalent to the original statement.   ◀

**BICONDITIONALS**   We now introduce another way to combine propositions that expresses that two propositions have the same truth value.

**DEFINITION 6**   Let *p* and *q* be propositions. The *biconditional statement* $p \leftrightarrow q$ is the proposition "*p* if and only if *q*." The biconditional statement $p \leftrightarrow q$ is true when *p* and *q* have the same truth values, and is false otherwise. Biconditional statements are also called *bi-implications*.

The truth table for $p \leftrightarrow q$ is shown in Table 6. Note that the statement $p \leftrightarrow q$ is true when both the conditional statements $p \rightarrow q$ and $q \rightarrow p$ are true and is false otherwise. That is why we use the words "if and only if" to express this logical connective and why it is symbolically written by combining the symbols $\rightarrow$ and $\leftarrow$. There are some other common ways to express $p \leftrightarrow q$:

"*p* is necessary and sufficient for *q*"
"if *p* then *q*, and conversely"
"*p* iff *q*."

The last way of expressing the biconditional statement $p \leftrightarrow q$ uses the abbreviation "iff" for "if and only if." Note that $p \leftrightarrow q$ has exactly the same truth value as $(p \rightarrow q) \wedge (q \rightarrow p)$.

| TABLE 6  The Truth Table for the Biconditional $p \leftrightarrow q$. | | |
|:---:|:---:|:---:|
| *p* | *q* | $p \leftrightarrow q$ |
| T | T | T |
| T | F | F |
| F | T | F |
| F | F | T |

**EXAMPLE 10**    Let $p$ be the statement "You can take the flight," and let $q$ be the statement "You buy a ticket." Then $p \leftrightarrow q$ is the statement

"You can take the flight if and only if you buy a ticket."

This statement is true if $p$ and $q$ are either both true or both false, that is, if you buy a ticket and can take the flight or if you do not buy a ticket and you cannot take the flight. It is false when $p$ and $q$ have opposite truth values, that is, when you do not buy a ticket, but you can take the flight (such as when you get a free trip) and when you buy a ticket but you cannot take the flight (such as when the airline bumps you).    ◄

IMPLICIT USE OF BICONDITIONALS    You should be aware that biconditionals are not always explicit in natural language. In particular, the "if and only if" construction used in biconditionals is rarely used in common language. Instead, biconditionals are often expressed using an "if, then" or an "only if" construction. The other part of the "if and only if" is implicit. That is, the converse is implied, but not stated. For example, consider the statement in English "If you finish your meal, then you can have dessert." What is really meant is "You can have dessert if and only if you finish your meal." This last statement is logically equivalent to the two statements "If you finish your meal, then you can have dessert" and "You can have dessert only if you finish your meal." Because of this imprecision in natural language, we need to make an assumption whether a conditional statement in natural language implicitly includes its converse. Because precision is essential in mathematics and in logic, we will always distinguish between the conditional statement $p \rightarrow q$ and the biconditional statement $p \leftrightarrow q$.

## Truth Tables of Compound Propositions

We have now introduced four important logical connectives—conjunctions, disjunctions, conditional statements, and biconditional statements—as well as negations. We can use these connectives to build up complicated compound propositions involving any number of propositional variables. We can use truth tables to determine the truth values of these compound propositions, as Example 11 illustrates. We use a separate column to find the truth value of each compound expression that occurs in the compound proposition as it is built up. The truth values of the compound proposition for each combination of truth values of the propositional variables in it is found in the final column of the table.

**EXAMPLE 11**    Construct the truth table of the compound proposition

$$(p \vee \neg q) \rightarrow (p \wedge q).$$

*Solution:* Because this truth table involves two propositional variables $p$ and $q$, there are four rows in this truth table, one for each of the pairs of truth values TT, TF, FT, and FF. The first two columns are used for the truth values of $p$ and $q$, respectively. In the third column we find the truth value of $\neg q$, needed to find the truth value of $p \vee \neg q$, found in the fourth column. The fifth column gives the truth value of $p \wedge q$. Finally, the truth value of $(p \vee \neg q) \rightarrow (p \wedge q)$ is found in the last column. The resulting truth table is shown in Table 7.    ◄

| TABLE 7  The Truth Table of $(p \vee \neg q) \rightarrow (p \wedge q)$. | | | | | |
|---|---|---|---|---|---|
| $p$ | $q$ | $\neg q$ | $p \vee \neg q$ | $p \wedge q$ | $(p \vee \neg q) \rightarrow (p \wedge q)$ |
| T | T | F | T | T | T |
| T | F | T | T | F | F |
| F | T | F | F | F | T |
| F | F | T | T | F | F |

## Precedence of Logical Operators

| TABLE 8 Precedence of Logical Operators. | |
|---|---|
| *Operator* | *Precedence* |
| ¬ | 1 |
| ∧ | 2 |
| ∨ | 3 |
| → | 4 |
| ↔ | 5 |

We can construct compound propositions using the negation operator and the logical operators defined so far. We will generally use parentheses to specify the order in which logical operators in a compound proposition are to be applied. For instance, $(p \lor q) \land (\neg r)$ is the conjunction of $p \lor q$ and $\neg r$. However, to reduce the number of parentheses, we specify that the negation operator is applied before all other logical operators. This means that $\neg p \land q$ is the conjunction of $\neg p$ and $q$, namely, $(\neg p) \land q$, not the negation of the conjunction of $p$ and $q$, namely $\neg(p \land q)$.

Another general rule of precedence is that the conjunction operator takes precedence over the disjunction operator, so that $p \land q \lor r$ means $(p \land q) \lor r$ rather than $p \land (q \lor r)$. Because this rule may be difficult to remember, we will continue to use parentheses so that the order of the disjunction and conjunction operators is clear.

Finally, it is an accepted rule that the conditional and biconditional operators $\to$ and $\leftrightarrow$ have lower precedence than the conjunction and disjunction operators, $\land$ and $\lor$. Consequently, $p \lor q \to r$ is the same as $(p \lor q) \to r$. We will use parentheses when the order of the conditional operator and biconditional operator is at issue, although the conditional operator has precedence over the biconditional operator. Table 8 displays the precedence levels of the logical operators, $\neg$, $\land$, $\lor$, $\to$, and $\leftrightarrow$.

## Logic and Bit Operations

| *Truth Value* | *Bit* |
|---|---|
| T | 1 |
| F | 0 |

Computers represent information using bits. A **bit** is a symbol with two possible values, namely, 0 (zero) and 1 (one). This meaning of the word bit comes from *b*inary dig*it*, because zeros and ones are the digits used in binary representations of numbers. The well-known statistician John Tukey introduced this terminology in 1946. A bit can be used to represent a truth value, because there are two truth values, namely, *true* and *false*. As is customarily done, we will use a 1 bit to represent true and a 0 bit to represent false. That is, 1 represents T (true), 0 represents F (false). A variable is called a **Boolean variable** if its value is either true or false. Consequently, a Boolean variable can be represented using a bit.

Computer **bit operations** correspond to the logical connectives. By replacing true by a one and false by a zero in the truth tables for the operators $\land$, $\lor$, and $\oplus$, the tables shown in Table 9 for the corresponding bit operations are obtained. We will also use the notation *OR*, *AND*, and *XOR* for the operators $\lor$, $\land$, and $\oplus$, as is done in various programming languages.

JOHN WILDER TUKEY (1915–2000)   Tukey, born in New Bedford, Massachusetts, was an only child. His parents, both teachers, decided home schooling would best develop his potential. His formal education began at Brown University, where he studied mathematics and chemistry. He received a master's degree in chemistry from Brown and continued his studies at Princeton University, changing his field of study from chemistry to mathematics. He received his Ph.D. from Princeton in 1939 for work in topology, when he was appointed an instructor in mathematics at Princeton. With the start of World War II, he joined the Fire Control Research Office, where he began working in statistics. Tukey found statistical research to his liking and impressed several leading statisticians with his skills. In 1945, at the conclusion of the war, Tukey returned to the mathematics department at Princeton as a professor of statistics, and he also took a position at AT&T Bell Laboratories. Tukey founded the Statistics Department at Princeton in 1966 and was its first chairman. Tukey made significant contributions to many areas of statistics, including the analysis of variance, the estimation of spectra of time series, inferences about the values of a set of parameters from a single experiment, and the philosophy of statistics. However, he is best known for his invention, with J. W. Cooley, of the fast Fourier transform. In addition to his contributions to statistics, Tukey was noted as a skilled wordsmith; he is credited with coining the terms *bit* and *software*.

Tukey contributed his insight and expertise by serving on the President's Science Advisory Committee. He chaired several important committees dealing with the environment, education, and chemicals and health. He also served on committees working on nuclear disarmament. Tukey received many awards, including the National Medal of Science.

HISTORICAL NOTE   There were several other suggested words for a binary digit, including *binit* and *bigit*, that never were widely accepted. The adoption of the word *bit* may be due to its meaning as a common English word. For an account of Tukey's coining of the word *bit*, see the April 1984 issue of *Annals of the History of Computing*.

| TABLE 9 Table for the Bit Operators *OR*, *AND*, and *XOR*. | | | | |
|---|---|---|---|---|
| $x$ | $y$ | $x \vee y$ | $x \wedge y$ | $x \oplus y$ |
| 0 | 0 | 0 | 0 | 0 |
| 0 | 1 | 1 | 0 | 1 |
| 1 | 0 | 1 | 0 | 1 |
| 1 | 1 | 1 | 1 | 0 |

Information is often represented using bit strings, which are lists of zeros and ones. When this is done, operations on the bit strings can be used to manipulate this information.

**DEFINITION 7**   A *bit string* is a sequence of zero or more bits. The *length* of this string is the number of bits in the string.

**EXAMPLE 12**   101010011 is a bit string of length nine.   ◀

We can extend bit operations to bit strings. We define the **bitwise *OR***, **bitwise *AND***, and **bitwise *XOR*** of two strings of the same length to be the strings that have as their bits the *OR*, *AND*, and *XOR* of the corresponding bits in the two strings, respectively. We use the symbols $\vee$, $\wedge$, and $\oplus$ to represent the bitwise *OR*, bitwise *AND*, and bitwise *XOR* operations, respectively. We illustrate bitwise operations on bit strings with Example 13.

**EXAMPLE 13**   Find the bitwise *OR*, bitwise *AND*, and bitwise *XOR* of the bit strings 01 1011 0110 and 11 0001 1101. (Here, and throughout this book, bit strings will be split into blocks of four bits to make them easier to read.)

*Solution:* The bitwise *OR*, bitwise *AND*, and bitwise *XOR* of these strings are obtained by taking the *OR*, *AND*, and *XOR* of the corresponding bits, respectively. This gives us

```
  01 1011 0110
  11 0001 1101
  _____
  11 1011 1111    bitwise OR
  01 0001 0100    bitwise AND
  10 1010 1011    bitwise XOR
```
◀

## Exercises

**1.** Which of these sentences are propositions? What are the truth values of those that are propositions?

   **a)** Boston is the capital of Massachusetts.
   **b)** Miami is the capital of Florida.
   **c)** $2 + 3 = 5$.
   **d)** $5 + 7 = 10$.
   **e)** $x + 2 = 11$.
   **f)** Answer this question.

**2.** Which of these are propositions? What are the truth values of those that are propositions?

   **a)** Do not pass go.
   **b)** What time is it?
   **c)** There are no black flies in Maine.

   **d)** $4 + x = 5$.
   **e)** The moon is made of green cheese.
   **f)** $2^n \geq 100$.

**3.** What is the negation of each of these propositions?

   **a)** Mei has an MP3 player.
   **b)** There is no pollution in New Jersey.
   **c)** $2 + 1 = 3$.
   **d)** The summer in Maine is hot and sunny.

**4.** What is the negation of each of these propositions?

   **a)** Jennifer and Teja are friends.
   **b)** There are 13 items in a baker's dozen.
   **c)** Abby sent more than 100 text messages every day.
   **d)** 121 is a perfect square.

**5.** What is the negation of each of these propositions?

   **a)** Steve has more than 100 GB free disk space on his laptop.
   **b)** Zach blocks e-mails and texts from Jennifer.
   **c)** $7 \cdot 11 \cdot 13 = 999$.
   **d)** Diane rode her bicycle 100 miles on Sunday.

**6.** Suppose that Smartphone A has 256 MB RAM and 32 GB ROM, and the resolution of its camera is 8 MP; Smartphone B has 288 MB RAM and 64 GB ROM, and the resolution of its camera is 4 MP; and Smartphone C has 128 MB RAM and 32 GB ROM, and the resolution of its camera is 5 MP. Determine the truth value of each of these propositions.

   **a)** Smartphone B has the most RAM of these three smartphones.
   **b)** Smartphone C has more ROM or a higher resolution camera than Smartphone B.
   **c)** Smartphone B has more RAM, more ROM, and a higher resolution camera than Smartphone A.
   **d)** If Smartphone B has more RAM and more ROM than Smartphone C, then it also has a higher resolution camera.
   **e)** Smartphone A has more RAM than Smartphone B if and only if Smartphone B has more RAM than Smartphone A.

**7.** Suppose that during the most recent fiscal year, the annual revenue of Acme Computer was 138 billion dollars and its net profit was 8 billion dollars, the annual revenue of Nadir Software was 87 billion dollars and its net profit was 5 billion dollars, and the annual revenue of Quixote Media was 111 billion dollars and its net profit was 13 billion dollars. Determine the truth value of each of these propositions for the most recent fiscal year.

   **a)** Quixote Media had the largest annual revenue.
   **b)** Nadir Software had the lowest net profit and Acme Computer had the largest annual revenue.
   **c)** Acme Computer had the largest net profit or Quixote Media had the largest net profit.
   **d)** If Quixote Media had the smallest net profit, then Acme Computer had the largest annual revenue.
   **e)** Nadir Software had the smallest net profit if and only if Acme Computer had the largest annual revenue.

**8.** Let $p$ and $q$ be the propositions

   $p$ : I bought a lottery ticket this week.
   $q$ : I won the million dollar jackpot.

Express each of these propositions as an English sentence.

   **a)** $\neg p$
   **b)** $p \vee q$
   **c)** $p \rightarrow q$
   **d)** $p \wedge q$
   **e)** $p \leftrightarrow q$
   **f)** $\neg p \rightarrow \neg q$
   **g)** $\neg p \wedge \neg q$
   **h)** $\neg p \vee (p \wedge q)$

**9.** Let $p$ and $q$ be the propositions "Swimming at the New Jersey shore is allowed" and "Sharks have been spotted near the shore," respectively. Express each of these compound propositions as an English sentence.

   **a)** $\neg q$
   **b)** $p \wedge q$
   **c)** $\neg p \vee q$
   **d)** $p \rightarrow \neg q$
   **e)** $\neg q \rightarrow p$
   **f)** $\neg p \rightarrow \neg q$
   **g)** $p \leftrightarrow \neg q$
   **h)** $\neg p \wedge (p \vee \neg q)$

**10.** Let $p$ and $q$ be the propositions "The election is decided" and "The votes have been counted," respectively. Express each of these compound propositions as an English sentence.

   **a)** $\neg p$
   **b)** $p \vee q$
   **c)** $\neg p \wedge q$
   **d)** $q \rightarrow p$
   **e)** $\neg q \rightarrow \neg p$
   **f)** $\neg p \rightarrow \neg q$
   **g)** $p \leftrightarrow q$
   **h)** $\neg q \vee (\neg p \wedge q)$

**11.** Let $p$ and $q$ be the propositions

   $p$ : It is below freezing.
   $q$ : It is snowing.

Write these propositions using $p$ and $q$ and logical connectives (including negations).

   **a)** It is below freezing and snowing.
   **b)** It is below freezing but not snowing.
   **c)** It is not below freezing and it is not snowing.
   **d)** It is either snowing or below freezing (or both).
   **e)** If it is below freezing, it is also snowing.
   **f)** Either it is below freezing or it is snowing, but it is not snowing if it is below freezing.
   **g)** That it is below freezing is necessary and sufficient for it to be snowing.

**12.** Let $p, q$, and $r$ be the propositions

   $p$ : You have the flu.
   $q$ : You miss the final examination.
   $r$ : You pass the course.

Express each of these propositions as an English sentence.

   **a)** $p \rightarrow q$
   **b)** $\neg q \leftrightarrow r$
   **c)** $q \rightarrow \neg r$
   **d)** $p \vee q \vee r$
   **e)** $(p \rightarrow \neg r) \vee (q \rightarrow \neg r)$
   **f)** $(p \wedge q) \vee (\neg q \wedge r)$

**13.** Let $p$ and $q$ be the propositions

   $p$ : You drive over 65 miles per hour.
   $q$ : You get a speeding ticket.

Write these propositions using $p$ and $q$ and logical connectives (including negations).

   **a)** You do not drive over 65 miles per hour.
   **b)** You drive over 65 miles per hour, but you do not get a speeding ticket.
   **c)** You will get a speeding ticket if you drive over 65 miles per hour.
   **d)** If you do not drive over 65 miles per hour, then you will not get a speeding ticket.
   **e)** Driving over 65 miles per hour is sufficient for getting a speeding ticket.
   **f)** You get a speeding ticket, but you do not drive over 65 miles per hour.
   **g)** Whenever you get a speeding ticket, you are driving over 65 miles per hour.

**14.** Let $p, q$, and $r$ be the propositions

   $p$ : You get an A on the final exam.
   $q$ : You do every exercise in this book.
   $r$ : You get an A in this class.

Write these propositions using $p, q$, and $r$ and logical connectives (including negations).

a) You get an A in this class, but you do not do every exercise in this book.

b) You get an A on the final, you do every exercise in this book, and you get an A in this class.

c) To get an A in this class, it is necessary for you to get an A on the final.

d) You get an A on the final, but you don't do every exercise in this book; nevertheless, you get an A in this class.

e) Getting an A on the final and doing every exercise in this book is sufficient for getting an A in this class.

f) You will get an A in this class if and only if you either do every exercise in this book or you get an A on the final.

**15.** Let $p$, $q$, and $r$ be the propositions

   $p$ : Grizzly bears have been seen in the area.
   $q$ : Hiking is safe on the trail.
   $r$ : Berries are ripe along the trail.

Write these propositions using $p$, $q$, and $r$ and logical connectives (including negations).

a) Berries are ripe along the trail, but grizzly bears have not been seen in the area.

b) Grizzly bears have not been seen in the area and hiking on the trail is safe, but berries are ripe along the trail.

c) If berries are ripe along the trail, hiking is safe if and only if grizzly bears have not been seen in the area.

d) It is not safe to hike on the trail, but grizzly bears have not been seen in the area and the berries along the trail are ripe.

e) For hiking on the trail to be safe, it is necessary but not sufficient that berries not be ripe along the trail and for grizzly bears not to have been seen in the area.

f) Hiking is not safe on the trail whenever grizzly bears have been seen in the area and berries are ripe along the trail.

**16.** Determine whether these biconditionals are true or false.

a) $2 + 2 = 4$ if and only if $1 + 1 = 2$.

b) $1 + 1 = 2$ if and only if $2 + 3 = 4$.

c) $1 + 1 = 3$ if and only if monkeys can fly.

d) $0 > 1$ if and only if $2 > 1$.

**17.** Determine whether each of these conditional statements is true or false.

a) If $1 + 1 = 2$, then $2 + 2 = 5$.

b) If $1 + 1 = 3$, then $2 + 2 = 4$.

c) If $1 + 1 = 3$, then $2 + 2 = 5$.

d) If monkeys can fly, then $1 + 1 = 3$.

**18.** Determine whether each of these conditional statements is true or false.

a) If $1 + 1 = 3$, then unicorns exist.

b) If $1 + 1 = 3$, then dogs can fly.

c) If $1 + 1 = 2$, then dogs can fly.

d) If $2 + 2 = 4$, then $1 + 2 = 3$.

**19.** For each of these sentences, determine whether an inclusive or, or an exclusive or, is intended. Explain your answer.

a) Coffee or tea comes with dinner.

b) A password must have at least three digits or be at least eight characters long.

c) The prerequisite for the course is a course in number theory or a course in cryptography.

d) You can pay using U.S. dollars or euros.

**20.** For each of these sentences, determine whether an inclusive or, or an exclusive or, is intended. Explain your answer.

a) Experience with C++ or Java is required.

b) Lunch includes soup or salad.

c) To enter the country you need a passport or a voter registration card.

d) Publish or perish.

**21.** For each of these sentences, state what the sentence means if the logical connective or is an inclusive or (that is, a disjunction) versus an exclusive or. Which of these meanings of or do you think is intended?

a) To take discrete mathematics, you must have taken calculus or a course in computer science.

b) When you buy a new car from Acme Motor Company, you get $2000 back in cash or a 2% car loan.

c) Dinner for two includes two items from column A or three items from column B.

d) School is closed if more than 2 feet of snow falls or if the wind chill is below $-100$.

**22.** Write each of these statements in the form "if $p$, then $q$" in English. [*Hint:* Refer to the list of common ways to express conditional statements provided in this section.]

a) It is necessary to wash the boss's car to get promoted.

b) Winds from the south imply a spring thaw.

c) A sufficient condition for the warranty to be good is that you bought the computer less than a year ago.

d) Willy gets caught whenever he cheats.

e) You can access the website only if you pay a subscription fee.

f) Getting elected follows from knowing the right people.

g) Carol gets seasick whenever she is on a boat.

**23.** Write each of these statements in the form "if $p$, then $q$" in English. [*Hint:* Refer to the list of common ways to express conditional statements.]

a) It snows whenever the wind blows from the northeast.

b) The apple trees will bloom if it stays warm for a week.

c) That the Pistons win the championship implies that they beat the Lakers.

d) It is necessary to walk 8 miles to get to the top of Long's Peak.

e) To get tenure as a professor, it is sufficient to be world-famous.

f) If you drive more than 400 miles, you will need to buy gasoline.

g) Your guarantee is good only if you bought your CD player less than 90 days ago.

h) Jan will go swimming unless the water is too cold.

**24.** Write each of these statements in the form "if $p$, then $q$" in English. [*Hint:* Refer to the list of common ways to express conditional statements provided in this section.]

**a)** I will remember to send you the address only if you send me an e-mail message.

**b)** To be a citizen of this country, it is sufficient that you were born in the United States.

**c)** If you keep your textbook, it will be a useful reference in your future courses.

**d)** The Red Wings will win the Stanley Cup if their goalie plays well.

**e)** That you get the job implies that you had the best credentials.

**f)** The beach erodes whenever there is a storm.

**g)** It is necessary to have a valid password to log on to the server.

**h)** You will reach the summit unless you begin your climb too late.

**25.** Write each of these propositions in the form "$p$ if and only if $q$" in English.

**a)** If it is hot outside you buy an ice cream cone, and if you buy an ice cream cone it is hot outside.

**b)** For you to win the contest it is necessary and sufficient that you have the only winning ticket.

**c)** You get promoted only if you have connections, and you have connections only if you get promoted.

**d)** If you watch television your mind will decay, and conversely.

**e)** The trains run late on exactly those days when I take it.

**26.** Write each of these propositions in the form "$p$ if and only if $q$" in English.

**a)** For you to get an A in this course, it is necessary and sufficient that you learn how to solve discrete mathematics problems.

**b)** If you read the newspaper every day, you will be informed, and conversely.

**c)** It rains if it is a weekend day, and it is a weekend day if it rains.

**d)** You can see the wizard only if the wizard is not in, and the wizard is not in only if you can see him.

**27.** State the converse, contrapositive, and inverse of each of these conditional statements.

**a)** If it snows today, I will ski tomorrow.

**b)** I come to class whenever there is going to be a quiz.

**c)** A positive integer is a prime only if it has no divisors other than 1 and itself.

**28.** State the converse, contrapositive, and inverse of each of these conditional statements.

**a)** If it snows tonight, then I will stay at home.

**b)** I go to the beach whenever it is a sunny summer day.

**c)** When I stay up late, it is necessary that I sleep until noon.

**29.** How many rows appear in a truth table for each of these compound propositions?

**a)** $p \rightarrow \neg p$

**b)** $(p \vee \neg r) \wedge (q \vee \neg s)$

**c)** $q \vee p \vee \neg s \vee \neg r \vee \neg t \vee u$

**d)** $(p \wedge r \wedge t) \leftrightarrow (q \wedge t)$

**30.** How many rows appear in a truth table for each of these compound propositions?

**a)** $(q \rightarrow \neg p) \vee (\neg p \rightarrow \neg q)$

**b)** $(p \vee \neg t) \wedge (p \vee \neg s)$

**c)** $(p \rightarrow r) \vee (\neg s \rightarrow \neg t) \vee (\neg u \rightarrow v)$

**d)** $(p \wedge r \wedge s) \vee (q \wedge t) \vee (r \wedge \neg t)$

**31.** Construct a truth table for each of these compound propositions.

**a)** $p \wedge \neg p$      **b)** $p \vee \neg p$

**c)** $(p \vee \neg q) \rightarrow q$      **d)** $(p \vee q) \rightarrow (p \wedge q)$

**e)** $(p \rightarrow q) \leftrightarrow (\neg q \rightarrow \neg p)$

**f)** $(p \rightarrow q) \rightarrow (q \rightarrow p)$

**32.** Construct a truth table for each of these compound propositions.

**a)** $p \rightarrow \neg p$      **b)** $p \leftrightarrow \neg p$

**c)** $p \oplus (p \vee q)$      **d)** $(p \wedge q) \rightarrow (p \vee q)$

**e)** $(q \rightarrow \neg p) \leftrightarrow (p \leftrightarrow q)$

**f)** $(p \leftrightarrow q) \oplus (p \leftrightarrow \neg q)$

**33.** Construct a truth table for each of these compound propositions.

**a)** $(p \vee q) \rightarrow (p \oplus q)$    **b)** $(p \oplus q) \rightarrow (p \wedge q)$

**c)** $(p \vee q) \oplus (p \wedge q)$    **d)** $(p \leftrightarrow q) \oplus (\neg p \leftrightarrow q)$

**e)** $(p \leftrightarrow q) \oplus (\neg p \leftrightarrow \neg r)$

**f)** $(p \oplus q) \rightarrow (p \oplus \neg q)$

**34.** Construct a truth table for each of these compound propositions.

**a)** $p \oplus p$      **b)** $p \oplus \neg p$

**c)** $p \oplus \neg q$      **d)** $\neg p \oplus \neg q$

**e)** $(p \oplus q) \vee (p \oplus \neg q)$    **f)** $(p \oplus q) \wedge (p \oplus \neg q)$

**35.** Construct a truth table for each of these compound propositions.

**a)** $p \rightarrow \neg q$      **b)** $\neg p \leftrightarrow q$

**c)** $(p \rightarrow q) \vee (\neg p \rightarrow q)$   **d)** $(p \rightarrow q) \wedge (\neg p \rightarrow q)$

**e)** $(p \leftrightarrow q) \vee (\neg p \leftrightarrow q)$

**f)** $(\neg p \leftrightarrow \neg q) \leftrightarrow (p \leftrightarrow q)$

**36.** Construct a truth table for each of these compound propositions.

**a)** $(p \vee q) \vee r$      **b)** $(p \vee q) \wedge r$

**c)** $(p \wedge q) \vee r$      **d)** $(p \wedge q) \wedge r$

**e)** $(p \vee q) \wedge \neg r$      **f)** $(p \wedge q) \vee \neg r$

**37.** Construct a truth table for each of these compound propositions.

**a)** $p \rightarrow (\neg q \vee r)$

**b)** $\neg p \rightarrow (q \rightarrow r)$

**c)** $(p \rightarrow q) \vee (\neg p \rightarrow r)$

**d)** $(p \rightarrow q) \wedge (\neg p \rightarrow r)$

**e)** $(p \leftrightarrow q) \vee (\neg q \leftrightarrow r)$

**f)** $(\neg p \leftrightarrow \neg q) \leftrightarrow (q \leftrightarrow r)$

**38.** Construct a truth table for $((p \rightarrow q) \rightarrow r) \rightarrow s$.

**39.** Construct a truth table for $(p \leftrightarrow q) \leftrightarrow (r \leftrightarrow s)$.

**40.** Explain, without using a truth table, why $(p \vee \neg q) \wedge (q \vee \neg r) \wedge (r \vee \neg p)$ is true when $p$, $q$, and $r$ have the same truth value and it is false otherwise.

**41.** Explain, without using a truth table, why $(p \vee q \vee r) \wedge (\neg p \vee \neg q \vee \neg r)$ is true when at least one of $p$, $q$, and $r$ is true and at least one is false, but is false when all three variables have the same truth value.

**42.** What is the value of $x$ after each of these statements is encountered in a computer program, if $x = 1$ before the statement is reached?

  **a)** **if** $x + 2 = 3$ **then** $x := x + 1$
  **b)** **if** $(x + 1 = 3)$ *OR* $(2x + 2 = 3)$ **then** $x := x + 1$
  **c)** **if** $(2x + 3 = 5)$ *AND* $(3x + 4 = 7)$ **then** $x := x + 1$
  **d)** **if** $(x + 1 = 2)$ *XOR* $(x + 2 = 3)$ **then** $x := x + 1$
  **e)** **if** $x < 2$ **then** $x := x + 1$

**43.** Find the bitwise *OR*, bitwise *AND*, and bitwise *XOR* of each of these pairs of bit strings.

  **a)** 101 1110, 010 0001
  **b)** 1111 0000, 1010 1010
  **c)** 00 0111 0001, 10 0100 1000
  **d)** 11 1111 1111, 00 0000 0000

**44.** Evaluate each of these expressions.

  **a)** 1 1000 $\wedge$ (0 1011 $\vee$ 1 1011)
  **b)** (0 1111 $\wedge$ 1 0101) $\vee$ 0 1000
  **c)** (0 1010 $\oplus$ 1 1011) $\oplus$ 0 1000
  **d)** (1 1011 $\vee$ 0 1010) $\wedge$ (1 0001 $\vee$ 1 1011)

**Fuzzy logic** is used in artificial intelligence. In fuzzy logic, a proposition has a truth value that is a number between 0 and 1, inclusive. A proposition with a truth value of 0 is false and one with a truth value of 1 is true. Truth values that are between 0 and 1 indicate varying degrees of truth. For instance, the truth value 0.8 can be assigned to the statement "Fred is happy," because Fred is happy most of the time, and the truth value 0.4 can be assigned to the statement "John is happy," because John is happy slightly less than half the time. Use these truth values to solve Exercises 45–47.

**45.** The truth value of the negation of a proposition in fuzzy logic is 1 minus the truth value of the proposition. What are the truth values of the statements "Fred is not happy" and "John is not happy?"

**46.** The truth value of the conjunction of two propositions in fuzzy logic is the minimum of the truth values of the two propositions. What are the truth values of the statements "Fred and John are happy" and "Neither Fred nor John is happy?"

**47.** The truth value of the disjunction of two propositions in fuzzy logic is the maximum of the truth values of the two propositions. What are the truth values of the statements "Fred is happy, or John is happy" and "Fred is not happy, or John is not happy?"

**∗48.** Is the assertion "This statement is false" a proposition?

**∗49.** The $n$th statement in a list of 100 statements is "Exactly $n$ of the statements in this list are false."

  **a)** What conclusions can you draw from these statements?
  **b)** Answer part (a) if the $n$th statement is "At least $n$ of the statements in this list are false."
  **c)** Answer part (b) assuming that the list contains 99 statements.

**50.** An ancient Sicilian legend says that the barber in a remote town who can be reached only by traveling a dangerous mountain road shaves those people, and only those people, who do not shave themselves. Can there be such a barber?

## 1.2    Applications of Propositional Logic

### Introduction

Logic has many important applications to mathematics, computer science, and numerous other disciplines. Statements in mathematics and the sciences and in natural language often are imprecise or ambiguous. To make such statements precise, they can be translated into the language of logic. For example, logic is used in the specification of software and hardware, because these specifications need to be precise before development begins. Furthermore, propositional logic and its rules can be used to design computer circuits, to construct computer programs, to verify the correctness of programs, and to build expert systems. Logic can be used to analyze and solve many familiar puzzles. Software systems based on the rules of logic have been developed for constructing some, but not all, types of proofs automatically. We will discuss some of these applications of propositional logic in this section and in later chapters.

### Translating English Sentences

There are many reasons to translate English sentences into expressions involving propositional variables and logical connectives. In particular, English (and every other human language) is often ambiguous. Translating sentences into compound statements (and other types of logical expressions, which we will introduce later in this chapter) removes the ambiguity. Note that this may involve making a set of reasonable assumptions based on the intended meaning of the sentence. Moreover, once we have translated sentences from English into logical expressions we can analyze these logical expressions to determine their truth values, we can manipulate them, and we can use rules of inference (which are discussed in Section 1.6) to reason about them.

To illustrate the process of translating an English sentence into a logical expression, consider Examples 1 and 2.

**EXAMPLE 1**    How can this English sentence be translated into a logical expression?

"You can access the Internet from campus only if you are a computer science major or you are not a freshman."

*Extra Examples*

*Solution:* There are many ways to translate this sentence into a logical expression. Although it is possible to represent the sentence by a single propositional variable, such as $p$, this would not be useful when analyzing its meaning or reasoning with it. Instead, we will use propositional variables to represent each sentence part and determine the appropriate logical connectives between them. In particular, we let $a$, $c$, and $f$ represent "You can access the Internet from campus," "You are a computer science major," and "You are a freshman," respectively. Noting that "only if" is one way a conditional statement can be expressed, this sentence can be represented as

$$a \rightarrow (c \vee \neg f).$$ ◀

**EXAMPLE 2**    How can this English sentence be translated into a logical expression?

"You cannot ride the roller coaster if you are under 4 feet tall unless you are older than 16 years old."

*Solution:* Let $q$, $r$, and $s$ represent "You can ride the roller coaster," "You are under 4 feet tall," and "You are older than 16 years old," respectively. Then the sentence can be translated to

$$(r \wedge \neg s) \rightarrow \neg q.$$

Of course, there are other ways to represent the original sentence as a logical expression, but the one we have used should meet our needs. ◀

## System Specifications

Translating sentences in natural language (such as English) into logical expressions is an essential part of specifying both hardware and software systems. System and software engineers take requirements in natural language and produce precise and unambiguous specifications that can be used as the basis for system development. Example 3 shows how compound propositions can be used in this process.

**EXAMPLE 3**    Express the specification "The automated reply cannot be sent when the file system is full" using logical connectives.

*Extra Examples*

*Solution:* One way to translate this is to let $p$ denote "The automated reply can be sent" and $q$ denote "The file system is full." Then $\neg p$ represents "It is not the case that the automated reply can be sent," which can also be expressed as "The automated reply cannot be sent." Consequently, our specification can be represented by the conditional statement $q \rightarrow \neg p$.  ◀

System specifications should be **consistent**, that is, they should not contain conflicting requirements that could be used to derive a contradiction. When specifications are not consistent, there would be no way to develop a system that satisfies all specifications.

**EXAMPLE 4**    Determine whether these system specifications are consistent:

"The diagnostic message is stored in the buffer or it is retransmitted."
"The diagnostic message is not stored in the buffer."
"If the diagnostic message is stored in the buffer, then it is retransmitted."

*Solution:* To determine whether these specifications are consistent, we first express them using logical expressions. Let $p$ denote "The diagnostic message is stored in the buffer" and let $q$ denote "The diagnostic message is retransmitted." The specifications can then be written as $p \vee q$, $\neg p$, and $p \rightarrow q$. An assignment of truth values that makes all three specifications true must have $p$ false to make $\neg p$ true. Because we want $p \vee q$ to be true but $p$ must be false, $q$ must be true. Because $p \rightarrow q$ is true when $p$ is false and $q$ is true, we conclude that these specifications are consistent, because they are all true when $p$ is false and $q$ is true. We could come to the same conclusion by use of a truth table to examine the four possible assignments of truth values to $p$ and $q$.  ◀

**EXAMPLE 5**    Do the system specifications in Example 4 remain consistent if the specification "The diagnostic message is not retransmitted" is added?

*Solution:* By the reasoning in Example 4, the three specifications from that example are true only in the case when $p$ is false and $q$ is true. However, this new specification is $\neg q$, which is false when $q$ is true. Consequently, these four specifications are inconsistent.  ◀

## Boolean Searches

Links

Logical connectives are used extensively in searches of large collections of information, such as indexes of Web pages. Because these searches employ techniques from propositional logic, they are called **Boolean searches**.

In Boolean searches, the connective *AND* is used to match records that contain both of two search terms, the connective *OR* is used to match one or both of two search terms, and the connective *NOT* (sometimes written as *AND NOT* ) is used to exclude a particular search term. Careful planning of how logical connectives are used is often required when Boolean searches are used to locate information of potential interest. Example 6 illustrates how Boolean searches are carried out.

**EXAMPLE 6**    **Web Page Searching**    Most Web search engines support Boolean searching techniques, which usually can help find Web pages about particular subjects. For instance, using Boolean searching to find Web pages about universities in New Mexico, we can look for pages matching NEW *AND* MEXICO *AND* UNIVERSITIES. The results of this search will include those pages that contain the three words NEW, MEXICO, and UNIVERSITIES. This will include all of the pages of interest, together with others such as a page about new universities in Mexico. (Note that in Google, and many other search engines, the word "AND" is not needed, although it is

Extra
Examples

understood, because all search terms are included by default. These search engines also support the use of quotation marks to search for specific phrases. So, it may be more effective to search for pages matching "New Mexico" *AND* UNIVERSITIES.)

Next, to find pages that deal with universities in New Mexico or Arizona, we can search for pages matching (NEW *AND* MEXICO *OR* ARIZONA) *AND* UNIVERSITIES. (*Note:* Here the *AND* operator takes precedence over the *OR* operator. Also, in Google, the terms used for this search would be NEW MEXICO *OR* ARIZONA.) The results of this search will include all pages that contain the word UNIVERSITIES and either both the words NEW and MEXICO or the word ARIZONA. Again, pages besides those of interest will be listed. Finally, to find Web pages that deal with universities in Mexico (and not New Mexico), we might first look for pages matching MEXICO *AND* UNIVERSITIES, but because the results of this search will include pages about universities in New Mexico, as well as universities in Mexico, it might be better to search for pages matching (MEXICO *AND* UNIVERSITIES) *NOT* NEW. The results of this search include pages that contain both the words MEXICO and UNIVERSITIES but do not contain the word NEW. (In Google, and many other search engines, the word "NOT" is replaced by the symbol "-". In Google, the terms used for this last search would be MEXICO UNIVERSITIES -NEW.)    ◄

## Logic Puzzles

**Links**

Puzzles that can be solved using logical reasoning are known as **logic puzzles**. Solving logic puzzles is an excellent way to practice working with the rules of logic. Also, computer programs designed to carry out logical reasoning often use well-known logic puzzles to illustrate their capabilities. Many people enjoy solving logic puzzles, published in periodicals, books, and on the Web, as a recreational activity.

We will discuss two logic puzzles here. We begin with a puzzle originally posed by Raymond Smullyan, a master of logic puzzles, who has published more than a dozen books containing challenging puzzles that involve logical reasoning. In Section 1.3 we will also discuss the extremely popular logic puzzle Sudoku.

**EXAMPLE 7**

**Extra Examples**

In [Sm78] Smullyan posed many puzzles about an island that has two kinds of inhabitants, knights, who always tell the truth, and their opposites, knaves, who always lie. You encounter two people $A$ and $B$. What are $A$ and $B$ if $A$ says "$B$ is a knight" and $B$ says "The two of us are opposite types?"

*Solution:* Let $p$ and $q$ be the statements that $A$ is a knight and $B$ is a knight, respectively, so that $\neg p$ and $\neg q$ are the statements that $A$ is a knave and $B$ is a knave, respectively.

We first consider the possibility that $A$ is a knight; this is the statement that $p$ is true. If $A$ is a knight, then he is telling the truth when he says that $B$ is a knight, so that $q$ is true, and $A$ and $B$ are the same type. However, if $B$ is a knight, then $B$'s statement that $A$ and $B$ are of opposite types, the statement $(p \wedge \neg q) \vee (\neg p \wedge q)$, would have to be true, which it is not, because $A$ and $B$ are both knights. Consequently, we can conclude that $A$ is not a knight, that is, that $p$ is false.

If $A$ is a knave, then because everything a knave says is false, $A$'s statement that $B$ is a knight, that is, that $q$ is true, is a lie. This means that $q$ is false and $B$ is also a knave. Furthermore, if $B$ is a knave, then $B$'s statement that $A$ and $B$ are opposite types is a lie, which is consistent with both $A$ and $B$ being knaves. We can conclude that both $A$ and $B$ are knaves.    ◄

We pose more of Smullyan's puzzles about knights and knaves in Exercises 19–23. In Exercises 24–31 we introduce related puzzles where we have three types of people, knights and knaves as in this puzzle together with spies who can lie.

Next, we pose a puzzle known as the **muddy children puzzle** for the case of two children.

EXAMPLE 8   A father tells his two children, a boy and a girl, to play in their backyard without getting dirty. However, while playing, both children get mud on their foreheads. When the children stop playing, the father says "At least one of you has a muddy forehead," and then asks the children to answer "Yes" or "No" to the question: "Do you know whether you have a muddy forehead?" The father asks this question twice. What will the children answer each time this question is asked, assuming that a child can see whether his or her sibling has a muddy forehead, but cannot see his or her own forehead? Assume that both children are honest and that the children answer each question simultaneously.

*Solution:* Let $s$ be the statement that the son has a muddy forehead and let $d$ be the statement that the daughter has a muddy forehead. When the father says that at least one of the two children has a muddy forehead, he is stating that the disjunction $s \lor d$ is true. Both children will answer "No" the first time the question is asked because each sees mud on the other child's forehead. That is, the son knows that $d$ is true, but does not know whether $s$ is true, and the daughter knows that $s$ is true, but does not know whether $d$ is true.

After the son has answered "No" to the first question, the daughter can determine that $d$ must be true. This follows because when the first question is asked, the son knows that $s \lor d$ is true, but cannot determine whether $s$ is true. Using this information, the daughter can conclude that $d$ must be true, for if $d$ were false, the son could have reasoned that because $s \lor d$ is true, then $s$ must be true, and he would have answered "Yes" to the first question. The son can reason in a similar way to determine that $s$ must be true. It follows that both children answer "Yes" the second time the question is asked.                                                                    ◄

## Logic Circuits

Propositional logic can be applied to the design of computer hardware. This was first observed in 1938 by Claude Shannon in his MIT master's thesis. In Chapter 12 we will study this topic in depth. (See that chapter for a biography of Shannon.) We give a brief introduction to this application here.

A **logic circuit** (or **digital circuit**) receives input signals $p_1, p_2, \ldots, p_n$, each a bit [either 0 (off) or 1 (on)], and produces output signals $s_1, s_2, \ldots, s_n$, each a bit. In this section we will restrict our attention to logic circuits with a single output signal; in general, digital circuits may have multiple outputs.

*In Chapter 12 we design some useful circuits.*

RAYMOND SMULLYAN (BORN 1919)   Raymond Smullyan dropped out of high school. He wanted to study what he was really interested in and not standard high school material. After jumping from one university to the next, he earned an undergraduate degree in mathematics at the University of Chicago in 1955. He paid his college expenses by performing magic tricks at parties and clubs. He obtained a Ph.D. in logic in 1959 at Princeton, studying under Alonzo Church. After graduating from Princeton, he taught mathematics and logic at Dartmouth College, Princeton University, Yeshiva University, and the City University of New York. He joined the philosophy department at Indiana University in 1981 where he is now an emeritus professor.

Smullyan has written many books on recreational logic and mathematics, including *Satan, Cantor, and Infinity; What Is the Name of This Book?; The Lady or the Tiger?; Alice in Puzzleland; To Mock a Mockingbird; Forever Undecided;* and *The Riddle of Scheherazade: Amazing Logic Puzzles, Ancient and Modern.* Because his logic puzzles are challenging, entertaining, and thought-provoking, he is considered to be a modern-day Lewis Carroll. Smullyan has also written several books about the application of deductive logic to chess, three collections of philosophical essays and aphorisms, and several advanced books on mathematical logic and set theory. He is particularly interested in self-reference and has worked on extending some of Gödel's results that show that it is impossible to write a computer program that can solve all mathematical problems. He is also particularly interested in explaining ideas from mathematical logic to the public.

Smullyan is a talented musician and often plays piano with his wife, who is a concert-level pianist. Making telescopes is one of his hobbies. He is also interested in optics and stereo photography. He states "I've never had a conflict between teaching and research as some people do because when I'm teaching, I'm doing research." Smullyan is the subject of a documentary short film entitled *This Film Needs No Title.*

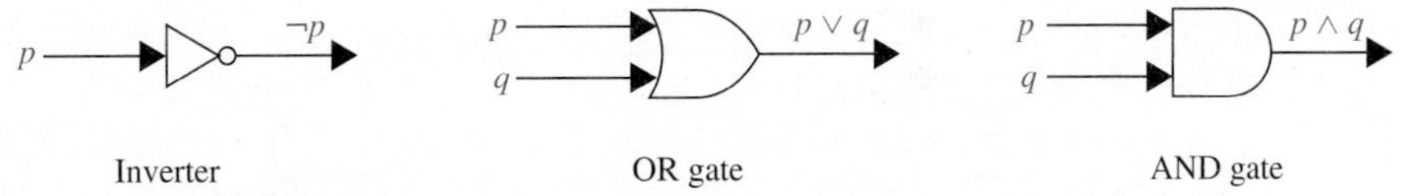

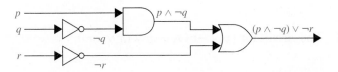

**FIGURE 1    Basic logic gates.**

**FIGURE 2    A combinatorial circuit.**

Complicated digital circuits can be constructed from three basic circuits, called **gates**, shown in Figure 1. The **inverter**, or **NOT gate**, takes an input bit $p$, and produces as output $\neg p$. The **OR gate** takes two input signals $p$ and $q$, each a bit, and produces as output the signal $p \vee q$. Finally, the **AND gate** takes two input signals $p$ and $q$, each a bit, and produces as output the signal $p \wedge q$. We use combinations of these three basic gates to build more complicated circuits, such as that shown in Figure 2.

Given a circuit built from the basic logic gates and the inputs to the circuit, we determine the output by tracing through the circuit, as Example 9 shows.

**EXAMPLE 9**    Determine the output for the combinatorial circuit in Figure 2.

*Solution:* In Figure 2 we display the output of each logic gate in the circuit. We see that the AND gate takes input of $p$ and $\neg q$, the output of the inverter with input $q$, and produces $p \wedge \neg q$. Next, we note that the OR gate takes input $p \wedge \neg q$ and $\neg r$, the output of the inverter with input $r$, and produces the final output $(p \wedge \neg q) \vee \neg r$.    ◀

Suppose that we have a formula for the output of a digital circuit in terms of negations, disjunctions, and conjunctions. Then, we can systematically build a digital circuit with the desired output, as illustrated in Example 10.

**EXAMPLE 10**    Build a digital circuit that produces the output $(p \vee \neg r) \wedge (\neg p \vee (q \vee \neg r))$ when given input bits $p$, $q$, and $r$.

*Solution:* To construct the desired circuit, we build separate circuits for $p \vee \neg r$ and for $\neg p \vee (q \vee \neg r)$ and combine them using an AND gate. To construct a circuit for $p \vee \neg r$, we use an inverter to produce $\neg r$ from the input $r$. Then, we use an OR gate to combine $p$ and $\neg r$. To build a circuit for $\neg p \vee (q \vee \neg r)$, we first use an inverter to obtain $\neg r$. Then we use an OR gate with inputs $q$ and $\neg r$ to obtain $q \vee \neg r$. Finally, we use another inverter and an OR gate to get $\neg p \vee (q \vee \neg r)$ from the inputs $p$ and $q \vee \neg r$.

To complete the construction, we employ a final AND gate, with inputs $p \vee \neg r$ and $\neg p \vee (q \vee \neg r)$. The resulting circuit is displayed in Figure 3.    ◀

We will study logic circuits in great detail in Chapter 12 in the context of Boolean algebra, and with different notation.

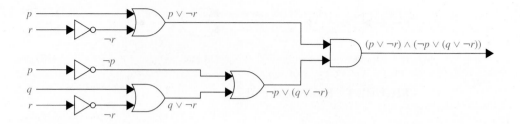

**FIGURE 3**    **The circuit for $(p \vee \neg r) \wedge (\neg p \vee (q \vee \neg r))$.**

# Exercises

In Exercises 1–6, translate the given statement into propositional logic using the propositions provided.

1. You cannot edit a protected Wikipedia entry unless you are an administrator. Express your answer in terms of $e$: "You can edit a protected Wikipedia entry" and $a$: "You are an administrator."

2. You can see the movie only if you are over 18 years old or you have the permission of a parent. Express your answer in terms of $m$: "You can see the movie," $e$: "You are over 18 years old," and $p$: "You have the permission of a parent."

3. You can graduate only if you have completed the requirements of your major and you do not owe money to the university and you do not have an overdue library book. Express your answer in terms of $g$: "You can graduate," $m$: "You owe money to the university," $r$: "You have completed the requirements of your major," and $b$: "You have an overdue library book."

4. To use the wireless network in the airport you must pay the daily fee unless you are a subscriber to the service. Express your answer in terms of $w$: "You can use the wireless network in the airport," $d$: "You pay the daily fee," and $s$: "You are a subscriber to the service."

5. You are eligible to be President of the U.S.A. only if you are at least 35 years old, were born in the U.S.A, or at the time of your birth both of your parents were citizens, and you have lived at least 14 years in the country. Express your answer in terms of $e$: "You are eligible to be President of the U.S.A.," $a$: "You are at least 35 years old," $b$: "You were born in the U.S.A," $p$: "At the time of your birth, both of your parents where citizens," and $r$: "You have lived at least 14 years in the U.S.A."

6. You can upgrade your operating system only if you have a 32-bit processor running at 1 GHz or faster, at least 1 GB RAM, and 16 GB free hard disk space, or a 64-bit processor running at 2 GHz or faster, at least 2 GB RAM, and at least 32 GB free hard disk space. Express you answer in terms of $u$: "You can upgrade your operating system," $b_{32}$: "You have a 32-bit processor," $b_{64}$:

"You have a 64-bit processor," $g_1$: "Your processor runs at 1 GHz or faster," $g_2$: "Your processor runs at 2 GHz or faster," $r_1$: "Your processor has at least 1 GB RAM," $r_2$: "Your processor has at least 2 GB RAM," $h_{16}$: "You have at least 16 GB free hard disk space," and $h_{32}$: "You have at least 32 GB free hard disk space."

7. Express these system specifications using the propositions $p$ "The message is scanned for viruses" and $q$ "The message was sent from an unknown system" together with logical connectives (including negations).

    a) "The message is scanned for viruses whenever the message was sent from an unknown system."

    b) "The message was sent from an unknown system but it was not scanned for viruses."

    c) "It is necessary to scan the message for viruses whenever it was sent from an unknown system."

    d) "When a message is not sent from an unknown system it is not scanned for viruses."

8. Express these system specifications using the propositions $p$ "The user enters a valid password," $q$ "Access is granted," and $r$ "The user has paid the subscription fee" and logical connectives (including negations).

    a) "The user has paid the subscription fee, but does not enter a valid password."

    b) "Access is granted whenever the user has paid the subscription fee and enters a valid password."

    c) "Access is denied if the user has not paid the subscription fee."

    d) "If the user has not entered a valid password but has paid the subscription fee, then access is granted."

9. Are these system specifications consistent? "The system is in multiuser state if and only if it is operating normally. If the system is operating normally, the kernel is functioning. The kernel is not functioning or the system is in interrupt mode. If the system is not in multiuser state, then it is in interrupt mode. The system is not in interrupt mode."

10. Are these system specifications consistent? "Whenever the system software is being upgraded, users cannot access the file system. If users can access the file system, then they can save new files. If users cannot save new files, then the system software is not being upgraded."

11. Are these system specifications consistent? "The router can send packets to the edge system only if it supports the new address space. For the router to support the new address space it is necessary that the latest software release be installed, The router can send packets to the edge system if the latest software release is installed, The router does not support the new address space."

12. Are these system specifications consistent? "If the file system is not locked, then new messages will be queued. If the file system is not locked, then the system is functioning normally, and conversely. If new messages are not queued, then they will be sent to the message buffer. If the file system is not locked, then new messages will be sent to the message buffer. New messages will not be sent to the message buffer."

13. What Boolean search would you use to look for Web pages about beaches in New Jersey? What if you wanted to find Web pages about beaches on the isle of Jersey (in the English Channel)?

14. What Boolean search would you use to look for Web pages about hiking in West Virginia? What if you wanted to find Web pages about hiking in Virginia, but not in West Virginia?

\*15. Each inhabitant of a remote village always tells the truth or always lies. A villager will give only a "Yes" or a "No" response to a question a tourist asks. Suppose you are a tourist visiting this area and come to a fork in the road. One branch leads to the ruins you want to visit; the other branch leads deep into the jungle. A villager is standing at the fork in the road. What one question can you ask the villager to determine which branch to take?

16. An explorer is captured by a group of cannibals. There are two types of cannibals—those who always tell the truth and those who always lie. The cannibals will barbecue the explorer unless he can determine whether a particular cannibal always lies or always tells the truth. He is allowed to ask the cannibal exactly one question.

    a) Explain why the question "Are you a liar?" does not work.

    b) Find a question that the explorer can use to determine whether the cannibal always lies or always tells the truth.

17. When three professors are seated in a restaurant, the hostess asks them: "Does everyone want coffee?" The first professor says: "I do not know." The second professor then says: "I do not know." Finally, the third professor says: "No, not everyone wants coffee." The hostess comes back and gives coffee to the professors who want it. How did she figure out who wanted coffee?

18. When planning a party you want to know whom to invite. Among the people you would like to invite are three touchy friends. You know that if Jasmine attends, she will become unhappy if Samir is there, Samir will attend only if Kanti will be there, and Kanti will not attend unless Jasmine also does. Which combinations of these three friends can you invite so as not to make someone unhappy?

Exercises 19–23 relate to inhabitants of the island of knights and knaves created by Smullyan, where knights always tell the truth and knaves always lie. You encounter two people, A and B. Determine, if possible, what A and B are if they address you in the ways described. If you cannot determine what these two people are, can you draw any conclusions?

19. A says "At least one of us is a knave" and B says nothing.

20. A says "The two of us are both knights" and B says "A is a knave."

21. A says "I am a knave or B is a knight" and B says nothing.

22. Both A and B say "I am a knight."

23. A says "We are both knaves" and B says nothing.

Exercises 24–31 relate to inhabitants of an island on which there are three kinds of people: knights who always tell the truth, knaves who always lie, and spies (called normals by Smullyan [Sm78]) who can either lie or tell the truth. You encounter three people, A, B, and C. You know one of these people is a knight, one is a knave, and one is a spy. Each of the three people knows the type of person each of other two is. For each of these situations, if possible, determine whether there is a unique solution and determine who the knave, knight, and spy are. When there is no unique solution, list all possible solutions or state that there are no solutions.

24. A says "C is the knave," B says, "A is the knight," and C says "I am the spy."

25. A says "I am the knight," B says "I am the knave," and C says "B is the knight."

26. A says "I am the knave," B says "I am the knave," and C says "I am the knave."

27. A says "I am the knight," B says "A is telling the truth," and C says "I am the spy."

28. A says "I am the knight," B says, "A is not the knave," and C says "B is not the knave."

29. A says "I am the knight," B says "I am the knight," and C says "I am the knight."

30. A says "I am not the spy," B says "I am not the spy," and C says "A is the spy."

31. A says "I am not the spy," B says "I am not the spy," and C says "I am not the spy."

Exercises 32–38 are puzzles that can be solved by translating statements into logical expressions and reasoning from these expressions using truth tables.

32. The police have three suspects for the murder of Mr. Cooper: Mr. Smith, Mr. Jones, and Mr. Williams. Smith, Jones, and Williams each declare that they did not kill Cooper. Smith also states that Cooper was a friend of Jones and that Williams disliked him. Jones also states that he did not know Cooper and that he was out of town the day Cooper was killed. Williams also states that he

saw both Smith and Jones with Cooper the day of the killing and that either Smith or Jones must have killed him. Can you determine who the murderer was if

a) one of the three men is guilty, the two innocent men are telling the truth, but the statements of the guilty man may or may not be true?

b) innocent men do not lie?

33. Steve would like to determine the relative salaries of three coworkers using two facts. First, he knows that if Fred is not the highest paid of the three, then Janice is. Second, he knows that if Janice is not the lowest paid, then Maggie is paid the most. Is it possible to determine the relative salaries of Fred, Maggie, and Janice from what Steve knows? If so, who is paid the most and who the least? Explain your reasoning.

34. Five friends have access to a chat room. Is it possible to determine who is chatting if the following information is known? Either Kevin or Heather, or both, are chatting. Either Randy or Vijay, but not both, are chatting. If Abby is chatting, so is Randy. Vijay and Kevin are either both chatting or neither is. If Heather is chatting, then so are Abby and Kevin. Explain your reasoning.

35. A detective has interviewed four witnesses to a crime. From the stories of the witnesses the detective has concluded that if the butler is telling the truth then so is the cook; the cook and the gardener cannot both be telling the truth; the gardener and the handyman are not both lying; and if the handyman is telling the truth then the cook is lying. For each of the four witnesses, can the detective determine whether that person is telling the truth or lying? Explain your reasoning.

36. Four friends have been identified as suspects for an unauthorized access into a computer system. They have made statements to the investigating authorities. Alice said "Carlos did it." John said "I did not do it." Carlos said "Diana did it." Diana said "Carlos lied when he said that I did it."

a) If the authorities also know that exactly one of the four suspects is telling the truth, who did it? Explain your reasoning.

b) If the authorities also know that exactly one is lying, who did it? Explain your reasoning.

37. Suppose there are signs on the doors to two rooms. The sign on the first door reads "In this room there is a lady, and in the other one there is a tiger"; and the sign on the second door reads "In one of these rooms, there is a lady, and in one of them there is a tiger." Suppose that you know that one of these signs is true and the other is false. Behind which door is the lady?

*38. Solve this famous logic puzzle, attributed to Albert Einstein, and known as the **zebra puzzle**. Five men with different nationalities and with different jobs live in consecutive houses on a street. These houses are painted different colors. The men have different pets and have different favorite drinks. Determine who owns a zebra and

whose favorite drink is mineral water (which is one of the favorite drinks) given these clues: The Englishman lives in the red house. The Spaniard owns a dog. The Japanese man is a painter. The Italian drinks tea. The Norwegian lives in the first house on the left. The green house is immediately to the right of the white one. The photographer breeds snails. The diplomat lives in the yellow house. Milk is drunk in the middle house. The owner of the green house drinks coffee. The Norwegian's house is next to the blue one. The violinist drinks orange juice. The fox is in a house next to that of the physician. The horse is in a house next to that of the diplomat. [*Hint:* Make a table where the rows represent the men and columns represent the color of their houses, their jobs, their pets, and their favorite drinks and use logical reasoning to determine the correct entries in the table.]

39. Freedonia has fifty senators. Each senator is either honest or corrupt. Suppose you know that at least one of the Freedonian senators is honest and that, given any two Freedonian senators, at least one is corrupt. Based on these facts, can you determine how many Freedonian senators are honest and how many are corrupt? If so, what is the answer?

40. Find the output of each of these combinatorial circuits.

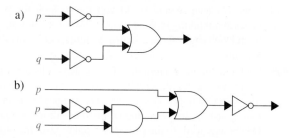

41. Find the output of each of these combinatorial circuits.

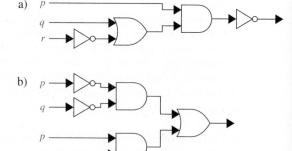

42. Construct a combinatorial circuit using inverters, OR gates, and AND gates that produces the output $(p \wedge \neg r) \vee (\neg q \wedge r)$ from input bits $p$, $q$, and $r$.

43. Construct a combinatorial circuit using inverters, OR gates, and AND gates that produces the output $((\neg p \vee \neg r) \wedge \neg q) \vee (\neg p \wedge (q \vee r))$ from input bits $p$, $q$, and $r$.

# 1.3 Propositional Equivalences

## Introduction

An important type of step used in a mathematical argument is the replacement of a statement with another statement with the same truth value. Because of this, methods that produce propositions with the same truth value as a given compound proposition are used extensively in the construction of mathematical arguments. Note that we will use the term "compound proposition" to refer to an expression formed from propositional variables using logical operators, such as $p \wedge q$.

We begin our discussion with a classification of compound propositions according to their possible truth values.

**DEFINITION 1**    A compound proposition that is always true, no matter what the truth values of the propositional variables that occur in it, is called a *tautology*. A compound proposition that is always false is called a *contradiction*. A compound proposition that is neither a tautology nor a contradiction is called a *contingency*.

Tautologies and contradictions are often important in mathematical reasoning. Example 1 illustrates these types of compound propositions.

**EXAMPLE 1**    We can construct examples of tautologies and contradictions using just one propositional variable. Consider the truth tables of $p \vee \neg p$ and $p \wedge \neg p$, shown in Table 1. Because $p \vee \neg p$ is always true, it is a tautology. Because $p \wedge \neg p$ is always false, it is a contradiction.    ◀

## Logical Equivalences

Demo

Compound propositions that have the same truth values in all possible cases are called **logically equivalent**. We can also define this notion as follows.

**DEFINITION 2**    The compound propositions $p$ and $q$ are called *logically equivalent* if $p \leftrightarrow q$ is a tautology. The notation $p \equiv q$ denotes that $p$ and $q$ are logically equivalent.

***Remark:*** The symbol $\equiv$ is not a logical connective, and $p \equiv q$ is not a compound proposition but rather is the statement that $p \leftrightarrow q$ is a tautology. The symbol $\Leftrightarrow$ is sometimes used instead of $\equiv$ to denote logical equivalence.

One way to determine whether two compound propositions are equivalent is to use a truth table. In particular, the compound propositions $p$ and $q$ are equivalent if and only if the columns

| TABLE 1  Examples of a Tautology and a Contradiction. | | | |
|---|---|---|---|
| $p$ | $\neg p$ | $p \vee \neg p$ | $p \wedge \neg p$ |
| T | F | T | F |
| F | T | T | F |

| TABLE 2 De Morgan's Laws. |
|---|
| $\neg(p \wedge q) \equiv \neg p \vee \neg q$ |
| $\neg(p \vee q) \equiv \neg p \wedge \neg q$ |

**Extra Examples**

giving their truth values agree. Example 2 illustrates this method to establish an extremely important and useful logical equivalence, namely, that of $\neg(p \vee q)$ with $\neg p \wedge \neg q$. This logical equivalence is one of the two **De Morgan laws**, shown in Table 2, named after the English mathematician Augustus De Morgan, of the mid-nineteenth century.

**EXAMPLE 2**    Show that $\neg(p \vee q)$ and $\neg p \wedge \neg q$ are logically equivalent.

*Solution:* The truth tables for these compound propositions are displayed in Table 3. Because the truth values of the compound propositions $\neg(p \vee q)$ and $\neg p \wedge \neg q$ agree for all possible combinations of the truth values of $p$ and $q$, it follows that $\neg(p \vee q) \leftrightarrow (\neg p \wedge \neg q)$ is a tautology and that these compound propositions are logically equivalent.    ◀

| TABLE 3 Truth Tables for $\neg(p \vee q)$ and $\neg p \wedge \neg q$. | | | | | | |
|---|---|---|---|---|---|---|
| $p$ | $q$ | $p \vee q$ | $\neg(p \vee q)$ | $\neg p$ | $\neg q$ | $\neg p \wedge \neg q$ |
| T | T | T | F | F | F | F |
| T | F | T | F | F | T | F |
| F | T | T | F | T | F | F |
| F | F | F | T | T | T | T |

**EXAMPLE 3**    Show that $p \rightarrow q$ and $\neg p \vee q$ are logically equivalent.

*Solution:* We construct the truth table for these compound propositions in Table 4. Because the truth values of $\neg p \vee q$ and $p \rightarrow q$ agree, they are logically equivalent.    ◀

| TABLE 4 Truth Tables for $\neg p \vee q$ and $p \rightarrow q$. | | | | |
|---|---|---|---|---|
| $p$ | $q$ | $\neg p$ | $\neg p \vee q$ | $p \rightarrow q$ |
| T | T | F | T | T |
| T | F | F | F | F |
| F | T | T | T | T |
| F | F | T | T | T |

We will now establish a logical equivalence of two compound propositions involving three different propositional variables $p$, $q$, and $r$. To use a truth table to establish such a logical equivalence, we need eight rows, one for each possible combination of truth values of these three variables. We symbolically represent these combinations by listing the truth values of $p$, $q$, and $r$, respectively. These eight combinations of truth values are TTT, TTF, TFT, TFF, FTT, FTF, FFT, and FFF; we use this order when we display the rows of the truth table. Note that we need to double the number of rows.in the truth tables we use to show that compound propositions are equivalent for each additional propositional variable, so that 16 rows are needed to establish the logical equivalence of two compound propositions involving four propositional variables, and so on. In general, $2^n$ rows are required if a compound proposition involves $n$ propositional variables.

**TABLE 5** A Demonstration That $p \vee (q \wedge r)$ and $(p \vee q) \wedge (p \vee r)$ Are Logically Equivalent.

| $p$ | $q$ | $r$ | $q \wedge r$ | $p \vee (q \wedge r)$ | $p \vee q$ | $p \vee r$ | $(p \vee q) \wedge (p \vee r)$ |
|-----|-----|-----|--------------|------------------------|------------|------------|----------------------------------|
| T | T | T | T | T | T | T | T |
| T | T | F | F | T | T | T | T |
| T | F | T | F | T | T | T | T |
| T | F | F | F | T | T | T | T |
| F | T | T | T | T | T | T | T |
| F | T | F | F | F | T | F | F |
| F | F | T | F | F | F | T | F |
| F | F | F | F | F | F | F | F |

**EXAMPLE 4**    Show that $p \vee (q \wedge r)$ and $(p \vee q) \wedge (p \vee r)$ are logically equivalent. This is the *distributive law* of disjunction over conjunction.

*Solution:* We construct the truth table for these compound propositions in Table 5. Because the truth values of $p \vee (q \wedge r)$ and $(p \vee q) \wedge (p \vee r)$ agree, these compound propositions are logically equivalent.    ◀

The identities in Table 6 are a special case of Boolean algebra identities found in Table 5 of Section 12.1. See Table 1 in Section 2.2 for analogous set identities.

Table 6 contains some important equivalences. In these equivalences, **T** denotes the compound proposition that is always true and **F** denotes the compound proposition that is always

**TABLE 6** Logical Equivalences.

| Equivalence | Name |
|-------------|------|
| $p \wedge \mathbf{T} \equiv p$ <br> $p \vee \mathbf{F} \equiv p$ | Identity laws |
| $p \vee \mathbf{T} \equiv \mathbf{T}$ <br> $p \wedge \mathbf{F} \equiv \mathbf{F}$ | Domination laws |
| $p \vee p \equiv p$ <br> $p \wedge p \equiv p$ | Idempotent laws |
| $\neg(\neg p) \equiv p$ | Double negation law |
| $p \vee q \equiv q \vee p$ <br> $p \wedge q \equiv q \wedge p$ | Commutative laws |
| $(p \vee q) \vee r \equiv p \vee (q \vee r)$ <br> $(p \wedge q) \wedge r \equiv p \wedge (q \wedge r)$ | Associative laws |
| $p \vee (q \wedge r) \equiv (p \vee q) \wedge (p \vee r)$ <br> $p \wedge (q \vee r) \equiv (p \wedge q) \vee (p \wedge r)$ | Distributive laws |
| $\neg(p \wedge q) \equiv \neg p \vee \neg q$ <br> $\neg(p \vee q) \equiv \neg p \wedge \neg q$ | De Morgan's laws |
| $p \vee (p \wedge q) \equiv p$ <br> $p \wedge (p \vee q) \equiv p$ | Absorption laws |
| $p \vee \neg p \equiv \mathbf{T}$ <br> $p \wedge \neg p \equiv \mathbf{F}$ | Negation laws |

| TABLE 7 Logical Equivalences Involving Conditional Statements. |
|---|
| $p \rightarrow q \equiv \neg p \vee q$ |
| $p \rightarrow q \equiv \neg q \rightarrow \neg p$ |
| $p \vee q \equiv \neg p \rightarrow q$ |
| $p \wedge q \equiv \neg(p \rightarrow \neg q)$ |
| $\neg(p \rightarrow q) \equiv p \wedge \neg q$ |
| $(p \rightarrow q) \wedge (p \rightarrow r) \equiv p \rightarrow (q \wedge r)$ |
| $(p \rightarrow r) \wedge (q \rightarrow r) \equiv (p \vee q) \rightarrow r$ |
| $(p \rightarrow q) \vee (p \rightarrow r) \equiv p \rightarrow (q \vee r)$ |
| $(p \rightarrow r) \vee (q \rightarrow r) \equiv (p \wedge q) \rightarrow r$ |

| TABLE 8 Logical Equivalences Involving Biconditional Statements. |
|---|
| $p \leftrightarrow q \equiv (p \rightarrow q) \wedge (q \rightarrow p)$ |
| $p \leftrightarrow q \equiv \neg p \leftrightarrow \neg q$ |
| $p \leftrightarrow q \equiv (p \wedge q) \vee (\neg p \wedge \neg q)$ |
| $\neg(p \leftrightarrow q) \equiv p \leftrightarrow \neg q$ |

false. We also display some useful equivalences for compound propositions involving conditional statements and biconditional statements in Tables 7 and 8, respectively. The reader is asked to verify the equivalences in Tables 6–8 in the exercises.

The associative law for disjunction shows that the expression $p \vee q \vee r$ is well defined, in the sense that it does not matter whether we first take the disjunction of $p$ with $q$ and then the disjunction of $p \vee q$ with $r$, or if we first take the disjunction of $q$ and $r$ and then take the disjunction of $p$ with $q \vee r$. Similarly, the expression $p \wedge q \wedge r$ is well defined. By extending this reasoning, it follows that $p_1 \vee p_2 \vee \cdots \vee p_n$ and $p_1 \wedge p_2 \wedge \cdots \wedge p_n$ are well defined whenever $p_1, p_2, \ldots, p_n$ are propositions.

Furthermore, note that De Morgan's laws extend to

$$\neg(p_1 \vee p_2 \vee \cdots \vee p_n) \equiv (\neg p_1 \wedge \neg p_2 \wedge \cdots \wedge \neg p_n)$$

and

$$\neg(p_1 \wedge p_2 \wedge \cdots \wedge p_n) \equiv (\neg p_1 \vee \neg p_2 \vee \cdots \vee \neg p_n).$$

We will sometimes use the notation $\bigvee_{j=1}^{n} p_j$ for $p_1 \vee p_2 \vee \cdots \vee p_n$ and $\bigwedge_{j=1}^{n} p_j$ for $p_1 \wedge p_2 \wedge \cdots \wedge p_n$. Using this notation, the extended version of De Morgan's laws can be written concisely as $\neg\left(\bigvee_{j=1}^{n} p_j\right) \equiv \bigwedge_{j=1}^{n} \neg p_j$ and $\neg\left(\bigwedge_{j=1}^{n} p_j\right) \equiv \bigvee_{j=1}^{n} \neg p_j$. (Methods for proving these identities will be given in Section 5.1.)

## Using De Morgan's Laws

When using De Morgan's laws, remember to change the logical connective after you negate.

The two logical equivalences known as De Morgan's laws are particularly important. They tell us how to negate conjunctions and how to negate disjunctions. In particular, the equivalence $\neg(p \vee q) \equiv \neg p \wedge \neg q$ tells us that the negation of a disjunction is formed by taking the conjunction of the negations of the component propositions. Similarly, the equivalence $\neg(p \wedge q) \equiv \neg p \vee \neg q$ tells us that the negation of a conjunction is formed by taking the disjunction of the negations of the component propositions. Example 5 illustrates the use of De Morgan's laws.

**EXAMPLE 5**   Use De Morgan's laws to express the negations of "Miguel has a cellphone and he has a laptop computer" and "Heather will go to the concert or Steve will go to the concert."

*Solution:* Let $p$ be "Miguel has a cellphone" and $q$ be "Miguel has a laptop computer." Then "Miguel has a cellphone and he has a laptop computer" can be represented by $p \wedge q$. By the first of De Morgan's laws, $\neg(p \wedge q)$ is equivalent to $\neg p \vee \neg q$. Consequently, we can express the negation of our original statement as "Miguel does not have a cellphone or he does not have a laptop computer."

Let $r$ be "Heather will go to the concert" and $s$ be "Steve will go to the concert." Then "Heather will go to the concert or Steve will go to the concert" can be represented by $r \vee s$. By the second of De Morgan's laws, $\neg(r \vee s)$ is equivalent to $\neg r \wedge \neg s$. Consequently, we can express the negation of our original statement as "Heather will not go to the concert and Steve will not go to the concert." ◀

## Constructing New Logical Equivalences

The logical equivalences in Table 6, as well as any others that have been established (such as those shown in Tables 7 and 8), can be used to construct additional logical equivalences. The reason for this is that a proposition in a compound proposition can be replaced by a compound proposition that is logically equivalent to it without changing the truth value of the original compound proposition. This technique is illustrated in Examples 6–8, where we also use the fact that if $p$ and $q$ are logically equivalent and $q$ and $r$ are logically equivalent, then $p$ and $r$ are logically equivalent (see Exercise 56).

**EXAMPLE 6**   Show that $\neg(p \rightarrow q)$ and $p \wedge \neg q$ are logically equivalent.

*Solution:* We could use a truth table to show that these compound propositions are equivalent (similar to what we did in Example 4). Indeed, it would not be hard to do so. However, we want to illustrate how to use logical identities that we already know to establish new logical identities, something that is of practical importance for establishing equivalences of compound propositions with a large number of variables. So, we will establish this equivalence by developing a series of

AUGUSTUS DE MORGAN (1806–1871)   Augustus De Morgan was born in India, where his father was a colonel in the Indian army. De Morgan's family moved to England when he was 7 months old. He attended private schools, where in his early teens he developed a strong interest in mathematics. De Morgan studied at Trinity College, Cambridge, graduating in 1827. Although he considered medicine or law, he decided on mathematics for his career. He won a position at University College, London, in 1828, but resigned after the college dismissed a fellow professor without giving reasons. However, he resumed this position in 1836 when his successor died, remaining until 1866.

De Morgan was a noted teacher who stressed principles over techniques. His students included many famous mathematicians, including Augusta Ada, Countess of Lovelace, who was Charles Babbage's collaborator in his work on computing machines (see page 31 for biographical notes on Augusta Ada). (De Morgan cautioned the countess against studying too much mathematics, because it might interfere with her childbearing abilities!)

De Morgan was an extremely prolific writer, publishing more than 1000 articles in more than 15 periodicals. De Morgan also wrote textbooks on many subjects, including logic, probability, calculus, and algebra. In 1838 he presented what was perhaps the first clear explanation of an important proof technique known as *mathematical induction* (discussed in Section 5.1 of this text), a term he coined. In the 1840s De Morgan made fundamental contributions to the development of symbolic logic. He invented notations that helped him prove propositional equivalences, such as the laws that are named after him. In 1842 De Morgan presented what is considered to be the first precise definition of a limit and developed new tests for convergence of infinite series. De Morgan was also interested in the history of mathematics and wrote biographies of Newton and Halley.

In 1837 De Morgan married Sophia Frend, who wrote his biography in 1882. De Morgan's research, writing, and teaching left little time for his family or social life. Nevertheless, he was noted for his kindness, humor, and wide range of knowledge.

logical equivalences, using one of the equivalences in Table 6 at a time, starting with $\neg(p \rightarrow q)$ and ending with $p \wedge \neg q$. We have the following equivalences.

$$
\begin{aligned}
\neg(p \rightarrow q) &\equiv \neg(\neg p \vee q) && \text{by Example 3} \\
&\equiv \neg(\neg p) \wedge \neg q && \text{by the second De Morgan law} \\
&\equiv p \wedge \neg q && \text{by the double negation law}
\end{aligned}
$$

◀

**EXAMPLE 7**   Show that $\neg(p \vee (\neg p \wedge q))$ and $\neg p \wedge \neg q$ are logically equivalent by developing a series of logical equivalences.

*Solution:* We will use one of the equivalences in Table 6 at a time, starting with $\neg(p \vee (\neg p \wedge q))$ and ending with $\neg p \wedge \neg q$. (*Note:* we could also easily establish this equivalence using a truth table.) We have the following equivalences.

$$
\begin{aligned}
\neg(p \vee (\neg p \wedge q)) &\equiv \neg p \wedge \neg(\neg p \wedge q) && \text{by the second De Morgan law} \\
&\equiv \neg p \wedge [\neg(\neg p) \vee \neg q] && \text{by the first De Morgan law} \\
&\equiv \neg p \wedge (p \vee \neg q) && \text{by the double negation law} \\
&\equiv (\neg p \wedge p) \vee (\neg p \wedge \neg q) && \text{by the second distributive law} \\
&\equiv \mathbf{F} \vee (\neg p \wedge \neg q) && \text{because } \neg p \wedge p \equiv \mathbf{F} \\
&\equiv (\neg p \wedge \neg q) \vee \mathbf{F} && \text{by the commutative law for disjunction} \\
&\equiv \neg p \wedge \neg q && \text{by the identity law for } \mathbf{F}
\end{aligned}
$$

Consequently $\neg(p \vee (\neg p \wedge q))$ and $\neg p \wedge \neg q$ are logically equivalent.   ◀

**EXAMPLE 8**   Show that $(p \wedge q) \rightarrow (p \vee q)$ is a tautology.

*Solution:* To show that this statement is a tautology, we will use logical equivalences to demonstrate that it is logically equivalent to $\mathbf{T}$. (*Note:* This could also be done using a truth table.)

$$
\begin{aligned}
(p \wedge q) \rightarrow (p \vee q) &\equiv \neg(p \wedge q) \vee (p \vee q) && \text{by Example 3} \\
&\equiv (\neg p \vee \neg q) \vee (p \vee q) && \text{by the first De Morgan law} \\
&\equiv (\neg p \vee p) \vee (\neg q \vee q) && \text{by the associative and commutative} \\
& && \quad \text{laws for disjunction} \\
&\equiv \mathbf{T} \vee \mathbf{T} && \text{by Example 1 and the commutative} \\
& && \quad \text{law for disjunction} \\
&\equiv \mathbf{T} && \text{by the domination law}
\end{aligned}
$$

◀

## Propositional Satisfiability

A compound proposition is **satisfiable** if there is an assignment of truth values to its variables that makes it true. When no such assignments exists, that is, when the compound proposition is false for all assignments of truth values to its variables, the compound proposition is **unsatisfiable**. Note that a compound proposition is unsatisfiable if and only if its negation is true for all assignments of truth values to the variables, that is, if and only if its negation is a tautology.

When we find a particular assignment of truth values that makes a compound proposition true, we have shown that it is satisfiable; such an assignment is called a **solution** of this particular satisfiability problem. However, to show that a compound proposition is unsatisfiable, we need to show that *every* assignment of truth values to its variables makes it false. Although we can always use a truth table to determine whether a compound proposition is satisfiable, it is often more efficient not to, as Example 9 demonstrates.

**EXAMPLE 9**  Determine whether each of the compound propositions $(p \vee \neg q) \wedge (q \vee \neg r) \wedge (r \vee \neg p)$, $(p \vee q \vee r) \wedge (\neg p \vee \neg q \vee \neg r)$, and $(p \vee \neg q) \wedge (q \vee \neg r) \wedge (r \vee \neg p) \wedge (p \vee q \vee r) \wedge (\neg p \vee \neg q \vee \neg r)$ is satisfiable.

*Solution:* Instead of using truth table to solve this problem, we will reason about truth values. Note that $(p \vee \neg q) \wedge (q \vee \neg r) \wedge (r \vee \neg p)$ is true when the three variable $p$, $q$, and $r$ have the same truth value (see Exercise 40 of Section 1.1). Hence, it is satisfiable as there is at least one assignment of truth values for $p$, $q$, and $r$ that makes it true. Similarly, note that $(p \vee q \vee r) \wedge (\neg p \vee \neg q \vee \neg r)$ is true when at least one of $p$, $q$, and $r$ is true and at least one is false (see Exercise 41 of Section 1.1). Hence, $(p \vee q \vee r) \wedge (\neg p \vee \neg q \vee \neg r)$ is satisfiable, as there is at least one assignment of truth values for $p$, $q$, and $r$ that makes it true.

Finally, note that for $(p \vee \neg q) \wedge (q \vee \neg r) \wedge (r \vee \neg p) \wedge (p \vee q \vee r) \wedge (\neg p \vee \neg q \vee \neg r)$ to be true, $(p \vee \neg q) \wedge (q \vee \neg r) \wedge (r \vee \neg p)$ and $(p \vee q \vee r) \wedge (\neg p \vee \neg q \vee \neg r)$ must both be true. For the first to be true, the three variables must have the same truth values, and for the second to be true, at least one of three variables must be true and at least one must be false. However, these conditions are contradictory. From these observations we conclude that no assignment of truth values to $p$, $q$, and $r$ makes $(p \vee \neg q) \wedge (q \vee \neg r) \wedge (r \vee \neg p) \wedge (p \vee q \vee r) \wedge (\neg p \vee \neg q \vee \neg r)$ true. Hence, it is unsatisfiable. ◀

AUGUSTA ADA, COUNTESS OF LOVELACE (1815–1852)  Augusta Ada was the only child from the marriage of the famous poet Lord Byron and Lady Byron, Annabella Millbanke, who separated when Ada was 1 month old, because of Lord Byron's scandalous affair with his half sister. The Lord Byron had quite a reputation, being described by one of his lovers as "mad, bad, and dangerous to know." Lady Byron was noted for her intellect and had a passion for mathematics; she was called by Lord Byron "The Princess of Parallelograms." Augusta was raised by her mother, who encouraged her intellectual talents especially in music and mathematics, to counter what Lady Byron considered dangerous poetic tendencies. At this time, women were not allowed to attend universities and could not join learned societies. Nevertheless, Augusta pursued her mathematical studies independently and with mathematicians, including William Frend. She was also encouraged by another female mathematician, Mary Somerville, and in 1834 at a dinner party hosted by Mary Somerville, she learned about Charles Babbage's ideas for a calculating machine, called the Analytic Engine. In 1838 Augusta Ada married Lord King, later elevated to Earl of Lovelace. Together they had three children.

Augusta Ada continued her mathematical studies after her marriage. Charles Babbage had continued work on his Analytic Engine and lectured on this in Europe. In 1842 Babbage asked Augusta Ada to translate an article in French describing Babbage's invention. When Babbage saw her translation, he suggested she add her own notes, and the resulting work was three times the length of the original. The most complete accounts of the Analytic Engine are found in Augusta Ada's notes. In her notes, she compared the working of the Analytic Engine to that of the Jacquard loom, with Babbage's punch cards analogous to the cards used to create patterns on the loom. Furthermore, she recognized the promise of the machine as a general purpose computer much better than Babbage did. She stated that the "engine is the material expression of any indefinite function of any degree of generality and complexity." Her notes on the Analytic Engine anticipate many future developments, including computer-generated music. Augusta Ada published her writings under her initials A.A.L. concealing her identity as a woman as did many women at a time when women were not considered to be the intellectual equals of men. After 1845 she and Babbage worked toward the development of a system to predict horse races. Unfortunately, their system did not work well, leaving Augusta Ada heavily in debt at the time of her death at an unfortunately young age from uterine cancer.

In 1953 Augusta Ada's notes on the Analytic Engine were republished more than 100 years after they were written, and after they had been long forgotten. In his work in the 1950s on the capacity of computers to think (and his famous Turing Test), Alan Turing responded to Augusta Ada's statement that "The Analytic Engine has no pretensions whatever to originate anything. It can do whatever we know how to order it to perform." This "dialogue" between Turing and Augusta Ada is still the subject of controversy. Because of her fundamental contributions to computing, the programming language Ada is named in honor of the Countess of Lovelace.

| | 2 | 9 | | | | 4 | | |
|---|---|---|---|---|---|---|---|---|
| | | | 5 | | | 1 | | |
| | 4 | | | | | | | |
| | | | | 4 | 2 | | | |
| 6 | | | | | | | 7 | |
| 5 | | | | | | | | |
| 7 | | | 3 | | | | | 5 |
| | 1 | | | 9 | | | | |
| | | | | | | 6 | | |

**FIGURE 1   A 9 × 9 Sudoku puzzle.**

# Applications of Satisfiability

Many problems, in diverse areas such as robotics, software testing, computer-aided design, machine vision, integrated circuit design, computer networking, and genetics, can be modeled in terms of propositional satisfiability. Although most of these applications are beyond the scope of this book, we will study one application here. In particular, we will show how to use propositional satisfiability to model Sudoku puzzles.

SUDOKU    A **Sudoku puzzle** is represented by a 9 × 9 grid made up of nine 3 × 3 subgrids, known as **blocks**, as shown in Figure 1. For each puzzle, some of the 81 cells, called **givens**,  are assigned one of the numbers 1, 2, . . . , 9, and the other cells are blank. The puzzle is solved by assigning a number to each blank cell so that every row, every column, and every one of the nine 3 × 3 blocks contains each of the nine possible numbers. Note that instead of using a 9 × 9 grid, Sudoku puzzles can be based on $n^2 \times n^2$ grids, for any positive integer $n$, with the $n^2 \times n^2$ grid made up of $n^2$ $n \times n$ subgrids.

Links

The popularity of Sudoku dates back to the 1980s when it was introduced in Japan. It took 20 years for Sudoku to spread to rest of the world, but by 2005, Sudoku puzzles were a worldwide craze. The name Sudoku is short for the Japanese *suuji wa dokushin ni kagiru*, which means "the digits must remain single." The modern game of Sudoku was apparently designed in the late 1970s by an American puzzle designer. The basic ideas of Sudoku date back even further; puzzles printed in French newspapers in the 1890s were quite similar, but not identical, to modern Sudoku.

Sudoku puzzles designed for entertainment have two additional important properties. First, they have exactly one solution. Second, they can be solved using reasoning alone, that is, without resorting to searching all possible assignments of numbers to the cells. As a Sudoku puzzle is solved, entries in blank cells are successively determined by already known values. For instance, in the grid in Figure 1, the number 4 must appear in exactly one cell in the second row. How can we determine which of the seven blank cells it must appear? First, we observe that 4 cannot appear in one of the first three cells or in one of the last three cells of this row, because it already appears in another cell in the block each of these cells is in. We can also see that 4 cannot appear in the fifth cell in this row, as it already appears in the fifth column in the fourth row. This means that 4 must appear in the sixth cell of the second row.

Many strategies based on logic and mathematics have been devised for solving Sudoku puzzles (see [Da10], for example). Here, we discuss one of the ways that have been developed for solving Sudoku puzzles with the aid of a computer, which depends on modeling the puzzle as a propositional satisfiability problem. Using the model we describe, particular Sudoku puzzles can be solved using software developed to solve satisfiability problems. Currently, Sudoku puzzles can be solved in less than 10 milliseconds this way. It should be noted that there are many other approaches for solving Sudoku puzzles via computers using other techniques.

To encode a Sudoku puzzle, let $p(i, j, n)$ denote the proposition that is true when the number $n$ is in the cell in the $i$th row and $j$th column. There are $9 \times 9 \times 9 = 729$ such propositions, as $i$, $j$, and $n$ all range from 1 to 9. For example, for the puzzle in Figure 1, the number 6 is given as the value in the fifth row and first column. Hence, we see that $p(5, 1, 6)$ is true, but $p(5, j, 6)$ is false for $j = 2, 3, \ldots, 9$.

Given a particular Sudoku puzzle, we begin by encoding each of the given values. Then, we construct compound propositions that assert that every row contains every number, every column contains every number, every $3 \times 3$ block contains every number, and each cell contains no more than one number. It follows, as the reader should verify, that the Sudoku puzzle is solved by finding an assignment of truth values to the 729 propositions $p(i, j, n)$ with $i$, $j$, and $n$ each ranging from 1 to 9 that makes the conjunction of all these compound propositions true. After listing these assertions, we will explain how to construct the assertion that every row contains every integer from 1 to 9. We will leave the construction of the other assertions that every column contains every number and each of the nine $3 \times 3$ blocks contains every number to the exercises.

- For each cell with a given value, we assert $p(i, j, n)$ when the cell in row $i$ and column $j$ has the given value $n$.
- We assert that every row contains every number:

$$\bigwedge_{i=1}^{9} \bigwedge_{n=1}^{9} \bigvee_{j=1}^{9} p(i, j, n)$$

- We assert that every column contains every number:

$$\bigwedge_{j=1}^{9} \bigwedge_{n=1}^{9} \bigvee_{i=1}^{9} p(i, j, n)$$

It is tricky setting up the two inner indices so that all nine cells in each square block are examined.

- We assert that each of the nine $3 \times 3$ blocks contains every number:

$$\bigwedge_{r=0}^{2} \bigwedge_{s=0}^{2} \bigwedge_{n=1}^{9} \bigvee_{i=1}^{3} \bigvee_{j=1}^{3} p(3r + i, 3s + j, n)$$

- To assert that no cell contains more than one number, we take the conjunction over all values of $n, n', i$, and $j$ where each variable ranges from 1 to 9 and $n \neq n'$ of $p(i, j, n) \rightarrow \neg p(i, j, n')$.

We now explain how to construct the assertion that every row contains every number. First, to assert that row $i$ contains the number $n$, we form $\bigvee_{j=1}^{9} p(i, j, n)$. To assert that row $i$ contains all $n$ numbers, we form the conjunction of these disjunctions over all nine possible values of $n$, giving us $\bigwedge_{n=1}^{9} \bigvee_{j=1}^{9} p(i, j, n)$. Finally, to assert that every row contains every number, we take the conjunction of $\bigwedge_{n=1}^{9} \bigvee_{j=1}^{9} p(i, j, n)$ over all nine rows. This gives us $\bigwedge_{i=1}^{9} \bigwedge_{n=1}^{9} \bigvee_{j=1}^{9} p(i, j, n)$. (Exercises 65 and 66 ask for explanations of the assertions that every column contains every number and that each of the nine $3 \times 3$ blocks contains every number.)

Given a particular Sudoku puzzle, to solve this puzzle we can find a solution to the satisfiability problems that asks for a set of truth values for the 729 variables $p(i, j, n)$ that makes the conjunction of all the listed assertions true.

## Solving Satisfiability Problems

A truth table can be used to determine whether a compound proposition is satisfiable, or equivalently, whether its negation is a tautology (see Exercise 60). This can be done by hand for a compound proposition with a small number of variables, but when the number of variables grows, this becomes impractical. For instance, there are $2^{20} = 1,048,576$ rows in the truth table for a compound proposition with 20 variables. Clearly, you need a computer to help you determine, in this way, whether a compound proposition in 20 variables is satisfiable.

When many applications are modeled, questions concerning the satisfiability of compound propositions with hundreds, thousands, or millions of variables arise. Note, for example, that when there are 1000 variables, checking every one of the $2^{1000}$ (a number with more than 300 decimal digits) possible combinations of truth values of the variables in a compound proposition cannot be done by a computer in even trillions of years. No procedure is known that a computer can follow to determine in a reasonable amount of time whether an arbitrary compound proposition in such a large number of variables is satisfiable. However, progress has been made developing methods for solving the satisfiability problem for the particular types of compound propositions that arise in practical applications, such as for the solution of Sudoku puzzles. Many computer programs have been developed for solving satisfiability problems which have practical use. In our discussion of the subject of algorithms in Chapter 3, we will discuss this question further. In particular, we will explain the important role the propositional satisfiability problem plays in the study of the complexity of algorithms.

**Links**

## Exercises

1. Use truth tables to verify these equivalences.
   a) $p \wedge \mathbf{T} \equiv p$          b) $p \vee \mathbf{F} \equiv p$
   c) $p \wedge \mathbf{F} \equiv \mathbf{F}$          d) $p \vee \mathbf{T} \equiv \mathbf{T}$
   e) $p \vee p \equiv p$          f) $p \wedge p \equiv p$
2. Show that $\neg(\neg p)$ and $p$ are logically equivalent.
3. Use truth tables to verify the commutative laws
   a) $p \vee q \equiv q \vee p$.          b) $p \wedge q \equiv q \wedge p$.
4. Use truth tables to verify the associative laws
   a) $(p \vee q) \vee r \equiv p \vee (q \vee r)$.

   b) $(p \wedge q) \wedge r \equiv p \wedge (q \wedge r)$.
5. Use a truth table to verify the distributive law
   $$p \wedge (q \vee r) \equiv (p \wedge q) \vee (p \wedge r).$$
6. Use a truth table to verify the first De Morgan law
   $$\neg(p \wedge q) \equiv \neg p \vee \neg q.$$
7. Use De Morgan's laws to find the negation of each of the following statements.
   a) Jan is rich and happy.
   b) Carlos will bicycle or run tomorrow.

HENRY MAURICE SHEFFER (1883–1964)   Henry Maurice Sheffer, born to Jewish parents in the western Ukraine, emigrated to the United States in 1892 with his parents and six siblings. He studied at the Boston Latin School before entering Harvard, where he completed his undergraduate degree in 1905, his master's in 1907, and his Ph.D. in philosophy in 1908. After holding a postdoctoral position at Harvard, Henry traveled to Europe on a fellowship. Upon returning to the United States, he became an academic nomad, spending one year each at the University of Washington, Cornell, the University of Minnesota, the University of Missouri, and City College in New York. In 1916 he returned to Harvard as a faculty member in the philosophy department. He remained at Harvard until his retirement in 1952.
    Sheffer introduced what is now known as the Sheffer stroke in 1913; it became well known only after its use in the 1925 edition of Whitehead and Russell's *Principia Mathematica*. In this same edition Russell wrote that Sheffer had invented a powerful method that could be used to simplify the *Principia*. Because of this comment, Sheffer was something of a mystery man to logicians, especially because Sheffer, who published little in his career, never published the details of this method, only describing it in mimeographed notes and in a brief published abstract.
    Sheffer was a dedicated teacher of mathematical logic. He liked his classes to be small and did not like auditors. When strangers appeared in his classroom, Sheffer would order them to leave, even his colleagues or distinguished guests visiting Harvard. Sheffer was barely five feet tall; he was noted for his wit and vigor, as well as for his nervousness and irritability. Although widely liked, he was quite lonely. He is noted for a quip he spoke at his retirement: "Old professors never die, they just become emeriti." Sheffer is also credited with coining the term "Boolean algebra" (the subject of Chapter 12 of this text). Sheffer was briefly married and lived most of his later life in small rooms at a hotel packed with his logic books and vast files of slips of paper he used to jot down his ideas. Unfortunately, Sheffer suffered from severe depression during the last two decades of his life.

c) Mei walks or takes the bus to class.

d) Ibrahim is smart and hard working.

**8.** Use De Morgan's laws to find the negation of each of the following statements.

  a) Kwame will take a job in industry or go to graduate school.

  b) Yoshiko knows Java and calculus.

  c) James is young and strong.

  d) Rita will move to Oregon or Washington.

**9.** Show that each of these conditional statements is a tautology by using truth tables.

  a) $(p \wedge q) \rightarrow p$   b) $p \rightarrow (p \vee q)$

  c) $\neg p \rightarrow (p \rightarrow q)$   d) $(p \wedge q) \rightarrow (p \rightarrow q)$

  e) $\neg (p \rightarrow q) \rightarrow p$   f) $\neg (p \rightarrow q) \rightarrow \neg q$

**10.** Show that each of these conditional statements is a tautology by using truth tables.

  a) $[\neg p \wedge (p \vee q)] \rightarrow q$

  b) $[(p \rightarrow q) \wedge (q \rightarrow r)] \rightarrow (p \rightarrow r)$

  c) $[p \wedge (p \rightarrow q)] \rightarrow q$

  d) $[(p \vee q) \wedge (p \rightarrow r) \wedge (q \rightarrow r)] \rightarrow r$

**11.** Show that each conditional statement in Exercise 9 is a tautology without using truth tables.

**12.** Show that each conditional statement in Exercise 10 is a tautology without using truth tables.

**13.** Use truth tables to verify the absorption laws.

  a) $p \vee (p \wedge q) \equiv p$   b) $p \wedge (p \vee q) \equiv p$

**14.** Determine whether $(\neg p \wedge (p \rightarrow q)) \rightarrow \neg q$ is a tautology.

**15.** Determine whether $(\neg q \wedge (p \rightarrow q)) \rightarrow \neg p$ is a tautology.

Each of Exercises 16–28 asks you to show that two compound propositions are logically equivalent. To do this, either show that both sides are true, or that both sides are false, for exactly the same combinations of truth values of the propositional variables in these expressions (whichever is easier).

**16.** Show that $p \leftrightarrow q$ and $(p \wedge q) \vee (\neg p \wedge \neg q)$ are logically equivalent.

**17.** Show that $\neg (p \leftrightarrow q)$ and $p \leftrightarrow \neg q$ are logically equivalent.

**18.** Show that $p \rightarrow q$ and $\neg q \rightarrow \neg p$ are logically equivalent.

**19.** Show that $\neg p \leftrightarrow q$ and $p \leftrightarrow \neg q$ are logically equivalent.

**20.** Show that $\neg (p \oplus q)$ and $p \leftrightarrow q$ are logically equivalent.

**21.** Show that $\neg (p \leftrightarrow q)$ and $\neg p \leftrightarrow q$ are logically equivalent.

**22.** Show that $(p \rightarrow q) \wedge (p \rightarrow r)$ and $p \rightarrow (q \wedge r)$ are logically equivalent.

**23.** Show that $(p \rightarrow r) \wedge (q \rightarrow r)$ and $(p \vee q) \rightarrow r$ are logically equivalent.

**24.** Show that $(p \rightarrow q) \vee (p \rightarrow r)$ and $p \rightarrow (q \vee r)$ are logically equivalent.

**25.** Show that $(p \rightarrow r) \vee (q \rightarrow r)$ and $(p \wedge q) \rightarrow r$ are logically equivalent.

**26.** Show that $\neg p \rightarrow (q \rightarrow r)$ and $q \rightarrow (p \vee r)$ are logically equivalent.

**27.** Show that $p \leftrightarrow q$ and $(p \rightarrow q) \wedge (q \rightarrow p)$ are logically equivalent.

**28.** Show that $p \leftrightarrow q$ and $\neg p \leftrightarrow \neg q$ are logically equivalent.

**29.** Show that $(p \rightarrow q) \wedge (q \rightarrow r) \rightarrow (p \rightarrow r)$ is a tautology.

**30.** Show that $(p \vee q) \wedge (\neg p \vee r) \rightarrow (q \vee r)$ is a tautology.

**31.** Show that $(p \rightarrow q) \rightarrow r$ and $p \rightarrow (q \rightarrow r)$ are not logically equivalent.

**32.** Show that $(p \wedge q) \rightarrow r$ and $(p \rightarrow r) \wedge (q \rightarrow r)$ are not logically equivalent.

**33.** Show that $(p \rightarrow q) \rightarrow (r \rightarrow s)$ and $(p \rightarrow r) \rightarrow (q \rightarrow s)$ are not logically equivalent.

The **dual** of a compound proposition that contains only the logical operators $\vee$, $\wedge$, and $\neg$ is the compound proposition obtained by replacing each $\vee$ by $\wedge$, each $\wedge$ by $\vee$, each **T** by **F**, and each **F** by **T**. The dual of $s$ is denoted by $s^*$.

**34.** Find the dual of each of these compound propositions.

  a) $p \vee \neg q$   b) $p \wedge (q \vee (r \wedge \mathbf{T}))$

  c) $(p \wedge \neg q) \vee (q \wedge \mathbf{F})$

**35.** Find the dual of each of these compound propositions.

  a) $p \wedge \neg q \wedge \neg r$   b) $(p \wedge q \wedge r) \vee s$

  c) $(p \vee \mathbf{F}) \wedge (q \vee \mathbf{T})$

**36.** When does $s^* = s$, where $s$ is a compound proposition?

**37.** Show that $(s^*)^* = s$ when $s$ is a compound proposition.

**38.** Show that the logical equivalences in Table 6, except for the double negation law, come in pairs, where each pair contains compound propositions that are duals of each other.

**\*\*39.** Why are the duals of two equivalent compound propositions also equivalent, where these compound propositions contain only the operators $\wedge$, $\vee$, and $\neg$?

**40.** Find a compound proposition involving the propositional variables $p$, $q$, and $r$ that is true when $p$ and $q$ are true and $r$ is false, but is false otherwise. [*Hint:* Use a conjunction of each propositional variable or its negation.]

**41.** Find a compound proposition involving the propositional variables $p$, $q$, and $r$ that is true when exactly two of $p, q$, and $r$ are true and is false otherwise. [*Hint:* Form a disjunction of conjunctions. Include a conjunction for each combination of values for which the compound proposition is true. Each conjunction should include each of the three propositional variables or its negations.]

**42.** Suppose that a truth table in $n$ propositional variables is specified. Show that a compound proposition with this truth table can be formed by taking the disjunction of conjunctions of the variables or their negations, with one conjunction included for each combination of values for which the compound proposition is true. The resulting compound proposition is said to be in **disjunctive normal form**.

A collection of logical operators is called **functionally complete** if every compound proposition is logically equivalent to a compound proposition involving only these logical operators.

**43.** Show that $\neg$, $\wedge$, and $\vee$ form a functionally complete collection of logical operators. [*Hint:* Use the fact that every compound proposition is logically equivalent to one in disjunctive normal form, as shown in Exercise 42.]

**\*44.** Show that ¬ and ∧ form a functionally complete collection of logical operators. [*Hint:* First use a De Morgan law to show that $p \lor q$ is logically equivalent to $\neg(\neg p \land \neg q)$.]

**\*45.** Show that ¬ and ∨ form a functionally complete collection of logical operators.

The following exercises involve the logical operators *NAND* and *NOR*. The proposition $p$ *NAND* $q$ is true when either $p$ or $q$, or both, are false; and it is false when both $p$ and $q$ are true. The proposition $p$ *NOR* $q$ is true when both $p$ and $q$ are false, and it is false otherwise. The propositions $p$ *NAND* $q$ and $p$ *NOR* $q$ are denoted by $p \mid q$ and $p \downarrow q$, respectively. (The operators $\mid$ and $\downarrow$ are called the **Sheffer stroke** and the **Peirce arrow** after H. M. Sheffer and C. S. Peirce, respectively.)

**46.** Construct a truth table for the logical operator *NAND*.

**47.** Show that $p \mid q$ is logically equivalent to $\neg(p \land q)$.

**48.** Construct a truth table for the logical operator *NOR*.

**49.** Show that $p \downarrow q$ is logically equivalent to $\neg(p \lor q)$.

**50.** In this exercise we will show that $\{\downarrow\}$ is a functionally complete collection of logical operators.
  a) Show that $p \downarrow p$ is logically equivalent to $\neg p$.
  b) Show that $(p \downarrow q) \downarrow (p \downarrow q)$ is logically equivalent to $p \lor q$.
  c) Conclude from parts (a) and (b), and Exercise 49, that $\{\downarrow\}$ is a functionally complete collection of logical operators.

**\*51.** Find a compound proposition logically equivalent to $p \to q$ using only the logical operator $\downarrow$.

**52.** Show that $\{\mid\}$ is a functionally complete collection of logical operators.

**53.** Show that $p \mid q$ and $q \mid p$ are equivalent.

**54.** Show that $p \mid (q \mid r)$ and $(p \mid q) \mid r$ are not equivalent, so that the logical operator $\mid$ is not associative.

**\*55.** How many different truth tables of compound propositions are there that involve the propositional variables $p$ and $q$?

**56.** Show that if $p$, $q$, and $r$ are compound propositions such that $p$ and $q$ are logically equivalent and $q$ and $r$ are logically equivalent, then $p$ and $r$ are logically equivalent.

**57.** The following sentence is taken from the specification of a telephone system: "If the directory database is opened, then the monitor is put in a closed state, if the system is not in its initial state." This specification is hard to understand because it involves two conditional statements. Find an equivalent, easier-to-understand specification that involves disjunctions and negations but not conditional statements.

**58.** How many of the disjunctions $p \lor \neg q$, $\neg p \lor q$, $q \lor r$, $q \lor \neg r$, and $\neg q \lor \neg r$ can be made simultaneously true by an assignment of truth values to $p$, $q$, and $r$?

**59.** How many of the disjunctions $p \lor \neg q \lor s$, $\neg p \lor \neg r \lor s$, $\neg p \lor \neg r \lor \neg s$, $\neg p \lor q \lor \neg s$, $q \lor r \lor \neg s$, $q \lor \neg r \lor \neg s$, $\neg p \lor \neg q \lor \neg s$, $p \lor r \lor s$, and $p \lor r \lor \neg s$ can be made simultaneously true by an assignment of truth values to $p$, $q$, $r$, and $s$?

**60.** Show that the negation of an unsatisfiable compound proposition is a tautology and the negation of a compound proposition that is a tautology is unsatisfiable.

**61.** Determine whether each of these compound propositions is satisfiable.
  **a)** $(p \lor \neg q) \land (\neg p \lor q) \land (\neg p \lor \neg q)$
  **b)** $(p \to q) \land (p \to \neg q) \land (\neg p \to q) \land (\neg p \to \neg q)$
  **c)** $(p \leftrightarrow q) \land (\neg p \leftrightarrow q)$

**62.** Determine whether each of these compound propositions is satisfiable.
  **a)** $(p \lor q \lor \neg r) \land (p \lor \neg q \lor \neg s) \land (p \lor \neg r \lor \neg s) \land (\neg p \lor \neg q \lor \neg s) \land (p \lor q \lor \neg s)$
  **b)** $(\neg p \lor \neg q \lor r) \land (\neg p \lor q \lor \neg s) \land (p \lor \neg q \lor \neg s) \land (\neg p \lor \neg r \lor \neg s) \land (p \lor q \lor \neg r) \land (p \lor \neg r \lor \neg s)$
  **c)** $(p \lor q \lor r) \land (p \lor \neg q \lor \neg s) \land (q \lor \neg r \lor s) \land (\neg p \lor r \lor s) \land (\neg p \lor q \lor \neg s) \land (p \lor \neg q \lor \neg r) \land (\neg p \lor \neg q \lor s) \land (\neg p \lor \neg r \lor \neg s)$

**63.** Show how the solution of a given $4 \times 4$ Sudoku puzzle can be found by solving a satisfiability problem.

**64.** Construct a compound proposition that asserts that every cell of a $9 \times 9$ Sudoku puzzle contains at least one number.

**65.** Explain the steps in the construction of the compound proposition given in the text that asserts that every column of a $9 \times 9$ Sudoku puzzle contains every number.

**\*66.** Explain the steps in the construction of the compound proposition given in the text that asserts that each of the nine $3 \times 3$ blocks of a $9 \times 9$ Sudoku puzzle contains every number.

# 1.4    Predicates and Quantifiers

## Introduction

Propositional logic, studied in Sections 1.1–1.3, cannot adequately express the meaning of all statements in mathematics and in natural language. For example, suppose that we know that

"Every computer connected to the university network is functioning properly."

No rules of propositional logic allow us to conclude the truth of the statement

"MATH3 is functioning properly,"

where MATH3 is one of the computers connected to the university network. Likewise, we cannot use the rules of propositional logic to conclude from the statement

"CS2 is under attack by an intruder,"

where CS2 is a computer on the university network, to conclude the truth of

"There is a computer on the university network that is under attack by an intruder."

In this section we will introduce a more powerful type of logic called **predicate logic**. We will see how predicate logic can be used to express the meaning of a wide range of statements in mathematics and computer science in ways that permit us to reason and explore relationships between objects. To understand predicate logic, we first need to introduce the concept of a predicate. Afterward, we will introduce the notion of quantifiers, which enable us to reason with statements that assert that a certain property holds for all objects of a certain type and with statements that assert the existence of an object with a particular property.

## Predicates

Statements involving variables, such as

"$x > 3$,"   "$x = y + 3$,"   "$x + y = z$,"

and

"computer $x$ is under attack by an intruder,"

and

"computer $x$ is functioning properly,"

are often found in mathematical assertions, in computer programs, and in system specifications. These statements are neither true nor false when the values of the variables are not specified. In this section, we will discuss the ways that propositions can be produced from such statements.

The statement "$x$ is greater than 3" has two parts. The first part, the variable $x$, is the subject of the statement. The second part—the **predicate**, "is greater than 3"—refers to a property that the subject of the statement can have. We can denote the statement "$x$ is greater than 3" by $P(x)$, where $P$ denotes the predicate "is greater than 3" and $x$ is the variable. The statement $P(x)$ is also said to be the value of the **propositional function** $P$ at $x$. Once a value has been assigned to the variable $x$, the statement $P(x)$ becomes a proposition and has a truth value. Consider Examples 1 and 2.

EXAMPLE 1   Let $P(x)$ denote the statement "$x > 3$." What are the truth values of $P(4)$ and $P(2)$?

*Solution:* We obtain the statement $P(4)$ by setting $x = 4$ in the statement "$x > 3$." Hence, $P(4)$, which is the statement "$4 > 3$," is true. However, $P(2)$, which is the statement "$2 > 3$," is false.  ◀

**EXAMPLE 2** Let $A(x)$ denote the statement "Computer $x$ is under attack by an intruder." Suppose that of the computers on campus, only CS2 and MATH1 are currently under attack by intruders. What are truth values of $A(\text{CS1})$, $A(\text{CS2})$, and $A(\text{MATH1})$?

*Solution:* We obtain the statement $A(\text{CS1})$ by setting $x = \text{CS1}$ in the statement "Computer $x$ is under attack by an intruder." Because CS1 is not on the list of computers currently under attack, we conclude that $A(\text{CS1})$ is false. Similarly, because CS2 and MATH1 are on the list of computers under attack, we know that $A(\text{CS2})$ and $A(\text{MATH1})$ are true. ◄

We can also have statements that involve more than one variable. For instance, consider the statement "$x = y + 3$." We can denote this statement by $Q(x, y)$, where $x$ and $y$ are variables and $Q$ is the predicate. When values are assigned to the variables $x$ and $y$, the statement $Q(x, y)$ has a truth value.

**EXAMPLE 3** Let $Q(x, y)$ denote the statement "$x = y + 3$." What are the truth values of the propositions $Q(1, 2)$ and $Q(3, 0)$?

 Extra Examples

*Solution:* To obtain $Q(1, 2)$, set $x = 1$ and $y = 2$ in the statement $Q(x, y)$. Hence, $Q(1, 2)$ is the statement "$1 = 2 + 3$," which is false. The statement $Q(3, 0)$ is the proposition "$3 = 0 + 3$," which is true. ◄

 Links

CHARLES SANDERS PEIRCE (1839–1914)   Many  consider Charles Peirce, born in Cambridge, Massachusetts, to be the most original and versatile American intellect. He made important contributions to an amazing number of disciplines, including mathematics, astronomy, chemistry, geodesy, metrology, engineering, psychology, philology, the history of science, and economics. Peirce was also an inventor, a lifelong student of medicine, a book reviewer, a dramatist and an actor, a short story writer, a phenomenologist, a logician, and a metaphysician. He is noted as the preeminent system-building philosopher competent and productive in logic, mathematics, and a wide range of sciences. He was encouraged by his father, Benjamin Peirce, a professor of mathematics and natural philosophy at Harvard, to pursue a career in science. Instead, he decided to study logic and scientific methodology. Peirce attended Harvard (1855–1859) and received a Harvard master of arts degree (1862) and an advanced degree in chemistry from the Lawrence Scientific School (1863).

In 1861, Peirce became an aide in the U.S. Coast Survey, with the goal of better understanding scientific methodology. His service for the Survey exempted him from military service during the Civil War. While working for the Survey, Peirce did astronomical and geodesic work. He made fundamental contributions to the design of pendulums and to map projections, applying new mathematical developments in the theory of elliptic functions. He was the first person to use the wavelength of light as a unit of measurement. Peirce rose to the position of Assistant for the Survey, a position he held until forced to resign in 1891 when he disagreed with the direction taken by the Survey's new administration.

While making his living from work in the physical sciences, Peirce developed a hierarchy of sciences, with mathematics at the top rung, in which the methods of one science could be adapted for use by those sciences under it in the hierarchy. During this time, he also founded the American philosophical theory of pragmatism.

The only academic position Peirce ever held was lecturer in logic at Johns Hopkins University in Baltimore (1879–1884). His mathematical work during this time included contributions to logic, set theory, abstract algebra, and the philosophy of mathematics. His work is still relevant today, with recent applications of this work on logic to artificial intelligence. Peirce believed that the study of mathematics could develop the mind's powers of imagination, abstraction, and generalization. His diverse activities after retiring from the Survey included writing for periodicals, contributing to scholarly dictionaries, translating scientific papers, guest lecturing, and textbook writing. Unfortunately, his income from these pursuits was insufficient to protect him and his second wife from abject poverty. He was supported in his later years by a fund created by his many admirers and administered by the philosopher William James, his lifelong friend. Although Peirce wrote and published voluminously in a vast range of subjects, he left more than 100,000 pages of unpublished manuscripts. Because of the difficulty of studying his unpublished writings, scholars have only recently started to understand some of his varied contributions. A group of people is devoted to making his work available over the Internet to bring a better appreciation of Peirce's accomplishments to the world.

**EXAMPLE 4** Let $A(c, n)$ denote the statement "Computer $c$ is connected to network $n$," where $c$ is a variable representing a computer and $n$ is a variable representing a network. Suppose that the computer MATH1 is connected to network CAMPUS2, but not to network CAMPUS1. What are the values of $A$(MATH1, CAMPUS1) and $A$(MATH1, CAMPUS2)?

*Solution:* Because MATH1 is not connected to the CAMPUS1 network, we see that $A$(MATH1, CAMPUS1) is false. However, because MATH1 is connected to the CAMPUS2 network, we see that $A$(MATH1, CAMPUS2) is true. ◀

Similarly, we can let $R(x, y, z)$ denote the statement "$x + y = z$." When values are assigned to the variables $x$, $y$, and $z$, this statement has a truth value.

**EXAMPLE 5** What are the truth values of the propositions $R(1, 2, 3)$ and $R(0, 0, 1)$?

*Solution:* The proposition $R(1, 2, 3)$ is obtained by setting $x = 1$, $y = 2$, and $z = 3$ in the statement $R(x, y, z)$. We see that $R(1, 2, 3)$ is the statement "$1 + 2 = 3$," which is true. Also note that $R(0, 0, 1)$, which is the statement "$0 + 0 = 1$," is false. ◀

In general, a statement involving the $n$ variables $x_1, x_2, \ldots, x_n$ can be denoted by

$$P(x_1, x_2, \ldots, x_n).$$

A statement of the form $P(x_1, x_2, \ldots, x_n)$ is the value of the **propositional function** $P$ at the $n$-tuple $(x_1, x_2, \ldots, x_n)$, and $P$ is also called an $n$-**place predicate** or a $n$-**ary predicate**.

Propositional functions occur in computer programs, as Example 6 demonstrates.

**EXAMPLE 6** Consider the statement

**if** $x > 0$ **then** $x := x + 1$.

When this statement is encountered in a program, the value of the variable $x$ at that point in the execution of the program is inserted into $P(x)$, which is "$x > 0$." If $P(x)$ is true for this value of $x$, the assignment statement $x := x + 1$ is executed, so the value of $x$ is increased by 1. If $P(x)$ is false for this value of $x$, the assignment statement is not executed, so the value of $x$ is not changed. ◀

PRECONDITIONS AND POSTCONDITIONS    Predicates are also used to establish the correctness of computer programs, that is, to show that computer programs always produce the desired output when given valid input. (Note that unless the correctness of a computer program is established, no amount of testing can show that it produces the desired output for all input values, unless every input value is tested.) The statements that describe valid input are known as **preconditions** and the conditions that the output should satisfy when the program has run are known as **postconditions**. As Example 7 illustrates, we use predicates to describe both preconditions and postconditions. We will study this process in greater detail in Section 5.5.

**EXAMPLE 7** Consider the following program, designed to interchange the values of two variables $x$ and $y$.

```
temp := x
x := y
y := temp
```

Find predicates that we can use as the precondition and the postcondition to verify the correctness of this program. Then explain how to use them to verify that for all valid input the program does what is intended.

*Solution:* For the precondition, we need to express that $x$ and $y$ have particular values before we run the program. So, for this precondition we can use the predicate $P(x, y)$, where $P(x, y)$ is the statement "$x = a$ and $y = b$," where $a$ and $b$ are the values of $x$ and $y$ before we run the program. Because we want to verify that the program swaps the values of $x$ and $y$ for all input values, for the postcondition we can use $Q(x, y)$, where $Q(x, y)$ is the statement "$x = b$ and $y = a$."

To verify that the program always does what it is supposed to do, suppose that the precondition $P(x, y)$ holds. That is, we suppose that the statement "$x = a$ and $y = b$" is true. This means that $x = a$ and $y = b$. The first step of the program, *temp* := $x$, assigns the value of $x$ to the variable *temp*, so after this step we know that $x = a$, *temp* $= a$, and $y = b$. After the second step of the program, $x := y$, we know that $x = b$, *temp* $= a$, and $y = b$. Finally, after the third step, we know that $x = b$, *temp* $= a$, and $y = a$. Consequently, after this program is run, the postcondition $Q(x, y)$ holds, that is, the statement "$x = b$ and $y = a$" is true.    ◀

## Quantifiers

When the variables in a propositional function are assigned values, the resulting statement becomes a proposition with a certain truth value. However, there is another important way, called **quantification**, to create a proposition from a propositional function. Quantification expresses the extent to which a predicate is true over a range of elements. In English, the words *all*, *some*, *many*, *none*, and *few* are used in quantifications. We will focus on two types of quantification here: universal quantification, which tells us that a predicate is true for every element under consideration, and existential quantification, which tells us that there is one or more element under consideration for which the predicate is true. The area of logic that deals with predicates and quantifiers is called the **predicate calculus**.

Assessment

Assessment

THE UNIVERSAL QUANTIFIER   Many mathematical statements assert that a property is true for all values of a variable in a particular domain, called the **domain of discourse** (or the **universe of discourse**), often just referred to as the **domain**. Such a statement is expressed using universal quantification. The universal quantification of $P(x)$ for a particular domain is the proposition that asserts that $P(x)$ is true for all values of $x$ in this domain. Note that the domain specifies the possible values of the variable $x$. The meaning of the universal quantification of $P(x)$ changes when we change the domain. The domain must always be specified when a universal quantifier is used; without it, the universal quantification of a statement is not defined.

**DEFINITION 1**

The *universal quantification* of $P(x)$ is the statement

"$P(x)$ for all values of $x$ in the domain."

The notation $\forall x\, P(x)$ denotes the universal quantification of $P(x)$. Here $\forall$ is called the **universal quantifier.** We read $\forall x\, P(x)$ as "for all $x\, P(x)$" or "for every $x\, P(x)$." An element for which $P(x)$ is false is called a **counterexample** of $\forall x\, P(x)$.

The meaning of the universal quantifier is summarized in the first row of Table 1. We illustrate the use of the universal quantifier in Examples 8–13.

| **TABLE 1  Quantifiers.** | | |
|---|---|---|
| **Statement** | **When True?** | **When False?** |
| $\forall x\, P(x)$ | $P(x)$ is true for every $x$. | There is an $x$ for which $P(x)$ is false. |
| $\exists x\, P(x)$ | There is an $x$ for which $P(x)$ is true. | $P(x)$ is false for every $x$. |

**EXAMPLE 8**  Let $P(x)$ be the statement "$x + 1 > x$." What is the truth value of the quantification $\forall x\, P(x)$, where the domain consists of all real numbers?

*Solution:* Because $P(x)$ is true for all real numbers $x$, the quantification

$$\forall x\, P(x)$$

is true.  ◀

**Remark:** Generally, an implicit assumption is made that all domains of discourse for quantifiers are nonempty. Note that if the domain is empty, then $\forall x\, P(x)$ is true for any propositional function $P(x)$ because there are no elements $x$ in the domain for which $P(x)$ is false.

Remember that the truth value of $\forall x\, P(x)$ depends on the domain!

Besides "for all" and "for every," universal quantification can be expressed in many other ways, including "all of," "for each," "given any," "for arbitrary," "for each," and "for any."

**Remark:** It is best to avoid using "for any $x$" because it is often ambiguous as to whether "any" means "every" or "some." In some cases, "any" is unambiguous, such as when it is used in negatives, for example, "there is not any reason to avoid studying."

A statement $\forall x\, P(x)$ is false, where $P(x)$ is a propositional function, if and only if $P(x)$ is not always true when $x$ is in the domain. One way to show that $P(x)$ is not always true when $x$ is in the domain is to find a counterexample to the statement $\forall x\, P(x)$. Note that a single counterexample is all we need to establish that $\forall x\, P(x)$ is false. Example 9 illustrates how counterexamples are used.

**EXAMPLE 9**  Let $Q(x)$ be the statement "$x < 2$." What is the truth value of the quantification $\forall x\, Q(x)$, where the domain consists of all real numbers?

*Solution:* $Q(x)$ is not true for every real number $x$, because, for instance, $Q(3)$ is false. That is, $x = 3$ is a counterexample for the statement $\forall x\, Q(x)$. Thus

$$\forall x\, Q(x)$$

is false.  ◀

**EXAMPLE 10**  Suppose that $P(x)$ is "$x^2 > 0$." To show that the statement $\forall x\, P(x)$ is false where the universe of discourse consists of all integers, we give a counterexample. We see that $x = 0$ is a counterexample because $x^2 = 0$ when $x = 0$, so that $x^2$ is not greater than 0 when $x = 0$.  ◀

Looking for counterexamples to universally quantified statements is an important activity in the study of mathematics, as we will see in subsequent sections of this book.

When all the elements in the domain can be listed—say, $x_1, x_2, \ldots, x_n$—it follows that the universal quantification $\forall x\, P(x)$ is the same as the conjunction

$$P(x_1) \wedge P(x_2) \wedge \cdots \wedge P(x_n),$$

because this conjunction is true if and only if $P(x_1), P(x_2), \ldots, P(x_n)$ are all true.

**EXAMPLE 11**    What is the truth value of $\forall x\, P(x)$, where $P(x)$ is the statement "$x^2 < 10$" and the domain consists of the positive integers not exceeding 4?

*Solution:* The statement $\forall x\, P(x)$ is the same as the conjunction

$$P(1) \wedge P(2) \wedge P(3) \wedge P(4),$$

because the domain consists of the integers 1, 2, 3, and 4. Because $P(4)$, which is the statement "$4^2 < 10$," is false, it follows that $\forall x\, P(x)$ is false.    ◄

**EXAMPLE 12**    What does the statement $\forall x\, N(x)$ mean if $N(x)$ is "Computer $x$ is connected to the network" and the domain consists of all computers on campus?

*Solution:* The statement $\forall x\, N(x)$ means that for every computer $x$ on campus, that computer $x$ is connected to the network. This statement can be expressed in English as "Every computer on campus is connected to the network."    ◄

As we have pointed out, specifying the domain is mandatory when quantifiers are used. The truth value of a quantified statement often depends on which elements are in this domain, as Example 13 shows.

**EXAMPLE 13**    What is the truth value of $\forall x(x^2 \geq x)$ if the domain consists of all real numbers? What is the truth value of this statement if the domain consists of all integers?

*Solution:* The universal quantification $\forall x(x^2 \geq x)$, where the domain consists of all real numbers, is false. For example, $(\frac{1}{2})^2 \not\geq \frac{1}{2}$. Note that $x^2 \geq x$ if and only if $x^2 - x = x(x - 1) \geq 0$. Consequently, $x^2 \geq x$ if and only if $x \leq 0$ or $x \geq 1$. It follows that $\forall x(x^2 \geq x)$ is false if the domain consists of all real numbers (because the inequality is false for all real numbers $x$ with $0 < x < 1$). However, if the domain consists of the integers, $\forall x(x^2 \geq x)$ is true, because there are no integers $x$ with $0 < x < 1$.    ◄

**THE EXISTENTIAL QUANTIFIER**    Many mathematical statements assert that there is an element with a certain property. Such statements are expressed using existential quantification. With existential quantification, we form a proposition that is true if and only if $P(x)$ is true for at least one value of $x$ in the domain.

**DEFINITION 2**

The *existential quantification* of $P(x)$ is the proposition

"There exists an element $x$ in the domain such that $P(x)$."

We use the notation $\exists x\, P(x)$ for the existential quantification of $P(x)$. Here $\exists$ is called the *existential quantifier*.

A domain must always be specified when a statement $\exists x\, P(x)$ is used. Furthermore, the meaning of $\exists x\, P(x)$ changes when the domain changes. Without specifying the domain, the statement $\exists x\, P(x)$ has no meaning.

Besides the phrase "there exists," we can also express existential quantification in many other ways, such as by using the words "for some," "for at least one," or "there is." The existential quantification $\exists x\, P(x)$ is read as

"There is an $x$ such that $P(x)$,"
"There is at least one $x$ such that $P(x)$,"

or

"For some $x\, P(x)$."

The meaning of the existential quantifier is summarized in the second row of Table 1. We illustrate the use of the existential quantifier in Examples 14–16.

**EXAMPLE 14**    Let $P(x)$ denote the statement "$x > 3$." What is the truth value of the quantification $\exists x\, P(x)$, where the domain consists of all real numbers?

*Solution:* Because "$x > 3$" is sometimes true—for instance, when $x = 4$—the existential quantification of $P(x)$, which is $\exists x\, P(x)$, is true.    ◄

Observe that the statement $\exists x\, P(x)$ is false if and only if there is no element $x$ in the domain for which $P(x)$ is true. That is, $\exists x\, P(x)$ is false if and only if $P(x)$ is false for every element of the domain. We illustrate this observation in Example 15.

**EXAMPLE 15**    Let $Q(x)$ denote the statement "$x = x + 1$." What is the truth value of the quantification $\exists x\, Q(x)$, where the domain consists of all real numbers?

*Solution:* Because $Q(x)$ is false for every real number $x$, the existential quantification of $Q(x)$, which is $\exists x\, Q(x)$, is false.    ◄

Remember that the truth value of $\exists x\, P(x)$ depends on the domain!

**Remark:** Generally, an implicit assumption is made that all domains of discourse for quantifiers are nonempty. If the domain is empty, then $\exists x\, Q(x)$ is false whenever $Q(x)$ is a propositional function because when the domain is empty, there can be no element $x$ in the domain for which $Q(x)$ is true.

When all elements in the domain can be listed—say, $x_1, x_2, \ldots, x_n$— the existential quantification $\exists x\, P(x)$ is the same as the disjunction

$$P(x_1) \vee P(x_2) \vee \cdots \vee P(x_n),$$

because this disjunction is true if and only if at least one of $P(x_1), P(x_2), \ldots, P(x_n)$ is true.

**EXAMPLE 16**    What is the truth value of $\exists x\, P(x)$, where $P(x)$ is the statement "$x^2 > 10$" and the universe of discourse consists of the positive integers not exceeding 4?

*Solution:* Because the domain is $\{1, 2, 3, 4\}$, the proposition $\exists x\, P(x)$ is the same as the disjunction

$$P(1) \vee P(2) \vee P(3) \vee P(4).$$

Because $P(4)$, which is the statement "$4^2 > 10$," is true, it follows that $\exists x\, P(x)$ is true.    ◄

It is sometimes helpful to think in terms of looping and searching when determining the truth value of a quantification. Suppose that there are $n$ objects in the domain for the variable $x$. To determine whether $\forall x\, P(x)$ is true, we can loop through all $n$ values of $x$ to see whether $P(x)$ is always true. If we encounter a value $x$ for which $P(x)$ is false, then we have shown that $\forall x\, P(x)$ is false. Otherwise, $\forall x\, P(x)$ is true. To see whether $\exists x\, P(x)$ is true, we loop through the $n$ values of $x$ searching for a value for which $P(x)$ is true. If we find one, then $\exists x\, P(x)$ is true. If we never find such an $x$, then we have determined that $\exists x\, P(x)$ is false. (Note that this searching procedure does not apply if there are infinitely many values in the domain. However, it is still a useful way of thinking about the truth values of quantifications.)

THE UNIQUENESS QUANTIFIER   We have now introduced universal and existential quantifiers. These are the most important quantifiers in mathematics and computer science. However, there is no limitation on the number of different quantifiers we can define, such as "there are exactly two," "there are no more than three," "there are at least 100," and so on. Of these other quantifiers, the one that is most often seen is the **uniqueness quantifier**, denoted by $\exists!$ or $\exists_1$. The notation $\exists! x P(x)$ [or $\exists_1 x P(x)$] states "There exists a unique $x$ such that $P(x)$ is true." (Other phrases for uniqueness quantification include "there is exactly one" and "there is one and only one.") For instance, $\exists! x (x - 1 = 0)$, where the domain is the set of real numbers, states that there is a unique real number $x$ such that $x - 1 = 0$. This is a true statement, as $x = 1$ is the unique real number such that $x - 1 = 0$. Observe that we can use quantifiers and propositional logic to express uniqueness (see Exercise 52 in Section 1.5), so the uniqueness quantifier can be avoided. Generally, it is best to stick with existential and universal quantifiers so that rules of inference for these quantifiers can be used.

## Quantifiers with Restricted Domains

An abbreviated notation is often used to restrict the domain of a quantifier. In this notation, a condition a variable must satisfy is included after the quantifier. This is illustrated in Example 17. We will also describe other forms of this notation involving set membership in Section 2.1.

EXAMPLE 17    What do the statements $\forall x < 0\,(x^2 > 0)$, $\forall y \neq 0\,(y^3 \neq 0)$, and $\exists z > 0\,(z^2 = 2)$ mean, where the domain in each case consists of the real numbers?

*Solution:* The statement $\forall x < 0\,(x^2 > 0)$ states that for every real number $x$ with $x < 0$, $x^2 > 0$. That is, it states "The square of a negative real number is positive." This statement is the same as $\forall x (x < 0 \rightarrow x^2 > 0)$.

The statement $\forall y \neq 0\,(y^3 \neq 0)$ states that for every real number $y$ with $y \neq 0$, we have $y^3 \neq 0$. That is, it states "The cube of every nonzero real number is nonzero." Note that this statement is equivalent to $\forall y(y \neq 0 \rightarrow y^3 \neq 0)$.

Finally, the statement $\exists z > 0\,(z^2 = 2)$ states that there exists a real number $z$ with $z > 0$ such that $z^2 = 2$. That is, it states "There is a positive square root of 2." This statement is equivalent to $\exists z(z > 0 \wedge z^2 = 2)$.    ◀

Note that the restriction of a universal quantification is the same as the universal quantification of a conditional statement. For instance, $\forall x < 0\,(x^2 > 0)$ is another way of expressing $\forall x(x < 0 \rightarrow x^2 > 0)$. On the other hand, the restriction of an existential quantification is the same as the existential quantification of a conjunction. For instance, $\exists z > 0\,(z^2 = 2)$ is another way of expressing $\exists z(z > 0 \wedge z^2 = 2)$.

## Precedence of Quantifiers

The quantifiers $\forall$ and $\exists$ have higher precedence than all logical operators from propositional calculus. For example, $\forall x P(x) \vee Q(x)$ is the disjunction of $\forall x P(x)$ and $Q(x)$. In other words, it means $(\forall x P(x)) \vee Q(x)$ rather than $\forall x(P(x) \vee Q(x))$.

## Binding Variables

When a quantifier is used on the variable $x$, we say that this occurrence of the variable is **bound**. An occurrence of a variable that is not bound by a quantifier or set equal to a particular value is said to be **free**. All the variables that occur in a propositional function must be bound or set equal to a particular value to turn it into a proposition. This can be done using a combination of universal quantifiers, existential quantifiers, and value assignments.

The part of a logical expression to which a quantifier is applied is called the **scope** of this quantifier. Consequently, a variable is free if it is outside the scope of all quantifiers in the formula that specify this variable.

**EXAMPLE 18**    In the statement $\exists x(x + y = 1)$, the variable $x$ is bound by the existential quantification $\exists x$, but the variable $y$ is free because it is not bound by a quantifier and no value is assigned to this variable. This illustrates that in the statement $\exists x(x + y = 1)$, $x$ is bound, but $y$ is free.

In the statement $\exists x(P(x) \wedge Q(x)) \vee \forall x R(x)$, all variables are bound. The scope of the first quantifier, $\exists x$, is the expression $P(x) \wedge Q(x)$ because $\exists x$ is applied only to $P(x) \wedge Q(x)$, and not to the rest of the statement. Similarly, the scope of the second quantifier, $\forall x$, is the expression $R(x)$. That is, the existential quantifier binds the variable $x$ in $P(x) \wedge Q(x)$ and the universal quantifier $\forall x$ binds the variable $x$ in $R(x)$. Observe that we could have written our statement using two different variables $x$ and $y$, as $\exists x(P(x) \wedge Q(x)) \vee \forall y R(y)$, because the scopes of the two quantifiers do not overlap. The reader should be aware that in common usage, the same letter is often used to represent variables bound by different quantifiers with scopes that do not overlap.    ◄

## Logical Equivalences Involving Quantifiers

In Section 1.3 we introduced the notion of logical equivalences of compound propositions. We can extend this notion to expressions involving predicates and quantifiers.

**DEFINITION 3**    Statements involving predicates and quantifiers are *logically equivalent* if and only if they have the same truth value no matter which predicates are substituted into these statements and which domain of discourse is used for the variables in these propositional functions. We use the notation $S \equiv T$ to indicate that two statements $S$ and $T$ involving predicates and quantifiers are logically equivalent.

Example 19 illustrates how to show that two statements involving predicates and quantifiers are logically equivalent.

**EXAMPLE 19**    Show that $\forall x(P(x) \wedge Q(x))$ and $\forall x P(x) \wedge \forall x Q(x)$ are logically equivalent (where the same domain is used throughout). This logical equivalence shows that we can distribute a universal quantifier over a conjunction. Furthermore, we can also distribute an existential quantifier over a disjunction. However, we cannot distribute a universal quantifier over a disjunction, nor can we distribute an existential quantifier over a conjunction. (See Exercises 50 and 51.)

*Solution:* To show that these statements are logically equivalent, we must show that they always take the same truth value, no matter what the predicates $P$ and $Q$ are, and no matter which domain of discourse is used. Suppose we have particular predicates $P$ and $Q$, with a common domain. We can show that $\forall x(P(x) \wedge Q(x))$ and $\forall x P(x) \wedge \forall x Q(x)$ are logically equivalent by doing two things. First, we show that if $\forall x(P(x) \wedge Q(x))$ is true, then $\forall x P(x) \wedge \forall x Q(x)$ is true. Second, we show that if $\forall x P(x) \wedge \forall x Q(x)$ is true, then $\forall x(P(x) \wedge Q(x))$ is true.

So, suppose that $\forall x(P(x) \wedge Q(x))$ is true. This means that if $a$ is in the domain, then $P(a) \wedge Q(a)$ is true. Hence, $P(a)$ is true and $Q(a)$ is true. Because $P(a)$ is true and $Q(a)$ is true for every element in the domain, we can conclude that $\forall x P(x)$ and $\forall x Q(x)$ are both true. This means that $\forall x P(x) \wedge \forall x Q(x)$ is true.

Next, suppose that $\forall x P(x) \wedge \forall x Q(x)$ is true. It follows that $\forall x P(x)$ is true and $\forall x Q(x)$ is true. Hence, if $a$ is in the domain, then $P(a)$ is true and $Q(a)$ is true [because $P(x)$ and $Q(x)$ are both true for all elements in the domain, there is no conflict using the same value of $a$ here].

It follows that for all $a$, $P(a) \wedge Q(a)$ is true. It follows that $\forall x (P(x) \wedge Q(x))$ is true. We can now conclude that

$$\forall x (P(x) \wedge Q(x)) \equiv \forall x \, P(x) \wedge \forall x \, Q(x).$$     ◀

## Negating Quantified Expressions

We will often want to consider the negation of a quantified expression. For instance, consider the negation of the statement

"Every student in your class has taken a course in calculus."

This statement is a universal quantification, namely,

$$\forall x \, P(x),$$

Assessment

where $P(x)$ is the statement "$x$ has taken a course in calculus" and the domain consists of the students in your class. The negation of this statement is "It is not the case that every student in your class has taken a course in calculus." This is equivalent to "There is a student in your class who has not taken a course in calculus." And this is simply the existential quantification of the negation of the original propositional function, namely,

$$\exists x \, \neg P(x).$$

This example illustrates the following logical equivalence:

$$\neg \forall x \, P(x) \equiv \exists x \, \neg P(x).$$

To show that $\neg \forall x \, P(x)$ and $\exists x \, P(x)$ are logically equivalent no matter what the propositional function $P(x)$ is and what the domain is, first note that $\neg \forall x \, P(x)$ is true if and only if $\forall x \, P(x)$ is false. Next, note that $\forall x \, P(x)$ is false if and only if there is an element $x$ in the domain for which $P(x)$ is false. This holds if and only if there is an element $x$ in the domain for which $\neg P(x)$ is true. Finally, note that there is an element $x$ in the domain for which $\neg P(x)$ is true if and only if $\exists x \, \neg P(x)$ is true. Putting these steps together, we can conclude that $\neg \forall x \, P(x)$ is true if and only if $\exists x \, \neg P(x)$ is true. It follows that $\neg \forall x \, P(x)$ and $\exists x \, \neg P(x)$ are logically equivalent.

Suppose we wish to negate an existential quantification. For instance, consider the proposition "There is a student in this class who has taken a course in calculus." This is the existential quantification

$$\exists x \, Q(x),$$

where $Q(x)$ is the statement "$x$ has taken a course in calculus." The negation of this statement is the proposition "It is not the case that there is a student in this class who has taken a course in calculus." This is equivalent to "Every student in this class has not taken calculus," which is just the universal quantification of the negation of the original propositional function, or, phrased in the language of quantifiers,

$$\forall x \, \neg Q(x).$$

This example illustrates the equivalence

$$\neg \exists x \, Q(x) \equiv \forall x \, \neg Q(x).$$

To show that $\neg \exists x \, Q(x)$ and $\forall x \, \neg Q(x)$ are logically equivalent no matter what $Q(x)$ is and what the domain is, first note that $\neg \exists x \, Q(x)$ is true if and only if $\exists x \, Q(x)$ is false. This is true if and

| TABLE 2 De Morgan's Laws for Quantifiers. | | | |
|---|---|---|---|
| **Negation** | **Equivalent Statement** | **When Is Negation True?** | **When False?** |
| $\neg \exists x P(x)$ | $\forall x \neg P(x)$ | For every $x$, $P(x)$ is false. | There is an $x$ for which $P(x)$ is true. |
| $\neg \forall x P(x)$ | $\exists x \neg P(x)$ | There is an $x$ for which $P(x)$ is false. | $P(x)$ is true for every $x$. |

only if no $x$ exists in the domain for which $Q(x)$ is true. Next, note that no $x$ exists in the domain for which $Q(x)$ is true if and only if $Q(x)$ is false for every $x$ in the domain. Finally, note that $Q(x)$ is false for every $x$ in the domain if and only if $\neg Q(x)$ is true for all $x$ in the domain, which holds if and only if $\forall x \neg Q(x)$ is true. Putting these steps together, we see that $\neg \exists x Q(x)$ is true if and only if $\forall x \neg Q(x)$ is true. We conclude that $\neg \exists x Q(x)$ and $\forall x \neg Q(x)$ are logically equivalent.

The rules for negations for quantifiers are called **De Morgan's laws for quantifiers**. These rules are summarized in Table 2.

*Remark:* When the domain of a predicate $P(x)$ consists of $n$ elements, where $n$ is a positive integer greater than one, the rules for negating quantified statements are exactly the same as De Morgan's laws discussed in Section 1.3. This is why these rules are called De Morgan's laws for quantifiers. When the domain has $n$ elements $x_1, x_2, \ldots, x_n$, it follows that $\neg \forall x P(x)$ is the same as $\neg (P(x_1) \wedge P(x_2) \wedge \cdots \wedge P(x_n))$, which is equivalent to $\neg P(x_1) \vee \neg P(x_2) \vee \cdots \vee \neg P(x_n)$ by De Morgan's laws, and this is the same as $\exists x \neg P(x)$. Similarly, $\neg \exists x P(x)$ is the same as $\neg (P(x_1) \vee P(x_2) \vee \cdots \vee P(x_n))$, which by De Morgan's laws is equivalent to $\neg P(x_1) \wedge \neg P(x_2) \wedge \cdots \wedge \neg P(x_n)$, and this is the same as $\forall x \neg P(x)$.

We illustrate the negation of quantified statements in Examples 20 and 21.

**EXAMPLE 20**  What are the negations of the statements "There is an honest politician" and "All Americans eat cheeseburgers"?

*Solution:* Let $H(x)$ denote "$x$ is honest." Then the statement "There is an honest politician" is represented by $\exists x H(x)$, where the domain consists of all politicians. The negation of this statement is $\neg \exists x H(x)$, which is equivalent to $\forall x \neg H(x)$. This negation can be expressed as "Every politician is dishonest." (*Note:* In English, the statement "All politicians are not honest" is ambiguous. In common usage, this statement often means "Not all politicians are honest." Consequently, we do not use this statement to express this negation.)

Extra Examples

Let $C(x)$ denote "$x$ eats cheeseburgers." Then the statement "All Americans eat cheeseburgers" is represented by $\forall x C(x)$, where the domain consists of all Americans. The negation of this statement is $\neg \forall x C(x)$, which is equivalent to $\exists x \neg C(x)$. This negation can be expressed in several different ways, including "Some American does not eat cheeseburgers" and "There is an American who does not eat cheeseburgers." ◀

**EXAMPLE 21**  What are the negations of the statements $\forall x (x^2 > x)$ and $\exists x (x^2 = 2)$?

*Solution:* The negation of $\forall x (x^2 > x)$ is the statement $\neg \forall x (x^2 > x)$, which is equivalent to $\exists x \neg (x^2 > x)$. This can be rewritten as $\exists x (x^2 \leq x)$. The negation of $\exists x (x^2 = 2)$ is the statement $\neg \exists x (x^2 = 2)$, which is equivalent to $\forall x \neg (x^2 = 2)$. This can be rewritten as $\forall x (x^2 \neq 2)$. The truth values of these statements depend on the domain. ◀

We use De Morgan's laws for quantifiers in Example 22.

**EXAMPLE 22**  Show that $\neg\forall x(P(x) \to Q(x))$ and $\exists x(P(x) \land \neg Q(x))$ are logically equivalent.

*Solution:* By De Morgan's law for universal quantifiers, we know that $\neg\forall x(P(x) \to Q(x))$ and $\exists x(\neg(P(x) \to Q(x)))$ are logically equivalent. By the fifth logical equivalence in Table 7 in Section 1.3, we know that $\neg(P(x) \to Q(x))$ and $P(x) \land \neg Q(x)$ are logically equivalent for every $x$. Because we can substitute one logically equivalent expression for another in a logical equivalence, it follows that $\neg\forall x(P(x) \to Q(x))$ and $\exists x(P(x) \land \neg Q(x))$ are logically equivalent.  ◀

## Translating from English into Logical Expressions

Translating sentences in English (or other natural languages) into logical expressions is a crucial task in mathematics, logic programming, artificial intelligence, software engineering, and many other disciplines. We began studying this topic in Section 1.1, where we used propositions to express sentences in logical expressions. In that discussion, we purposely avoided sentences whose translations required predicates and quantifiers. Translating from English to logical expressions becomes even more complex when quantifiers are needed. Furthermore, there can be many ways to translate a particular sentence. (As a consequence, there is no "cookbook" approach that can be followed step by step.) We will use some examples to illustrate how to translate sentences from English into logical expressions. The goal in this translation is to produce simple and useful logical expressions. In this section, we restrict ourselves to sentences that can be translated into logical expressions using a single quantifier; in the next section, we will look at more complicated sentences that require multiple quantifiers.

**EXAMPLE 23**  Express the statement "Every student in this class has studied calculus" using predicates and quantifiers.

*Solution:* First, we rewrite the statement so that we can clearly identify the appropriate quantifiers to use. Doing so, we obtain:

"For every student in this class, that student has studied calculus."

Next, we introduce a variable $x$ so that our statement becomes

"For every student $x$ in this class, $x$ has studied calculus."

Continuing, we introduce $C(x)$, which is the statement "$x$ has studied calculus." Consequently, if the domain for $x$ consists of the students in the class, we can translate our statement as $\forall x\, C(x)$.

However, there are other correct approaches; different domains of discourse and other predicates can be used. The approach we select depends on the subsequent reasoning we want to carry out. For example, we may be interested in a wider group of people than only those in this class. If we change the domain to consist of all people, we will need to express our statement as

"For every person $x$, if person $x$ is a student in this class then $x$ has studied calculus."

If $S(x)$ represents the statement that person $x$ is in this class, we see that our statement can be expressed as $\forall x(S(x) \to C(x))$. [*Caution!* Our statement *cannot* be expressed as $\forall x(S(x) \land C(x))$ because this statement says that all people are students in this class and have studied calculus!]

Finally, when we are interested in the background of people in subjects besides calculus, we may prefer to use the two-variable quantifier $Q(x, y)$ for the statement "student $x$ has studied subject $y$." Then we would replace $C(x)$ by $Q(x, \text{calculus})$ in both approaches to obtain $\forall x\, Q(x, \text{calculus})$ or $\forall x(S(x) \to Q(x, \text{calculus}))$.  ◀

In Example 23 we displayed different approaches for expressing the same statement using predicates and quantifiers. However, we should always adopt the simplest approach that is adequate for use in subsequent reasoning.

**EXAMPLE 24**    Express the statements "Some student in this class has visited Mexico" and "Every student in this class has visited either Canada or Mexico" using predicates and quantifiers.

*Solution:* The statement "Some student in this class has visited Mexico" means that

"There is a student in this class with the property that the student has visited Mexico."

We can introduce a variable $x$, so that our statement becomes

"There is a student $x$ in this class having the property that $x$ has visited Mexico."

We introduce $M(x)$, which is the statement "$x$ has visited Mexico." If the domain for $x$ consists of the students in this class, we can translate this first statement as $\exists x\, M(x)$.

However, if we are interested in people other than those in this class, we look at the statement a little differently. Our statement can be expressed as

"There is a person $x$ having the properties that $x$ is a student in this class and $x$ has visited Mexico."

 In this case, the domain for the variable $x$ consists of all people. We introduce $S(x)$ to represent "$x$ is a student in this class." Our solution becomes $\exists x(S(x) \wedge M(x))$ because the statement is that there is a person $x$ who is a student in this class and who has visited Mexico. [*Caution!* Our statement cannot be expressed as $\exists x(S(x) \rightarrow M(x))$, which is true when there is someone not in the class because, in that case, for such a person $x$, $S(x) \rightarrow M(x)$ becomes either $\mathbf{F} \rightarrow \mathbf{T}$ or $\mathbf{F} \rightarrow \mathbf{F}$, both of which are true.]

Similarly, the second statement can be expressed as

"For every $x$ in this class, $x$ has the property that $x$ has visited Mexico or $x$ has visited Canada."

(Note that we are assuming the inclusive, rather than the exclusive, or here.) We let $C(x)$ be "$x$ has visited Canada." Following our earlier reasoning, we see that if the domain for $x$ consists of the students in this class, this second statement can be expressed as $\forall x(C(x) \vee M(x))$. However, if the domain for $x$ consists of all people, our statement can be expressed as

"For every person $x$, if $x$ is a student in this class, then $x$ has visited Mexico or $x$ has visited Canada."

In this case, the statement can be expressed as $\forall x(S(x) \rightarrow (C(x) \vee M(x)))$.

Instead of using $M(x)$ and $C(x)$ to represent that $x$ has visited Mexico and $x$ has visited Canada, respectively, we could use a two-place predicate $V(x, y)$ to represent "$x$ has visited country $y$." In this case, $V(x, \text{Mexico})$ and $V(x, \text{Canada})$ would have the same meaning as $M(x)$ and $C(x)$ and could replace them in our answers. If we are working with many statements that involve people visiting different countries, we might prefer to use this two-variable approach. Otherwise, for simplicity, we would stick with the one-variable predicates $M(x)$ and $C(x)$. ◀

## Using Quantifiers in System Specifications

In Section 1.2 we used propositions to represent system specifications. However, many system specifications involve predicates and quantifications. This is illustrated in Example 25.

EXAMPLE 25    Use predicates and quantifiers to express the system specifications "Every mail message larger than one megabyte will be compressed" and "If a user is active, at least one network link will be available."

*Solution:* Let $S(m, y)$ be "Mail message $m$ is larger than $y$ megabytes," where the variable $x$ has the domain of all mail messages and the variable $y$ is a positive real number, and let $C(m)$ denote "Mail message $m$ will be compressed." Then the specification "Every mail message larger than one megabyte will be compressed" can be represented as $\forall m(S(m, 1) \rightarrow C(m))$.

Remember the rules of precedence for quantifiers and logical connectives!

Let $A(u)$ represent "User $u$ is active," where the variable $u$ has the domain of all users, let $S(n, x)$ denote "Network link $n$ is in state $x$," where $n$ has the domain of all network links and $x$ has the domain of all possible states for a network link. Then the specification "If a user is active, at least one network link will be available" can be represented by $\exists u A(u) \rightarrow \exists n S(n, \text{available})$.    ◄

## Examples from Lewis Carroll

Lewis Carroll (really C. L. Dodgson writing under a pseudonym), the author of *Alice in Wonderland*, is also the author of several works on symbolic logic. His books contain many examples of reasoning using quantifiers. Examples 26 and 27 come from his book *Symbolic Logic;* other examples from that book are given in the exercises at the end of this section. These examples illustrate how quantifiers are used to express various types of statements.

EXAMPLE 26    Consider these statements. The first two are called *premises* and the third is called the *conclusion*. The entire set is called an *argument*.

> "All lions are fierce."
> "Some lions do not drink coffee."
> "Some fierce creatures do not drink coffee."

(In Section 1.6 we will discuss the issue of determining whether the conclusion is a valid consequence of the premises. In this example, it is.) Let $P(x)$, $Q(x)$, and $R(x)$ be the statements "$x$ is a lion," "$x$ is fierce," and "$x$ drinks coffee," respectively. Assuming that the domain consists of all creatures, express the statements in the argument using quantifiers and $P(x)$, $Q(x)$, and $R(x)$.

CHARLES LUTWIDGE DODGSON (1832–1898)    We know Charles Dodgson as Lewis Carroll—the pseudonym he used in his literary works. Dodgson, the son of a clergyman, was the third of 11 children, all of whom stuttered. He was uncomfortable in the company of adults and is said to have spoken without stuttering only to young girls, many of whom he entertained, corresponded with, and photographed (sometimes in poses that today would be considered inappropriate). Although attracted to young girls, he was extremely puritanical and religious. His friendship with the three young daughters of Dean Liddell led to his writing *Alice in Wonderland*, which brought him money and fame.

Dodgson graduated from Oxford in 1854 and obtained his master of arts degree in 1857. He was appointed lecturer in mathematics at Christ Church College, Oxford, in 1855. He was ordained in the Church of England in 1861 but never practiced his ministry. His writings published under this real name include articles and books on geometry, determinants, and the mathematics of tournaments and elections. (He also used the pseudonym Lewis Carroll for his many works on recreational logic.)

*Solution:* We can express these statements as:

$$\forall x (P(x) \rightarrow Q(x)).$$
$$\exists x (P(x) \wedge \neg R(x)).$$
$$\exists x (Q(x) \wedge \neg R(x)).$$

Notice that the second statement cannot be written as $\exists x (P(x) \rightarrow \neg R(x))$. The reason is that $P(x) \rightarrow \neg R(x)$ is true whenever $x$ is not a lion, so that $\exists x (P(x) \rightarrow \neg R(x))$ is true as long as there is at least one creature that is not a lion, even if every lion drinks coffee. Similarly, the third statement cannot be written as

$$\exists x (Q(x) \rightarrow \neg R(x)). \qquad \blacktriangleleft$$

**EXAMPLE 27** Consider these statements, of which the first three are premises and the fourth is a valid conclusion.

"All hummingbirds are richly colored."
"No large birds live on honey."
"Birds that do not live on honey are dull in color."
"Hummingbirds are small."

Let $P(x)$, $Q(x)$, $R(x)$, and $S(x)$ be the statements "$x$ is a hummingbird," "$x$ is large," "$x$ lives on honey," and "$x$ is richly colored," respectively. Assuming that the domain consists of all birds, express the statements in the argument using quantifiers and $P(x)$, $Q(x)$, $R(x)$, and $S(x)$.

*Solution:* We can express the statements in the argument as

$$\forall x (P(x) \rightarrow S(x)).$$
$$\neg \exists x (Q(x) \wedge R(x)).$$
$$\forall x (\neg R(x) \rightarrow \neg S(x)).$$
$$\forall x (P(x) \rightarrow \neg Q(x)).$$

(Note we have assumed that "small" is the same as "not large" and that "dull in color" is the same as "not richly colored." To show that the fourth statement is a valid conclusion of the first three, we need to use rules of inference that will be discussed in Section 1.6.) $\qquad \blacktriangleleft$

## Logic Programming

An important type of programming language is designed to reason using the rules of predicate logic. Prolog (from *Pro*gramming in *Log*ic), developed in the 1970s by computer scientists working in the area of artificial intelligence, is an example of such a language. Prolog programs include a set of declarations consisting of two types of statements, **Prolog facts** and **Prolog rules**. Prolog facts define predicates by specifying the elements that satisfy these predicates. Prolog rules are used to define new predicates using those already defined by Prolog facts. Example 28 illustrates these notions.

Links

**EXAMPLE 28** Consider a Prolog program given facts telling it the instructor of each class and in which classes students are enrolled. The program uses these facts to answer queries concerning the professors who teach particular students. Such a program could use the predicates *instructor*(*p, c*) and *enrolled*(*s, c*) to represent that professor *p* is the instructor of course *c* and that student *s* is enrolled in course *c*, respectively. For example, the Prolog facts in such a program might include:

```
instructor(chan,math273)
instructor(patel,ee222)
instructor(grossman,cs301)
enrolled(kevin,math273)
enrolled(juana,ee222)
enrolled(juana,cs301)
enrolled(kiko,math273)
enrolled(kiko,cs301)
```

(Lowercase letters have been used for entries because Prolog considers names beginning with an uppercase letter to be variables.)

A new predicate *teaches*(*p, s*), representing that professor *p* teaches student *s*, can be defined using the Prolog rule

```
teaches(P,S) :- instructor(P,C), enrolled(S,C)
```

which means that *teaches*(*p, s*) is true if there exists a class *c* such that professor *p* is the instructor of class *c* and student *s* is enrolled in class *c*. (Note that a comma is used to represent a conjunction of predicates in Prolog. Similarly, a semicolon is used to represent a disjunction of predicates.)

Prolog answers queries using the facts and rules it is given. For example, using the facts and rules listed, the query

```
?enrolled(kevin,math273)
```

produces the response

```
yes
```

because the fact *enrolled*(kevin, math273) was provided as input. The query

```
?enrolled(X,math273)
```

produces the response

```
kevin
kiko
```

To produce this response, Prolog determines all possible values of *X* for which *enrolled*(*X*, math273) has been included as a Prolog fact. Similarly, to find all the professors who are instructors in classes being taken by Juana, we use the query

```
?teaches(X,juana)
```

This query returns

```
patel
grossman
```

# Exercises

**1.** Let $P(x)$ denote the statement "$x \leq 4$." What are these truth values?

**a)** $P(0)$      **b)** $P(4)$      **c)** $P(6)$

**2.** Let $P(x)$ be the statement "the word $x$ contains the letter $a$." What are these truth values?

**a)** $P(\text{orange})$      **b)** $P(\text{lemon})$
**c)** $P(\text{true})$      **d)** $P(\text{false})$

**3.** Let $Q(x, y)$ denote the statement "$x$ is the capital of $y$." What are these truth values?

**a)** $Q(\text{Denver, Colorado})$
**b)** $Q(\text{Detroit, Michigan})$
**c)** $Q(\text{Massachusetts, Boston})$
**d)** $Q(\text{New York, New York})$

**4.** State the value of $x$ after the statement **if** $P(x)$ **then** $x := 1$ is executed, where $P(x)$ is the statement "$x > 1$," if the value of $x$ when this statement is reached is

**a)** $x = 0$.      **b)** $x = 1$.
**c)** $x = 2$.

**5.** Let $P(x)$ be the statement "$x$ spends more than five hours every weekday in class," where the domain for $x$ consists of all students. Express each of these quantifications in English.

**a)** $\exists x \, P(x)$      **b)** $\forall x \, P(x)$
**c)** $\exists x \, \neg P(x)$      **d)** $\forall x \, \neg P(x)$

**6.** Let $N(x)$ be the statement "$x$ has visited North Dakota," where the domain consists of the students in your school. Express each of these quantifications in English.

**a)** $\exists x \, N(x)$    **b)** $\forall x \, N(x)$    **c)** $\neg \exists x \, N(x)$
**d)** $\exists x \, \neg N(x)$    **e)** $\neg \forall x \, N(x)$    **f)** $\forall x \, \neg N(x)$

**7.** Translate these statements into English, where $C(x)$ is "$x$ is a comedian" and $F(x)$ is "$x$ is funny" and the domain consists of all people.

**a)** $\forall x (C(x) \rightarrow F(x))$      **b)** $\forall x (C(x) \wedge F(x))$
**c)** $\exists x (C(x) \rightarrow F(x))$      **d)** $\exists x (C(x) \wedge F(x))$

**8.** Translate these statements into English, where $R(x)$ is "$x$ is a rabbit" and $H(x)$ is "$x$ hops" and the domain consists of all animals.

**a)** $\forall x (R(x) \rightarrow H(x))$      **b)** $\forall x (R(x) \wedge H(x))$
**c)** $\exists x (R(x) \rightarrow H(x))$      **d)** $\exists x (R(x) \wedge H(x))$

**9.** Let $P(x)$ be the statement "$x$ can speak Russian" and let $Q(x)$ be the statement "$x$ knows the computer language C++." Express each of these sentences in terms of $P(x)$, $Q(x)$, quantifiers, and logical connectives. The domain for quantifiers consists of all students at your school.

**a)** There is a student at your school who can speak Russian and who knows C++.
**b)** There is a student at your school who can speak Russian but who doesn't know C++.
**c)** Every student at your school either can speak Russian or knows C++.
**d)** No student at your school can speak Russian or knows C++.

**10.** Let $C(x)$ be the statement "$x$ has a cat," let $D(x)$ be the statement "$x$ has a dog," and let $F(x)$ be the statement "$x$ has a ferret." Express each of these statements in terms of $C(x)$, $D(x)$, $F(x)$, quantifiers, and logical connectives. Let the domain consist of all students in your class.

**a)** A student in your class has a cat, a dog, and a ferret.
**b)** All students in your class have a cat, a dog, or a ferret.
**c)** Some student in your class has a cat and a ferret, but not a dog.
**d)** No student in your class has a cat, a dog, and a ferret.
**e)** For each of the three animals, cats, dogs, and ferrets, there is a student in your class who has this animal as a pet.

**11.** Let $P(x)$ be the statement "$x = x^2$." If the domain consists of the integers, what are these truth values?

**a)** $P(0)$      **b)** $P(1)$      **c)** $P(2)$
**d)** $P(-1)$      **e)** $\exists x \, P(x)$      **f)** $\forall x \, P(x)$

**12.** Let $Q(x)$ be the statement "$x + 1 > 2x$." If the domain consists of all integers, what are these truth values?

**a)** $Q(0)$      **b)** $Q(-1)$      **c)** $Q(1)$
**d)** $\exists x \, Q(x)$      **e)** $\forall x \, Q(x)$      **f)** $\exists x \neg Q(x)$
**g)** $\forall x \neg Q(x)$

**13.** Determine the truth value of each of these statements if the domain consists of all integers.

**a)** $\forall n (n + 1 > n)$      **b)** $\exists n (2n = 3n)$
**c)** $\exists n (n = -n)$      **d)** $\forall n (3n \leq 4n)$

**14.** Determine the truth value of each of these statements if the domain consists of all real numbers.

**a)** $\exists x (x^3 = -1)$      **b)** $\exists x (x^4 < x^2)$
**c)** $\forall x ((-x)^2 = x^2)$      **d)** $\forall x (2x > x)$

**15.** Determine the truth value of each of these statements if the domain for all variables consists of all integers.

**a)** $\forall n (n^2 \geq 0)$      **b)** $\exists n (n^2 = 2)$
**c)** $\forall n (n^2 \geq n)$      **d)** $\exists n (n^2 < 0)$

**16.** Determine the truth value of each of these statements if the domain of each variable consists of all real numbers.

**a)** $\exists x (x^2 = 2)$      **b)** $\exists x (x^2 = -1)$
**c)** $\forall x (x^2 + 2 \geq 1)$      **d)** $\forall x (x^2 \neq x)$

**17.** Suppose that the domain of the propositional function $P(x)$ consists of the integers 0, 1, 2, 3, and 4. Write out each of these propositions using disjunctions, conjunctions, and negations.

**a)** $\exists x \, P(x)$      **b)** $\forall x \, P(x)$      **c)** $\exists x \neg P(x)$
**d)** $\forall x \neg P(x)$      **e)** $\neg \exists x \, P(x)$      **f)** $\neg \forall x \, P(x)$

**18.** Suppose that the domain of the propositional function $P(x)$ consists of the integers $-2$, $-1$, 0, 1, and 2. Write out each of these propositions using disjunctions, conjunctions, and negations.

**a)** $\exists x \, P(x)$      **b)** $\forall x \, P(x)$      **c)** $\exists x \neg P(x)$
**d)** $\forall x \neg P(x)$      **e)** $\neg \exists x \, P(x)$      **f)** $\neg \forall x \, P(x)$

**19.** Suppose that the domain of the propositional function $P(x)$ consists of the integers 1, 2, 3, 4, and 5. Express these statements without using quantifiers, instead using only negations, disjunctions, and conjunctions.

**a)** $\exists x\, P(x)$            **b)** $\forall x\, P(x)$
**c)** $\neg\exists x\, P(x)$        **d)** $\neg\forall x\, P(x)$
**e)** $\forall x((x \neq 3) \to P(x)) \vee \exists x \neg P(x)$

**20.** Suppose that the domain of the propositional function $P(x)$ consists of $-5, -3, -1, 1, 3$, and 5. Express these statements without using quantifiers, instead using only negations, disjunctions, and conjunctions.

**a)** $\exists x\, P(x)$            **b)** $\forall x\, P(x)$
**c)** $\forall x((x \neq 1) \to P(x))$
**d)** $\exists x((x \geq 0) \wedge P(x))$
**e)** $\exists x(\neg P(x)) \wedge \forall x((x < 0) \to P(x))$

**21.** For each of these statements find a domain for which the statement is true and a domain for which the statement is false.

**a)** Everyone is studying discrete mathematics.
**b)** Everyone is older than 21 years.
**c)** Every two people have the same mother.
**d)** No two different people have the same grandmother.

**22.** For each of these statements find a domain for which the statement is true and a domain for which the statement is false.

**a)** Everyone speaks Hindi.
**b)** There is someone older than 21 years.
**c)** Every two people have the same first name.
**d)** Someone knows more than two other people.

**23.** Translate in two ways each of these statements into logical expressions using predicates, quantifiers, and logical connectives. First, let the domain consist of the students in your class and second, let it consist of all people.

**a)** Someone in your class can speak Hindi.
**b)** Everyone in your class is friendly.
**c)** There is a person in your class who was not born in California.
**d)** A student in your class has been in a movie.
**e)** No student in your class has taken a course in logic programming.

**24.** Translate in two ways each of these statements into logical expressions using predicates, quantifiers, and logical connectives. First, let the domain consist of the students in your class and second, let it consist of all people.

**a)** Everyone in your class has a cellular phone.
**b)** Somebody in your class has seen a foreign movie.
**c)** There is a person in your class who cannot swim.
**d)** All students in your class can solve quadratic equations.
**e)** Some student in your class does not want to be rich.

**25.** Translate each of these statements into logical expressions using predicates, quantifiers, and logical connectives.

**a)** No one is perfect.
**b)** Not everyone is perfect.
**c)** All your friends are perfect.
**d)** At least one of your friends is perfect.

**e)** Everyone is your friend and is perfect.
**f)** Not everybody is your friend or someone is not perfect.

**26.** Translate each of these statements into logical expressions in three different ways by varying the domain and by using predicates with one and with two variables.

**a)** Someone in your school has visited Uzbekistan.
**b)** Everyone in your class has studied calculus and C++.
**c)** No one in your school owns both a bicycle and a motorcycle.
**d)** There is a person in your school who is not happy.
**e)** Everyone in your school was born in the twentieth century.

**27.** Translate each of these statements into logical expressions in three different ways by varying the domain and by using predicates with one and with two variables.

**a)** A student in your school has lived in Vietnam.
**b)** There is a student in your school who cannot speak Hindi.
**c)** A student in your school knows Java, Prolog, and C++.
**d)** Everyone in your class enjoys Thai food.
**e)** Someone in your class does not play hockey.

**28.** Translate each of these statements into logical expressions using predicates, quantifiers, and logical connectives.

**a)** Something is not in the correct place.
**b)** All tools are in the correct place and are in excellent condition.
**c)** Everything is in the correct place and in excellent condition.
**d)** Nothing is in the correct place and is in excellent condition.
**e)** One of your tools is not in the correct place, but it is in excellent condition.

**29.** Express each of these statements using logical operators, predicates, and quantifiers.

**a)** Some propositions are tautologies.
**b)** The negation of a contradiction is a tautology.
**c)** The disjunction of two contingencies can be a tautology.
**d)** The conjunction of two tautologies is a tautology.

**30.** Suppose the domain of the propositional function $P(x, y)$ consists of pairs $x$ and $y$, where $x$ is 1, 2, or 3 and $y$ is 1, 2, or 3. Write out these propositions using disjunctions and conjunctions.

**a)** $\exists x\, P(x, 3)$        **b)** $\forall y\, P(1, y)$
**c)** $\exists y \neg P(2, y)$      **d)** $\forall x \neg P(x, 2)$

**31.** Suppose that the domain of $Q(x, y, z)$ consists of triples $x, y, z$, where $x = 0, 1$, or 2, $y = 0$ or 1, and $z = 0$ or 1. Write out these propositions using disjunctions and conjunctions.

**a)** $\forall y\, Q(0, y, 0)$      **b)** $\exists x\, Q(x, 1, 1)$
**c)** $\exists z \neg Q(0, 0, z)$    **d)** $\exists x \neg Q(x, 0, 1)$

**32.** Express each of these statements using quantifiers. Then form the negation of the statement so that no negation is to the left of a quantifier. Next, express the negation in simple English. (Do not simply use the phrase "It is not the case that.")

a) All dogs have fleas.

b) There is a horse that can add.

c) Every koala can climb.

d) No monkey can speak French.

e) There exists a pig that can swim and catch fish.

**33.** Express each of these statements using quantifiers. Then form the negation of the statement, so that no negation is to the left of a quantifier. Next, express the negation in simple English. (Do not simply use the phrase "It is not the case that.")

a) Some old dogs can learn new tricks.

b) No rabbit knows calculus.

c) Every bird can fly.

d) There is no dog that can talk.

e) There is no one in this class who knows French and Russian.

**34.** Express the negation of these propositions using quantifiers, and then express the negation in English.

a) Some drivers do not obey the speed limit.

b) All Swedish movies are serious.

c) No one can keep a secret.

d) There is someone in this class who does not have a good attitude.

**35.** Find a counterexample, if possible, to these universally quantified statements, where the domain for all variables consists of all integers.

a) $\forall x(x^2 \geq x)$

b) $\forall x(x > 0 \lor x < 0)$

c) $\forall x(x = 1)$

**36.** Find a counterexample, if possible, to these universally quantified statements, where the domain for all variables consists of all real numbers.

a) $\forall x(x^2 \neq x)$   b) $\forall x(x^2 \neq 2)$

c) $\forall x(|x| > 0)$

**37.** Express each of these statements using predicates and quantifiers.

a) A passenger on an airline qualifies as an elite flyer if the passenger flies more than 25,000 miles in a year or takes more than 25 flights during that year.

b) A man qualifies for the marathon if his best previous time is less than 3 hours and a woman qualifies for the marathon if her best previous time is less than 3.5 hours.

c) A student must take at least 60 course hours, or at least 45 course hours and write a master's thesis, and receive a grade no lower than a B in all required courses, to receive a master's degree.

d) There is a student who has taken more than 21 credit hours in a semester and received all A's.

Exercises 38–42 deal with the translation between system specification and logical expressions involving quantifiers.

**38.** Translate these system specifications into English where the predicate $S(x, y)$ is "$x$ is in state $y$" and where the domain for $x$ and $y$ consists of all systems and all possible states, respectively.

a) $\exists x S(x, \text{open})$

b) $\forall x(S(x, \text{malfunctioning}) \lor S(x, \text{diagnostic}))$

c) $\exists x S(x, \text{open}) \lor \exists x S(x, \text{diagnostic})$

d) $\exists x \neg S(x, \text{available})$

e) $\forall x \neg S(x, \text{working})$

**39.** Translate these specifications into English where $F(p)$ is "Printer $p$ is out of service," $B(p)$ is "Printer $p$ is busy," $L(j)$ is "Print job $j$ is lost," and $Q(j)$ is "Print job $j$ is queued."

a) $\exists p(F(p) \land B(p)) \rightarrow \exists j L(j)$

b) $\forall p B(p) \rightarrow \exists j Q(j)$

c) $\exists j(Q(j) \land L(j)) \rightarrow \exists p F(p)$

d) $(\forall p B(p) \land \forall j Q(j)) \rightarrow \exists j L(j)$

**40.** Express each of these system specifications using predicates, quantifiers, and logical connectives.

a) When there is less than 30 megabytes free on the hard disk, a warning message is sent to all users.

b) No directories in the file system can be opened and no files can be closed when system errors have been detected.

c) The file system cannot be backed up if there is a user currently logged on.

d) Video on demand can be delivered when there are at least 8 megabytes of memory available and the connection speed is at least 56 kilobits per second.

**41.** Express each of these system specifications using predicates, quantifiers, and logical connectives.

a) At least one mail message, among the nonempty set of messages, can be saved if there is a disk with more than 10 kilobytes of free space.

b) Whenever there is an active alert, all queued messages are transmitted.

c) The diagnostic monitor tracks the status of all systems except the main console.

d) Each participant on the conference call whom the host of the call did not put on a special list was billed.

**42.** Express each of these system specifications using predicates, quantifiers, and logical connectives.

a) Every user has access to an electronic mailbox.

b) The system mailbox can be accessed by everyone in the group if the file system is locked.

c) The firewall is in a diagnostic state only if the proxy server is in a diagnostic state.

d) At least one router is functioning normally if the throughput is between 100 kbps and 500 kbps and the proxy server is not in diagnostic mode.

**43.** Determine whether $\forall x(P(x) \rightarrow Q(x))$ and $\forall x P(x) \rightarrow \forall x Q(x)$ are logically equivalent. Justify your answer.

**44.** Determine whether $\forall x(P(x) \leftrightarrow Q(x))$ and $\forall x\ P(x) \leftrightarrow \forall x Q(x)$ are logically equivalent. Justify your answer.

**45.** Show that $\exists x(P(x) \vee Q(x))$ and $\exists x P(x) \vee \exists x Q(x)$ are logically equivalent.

Exercises 46–49 establish rules for **null quantification** that we can use when a quantified variable does not appear in part of a statement.

**46.** Establish these logical equivalences, where $x$ does not occur as a free variable in $A$. Assume that the domain is nonempty.
 **a)** $(\forall x P(x)) \vee A \equiv \forall x(P(x) \vee A)$
 **b)** $(\exists x P(x)) \vee A \equiv \exists x(P(x) \vee A)$

**47.** Establish these logical equivalences, where $x$ does not occur as a free variable in $A$. Assume that the domain is nonempty.
 **a)** $(\forall x P(x)) \wedge A \equiv \forall x(P(x) \wedge A)$
 **b)** $(\exists x P(x)) \wedge A \equiv \exists x(P(x) \wedge A)$

**48.** Establish these logical equivalences, where $x$ does not occur as a free variable in $A$. Assume that the domain is nonempty.
 **a)** $\forall x(A \rightarrow P(x)) \equiv A \rightarrow \forall x P(x)$
 **b)** $\exists x(A \rightarrow P(x)) \equiv A \rightarrow \exists x P(x)$

**49.** Establish these logical equivalences, where $x$ does not occur as a free variable in $A$. Assume that the domain is nonempty.
 **a)** $\forall x(P(x) \rightarrow A) \equiv \exists x P(x) \rightarrow A$
 **b)** $\exists x(P(x) \rightarrow A) \equiv \forall x P(x) \rightarrow A$

**50.** Show that $\forall x P(x) \vee \forall x Q(x)$ and $\forall x(P(x) \vee Q(x))$ are not logically equivalent.

**51.** Show that $\exists x P(x) \wedge \exists x Q(x)$ and $\exists x(P(x) \wedge Q(x))$ are not logically equivalent.

**52.** As mentioned in the text, the notation $\exists! x P(x)$ denotes
   "There exists a unique $x$ such that $P(x)$ is true."
   If the domain consists of all integers, what are the truth values of these statements?
 **a)** $\exists! x(x > 1)$        **b)** $\exists! x(x^2 = 1)$
 **c)** $\exists! x(x + 3 = 2x)$   **d)** $\exists! x(x = x + 1)$

**53.** What are the truth values of these statements?
 **a)** $\exists! x P(x) \rightarrow \exists x P(x)$
 **b)** $\forall x P(x) \rightarrow \exists! x P(x)$
 **c)** $\exists! x \neg P(x) \rightarrow \neg \forall x P(x)$

**54.** Write out $\exists! x P(x)$, where the domain consists of the integers 1, 2, and 3, in terms of negations, conjunctions, and disjunctions.

**55.** Given the Prolog facts in Example 28, what would Prolog return given these queries?
 **a)** `?instructor(chan,math273)`
 **b)** `?instructor(patel,cs301)`
 **c)** `?enrolled(X,cs301)`
 **d)** `?enrolled(kiko,Y)`
 **e)** `?teaches(grossman,Y)`

**56.** Given the Prolog facts in Example 28, what would Prolog return when given these queries?
 **a)** `?enrolled(kevin,ee222)`
 **b)** `?enrolled(kiko,math273)`
 **c)** `?instructor(grossman,X)`
 **d)** `?instructor(X,cs301)`
 **e)** `?teaches(X,kevin)`

**57.** Suppose that Prolog facts are used to define the predicates $mother(M, Y)$ and $father(F, X)$, which represent that $M$ is the mother of $Y$ and $F$ is the father of $X$, respectively. Give a Prolog rule to define the predicate $sibling(X, Y)$, which represents that $X$ and $Y$ are siblings (that is, have the same mother and the same father).

**58.** Suppose that Prolog facts are used to define the predicates $mother(M, Y)$ and $father(F, X)$, which represent that $M$ is the mother of $Y$ and $F$ is the father of $X$, respectively. Give a Prolog rule to define the predicate $grandfather(X, Y)$, which represents that $X$ is the grandfather of $Y$. [*Hint:* You can write a disjunction in Prolog either by using a semicolon to separate predicates or by putting these predicates on separate lines.]

Exercises 59–62 are based on questions found in the book *Symbolic Logic* by Lewis Carroll.

**59.** Let $P(x)$, $Q(x)$, and $R(x)$ be the statements "$x$ is a professor," "$x$ is ignorant," and "$x$ is vain," respectively. Express each of these statements using quantifiers; logical connectives; and $P(x)$, $Q(x)$, and $R(x)$, where the domain consists of all people.
 **a)** No professors are ignorant.
 **b)** All ignorant people are vain.
 **c)** No professors are vain.
 **d)** Does (c) follow from (a) and (b)?

**60.** Let $P(x)$, $Q(x)$, and $R(x)$ be the statements "$x$ is a clear explanation," "$x$ is satisfactory," and "$x$ is an excuse," respectively. Suppose that the domain for $x$ consists of all English text. Express each of these statements using quantifiers, logical connectives, and $P(x)$, $Q(x)$, and $R(x)$.
 **a)** All clear explanations are satisfactory.
 **b)** Some excuses are unsatisfactory.
 **c)** Some excuses are not clear explanations.
 **\*d)** Does (c) follow from (a) and (b)?

**61.** Let $P(x)$, $Q(x)$, $R(x)$, and $S(x)$ be the statements "$x$ is a baby," "$x$ is logical," "$x$ is able to manage a crocodile," and "$x$ is despised," respectively. Suppose that the domain consists of all people. Express each of these statements using quantifiers; logical connectives; and $P(x)$, $Q(x)$, $R(x)$, and $S(x)$.
 **a)** Babies are illogical.
 **b)** Nobody is despised who can manage a crocodile.
 **c)** Illogical persons are despised.
 **d)** Babies cannot manage crocodiles.
 **\*e)** Does (d) follow from (a), (b), and (c)? If not, is there a correct conclusion?

**62.** Let $P(x)$, $Q(x)$, $R(x)$, and $S(x)$ be the statements "$x$ is a duck," "$x$ is one of my poultry," "$x$ is an officer," and "$x$ is willing to waltz," respectively. Express each of these statements using quantifiers; logical connectives; and $P(x)$, $Q(x)$, $R(x)$, and $S(x)$.

**a)** No ducks are willing to waltz.

**b)** No officers ever decline to waltz.

**c)** All my poultry are ducks.

**d)** My poultry are not officers.

**\*e)** Does (d) follow from (a), (b), and (c)? If not, is there a correct conclusion?

# 1.5  Nested Quantifiers

## Introduction

In Section 1.4 we defined the existential and universal quantifiers and showed how they can be used to represent mathematical statements. We also explained how they can be used to translate English sentences into logical expressions. However, in Section 1.4 we avoided **nested quantifiers**, where one quantifier is within the scope of another, such as

$$\forall x \exists y (x + y = 0).$$

Note that everything within the scope of a quantifier can be thought of as a propositional function. For example,

$$\forall x \exists y (x + y = 0)$$

is the same thing as $\forall x \, Q(x)$, where $Q(x)$ is $\exists y \, P(x, y)$, where $P(x, y)$ is $x + y = 0$.

Nested quantifiers commonly occur in mathematics and computer science. Although nested quantifiers can sometimes be difficult to understand, the rules we have already studied in Section 1.4 can help us use them. In this section we will gain experience working with nested quantifiers. We will see how to use nested quantifiers to express mathematical statements such as "The sum of two positive integers is always positive." We will show how nested quantifiers can be used to translate English sentences such as "Everyone has exactly one best friend" into logical statements. Moreover, we will gain experience working with the negations of statements involving nested quantifiers.

## Understanding Statements Involving Nested Quantifiers

To understand statements involving nested quantifiers, we need to unravel what the quantifiers and predicates that appear mean. This is illustrated in Examples 1 and 2.

EXAMPLE 1    Assume that the domain for the variables $x$ and $y$ consists of all real numbers. The statement

$$\forall x \forall y (x + y = y + x)$$

Extra
Examples

says that $x + y = y + x$ for all real numbers $x$ and $y$. This is the commutative law for addition of real numbers. Likewise, the statement

$$\forall x \exists y (x + y = 0)$$

says that for every real number $x$ there is a real number $y$ such that $x + y = 0$. This states that every real number has an additive inverse. Similarly, the statement

$$\forall x \forall y \forall z (x + (y + z) = (x + y) + z)$$

is the associative law for addition of real numbers. ◀

**EXAMPLE 2**    Translate into English the statement

$$\forall x \forall y ((x > 0) \wedge (y < 0) \rightarrow (xy < 0)),$$

where the domain for both variables consists of all real numbers.

*Solution:* This statement says that for every real number $x$ and for every real number $y$, if $x > 0$ and $y < 0$, then $xy < 0$. That is, this statement says that for real numbers $x$ and $y$, if $x$ is positive and $y$ is negative, then $xy$ is negative. This can be stated more succinctly as "The product of a positive real number and a negative real number is always a negative real number."    ◀

THINKING OF QUANTIFICATION AS LOOPS    In working with quantifications of more than one variable, it is sometimes helpful to think in terms of nested loops. (Of course, if there are infinitely many elements in the domain of some variable, we cannot actually loop through all values. Nevertheless, this way of thinking is helpful in understanding nested quantifiers.) For example, to see whether $\forall x \forall y P(x, y)$ is true, we loop through the values for $x$, and for each $x$ we loop through the values for $y$. If we find that $P(x, y)$ is true for all values for $x$ and $y$, we have determined that $\forall x \forall y P(x, y)$ is true. If we ever hit a value $x$ for which we hit a value $y$ for which $P(x, y)$ is false, we have shown that $\forall x \forall y P(x, y)$ is false.

Similarly, to determine whether $\forall x \exists y P(x, y)$ is true, we loop through the values for $x$. For each $x$ we loop through the values for $y$ until we find a $y$ for which $P(x, y)$ is true. If for every $x$ we hit such a $y$, then $\forall x \exists y P(x, y)$ is true; if for some $x$ we never hit such a $y$, then $\forall x \exists y P(x, y)$ is false.

To see whether $\exists x \forall y P(x, y)$ is true, we loop through the values for $x$ until we find an $x$ for which $P(x, y)$ is always true when we loop through all values for $y$. Once we find such an $x$, we know that $\exists x \forall y P(x, y)$ is true. If we never hit such an $x$, then we know that $\exists x \forall y P(x, y)$ is false.

Finally, to see whether $\exists x \exists y P(x, y)$ is true, we loop through the values for $x$, where for each $x$ we loop through the values for $y$ until we hit an $x$ for which we hit a $y$ for which $P(x, y)$ is true. The statement $\exists x \exists y P(x, y)$ is false only if we never hit an $x$ for which we hit a $y$ such that $P(x, y)$ is true.

## The Order of Quantifiers

Many mathematical statements involve multiple quantifications of propositional functions involving more than one variable. It is important to note that the order of the quantifiers is important, unless all the quantifiers are universal quantifiers or all are existential quantifiers.

These remarks are illustrated by Examples 3–5.

**EXAMPLE 3**    Let $P(x, y)$ be the statement "$x + y = y + x$." What are the truth values of the quantifications $\forall x \forall y P(x, y)$ and $\forall y \forall x P(x, y)$ where the domain for all variables consists of all real numbers?

*Solution:* The quantification

$$\forall x \forall y P(x, y)$$

Extra Examples

denotes the proposition

"For all real numbers $x$, for all real numbers $y$, $x + y = y + x$."

Because $P(x, y)$ is true for all real numbers $x$ and $y$ (it is the commutative law for addition, which is an axiom for the real numbers—see Appendix 1), the proposition $\forall x \forall y P(x, y)$ is true. Note that the statement $\forall y \forall x P(x, y)$ says "For all real numbers $y$, for all real numbers $x$, $x + y = y + x$." This has the same meaning as the statement "For all real numbers $x$, for all real numbers $y$, $x + y = y + x$." That is, $\forall x \forall y P(x, y)$ and $\forall y \forall x P(x, y)$ have the same meaning, and both are true. This illustrates the principle that the order of nested universal quantifiers in a statement without other quantifiers can be changed without changing the meaning of the quantified statement. ◄

**EXAMPLE 4**  Let $Q(x, y)$ denote "$x + y = 0$." What are the truth values of the quantifications $\exists y \forall x\, Q(x, y)$ and $\forall x \exists y\, Q(x, y)$, where the domain for all variables consists of all real numbers?

*Solution:* The quantification

$$\exists y \forall x\, Q(x, y)$$

denotes the proposition

"There is a real number $y$ such that for every real number $x$, $Q(x, y)$."

No matter what value of $y$ is chosen, there is only one value of $x$ for which $x + y = 0$. Because there is no real number $y$ such that $x + y = 0$ for all real numbers $x$, the statement $\exists y \forall x\, Q(x, y)$ is false.

The quantification

$$\forall x \exists y\, Q(x, y)$$

denotes the proposition

"For every real number $x$ there is a real number $y$ such that $Q(x, y)$."

Given a real number $x$, there is a real number $y$ such that $x + y = 0$; namely, $y = -x$. Hence, the statement $\forall x \exists y\, Q(x, y)$ is true. ◄

Be careful with the order of existential and universal quantifiers!

Example 4 illustrates that the order in which quantifiers appear makes a difference. The statements $\exists y \forall x\, P(x, y)$ and $\forall x \exists y\, P(x, y)$ are not logically equivalent. The statement $\exists y \forall x\, P(x, y)$ is true if and only if there is a $y$ that makes $P(x, y)$ true for every $x$. So, for this statement to be true, there must be a particular value of $y$ for which $P(x, y)$ is true regardless of the choice of $x$. On the other hand, $\forall x \exists y\, P(x, y)$ is true if and only if for every value of $x$ there is a value of $y$ for which $P(x, y)$ is true. So, for this statement to be true, no matter which $x$ you choose, there must be a value of $y$ (possibly depending on the $x$ you choose) for which $P(x, y)$ is true. In other words, in the second case, $y$ can depend on $x$, whereas in the first case, $y$ is a constant independent of $x$.

From these observations, it follows that if $\exists y \forall x\, P(x, y)$ is true, then $\forall x \exists y\, P(x, y)$ must also be true. However, if $\forall x \exists y\, P(x, y)$ is true, it is not necessary for $\exists y \forall x\, P(x, y)$ to be true. (See Supplementary Exercises 30 and 31.)

Table 1 summarizes the meanings of the different possible quantifications involving two variables.

Quantifications of more than two variables are also common, as Example 5 illustrates.

**EXAMPLE 5**  Let $Q(x, y, z)$ be the statement "$x + y = z$." What are the truth values of the statements $\forall x \forall y \exists z\, Q(x, y, z)$ and $\exists z \forall x \forall y\, Q(x, y, z)$, where the domain of all variables consists of all real numbers?

*Solution:* Suppose that $x$ and $y$ are assigned values. Then, there exists a real number $z$ such that $x + y = z$. Consequently, the quantification

$$\forall x \forall y \exists z\, Q(x, y, z),$$

which is the statement

"For all real numbers $x$ and for all real numbers $y$ there is a real number $z$ such that $x + y = z$,"

| TABLE 1 Quantifications of Two Variables. | | |
|---|---|---|
| *Statement* | *When True?* | *When False?* |
| $\forall x \forall y\, P(x, y)$<br>$\forall y \forall x\, P(x, y)$ | $P(x, y)$ is true for every pair $x, y$. | There is a pair $x, y$ for which $P(x, y)$ is false. |
| $\forall x \exists y\, P(x, y)$ | For every $x$ there is a $y$ for which $P(x, y)$ is true. | There is an $x$ such that $P(x, y)$ is false for every $y$. |
| $\exists x \forall y\, P(x, y)$ | There is an $x$ for which $P(x, y)$ is true for every $y$. | For every $x$ there is a $y$ for which $P(x, y)$ is false. |
| $\exists x \exists y\, P(x, y)$<br>$\exists y \exists x\, P(x, y)$ | There is a pair $x, y$ for which $P(x, y)$ is true. | $P(x, y)$ is false for every pair $x, y$. |

is true. The order of the quantification here is important, because the quantification

$$\exists z \forall x \forall y\, Q(x, y, z),$$

which is the statement

"There is a real number $z$ such that for all real numbers $x$ and for all real numbers $y$ it is true that $x + y = z$,"

is false, because there is no value of $z$ that satisfies the equation $x + y = z$ for all values of $x$ and $y$.    ◄

## Translating Mathematical Statements into Statements Involving Nested Quantifiers

Mathematical statements expressed in English can be translated into logical expressions, as Examples 6–8 show.

EXAMPLE 6    Translate the statement "The sum of two positive integers is always positive" into a logical expression.

*Solution:* To translate this statement into a logical expression, we first rewrite it so that the implied quantifiers and a domain are shown: "For every two integers, if these integers are both positive, then the sum of these integers is positive." Next, we introduce the variables $x$ and $y$ to obtain "For all positive integers $x$ and $y$, $x + y$ is positive." Consequently, we can express this statement as

Extra
Examples

$$\forall x \forall y((x > 0) \wedge (y > 0) \to (x + y > 0)),$$

where the domain for both variables consists of all integers. Note that we could also translate this using the positive integers as the domain. Then the statement "The sum of two positive integers is always positive" becomes "For every two positive integers, the sum of these integers is positive. We can express this as

$$\forall x \forall y(x + y > 0),$$

where the domain for both variables consists of all positive integers.    ◄

EXAMPLE 7    Translate the statement "Every real number except zero has a multiplicative inverse." (A **multiplicative inverse** of a real number $x$ is a real number $y$ such that $xy = 1$.)

*Solution:* We first rewrite this as "For every real number $x$ except zero, $x$ has a multiplicative inverse." We can rewrite this as "For every real number $x$, if $x \neq 0$, then there exists a real number $y$ such that $xy = 1$." This can be rewritten as

$$\forall x((x \neq 0) \to \exists y(xy = 1)).$$ ◀

One example that you may be familiar with is the concept of limit, which is important in calculus.

**EXAMPLE 8** (*Requires calculus*) Use quantifiers to express the definition of the limit of a real-valued function $f(x)$ of a real variable $x$ at a point $a$ in its domain.

*Solution:* Recall that the definition of the statement

$$\lim_{x \to a} f(x) = L$$

is: For every real number $\epsilon > 0$ there exists a real number $\delta > 0$ such that $|f(x) - L| < \epsilon$ whenever $0 < |x - a| < \delta$. This definition of a limit can be phrased in terms of quantifiers by

$$\forall \epsilon \exists \delta \forall x (0 < |x - a| < \delta \to |f(x) - L| < \epsilon),$$

where the domain for the variables $\delta$ and $\epsilon$ consists of all positive real numbers and for $x$ consists of all real numbers.

This definition can also be expressed as

$$\forall \epsilon > 0 \; \exists \delta > 0 \; \forall x (0 < |x - a| < \delta \to |f(x) - L| < \epsilon)$$

when the domain for the variables $\epsilon$ and $\delta$ consists of all real numbers, rather than just the positive real numbers. [Here, restricted quantifiers have been used. Recall that $\forall x > 0 \; P(x)$ means that for all $x$ with $x > 0$, $P(x)$ is true.] ◀

## Translating from Nested Quantifiers into English

Expressions with nested quantifiers expressing statements in English can be quite complicated. The first step in translating such an expression is to write out what the quantifiers and predicates in the expression mean. The next step is to express this meaning in a simpler sentence. This process is illustrated in Examples 9 and 10.

**EXAMPLE 9** Translate the statement

$$\forall x (C(x) \vee \exists y(C(y) \wedge F(x, y)))$$

into English, where $C(x)$ is "$x$ has a computer," $F(x, y)$ is "$x$ and $y$ are friends," and the domain for both $x$ and $y$ consists of all students in your school.

*Solution:* The statement says that for every student $x$ in your school, $x$ has a computer or there is a student $y$ such that $y$ has a computer and $x$ and $y$ are friends. In other words, every student in your school has a computer or has a friend who has a computer. ◀

**EXAMPLE 10** Translate the statement

$$\exists x \forall y \forall z ((F(x, y) \wedge F(x, z) \wedge (y \neq z)) \to \neg F(y, z))$$

into English, where $F(a,b)$ means $a$ and $b$ are friends and the domain for $x$, $y$, and $z$ consists of all students in your school.

*Solution:* We first examine the expression $(F(x, y) \land F(x, z) \land (y \neq z)) \to \neg F(y, z)$. This expression says that if students $x$ and $y$ are friends, and students $x$ and $z$ are friends, and furthermore, if $y$ and $z$ are not the same student, then $y$ and $z$ are not friends. It follows that the original statement, which is triply quantified, says that there is a student $x$ such that for all students $y$ and all students $z$ other than $y$, if $x$ and $y$ are friends and $x$ and $z$ are friends, then $y$ and $z$ are not friends. In other words, there is a student none of whose friends are also friends with each other. ◄

## Translating English Sentences into Logical Expressions

In Section 1.4 we showed how quantifiers can be used to translate sentences into logical expressions. However, we avoided sentences whose translation into logical expressions required the use of nested quantifiers. We now address the translation of such sentences.

**EXAMPLE 11**    Express the statement "If a person is female and is a parent, then this person is someone's mother" as a logical expression involving predicates, quantifiers with a domain consisting of all people, and logical connectives.

*Solution:* The statement "If a person is female and is a parent, then this person is someone's mother" can be expressed as "For every person $x$, if person $x$ is female and person $x$ is a parent, then there exists a person $y$ such that person $x$ is the mother of person $y$." We introduce the propositional functions $F(x)$ to represent "$x$ is female," $P(x)$ to represent "$x$ is a parent," and $M(x, y)$ to represent "$x$ is the mother of $y$." The original statement can be represented as

$$\forall x((F(x) \land P(x)) \to \exists y M(x, y)).$$

Using the null quantification rule in part (b) of Exercise 47 in Section 1.4, we can move $\exists y$ to the left so that it appears just after $\forall x$, because $y$ does not appear in $F(x) \land P(x)$. We obtain the logically equivalent expression

$$\forall x \exists y((F(x) \land P(x)) \to M(x, y)).$$ ◄

**EXAMPLE 12**    Express the statement "Everyone has exactly one best friend" as a logical expression involving predicates, quantifiers with a domain consisting of all people, and logical connectives.

*Solution:* The statement "Everyone has exactly one best friend" can be expressed as "For every person $x$, person $x$ has exactly one best friend." Introducing the universal quantifier, we see that this statement is the same as "$\forall x$(person $x$ has exactly one best friend)," where the domain consists of all people.

To say that $x$ has exactly one best friend means that there is a person $y$ who is the best friend of $x$, and furthermore, that for every person $z$, if person $z$ is not person $y$, then $z$ is not the best friend of $x$. When we introduce the predicate $B(x, y)$ to be the statement "$y$ is the best friend of $x$," the statement that $x$ has exactly one best friend can be represented as

$$\exists y(B(x, y) \land \forall z((z \neq y) \to \neg B(x, z))).$$

Consequently, our original statement can be expressed as

$$\forall x \exists y(B(x, y) \land \forall z((z \neq y) \to \neg B(x, z))).$$

[Note that we can write this statement as $\forall x \exists! y B(x, y)$, where $\exists!$ is the "uniqueness quantifier" defined in Section 1.4.] ◀

**EXAMPLE 13**    Use quantifiers to express the statement "There is a woman who has taken a flight on every airline in the world."

*Solution:* Let $P(w, f)$ be "$w$ has taken $f$" and $Q(f, a)$ be "$f$ is a flight on $a$." We can express the statement as

$$\exists w \forall a \exists f (P(w, f) \wedge Q(f, a)),$$

where the domains of discourse for $w$, $f$, and $a$ consist of all the women in the world, all airplane flights, and all airlines, respectively.

The statement could also be expressed as

$$\exists w \forall a \exists f R(w, f, a),$$

where $R(w, f, a)$ is "$w$ has taken $f$ on $a$." Although this is more compact, it somewhat obscures the relationships among the variables. Consequently, the first solution is usually preferable. ◀

## Negating Nested Quantifiers

**Assessment**

Statements involving nested quantifiers can be negated by successively applying the rules for negating statements involving a single quantifier. This is illustrated in Examples 14–16.

**EXAMPLE 14**    Express the negation of the statement $\forall x \exists y (xy = 1)$ so that no negation precedes a quantifier.

**Extra Examples**

*Solution:* By successively applying De Morgan's laws for quantifiers in Table 2 of Section 1.4, we can move the negation in $\neg \forall x \exists y (xy = 1)$ inside all the quantifiers. We find that $\neg \forall x \exists y (xy = 1)$ is equivalent to $\exists x \neg \exists y (xy = 1)$, which is equivalent to $\exists x \forall y \neg (xy = 1)$. Because $\neg (xy = 1)$ can be expressed more simply as $xy \neq 1$, we conclude that our negated statement can be expressed as $\exists x \forall y (xy \neq 1)$. ◀

**EXAMPLE 15**    Use quantifiers to express the statement that "There does not exist a woman who has taken a flight on every airline in the world."

*Solution:* This statement is the negation of the statement "There is a woman who has taken a flight on every airline in the world" from Example 13. By Example 13, our statement can be expressed as $\neg \exists w \forall a \exists f (P(w, f) \wedge Q(f, a))$, where $P(w, f)$ is "$w$ has taken $f$" and $Q(f, a)$ is "$f$ is a flight on $a$." By successively applying De Morgan's laws for quantifiers in Table 2 of Section 1.4 to move the negation inside successive quantifiers and by applying De Morgan's law for negating a conjunction in the last step, we find that our statement is equivalent to each of this sequence of statements:

$$\forall w \neg \forall a \exists f (P(w, f) \wedge Q(f, a)) \equiv \forall w \exists a \neg \exists f (P(w, f) \wedge Q(f, a))$$
$$\equiv \forall w \exists a \forall f \neg (P(w, f) \wedge Q(f, a))$$
$$\equiv \forall w \exists a \forall f (\neg P(w, f) \vee \neg Q(f, a)).$$

This last statement states "For every woman there is an airline such that for all flights, this woman has not taken that flight or that flight is not on this airline." ◀

**EXAMPLE 16**    (*Requires calculus*) Use quantifiers and predicates to express the fact that $\lim_{x \to a} f(x)$ does not exist where $f(x)$ is a real-valued function of a real variable $x$ and $a$ belongs to the domain of $f$.

*Solution:* To say that $\lim_{x \to a} f(x)$ does not exist means that for all real numbers $L$, $\lim_{x \to a} f(x) \neq L$. By using Example 8, the statement $\lim_{x \to a} f(x) \neq L$ can be expressed as

$$\neg \forall \epsilon > 0 \, \exists \delta > 0 \, \forall x (0 < |x - a| < \delta \to |f(x) - L| < \epsilon).$$

Successively applying the rules for negating quantified expressions, we construct this sequence of equivalent statements

$$\neg \forall \epsilon > 0 \, \exists \delta > 0 \, \forall x (0 < |x - a| < \delta \to |f(x) - L| < \epsilon)$$
$$\equiv \exists \epsilon > 0 \, \neg \exists \delta > 0 \, \forall x (0 < |x - a| < \delta \to |f(x) - L| < \epsilon)$$
$$\equiv \exists \epsilon > 0 \, \forall \delta > 0 \, \neg \forall x (0 < |x - a| < \delta \to |f(x) - L| < \epsilon)$$
$$\equiv \exists \epsilon > 0 \, \forall \delta > 0 \, \exists x \, \neg (0 < |x - a| < \delta \to |f(x) - L| < \epsilon)$$
$$\equiv \exists \epsilon > 0 \, \forall \delta > 0 \, \exists x (0 < |x - a| < \delta \wedge |f(x) - L| \geq \epsilon).$$

In the last step we used the equivalence $\neg(p \to q) \equiv p \wedge \neg q$, which follows from the fifth equivalence in Table 7 of Section 1.3.

Because the statement "$\lim_{x \to a} f(x)$ does not exist" means for all real numbers $L$, $\lim_{x \to a} f(x) \neq L$, this can be expressed as

$$\forall L \exists \epsilon > 0 \, \forall \delta > 0 \, \exists x (0 < |x - a| < \delta \wedge |f(x) - L| \geq \epsilon).$$

This last statement says that for every real number $L$ there is a real number $\epsilon > 0$ such that for every real number $\delta > 0$, there exists a real number $x$ such that $0 < |x - a| < \delta$ and $|f(x) - L| \geq \epsilon$.    ◀

# Exercises

**1.** Translate these statements into English, where the domain for each variable consists of all real numbers.

**a)** $\forall x \exists y (x < y)$
**b)** $\forall x \forall y (((x \geq 0) \wedge (y \geq 0)) \to (xy \geq 0))$
**c)** $\forall x \forall y \exists z (xy = z)$

**2.** Translate these statements into English, where the domain for each variable consists of all real numbers.

**a)** $\exists x \forall y (xy = y)$
**b)** $\forall x \forall y (((x \geq 0) \wedge (y < 0)) \to (x - y > 0))$
**c)** $\forall x \forall y \exists z (x = y + z)$

**3.** Let $Q(x, y)$ be the statement "$x$ has sent an e-mail message to $y$," where the domain for both $x$ and $y$ consists of all students in your class. Express each of these quantifications in English.

**a)** $\exists x \exists y \, Q(x, y)$      **b)** $\exists x \forall y \, Q(x, y)$
**c)** $\forall x \exists y \, Q(x, y)$      **d)** $\exists y \forall x \, Q(x, y)$
**e)** $\forall y \exists x \, Q(x, y)$      **f)** $\forall x \forall y \, Q(x, y)$

**4.** Let $P(x, y)$ be the statement "Student $x$ has taken class $y$," where the domain for $x$ consists of all students in your class and for $y$ consists of all computer science courses

at your school. Express each of these quantifications in English.

**a)** $\exists x \exists y \, P(x, y)$      **b)** $\exists x \forall y \, P(x, y)$
**c)** $\forall x \exists y \, P(x, y)$      **d)** $\exists y \forall x \, P(x, y)$
**e)** $\forall y \exists x \, P(x, y)$      **f)** $\forall x \forall y \, P(x, y)$

**5.** Let $W(x, y)$ mean that student $x$ has visited website $y$, where the domain for $x$ consists of all students in your school and the domain for $y$ consists of all websites. Express each of these statements by a simple English sentence.

**a)** $W(\text{Sarah Smith, www.att.com})$
**b)** $\exists x \, W(x, \text{www.imdb.org})$
**c)** $\exists y \, W(\text{José Orez}, y)$
**d)** $\exists y (W(\text{Ashok Puri}, y) \wedge W(\text{Cindy Yoon}, y))$
**e)** $\exists y \forall z (y \neq (\text{David Belcher}) \wedge (W(\text{David Belcher}, z) \to W(y, z)))$
**f)** $\exists x \exists y \forall z ((x \neq y) \wedge (W(x, z) \leftrightarrow W(y, z)))$

**6.** Let $C(x, y)$ mean that student $x$ is enrolled in class $y$, where the domain for $x$ consists of all students in your school and the domain for $y$ consists of all classes being given at your school. Express each of these statements by a simple English sentence.

**a)** $C$(Randy Goldberg, CS 252)
**b)** $\exists x C(x, \text{Math } 695)$
**c)** $\exists y C(\text{Carol Sitea}, y)$
**d)** $\exists x (C(x, \text{Math } 222) \land C(x, \text{CS } 252))$
**e)** $\exists x \exists y \forall z ((x \neq y) \land (C(x, z) \rightarrow C(y, z)))$
**f)** $\exists x \exists y \forall z ((x \neq y) \land (C(x, z) \leftrightarrow C(y, z)))$

**7.** Let $T(x, y)$ mean that student $x$ likes cuisine $y$, where the domain for $x$ consists of all students at your school and the domain for $y$ consists of all cuisines. Express each of these statements by a simple English sentence.

**a)** $\neg T$(Abdallah Hussein, Japanese)
**b)** $\exists x T(x, \text{Korean}) \land \forall x T(x, \text{Mexican})$
**c)** $\exists y (T(\text{Monique Arsenault}, y) \lor$
   $T(\text{Jay Johnson}, y))$
**d)** $\forall x \forall z \exists y ((x \neq z) \rightarrow \neg(T(x, y) \land T(z, y)))$
**e)** $\exists x \exists z \forall y (T(x, y) \leftrightarrow T(z, y))$
**f)** $\forall x \forall z \exists y (T(x, y) \leftrightarrow T(z, y))$

**8.** Let $Q(x, y)$ be the statement "student $x$ has been a contestant on quiz show $y$." Express each of these sentences in terms of $Q(x, y)$, quantifiers, and logical connectives, where the domain for $x$ consists of all students at your school and for $y$ consists of all quiz shows on television.

**a)** There is a student at your school who has been a contestant on a television quiz show.
**b)** No student at your school has ever been a contestant on a television quiz show.
**c)** There is a student at your school who has been a contestant on *Jeopardy* and on *Wheel of Fortune*.
**d)** Every television quiz show has had a student from your school as a contestant.
**e)** At least two students from your school have been contestants on *Jeopardy*.

**9.** Let $L(x, y)$ be the statement "$x$ loves $y$," where the domain for both $x$ and $y$ consists of all people in the world. Use quantifiers to express each of these statements.

**a)** Everybody loves Jerry.
**b)** Everybody loves somebody.
**c)** There is somebody whom everybody loves.
**d)** Nobody loves everybody.
**e)** There is somebody whom Lydia does not love.
**f)** There is somebody whom no one loves.
**g)** There is exactly one person whom everybody loves.
**h)** There are exactly two people whom Lynn loves.
**i)** Everyone loves himself or herself.
**j)** There is someone who loves no one besides himself or herself.

**10.** Let $F(x, y)$ be the statement "$x$ can fool $y$," where the domain consists of all people in the world. Use quantifiers to express each of these statements.

**a)** Everybody can fool Fred.
**b)** Evelyn can fool everybody.
**c)** Everybody can fool somebody.
**d)** There is no one who can fool everybody.
**e)** Everyone can be fooled by somebody.
**f)** No one can fool both Fred and Jerry.
**g)** Nancy can fool exactly two people.
**h)** There is exactly one person whom everybody can fool.
**i)** No one can fool himself or herself.
**j)** There is someone who can fool exactly one person besides himself or herself.

**11.** Let $S(x)$ be the predicate "$x$ is a student," $F(x)$ the predicate "$x$ is a faculty member," and $A(x, y)$ the predicate "$x$ has asked $y$ a question," where the domain consists of all people associated with your school. Use quantifiers to express each of these statements.

**a)** Lois has asked Professor Michaels a question.
**b)** Every student has asked Professor Gross a question.
**c)** Every faculty member has either asked Professor Miller a question or been asked a question by Professor Miller.
**d)** Some student has not asked any faculty member a question.
**e)** There is a faculty member who has never been asked a question by a student.
**f)** Some student has asked every faculty member a question.
**g)** There is a faculty member who has asked every other faculty member a question.
**h)** Some student has never been asked a question by a faculty member.

**12.** Let $I(x)$ be the statement "$x$ has an Internet connection" and $C(x, y)$ be the statement "$x$ and $y$ have chatted over the Internet," where the domain for the variables $x$ and $y$ consists of all students in your class. Use quantifiers to express each of these statements.

**a)** Jerry does not have an Internet connection.
**b)** Rachel has not chatted over the Internet with Chelsea.
**c)** Jan and Sharon have never chatted over the Internet.
**d)** No one in the class has chatted with Bob.
**e)** Sanjay has chatted with everyone except Joseph.
**f)** Someone in your class does not have an Internet connection.
**g)** Not everyone in your class has an Internet connection.
**h)** Exactly one student in your class has an Internet connection.
**i)** Everyone except one student in your class has an Internet connection.
**j)** Everyone in your class with an Internet connection has chatted over the Internet with at least one other student in your class.
**k)** Someone in your class has an Internet connection but has not chatted with anyone else in your class.
**l)** There are two students in your class who have not chatted with each other over the Internet.
**m)** There is a student in your class who has chatted with everyone in your class over the Internet.
**n)** There are at least two students in your class who have not chatted with the same person in your class.
**o)** There are two students in the class who between them have chatted with everyone else in the class.

**13.** Let $M(x, y)$ be "$x$ has sent $y$ an e-mail message" and $T(x, y)$ be "$x$ has telephoned $y$," where the domain consists of all students in your class. Use quantifiers to express each of these statements. (Assume that all e-mail messages that were sent are received, which is not the way things often work.)

  **a)** Chou has never sent an e-mail message to Koko.

  **b)** Arlene has never sent an e-mail message to or telephoned Sarah.

  **c)** José has never received an e-mail message from Deborah.

  **d)** Every student in your class has sent an e-mail message to Ken.

  **e)** No one in your class has telephoned Nina.

  **f)** Everyone in your class has either telephoned Avi or sent him an e-mail message.

  **g)** There is a student in your class who has sent everyone else in your class an e-mail message.

  **h)** There is someone in your class who has either sent an e-mail message or telephoned everyone else in your class.

  **i)** There are two different students in your class who have sent each other e-mail messages.

  **j)** There is a student who has sent himself or herself an e-mail message.

  **k)** There is a student in your class who has not received an e-mail message from anyone else in the class and who has not been called by any other student in the class.

  **l)** Every student in the class has either received an e-mail message or received a telephone call from another student in the class.

  **m)** There are at least two students in your class such that one student has sent the other e-mail and the second student has telephoned the first student.

  **n)** There are two different students in your class who between them have sent an e-mail message to or telephoned everyone else in the class.

**14.** Use quantifiers and predicates with more than one variable to express these statements.

  **a)** There is a student in this class who can speak Hindi.

  **b)** Every student in this class plays some sport.

  **c)** Some student in this class has visited Alaska but has not visited Hawaii.

  **d)** All students in this class have learned at least one programming language.

  **e)** There is a student in this class who has taken every course offered by one of the departments in this school.

  **f)** Some student in this class grew up in the same town as exactly one other student in this class.

  **g)** Every student in this class has chatted with at least one other student in at least one chat group.

**15.** Use quantifiers and predicates with more than one variable to express these statements.

  **a)** Every computer science student needs a course in discrete mathematics.

  **b)** There is a student in this class who owns a personal computer.

  **c)** Every student in this class has taken at least one computer science course.

  **d)** There is a student in this class who has taken at least one course in computer science.

  **e)** Every student in this class has been in every building on campus.

  **f)** There is a student in this class who has been in every room of at least one building on campus.

  **g)** Every student in this class has been in at least one room of every building on campus.

**16.** A discrete mathematics class contains 1 mathematics major who is a freshman, 12 mathematics majors who are sophomores, 15 computer science majors who are sophomores, 2 mathematics majors who are juniors, 2 computer science majors who are juniors, and 1 computer science major who is a senior. Express each of these statements in terms of quantifiers and then determine its truth value.

  **a)** There is a student in the class who is a junior.

  **b)** Every student in the class is a computer science major.

  **c)** There is a student in the class who is neither a mathematics major nor a junior.

  **d)** Every student in the class is either a sophomore or a computer science major.

  **e)** There is a major such that there is a student in the class in every year of study with that major.

**17.** Express each of these system specifications using predicates, quantifiers, and logical connectives, if necessary.

  **a)** Every user has access to exactly one mailbox.

  **b)** There is a process that continues to run during all error conditions only if the kernel is working correctly.

  **c)** All users on the campus network can access all websites whose url has a .edu extension.

  **\*d)** There are exactly two systems that monitor every remote server.

**18.** Express each of these system specifications using predicates, quantifiers, and logical connectives, if necessary.

  **a)** At least one console must be accessible during every fault condition.

  **b)** The e-mail address of every user can be retrieved whenever the archive contains at least one message sent by every user on the system.

  **c)** For every security breach there is at least one mechanism that can detect that breach if and only if there is a process that has not been compromised.

  **d)** There are at least two paths connecting every two distinct endpoints on the network.

  **e)** No one knows the password of every user on the system except for the system administrator, who knows all passwords.[

**19.** Express each of these statements using mathematical and logical operators, predicates, and quantifiers, where the domain consists of all integers.

  **a)** The sum of two negative integers is negative.

  **b)** The difference of two positive integers is not necessarily positive.

**c)** The sum of the squares of two integers is greater than or equal to the square of their sum.

**d)** The absolute value of the product of two integers is the product of their absolute values.

**20.** Express each of these statements using predicates, quantifiers, logical connectives, and mathematical operators where the domain consists of all integers.

**a)** The product of two negative integers is positive.

**b)** The average of two positive integers is positive.

**c)** The difference of two negative integers is not necessarily negative.

**d)** The absolute value of the sum of two integers does not exceed the sum of the absolute values of these integers.

**21.** Use predicates, quantifiers, logical connectives, and mathematical operators to express the statement that every positive integer is the sum of the squares of four integers.

**22.** Use predicates, quantifiers, logical connectives, and mathematical operators to express the statement that there is a positive integer that is not the sum of three squares.

**23.** Express each of these mathematical statements using predicates, quantifiers, logical connectives, and mathematical operators.

**a)** The product of two negative real numbers is positive.

**b)** The difference of a real number and itself is zero.

**c)** Every positive real number has exactly two square roots.

**d)** A negative real number does not have a square root that is a real number.

**24.** Translate each of these nested quantifications into an English statement that expresses a mathematical fact. The domain in each case consists of all real numbers.

**a)** $\exists x \forall y (x + y = y)$

**b)** $\forall x \forall y (((x \geq 0) \wedge (y < 0)) \rightarrow (x - y > 0))$

**c)** $\exists x \exists y (((x \leq 0) \wedge (y \leq 0)) \wedge (x - y > 0))$

**d)** $\forall x \forall y ((x \neq 0) \wedge (y \neq 0) \leftrightarrow (xy \neq 0))$

**25.** Translate each of these nested quantifications into an English statement that expresses a mathematical fact. The domain in each case consists of all real numbers.

**a)** $\exists x \forall y (xy = y)$

**b)** $\forall x \forall y (((x < 0) \wedge (y < 0)) \rightarrow (xy > 0))$

**c)** $\exists x \exists y ((x^2 > y) \wedge (x < y))$

**d)** $\forall x \forall y \exists z (x + y = z)$

**26.** Let $Q(x, y)$ be the statement "$x + y = x - y$." If the domain for both variables consists of all integers, what are the truth values?

**a)** $Q(1, 1)$      **b)** $Q(2, 0)$

**c)** $\forall y\, Q(1, y)$      **d)** $\exists x\, Q(x, 2)$

**e)** $\exists x \exists y\, Q(x, y)$      **f)** $\forall x \exists y\, Q(x, y)$

**g)** $\exists y \forall x\, Q(x, y)$      **h)** $\forall y \exists x\, Q(x, y)$

**i)** $\forall x \forall y\, Q(x, y)$

**27.** Determine the truth value of each of these statements if the domain for all variables consists of all integers.

**a)** $\forall n \exists m (n^2 < m)$      **b)** $\exists n \forall m (n < m^2)$

**c)** $\forall n \exists m (n + m = 0)$      **d)** $\exists n \forall m (nm = m)$

**e)** $\exists n \exists m (n^2 + m^2 = 5)$      **f)** $\exists n \exists m (n^2 + m^2 = 6)$

**g)** $\exists n \exists m (n + m = 4 \wedge n - m = 1)$

**h)** $\exists n \exists m (n + m = 4 \wedge n - m = 2)$

**i)** $\forall n \forall m \exists p (p = (m + n)/2)$

**28.** Determine the truth value of each of these statements if the domain of each variable consists of all real numbers.

**a)** $\forall x \exists y (x^2 = y)$      **b)** $\forall x \exists y (x = y^2)$

**c)** $\exists x \forall y (xy = 0)$      **d)** $\exists x \exists y (x + y \neq y + x)$

**e)** $\forall x (x \neq 0 \rightarrow \exists y (xy = 1))$

**f)** $\exists x \forall y (y \neq 0 \rightarrow xy = 1)$

**g)** $\forall x \exists y (x + y = 1)$

**h)** $\exists x \exists y (x + 2y = 2 \wedge 2x + 4y = 5)$

**i)** $\forall x \exists y (x + y = 2 \wedge 2x - y = 1)$

**j)** $\forall x \forall y \exists z (z = (x + y)/2)$

**29.** Suppose the domain of the propositional function $P(x, y)$ consists of pairs $x$ and $y$, where $x$ is 1, 2, or 3 and $y$ is 1, 2, or 3. Write out these propositions using disjunctions and conjunctions.

**a)** $\forall x \forall y\, P(x, y)$      **b)** $\exists x \exists y\, P(x, y)$

**c)** $\exists x \forall y\, P(x, y)$      **d)** $\forall y \exists x\, P(x, y)$

**30.** Rewrite each of these statements so that negations appear only within predicates (that is, so that no negation is outside a quantifier or an expression involving logical connectives).

**a)** $\neg \exists y \exists x\, P(x, y)$      **b)** $\neg \forall x \exists y\, P(x, y)$

**c)** $\neg \exists y (Q(y) \wedge \forall x \neg R(x, y))$

**d)** $\neg \exists y (\exists x R(x, y) \vee \forall x S(x, y))$

**e)** $\neg \exists y (\forall x \exists z T(x, y, z) \vee \exists x \forall z U(x, y, z))$

**31.** Express the negations of each of these statements so that all negation symbols immediately precede predicates.

**a)** $\forall x \exists y \forall z T(x, y, z)$

**b)** $\forall x \exists y P(x, y) \vee \forall x \exists y Q(x, y)$

**c)** $\forall x \exists y (P(x, y) \wedge \exists z R(x, y, z))$

**d)** $\forall x \exists y (P(x, y) \rightarrow Q(x, y))$

**32.** Express the negations of each of these statements so that all negation symbols immediately precede predicates.

**a)** $\exists z \forall y \forall x T(x, y, z)$

**b)** $\exists x \exists y P(x, y) \wedge \forall x \forall y Q(x, y)$

**c)** $\exists x \exists y (Q(x, y) \leftrightarrow Q(y, x))$

**d)** $\forall y \exists x \exists z (T(x, y, z) \vee Q(x, y))$

**33.** Rewrite each of these statements so that negations appear only within predicates (that is, so that no negation is outside a quantifier or an expression involving logical connectives).

**a)** $\neg \forall x \forall y\, P(x, y)$      **b)** $\neg \forall y \exists x\, P(x, y)$

**c)** $\neg \forall y \forall x (P(x, y) \vee Q(x, y))$

**d)** $\neg (\exists x \exists y \neg P(x, y) \wedge \forall x \forall y Q(x, y))$

**e)** $\neg \forall x (\exists y \forall z P(x, y, z) \wedge \exists z \forall y P(x, y, z))$

**34.** Find a common domain for the variables $x$, $y$, and $z$ for which the statement $\forall x \forall y ((x \neq y) \rightarrow \forall z ((z = x) \vee (z = y)))$ is true and another domain for which it is false.

**35.** Find a common domain for the variables $x, y, z$, and $w$ for which the statement $\forall x \forall y \forall z \exists w ((w \neq x) \wedge (w \neq y) \wedge (w \neq z))$ is true and another common domain for these variables for which it is false.

**36.** Express each of these statements using quantifiers. Then form the negation of the statement so that no negation is to the left of a quantifier. Next, express the negation in simple English. (Do not simply use the phrase "It is not the case that.")

**a)** No one has lost more than one thousand dollars playing the lottery.
**b)** There is a student in this class who has chatted with exactly one other student.
**c)** No student in this class has sent e-mail to exactly two other students in this class.
**d)** Some student has solved every exercise in this book.
**e)** No student has solved at least one exercise in every section of this book.

**37.** Express each of these statements using quantifiers. Then form the negation of the statement so that no negation is to the left of a quantifier. Next, express the negation in simple English. (Do not simply use the phrase "It is not the case that.")

**a)** Every student in this class has taken exactly two mathematics classes at this school.
**b)** Someone has visited every country in the world except Libya.
**c)** No one has climbed every mountain in the Himalayas.
**d)** Every movie actor has either been in a movie with Kevin Bacon or has been in a movie with someone who has been in a movie with Kevin Bacon.

**38.** Express the negations of these propositions using quantifiers, and in English.

**a)** Every student in this class likes mathematics.
**b)** There is a student in this class who has never seen a computer.
**c)** There is a student in this class who has taken every mathematics course offered at this school.
**d)** There is a student in this class who has been in at least one room of every building on campus.

**39.** Find a counterexample, if possible, to these universally quantified statements, where the domain for all variables consists of all integers.

**a)** $\forall x \forall y (x^2 = y^2 \rightarrow x = y)$
**b)** $\forall x \exists y (y^2 = x)$
**c)** $\forall x \forall y (xy \geq x)$

**40.** Find a counterexample, if possible, to these universally quantified statements, where the domain for all variables consists of all integers.

**a)** $\forall x \exists y (x = 1/y)$
**b)** $\forall x \exists y (y^2 - x < 100)$
**c)** $\forall x \forall y (x^2 \neq y^3)$

**41.** Use quantifiers to express the associative law for multiplication of real numbers.

**42.** Use quantifiers to express the distributive laws of multiplication over addition for real numbers.

**43.** Use quantifiers and logical connectives to express the fact that every linear polynomial (that is, polynomial of degree 1) with real coefficients and where the coefficient of $x$ is nonzero, has exactly one real root.

**44.** Use quantifiers and logical connectives to express the fact that a quadratic polynomial with real number coefficients has at most two real roots.

**45.** Determine the truth value of the statement $\forall x \exists y (xy = 1)$ if the domain for the variables consists of

**a)** the nonzero real numbers.
**b)** the nonzero integers.
**c)** the positive real numbers.

**46.** Determine the truth value of the statement $\exists x \forall y (x \leq y^2)$ if the domain for the variables consists of

**a)** the positive real numbers.
**b)** the integers.
**c)** the nonzero real numbers.

**47.** Show that the two statements $\neg \exists x \forall y P(x, y)$ and $\forall x \exists y \neg P(x, y)$, where both quantifiers over the first variable in $P(x, y)$ have the same domain, and both quantifiers over the second variable in $P(x, y)$ have the same domain, are logically equivalent.

**\*48.** Show that $\forall x P(x) \vee \forall x Q(x)$ and $\forall x \forall y (P(x) \vee Q(y))$, where all quantifiers have the same nonempty domain, are logically equivalent. (The new variable $y$ is used to combine the quantifications correctly.)

**\*49. a)** Show that $\forall x P(x) \wedge \exists x Q(x)$ is logically equivalent to $\forall x \exists y (P(x) \wedge Q(y))$, where all quantifiers have the same nonempty domain.

**b)** Show that $\forall x P(x) \vee \exists x Q(x)$ is equivalent to $\forall x \exists y (P(x) \vee Q(y))$, where all quantifiers have the same nonempty domain.

A statement is in **prenex normal form (PNF)** if and only if it is of the form

$$Q_1 x_1 Q_2 x_2 \cdots Q_k x_k P(x_1, x_2, \ldots, x_k),$$

where each $Q_i$, $i = 1, 2, \ldots, k$, is either the existential quantifier or the universal quantifier, and $P(x_1, \ldots, x_k)$ is a predicate involving no quantifiers. For example, $\exists x \forall y (P(x, y) \wedge Q(y))$ is in prenex normal form, whereas $\exists x P(x) \vee \forall x Q(x)$ is not (because the quantifiers do not all occur first).

Every statement formed from propositional variables, predicates, **T**, and **F** using logical connectives and quantifiers is equivalent to a statement in prenex normal form. Exercise 51 asks for a proof of this fact.

**\*50.** Put these statements in prenex normal form. [*Hint:* Use logical equivalence from Tables 6 and 7 in Section 1.3, Table 2 in Section 1.4, Example 19 in Section 1.4, Exercises 45 and 46 in Section 1.4, and Exercises 48 and 49.]

**a)** $\exists x P(x) \vee \exists x Q(x) \vee A$, where $A$ is a proposition not involving any quantifiers.
**b)** $\neg(\forall x P(x) \vee \forall x Q(x))$
**c)** $\exists x P(x) \rightarrow \exists x Q(x)$

**\*\*51.** Show how to transform an arbitrary statement to a statement in prenex normal form that is equivalent to the given statement. (Note: A formal solution of this exercise requires use of structural induction, covered in Section 5.3.)

**\*52.** Express the quantification $\exists! x P(x)$, introduced in Section 1.4, using universal quantifications, existential quantifications, and logical operators.

# 1.6    Rules of Inference

## Introduction

Later in this chapter we will study proofs. Proofs in mathematics are valid arguments that establish the truth of mathematical statements. By an **argument**, we mean a sequence of statements that end with a conclusion. By **valid**, we mean that the conclusion, or final statement of the argument, must follow from the truth of the preceding statements, or **premises**, of the argument. That is, an argument is valid if and only if it is impossible for all the premises to be true and the conclusion to be false. To deduce new statements from statements we already have, we use rules of inference which are templates for constructing valid arguments. Rules of inference are our basic tools for establishing the truth of statements.

Before we study mathematical proofs, we will look at arguments that involve only compound propositions. We will define what it means for an argument involving compound propositions to be valid. Then we will introduce a collection of rules of inference in propositional logic. These rules of inference are among the most important ingredients in producing valid arguments. After we illustrate how rules of inference are used to produce valid arguments, we will describe some common forms of incorrect reasoning, called **fallacies**, which lead to invalid arguments.

After studying rules of inference in propositional logic, we will introduce rules of inference for quantified statements. We will describe how these rules of inference can be used to produce valid arguments. These rules of inference for statements involving existential and universal quantifiers play an important role in proofs in computer science and mathematics, although they are often used without being explicitly mentioned.

Finally, we will show how rules of inference for propositions and for quantified statements can be combined. These combinations of rule of inference are often used together in complicated arguments.

## Valid Arguments in Propositional Logic

Consider the following argument involving propositions (which, by definition, is a sequence of propositions):

"If you have a current password, then you can log onto the network."

"You have a current password."

Therefore,

"You can log onto the network."

We would like to determine whether this is a valid argument. That is, we would like to determine whether the conclusion "You can log onto the network" must be true when the premises "If you have a current password, then you can log onto the network" and "You have a current password" are both true.

Before we discuss the validity of this particular argument, we will look at its form. Use $p$ to represent "You have a current password" and $q$ to represent "You can log onto the network." Then, the argument has the form

$$p \to q$$
$$\underline{p}$$
$$\therefore q$$

where $\therefore$ is the symbol that denotes "therefore."

We know that when $p$ and $q$ are propositional variables, the statement $((p \to q) \land p) \to q$ is a tautology (see Exercise 10(c) in Section 1.3). In particular, when both $p \to q$ and $p$ are true, we know that $q$ must also be true. We say this form of argument is **valid** because whenever all its premises (all statements in the argument other than the final one, the conclusion) are true, the conclusion must also be true. Now suppose that both "If you have a current password, then you can log onto the network" and "You have a current password" are true statements. When we replace $p$ by "You have a current password" and $q$ by "You can log onto the network," it necessarily follows that the conclusion "You can log onto the network" is true. This argument is **valid** because its form is valid. Note that whenever we replace $p$ and $q$ by propositions where $p \to q$ and $p$ are both true, then $q$ must also be true.

What happens when we replace $p$ and $q$ in this argument form by propositions where not both $p$ and $p \to q$ are true? For example, suppose that $p$ represents "You have access to the network" and $q$ represents "You can change your grade" and that $p$ is true, but $p \to q$ is false. The argument we obtain by substituting these values of $p$ and $q$ into the argument form is

"If you have access to the network, then you can change your grade."
"You have access to the network."

$\therefore$ "You can change your grade."

The argument we obtained is a valid argument, but because one of the premises, namely the first premise, is false, we cannot conclude that the conclusion is true. (Most likely, this conclusion is false.)

In our discussion, to analyze an argument, we replaced propositions by propositional variables. This changed an argument to an **argument form**. We saw that the validity of an argument follows from the validity of the form of the argument. We summarize the terminology used to discuss the validity of arguments with our definition of the key notions.

**DEFINITION 1**

An *argument* in propositional logic is a sequence of propositions. All but the final proposition in the argument are called *premises* and the final proposition is called the *conclusion*. An argument is *valid* if the truth of all its premises implies that the conclusion is true.

An *argument form* in propositional logic is a sequence of compound propositions involving propositional variables. An argument form is *valid* no matter which particular propositions are substituted for the propositional variables in its premises, the conclusion is true if the premises are all true.

From the definition of a valid argument form we see that the argument form with premises $p_1, p_2, \ldots, p_n$ and conclusion $q$ is valid, when $(p_1 \land p_2 \land \cdots \land p_n) \to q$ is a tautology.

The key to showing that an argument in propositional logic is valid is to show that its argument form is valid. Consequently, we would like techniques to show that argument forms are valid. We will now develop methods for accomplishing this task.

# Rules of Inference for Propositional Logic

We can always use a truth table to show that an argument form is valid. We do this by showing that whenever the premises are true, the conclusion must also be true. However, this can be a tedious approach. For example, when an argument form involves 10 different propositional variables, to use a truth table to show this argument form is valid requires $2^{10} = 1024$ different rows. Fortunately, we do not have to resort to truth tables. Instead, we can first establish the validity of some relatively simple argument forms, called **rules of inference**. These rules of inference can be used as building blocks to construct more complicated valid argument forms. We will now introduce the most important rules of inference in propositional logic.

The tautology $(p \land (p \to q)) \to q$ is the basis of the rule of inference called **modus ponens**, or the **law of detachment**. (Modus ponens is Latin for *mode that affirms*.) This tautology leads to the following valid argument form, which we have already seen in our initial discussion about arguments (where, as before, the symbol $\therefore$ denotes "therefore"):

$$
\begin{array}{l}
p \\
\underline{p \to q} \\
\therefore q
\end{array}
$$

Using this notation, the hypotheses are written in a column, followed by a horizontal bar, followed by a line that begins with the therefore symbol and ends with the conclusion. In particular, modus ponens tells us that if a conditional statement and the hypothesis of this conditional statement are both true, then the conclusion must also be true. Example 1 illustrates the use of modus ponens.

**EXAMPLE 1**     Suppose that the conditional statement "If it snows today, then we will go skiing" and its hypothesis, "It is snowing today," are true. Then, by modus ponens, it follows that the conclusion of the conditional statement, "We will go skiing," is true.     ◀

As we mentioned earlier, a valid argument can lead to an incorrect conclusion if one or more of its premises is false. We illustrate this again in Example 2.

**EXAMPLE 2**     Determine whether the argument given here is valid and determine whether its conclusion must be true because of the validity of the argument.

"If $\sqrt{2} > \frac{3}{2}$, then $\left(\sqrt{2}\right)^2 > \left(\frac{3}{2}\right)^2$. We know that $\sqrt{2} > \frac{3}{2}$. Consequently, $\left(\sqrt{2}\right)^2 = 2 > \left(\frac{3}{2}\right)^2 = \frac{9}{4}$."

*Solution:* Let $p$ be the proposition "$\sqrt{2} > \frac{3}{2}$" and $q$ the proposition "$2 > (\frac{3}{2})^2$." The premises of the argument are $p \to q$ and $p$, and $q$ is its conclusion. This argument is valid because it is constructed by using modus ponens, a valid argument form. However, one of its premises, $\sqrt{2} > \frac{3}{2}$, is false. Consequently, we cannot conclude that the conclusion is true. Furthermore, note that the conclusion of this argument is false, because $2 < \frac{9}{4}$.     ◀

There are many useful rules of inference for propositional logic. Perhaps the most widely used of these are listed in Table 1. Exercises 9, 10, 15, and 30 in Section 1.3 ask for the verifications that these rules of inference are valid argument forms. We now give examples of arguments that use these rules of inference. In each argument, we first use propositional variables to express the propositions in the argument. We then show that the resulting argument form is a rule of inference from Table 1.

| TABLE 1  Rules of Inference. | | |
|---|---|---|
| *Rule of Inference* | *Tautology* | *Name* |
| $p$ <br> $p \rightarrow q$ <br> $\therefore q$ | $(p \wedge (p \rightarrow q)) \rightarrow q$ | Modus ponens |
| $\neg q$ <br> $p \rightarrow q$ <br> $\therefore \neg p$ | $(\neg q \wedge (p \rightarrow q)) \rightarrow \neg p$ | Modus tollens |
| $p \rightarrow q$ <br> $q \rightarrow r$ <br> $\therefore p \rightarrow r$ | $((p \rightarrow q) \wedge (q \rightarrow r)) \rightarrow (p \rightarrow r)$ | Hypothetical syllogism |
| $p \vee q$ <br> $\neg p$ <br> $\therefore q$ | $((p \vee q) \wedge \neg p) \rightarrow q$ | Disjunctive syllogism |
| $p$ <br> $\therefore p \vee q$ | $p \rightarrow (p \vee q)$ | Addition |
| $p \wedge q$ <br> $\therefore p$ | $(p \wedge q) \rightarrow p$ | Simplification |
| $p$ <br> $q$ <br> $\therefore p \wedge q$ | $((p) \wedge (q)) \rightarrow (p \wedge q)$ | Conjunction |
| $p \vee q$ <br> $\neg p \vee r$ <br> $\therefore q \vee r$ | $((p \vee q) \wedge (\neg p \vee r)) \rightarrow (q \vee r)$ | Resolution |

**EXAMPLE 3**   State which rule of inference is the basis of the following argument: "It is below freezing now. Therefore, it is either below freezing or raining now."

*Solution:* Let $p$ be the proposition "It is below freezing now" and $q$ the proposition "It is raining now." Then this argument is of the form

$$\frac{p}{\therefore p \vee q}$$

This is an argument that uses the addition rule.    ◀

**EXAMPLE 4**   State which rule of inference is the basis of the following argument: "It is below freezing and raining now. Therefore, it is below freezing now."

*Solution:* Let $p$ be the proposition "It is below freezing now," and let $q$ be the proposition "It is raining now." This argument is of the form

$$\frac{p \wedge q}{\therefore p}$$

This argument uses the simplification rule.    ◀

**EXAMPLE 5**   State which rule of inference is used in the argument:

If it rains today, then we will not have a barbecue today. If we do not have a barbecue today, then we will have a barbecue tomorrow. Therefore, if it rains today, then we will have a barbecue tomorrow.

*Solution:* Let $p$ be the proposition "It is raining today," let $q$ be the proposition "We will not have a barbecue today," and let $r$ be the proposition "We will have a barbecue tomorrow." Then this argument is of the form

$$
\begin{array}{r}
p \to q \\
q \to r \\
\hline
\therefore \ p \to r
\end{array}
$$

Hence, this argument is a hypothetical syllogism.    ◀

## Using Rules of Inference to Build Arguments

When there are many premises, several rules of inference are often needed to show that an argument is valid. This is illustrated by Examples 6 and 7, where the steps of arguments are displayed on separate lines, with the reason for each step explicitly stated. These examples also show how arguments in English can be analyzed using rules of inference.

**EXAMPLE 6**   Show that the premises "It is not sunny this afternoon and it is colder than yesterday," "We will go swimming only if it is sunny," "If we do not go swimming, then we will take a canoe trip," and "If we take a canoe trip, then we will be home by sunset" lead to the conclusion "We will be home by sunset."

Extra Examples

*Solution:* Let $p$ be the proposition "It is sunny this afternoon," $q$ the proposition "It is colder than yesterday," $r$ the proposition "We will go swimming," $s$ the proposition "We will take a canoe trip," and $t$ the proposition "We will be home by sunset." Then the premises become $\neg p \land q$, $r \to p$, $\neg r \to s$, and $s \to t$. The conclusion is simply $t$. We need to give a valid argument with premises $\neg p \land q$, $r \to p$, $\neg r \to s$, and $s \to t$ and conclusion $t$.

We construct an argument to show that our premises lead to the desired conclusion as follows.

| Step | Reason |
|------|--------|
| 1. $\neg p \land q$ | Premise |
| 2. $\neg p$ | Simplification using (1) |
| 3. $r \to p$ | Premise |
| 4. $\neg r$ | Modus tollens using (2) and (3) |
| 5. $\neg r \to s$ | Premise |
| 6. $s$ | Modus ponens using (4) and (5) |
| 7. $s \to t$ | Premise |
| 8. $t$ | Modus ponens using (6) and (7) |

Note that we could have used a truth table to show that whenever each of the four hypotheses is true, the conclusion is also true. However, because we are working with five propositional variables, $p$, $q$, $r$, $s$, and $t$, such a truth table would have 32 rows.    ◀

**EXAMPLE 7** Show that the premises "If you send me an e-mail message, then I will finish writing the program," "If you do not send me an e-mail message, then I will go to sleep early," and "If I go to sleep early, then I will wake up feeling refreshed" lead to the conclusion "If I do not finish writing the program, then I will wake up feeling refreshed."

*Solution:* Let $p$ be the proposition "You send me an e-mail message," $q$ the proposition "I will finish writing the program," $r$ the proposition "I will go to sleep early," and $s$ the proposition "I will wake up feeling refreshed." Then the premises are $p \rightarrow q$, $\neg p \rightarrow r$, and $r \rightarrow s$. The desired conclusion is $\neg q \rightarrow s$. We need to give a valid argument with premises $p \rightarrow q$, $\neg p \rightarrow r$, and $r \rightarrow s$ and conclusion $\neg q \rightarrow s$.

This argument form shows that the premises lead to the desired conclusion.

| Step | Reason |
|------|--------|
| 1. $p \rightarrow q$ | Premise |
| 2. $\neg q \rightarrow \neg p$ | Contrapositive of (1) |
| 3. $\neg p \rightarrow r$ | Premise |
| 4. $\neg q \rightarrow r$ | Hypothetical syllogism using (2) and (3) |
| 5. $r \rightarrow s$ | Premise |
| 6. $\neg q \rightarrow s$ | Hypothetical syllogism using (4) and (5) |

◄

## Resolution

Computer programs have been developed to automate the task of reasoning and proving theorems. Many of these programs make use of a rule of inference known as **resolution**. This rule of inference is based on the tautology

**Links**

$$((p \vee q) \wedge (\neg p \vee r)) \rightarrow (q \vee r).$$

(Exercise 30 in Section 1.3 asks for the verification that this is a tautology.) The final disjunction in the resolution rule, $q \vee r$, is called the **resolvent**. When we let $q = r$ in this tautology, we obtain $(p \vee q) \wedge (\neg p \vee q) \rightarrow q$. Furthermore, when we let $r = \mathbf{F}$, we obtain $(p \vee q) \wedge (\neg p) \rightarrow q$ (because $q \vee \mathbf{F} \equiv q$), which is the tautology on which the rule of disjunctive syllogism is based.

**EXAMPLE 8** Use resolution to show that the hypotheses "Jasmine is skiing or it is not snowing" and "It is snowing or Bart is playing hockey" imply that "Jasmine is skiing or Bart is playing hockey."

**Extra Examples**

*Solution:* Let $p$ be the proposition "It is snowing," $q$ the proposition "Jasmine is skiing," and $r$ the proposition "Bart is playing hockey." We can represent the hypotheses as $\neg p \vee q$ and $p \vee r$, respectively. Using resolution, the proposition $q \vee r$, "Jasmine is skiing or Bart is playing hockey," follows. ◄

Resolution plays an important role in programming languages based on the rules of logic, such as Prolog (where resolution rules for quantified statements are applied). Furthermore, it can be used to build automatic theorem proving systems. To construct proofs in propositional logic using resolution as the only rule of inference, the hypotheses and the conclusion must be expressed as **clauses**, where a clause is a disjunction of variables or negations of these variables. We can replace a statement in propositional logic that is not a clause by one or more equivalent statements that are clauses. For example, suppose we have a statement of the form $p \vee (q \wedge r)$. Because $p \vee (q \wedge r) \equiv (p \vee q) \wedge (p \vee r)$, we can replace the single statement $p \vee (q \wedge r)$ by two statements $p \vee q$ and $p \vee r$, each of which is a clause. We can replace a statement of the form $\neg(p \vee q)$ by the two statements $\neg p$ and $\neg q$ because De Morgan's law tells us that $\neg(p \vee q) \equiv \neg p \wedge \neg q$. We can also replace a conditional statement $p \rightarrow q$ with the equivalent disjunction $\neg p \vee q$.

**EXAMPLE 9** Show that the premises $(p \wedge q) \vee r$ and $r \rightarrow s$ imply the conclusion $p \vee s$.

*Solution:* We can rewrite the premises $(p \wedge q) \vee r$ as two clauses, $p \vee r$ and $q \vee r$. We can also replace $r \rightarrow s$ by the equivalent clause $\neg r \vee s$. Using the two clauses $p \vee r$ and $\neg r \vee s$, we can use resolution to conclude $p \vee s$. ◀

## Fallacies

Several common fallacies arise in incorrect arguments. These fallacies resemble rules of inference, but are based on contingencies rather than tautologies. These are discussed here to show the distinction between correct and incorrect reasoning.

Links

The proposition $((p \rightarrow q) \wedge q) \rightarrow p$ is not a tautology, because it is false when $p$ is false and $q$ is true. However, there are many incorrect arguments that treat this as a tautology. In other words, they treat the argument with premises $p \rightarrow q$ and $q$ and conclusion $p$ as a valid argument form, which it is not. This type of incorrect reasoning is called the **fallacy of affirming the conclusion**.

**EXAMPLE 10** Is the following argument valid?

If you do every problem in this book, then you will learn discrete mathematics. You learned discrete mathematics.

Therefore, you did every problem in this book.

*Solution:* Let $p$ be the proposition "You did every problem in this book." Let $q$ be the proposition "You learned discrete mathematics." Then this argument is of the form: if $p \rightarrow q$ and $q$, then $p$. This is an example of an incorrect argument using the fallacy of affirming the conclusion. Indeed, it is possible for you to learn discrete mathematics in some way other than by doing every problem in this book. (You may learn discrete mathematics by reading, listening to lectures, doing some, but not all, the problems in this book, and so on.) ◀

The proposition $((p \rightarrow q) \wedge \neg p) \rightarrow \neg q$ is not a tautology, because it is false when $p$ is false and $q$ is true. Many incorrect arguments use this incorrectly as a rule of inference. This type of incorrect reasoning is called the **fallacy of denying the hypothesis**.

**EXAMPLE 11** Let $p$ and $q$ be as in Example 10. If the conditional statement $p \rightarrow q$ is true, and $\neg p$ is true, is it correct to conclude that $\neg q$ is true? In other words, is it correct to assume that you did not learn discrete mathematics if you did not do every problem in the book, assuming that if you do every problem in this book, then you will learn discrete mathematics?

*Solution:* It is possible that you learned discrete mathematics even if you did not do every problem in this book. This incorrect argument is of the form $p \rightarrow q$ and $\neg p$ imply $\neg q$, which is an example of the fallacy of denying the hypothesis. ◀

## Rules of Inference for Quantified Statements

We have discussed rules of inference for propositions. We will now describe some important rules of inference for statements involving quantifiers. These rules of inference are used extensively in mathematical arguments, often without being explicitly mentioned.

**Universal instantiation** is the rule of inference used to conclude that $P(c)$ is true, where $c$ is a particular member of the domain, given the premise $\forall x P(x)$. Universal instantiation is used when we conclude from the statement "All women are wise" that "Lisa is wise," where Lisa is a member of the domain of all women.

| TABLE 2   Rules of Inference for Quantified Statements. | |
| --- | --- |
| *Rule of Inference* | *Name* |
| $\forall x\, P(x)$ <br> $\therefore\ \overline{P(c)}$ | Universal instantiation |
| $P(c)$ for an arbitrary $c$ <br> $\therefore\ \overline{\forall x\, P(x)}$ | Universal generalization |
| $\exists x\, P(x)$ <br> $\therefore\ \overline{P(c) \text{ for some element } c}$ | Existential instantiation |
| $P(c)$ for some element $c$ <br> $\therefore\ \overline{\exists x\, P(x)}$ | Existential generalization |

**Universal generalization** is the rule of inference that states that $\forall x\, P(x)$ is true, given the premise that $P(c)$ is true for all elements $c$ in the domain. Universal generalization is used when we show that $\forall x\, P(x)$ is true by taking an arbitrary element $c$ from the domain and showing that $P(c)$ is true. The element $c$ that we select must be an arbitrary, and not a specific, element of the domain. That is, when we assert from $\forall x\, P(x)$ the existence of an element $c$ in the domain, we have no control over $c$ and cannot make any other assumptions about $c$ other than it comes from the domain. Universal generalization is used implicitly in many proofs in mathematics and is seldom mentioned explicitly. However, the error of adding unwarranted assumptions about the arbitrary element $c$ when universal generalization is used is all too common in incorrect reasoning.

**Existential instantiation** is the rule that allows us to conclude that there is an element $c$ in the domain for which $P(c)$ is true if we know that $\exists x\, P(x)$ is true. We cannot select an arbitrary value of $c$ here, but rather it must be a $c$ for which $P(c)$ is true. Usually we have no knowledge of what $c$ is, only that it exists. Because it exists, we may give it a name ($c$) and continue our argument.

**Existential generalization** is the rule of inference that is used to conclude that $\exists x\, P(x)$ is true when a particular element $c$ with $P(c)$ true is known. That is, if we know one element $c$ in the domain for which $P(c)$ is true, then we know that $\exists x\, P(x)$ is true.

We summarize these rules of inference in Table 2. We will illustrate how some of these rules of inference for quantified statements are used in Examples 12 and 13.

**EXAMPLE 12**   Show that the premises "Everyone in this discrete mathematics class has taken a course in computer science" and "Marla is a student in this class" imply the conclusion "Marla has taken a course in computer science."

*Solution:* Let $D(x)$ denote "$x$ is in this discrete mathematics class," and let $C(x)$ denote "$x$ has taken a course in computer science." Then the premises are $\forall x(D(x) \rightarrow C(x))$ and $D(\text{Marla})$. The conclusion is $C(\text{Marla})$.

Extra
Examples

The following steps can be used to establish the conclusion from the premises.

| Step | Reason |
| --- | --- |
| 1. $\forall x(D(x) \rightarrow C(x))$ | Premise |
| 2. $D(\text{Marla}) \rightarrow C(\text{Marla})$ | Universal instantiation from (1) |
| 3. $D(\text{Marla})$ | Premise |
| 4. $C(\text{Marla})$ | Modus ponens from (2) and (3) |

◀

**EXAMPLE 13**  Show that the premises "A student in this class has not read the book," and "Everyone in this class passed the first exam" imply the conclusion "Someone who passed the first exam has not read the book."

*Solution:* Let $C(x)$ be "$x$ is in this class," $B(x)$ be "$x$ has read the book," and $P(x)$ be "$x$ passed the first exam." The premises are $\exists x(C(x) \land \neg B(x))$ and $\forall x(C(x) \to P(x))$. The conclusion is $\exists x(P(x) \land \neg B(x))$. These steps can be used to establish the conclusion from the premises.

| Step | Reason |
|------|--------|
| 1. $\exists x(C(x) \land \neg B(x))$ | Premise |
| 2. $C(a) \land \neg B(a)$ | Existential instantiation from (1) |
| 3. $C(a)$ | Simplification from (2) |
| 4. $\forall x(C(x) \to P(x))$ | Premise |
| 5. $C(a) \to P(a)$ | Universal instantiation from (4) |
| 6. $P(a)$ | Modus ponens from (3) and (5) |
| 7. $\neg B(a)$ | Simplification from (2) |
| 8. $P(a) \land \neg B(a)$ | Conjunction from (6) and (7) |
| 9. $\exists x(P(x) \land \neg B(x))$ | Existential generalization from (8) |

◀

## Combining Rules of Inference for Propositions and Quantified Statements

We have developed rules of inference both for propositions and for quantified statements. Note that in our arguments in Examples 12 and 13 we used both universal instantiation, a rule of inference for quantified statements, and modus ponens, a rule of inference for propositional logic. We will often need to use this combination of rules of inference. Because universal instantiation and modus ponens are used so often together, this combination of rules is sometimes called **universal modus ponens**. This rule tells us that if $\forall x(P(x) \to Q(x))$ is true, and if $P(a)$ is true for a particular element $a$ in the domain of the universal quantifier, then $Q(a)$ must also be true. To see this, note that by universal instantiation, $P(a) \to Q(a)$ is true. Then, by modus ponens, $Q(a)$ must also be true. We can describe universal modus ponens as follows:

$\forall x(P(x) \to Q(x))$

$P(a)$, where $a$ is a particular element in the domain

_____

$\therefore Q(a)$

Universal modus ponens is commonly used in mathematical arguments. This is illustrated in Example 14.

**EXAMPLE 14**  Assume that "For all positive integers $n$, if $n$ is greater than 4, then $n^2$ is less than $2^n$" is true. Use universal modus ponens to show that $100^2 < 2^{100}$.

*Solution:* Let $P(n)$ denote "$n > 4$" and $Q(n)$ denote "$n^2 < 2^n$." The statement "For all positive integers $n$, if $n$ is greater than 4, then $n^2$ is less than $2^n$" can be represented by $\forall n(P(n) \to Q(n))$, where the domain consists of all positive integers. We are assuming that $\forall n(P(n) \to Q(n))$ is true. Note that $P(100)$ is true because $100 > 4$. It follows by universal modus ponens that $Q(100)$ is true, namely that $100^2 < 2^{100}$.  ◀

Another useful combination of a rule of inference from propositional logic and a rule of inference for quantified statements is **universal modus tollens**. Universal modus tollens combines universal instantiation and modus tollens and can be expressed in the following way:

$$\forall x (P(x) \rightarrow Q(x))$$
$$\neg Q(a), \text{ where } a \text{ is a particular element in the domain}$$
$$\therefore \neg P(a)$$

The verification of universal modus tollens is left as Exercise 25. Exercises 26–29 develop additional combinations of rules of inference in propositional logic and quantified statements.

# Exercises

**1.** Find the argument form for the following argument and determine whether it is valid. Can we conclude that the conclusion is true if the premises are true?

> If Socrates is human, then Socrates is mortal.
> Socrates is human.
> _____
>
> ∴ Socrates is mortal.

**2.** Find the argument form for the following argument and determine whether it is valid. Can we conclude that the conclusion is true if the premises are true?

> If George does not have eight legs, then he is not a spider.
> George is a spider.
> _____
>
> ∴ George has eight legs.

**3.** What rule of inference is used in each of these arguments?

**a)** Alice is a mathematics major. Therefore, Alice is either a mathematics major or a computer science major.

**b)** Jerry is a mathematics major and a computer science major. Therefore, Jerry is a mathematics major.

**c)** If it is rainy, then the pool will be closed. It is rainy. Therefore, the pool is closed.

**d)** If it snows today, the university will close. The university is not closed today. Therefore, it did not snow today.

**e)** If I go swimming, then I will stay in the sun too long. If I stay in the sun too long, then I will sunburn. Therefore, if I go swimming, then I will sunburn.

**4.** What rule of inference is used in each of these arguments?

**a)** Kangaroos live in Australia and are marsupials. Therefore, kangaroos are marsupials.

**b)** It is either hotter than 100 degrees today or the pollution is dangerous. It is less than 100 degrees outside today. Therefore, the pollution is dangerous.

**c)** Linda is an excellent swimmer. If Linda is an excellent swimmer, then she can work as a lifeguard. Therefore, Linda can work as a lifeguard.

**d)** Steve will work at a computer company this summer. Therefore, this summer Steve will work at a computer company or he will be a beach bum.

**e)** If I work all night on this homework, then I can answer all the exercises. If I answer all the exercises, I will understand the material. Therefore, if I work all night on this homework, then I will understand the material.

**5.** Use rules of inference to show that the hypotheses "Randy works hard," "If Randy works hard, then he is a dull boy," and "If Randy is a dull boy, then he will not get the job" imply the conclusion "Randy will not get the job."

**6.** Use rules of inference to show that the hypotheses "If it does not rain or if it is not foggy, then the sailing race will be held and the lifesaving demonstration will go on," "If the sailing race is held, then the trophy will be awarded," and "The trophy was not awarded" imply the conclusion "It rained."

**7.** What rules of inference are used in this famous argument? "All men are mortal. Socrates is a man. Therefore, Socrates is mortal."

**8.** What rules of inference are used in this argument? "No man is an island. Manhattan is an island. Therefore, Manhattan is not a man."

**9.** For each of these collections of premises, what relevant conclusion or conclusions can be drawn? Explain the rules of inference used to obtain each conclusion from the premises.

**a)** "If I take the day off, it either rains or snows." "I took Tuesday off or I took Thursday off." "It was sunny on Tuesday." "It did not snow on Thursday."

**b)** "If I eat spicy foods, then I have strange dreams." "I have strange dreams if there is thunder while I sleep." "I did not have strange dreams."

**c)** "I am either clever or lucky." "I am not lucky." "If I am lucky, then I will win the lottery."

**d)** "Every computer science major has a personal computer." "Ralph does not have a personal computer." "Ann has a personal computer."

**e)** "What is good for corporations is good for the United States." "What is good for the United States is good for you." "What is good for corporations is for you to buy lots of stuff."

**f)** "All rodents gnaw their food." "Mice are rodents." "Rabbits do not gnaw their food." "Bats are not rodents."

**10.** For each of these sets of premises, what relevant conclusion or conclusions can be drawn? Explain the rules of inference used to obtain each conclusion from the premises.

   **a)** "If I play hockey, then I am sore the next day." "I use the whirlpool if I am sore." "I did not use the whirlpool."

   **b)** "If I work, it is either sunny or partly sunny." "I worked last Monday or I worked last Friday." "It was not sunny on Tuesday." "It was not partly sunny on Friday."

   **c)** "All insects have six legs." "Dragonflies are insects." "Spiders do not have six legs." "Spiders eat dragonflies."

   **d)** "Every student has an Internet account." "Homer does not have an Internet account." "Maggie has an Internet account."

   **e)** "All foods that are healthy to eat do not taste good." "Tofu is healthy to eat." "You only eat what tastes good." "You do not eat tofu." "Cheeseburgers are not healthy to eat."

   **f)** "I am either dreaming or hallucinating." "I am not dreaming." "If I am hallucinating, I see elephants running down the road."

**11.** Show that the argument form with premises $p_1, p_2, \ldots, p_n$ and conclusion $q \to r$ is valid if the argument form with premises $p_1, p_2, \ldots, p_n, q$, and conclusion $r$ is valid.

**12.** Show that the argument form with premises $(p \wedge t) \to (r \vee s)$, $q \to (u \wedge t)$, $u \to p$, and $\neg s$ and conclusion $q \to r$ is valid by first using Exercise 11 and then using rules of inference from Table 1.

**13.** For each of these arguments, explain which rules of inference are used for each step.

   **a)** "Doug, a student in this class, knows how to write programs in JAVA. Everyone who knows how to write programs in JAVA can get a high-paying job. Therefore, someone in this class can get a high-paying job."

   **b)** "Somebody in this class enjoys whale watching. Every person who enjoys whale watching cares about ocean pollution. Therefore, there is a person in this class who cares about ocean pollution."

   **c)** "Each of the 93 students in this class owns a personal computer. Everyone who owns a personal computer can use a word processing program. Therefore, Zeke, a student in this class, can use a word processing program."

   **d)** "Everyone in New Jersey lives within 50 miles of the ocean. Someone in New Jersey has never seen the ocean. Therefore, someone who lives within 50 miles of the ocean has never seen the ocean."

**14.** For each of these arguments, explain which rules of inference are used for each step.

   **a)** "Linda, a student in this class, owns a red convertible. Everyone who owns a red convertible has gotten at least one speeding ticket. Therefore, someone in this class has gotten a speeding ticket."

   **b)** "Each of five roommates, Melissa, Aaron, Ralph, Veneesha, and Keeshawn, has taken a course in discrete mathematics. Every student who has taken a course in discrete mathematics can take a course in algorithms. Therefore, all five roommates can take a course in algorithms next year."

   **c)** "All movies produced by John Sayles are wonderful. John Sayles produced a movie about coal miners. Therefore, there is a wonderful movie about coal miners."

   **d)** "There is someone in this class who has been to France. Everyone who goes to France visits the Louvre. Therefore, someone in this class has visited the Louvre."

**15.** For each of these arguments determine whether the argument is correct or incorrect and explain why.

   **a)** All students in this class understand logic. Xavier is a student in this class. Therefore, Xavier understands logic.

   **b)** Every computer science major takes discrete mathematics. Natasha is taking discrete mathematics. Therefore, Natasha is a computer science major.

   **c)** All parrots like fruit. My pet bird is not a parrot. Therefore, my pet bird does not like fruit.

   **d)** Everyone who eats granola every day is healthy. Linda is not healthy. Therefore, Linda does not eat granola every day.

**16.** For each of these arguments determine whether the argument is correct or incorrect and explain why.

   **a)** Everyone enrolled in the university has lived in a dormitory. Mia has never lived in a dormitory. Therefore, Mia is not enrolled in the university.

   **b)** A convertible car is fun to drive. Isaac's car is not a convertible. Therefore, Isaac's car is not fun to drive.

   **c)** Quincy likes all action movies. Quincy likes the movie *Eight Men Out*. Therefore, *Eight Men Out* is an action movie.

   **d)** All lobstermen set at least a dozen traps. Hamilton is a lobsterman. Therefore, Hamilton sets at least a dozen traps.

**17.** What is wrong with this argument? Let $H(x)$ be "$x$ is happy." Given the premise $\exists x H(x)$, we conclude that $H(\text{Lola})$. Therefore, Lola is happy.

**18.** What is wrong with this argument? Let $S(x, y)$ be "$x$ is shorter than $y$." Given the premise $\exists s S(s, \text{Max})$, it follows that $S(\text{Max}, \text{Max})$. Then by existential generalization it follows that $\exists x S(x, x)$, so that someone is shorter than himself.

**19.** Determine whether each of these arguments is valid. If an argument is correct, what rule of inference is being used? If it is not, what logical error occurs?

   **a)** If $n$ is a real number such that $n > 1$, then $n^2 > 1$. Suppose that $n^2 > 1$. Then $n > 1$.

   **b)** If $n$ is a real number with $n > 3$, then $n^2 > 9$. Suppose that $n^2 \leq 9$. Then $n \leq 3$.

   **c)** If $n$ is a real number with $n > 2$, then $n^2 > 4$. Suppose that $n \leq 2$. Then $n^2 \leq 4$.

**20.** Determine whether these are valid arguments.

    **a)** If $x$ is a positive real number, then $x^2$ is a positive real number. Therefore, if $a^2$ is positive, where $a$ is a real number, then $a$ is a positive real number.

    **b)** If $x^2 \neq 0$, where $x$ is a real number, then $x \neq 0$. Let $a$ be a real number with $a^2 \neq 0$; then $a \neq 0$.

**21.** Which rules of inference are used to establish the conclusion of Lewis Carroll's argument described in Example 26 of Section 1.4?

**22.** Which rules of inference are used to establish the conclusion of Lewis Carroll's argument described in Example 27 of Section 1.4?

**23.** Identify the error or errors in this argument that supposedly shows that if $\exists x\, P(x) \wedge \exists x\, Q(x)$ is true then $\exists x (P(x) \wedge Q(x))$ is true.

| | |
|---|---|
| 1. $\exists x\, P(x) \vee \exists x\, Q(x)$ | Premise |
| 2. $\exists x\, P(x)$ | Simplification from (1) |
| 3. $P(c)$ | Existential instantiation from (2) |
| 4. $\exists x\, Q(x)$ | Simplification from (1) |
| 5. $Q(c)$ | Existential instantiation from (4) |
| 6. $P(c) \wedge Q(c)$ | Conjunction from (3) and (5) |
| 7. $\exists x (P(x) \wedge Q(x))$ | Existential generalization |

**24.** Identify the error or errors in this argument that supposedly shows that if $\forall x (P(x) \vee Q(x))$ is true then $\forall x\, P(x) \vee \forall x\, Q(x)$ is true.

| | |
|---|---|
| 1. $\forall x (P(x) \vee Q(x))$ | Premise |
| 2. $P(c) \vee Q(c)$ | Universal instantiation from (1) |
| 3. $P(c)$ | Simplification from (2) |
| 4. $\forall x\, P(x)$ | Universal generalization from (3) |
| 5. $Q(c)$ | Simplification from (2) |
| 6. $\forall x\, Q(x)$ | Universal generalization from (5) |
| 7. $\forall x (P(x) \vee \forall x\, Q(x))$ | Conjunction from (4) and (6) |

**25.** Justify the rule of universal modus tollens by showing that the premises $\forall x (P(x) \rightarrow Q(x))$ and $\neg Q(a)$ for a particular element $a$ in the domain, imply $\neg P(a)$.

**26.** Justify the rule of **universal transitivity**, which states that if $\forall x (P(x) \rightarrow Q(x))$ and $\forall x (Q(x) \rightarrow R(x))$ are true, then $\forall x (P(x) \rightarrow R(x))$ is true, where the domains of all quantifiers are the same.

**27.** Use rules of inference to show that if $\forall x (P(x) \rightarrow (Q(x) \wedge S(x)))$ and $\forall x (P(x) \wedge R(x))$ are true, then $\forall x (R(x) \wedge S(x))$ is true.

**28.** Use rules of inference to show that if $\forall x (P(x) \vee Q(x))$ and $\forall x ((\neg P(x) \wedge Q(x)) \rightarrow R(x))$ are true, then $\forall x (\neg R(x) \rightarrow P(x))$ is also true, where the domains of all quantifiers are the same.

**29.** Use rules of inference to show that if $\forall x (P(x) \vee Q(x))$, $\forall x (\neg Q(x) \vee S(x))$, $\forall x (R(x) \rightarrow \neg S(x))$, and $\exists x \neg P(x)$ are true, then $\exists x \neg R(x)$ is true.

**30.** Use resolution to show the hypotheses "Allen is a bad boy or Hillary is a good girl" and "Allen is a good boy or David is happy" imply the conclusion "Hillary is a good girl or David is happy."

**31.** Use resolution to show that the hypotheses "It is not raining or Yvette has her umbrella," "Yvette does not have her umbrella or she does not get wet," and "It is raining or Yvette does not get wet" imply that "Yvette does not get wet."

**32.** Show that the equivalence $p \wedge \neg p \equiv \mathbf{F}$ can be derived using resolution together with the fact that a conditional statement with a false hypothesis is true. [*Hint:* Let $q = r = \mathbf{F}$ in resolution.]

**33.** Use resolution to show that the compound proposition $(p \vee q) \wedge (\neg p \vee q) \wedge (p \vee \neg q) \wedge (\neg p \vee \neg q)$ is not satisfiable.

**\*34.** The Logic Problem, taken from *WFF'N PROOF, The Game of Logic*, has these two assumptions:

    *1.* "Logic is difficult or not many students like logic."

    *2.* "If mathematics is easy, then logic is not difficult."

By translating these assumptions into statements involving propositional variables and logical connectives, determine whether each of the following are valid conclusions of these assumptions:

    **a)** That mathematics is not easy, if many students like logic.

    **b)** That not many students like logic, if mathematics is not easy.

    **c)** That mathematics is not easy or logic is difficult.

    **d)** That logic is not difficult or mathematics is not easy.

    **e)** That if not many students like logic, then either mathematics is not easy or logic is not difficult.

**\*35.** Determine whether this argument, taken from Kalish and Montague [KaMo64], is valid.

> If Superman were able and willing to prevent evil, he would do so. If Superman were unable to prevent evil, he would be impotent; if he were unwilling to prevent evil, he would be malevolent. Superman does not prevent evil. If Superman exists, he is neither impotent nor malevolent. Therefore, Superman does not exist.

# 1.7  Introduction to Proofs

## Introduction

In this section we introduce the notion of a proof and describe methods for constructing proofs. A proof is a valid argument that establishes the truth of a mathematical statement. A proof can use the hypotheses of the theorem, if any, axioms assumed to be true, and previously proven theorems. Using these ingredients and rules of inference, the final step of the proof establishes the truth of the statement being proved.

In our discussion we move from formal proofs of theorems toward more informal proofs. The arguments we introduced in Section 1.6 to show that statements involving propositions and quantified statements are true were formal proofs, where all steps were supplied, and the rules for each step in the argument were given. However, formal proofs of useful theorems can be extremely long and hard to follow. In practice, the proofs of theorems designed for human consumption are almost always **informal proofs**, where more than one rule of inference may be used in each step, where steps may be skipped, where the axioms being assumed and the rules of inference used are not explicitly stated. Informal proofs can often explain to humans why theorems are true, while computers are perfectly happy producing formal proofs using automated reasoning systems.

The methods of proof discussed in this chapter are important not only because they are used to prove mathematical theorems, but also for their many applications to computer science. These applications include verifying that computer programs are correct, establishing that operating systems are secure, making inferences in artificial intelligence, showing that system specifications are consistent, and so on. Consequently, understanding the techniques used in proofs is essential both in mathematics and in computer science.

## Some Terminology

Links

Formally, a **theorem** is a statement that can be shown to be true. In mathematical writing, the term theorem is usually reserved for a statement that is considered at least somewhat important. Less important theorems sometimes are called **propositions**. (Theorems can also be referred to as **facts** or **results**.) A theorem may be the universal quantification of a conditional statement with one or more premises and a conclusion. However, it may be some other type of logical statement, as the examples later in this chapter will show. We demonstrate that a theorem is true with a **proof**. A proof is a valid argument that establishes the truth of a theorem. The statements used in a proof can include **axioms** (or **postulates**), which are statements we assume to be true (for example, the axioms for the real numbers, given in Appendix 1, and the axioms of plane geometry), the premises, if any, of the theorem, and previously proven theorems. Axioms may be stated using primitive terms that do not require definition, but all other terms used in theorems and their proofs must be defined. Rules of inference, together with definitions of terms, are used to draw conclusions from other assertions, tying together the steps of a proof. In practice, the final step of a proof is usually just the conclusion of the theorem. However, for clarity, we will often recap the statement of the theorem as the final step of a proof.

A less important theorem that is helpful in the proof of other results is called a **lemma** (plural *lemmas* or *lemmata*). Complicated proofs are usually easier to understand when they are proved using a series of lemmas, where each lemma is proved individually. A **corollary** is a theorem that can be established directly from a theorem that has been proved. A **conjecture** is a statement that is being proposed to be a true statement, usually on the basis of some partial evidence, a heuristic argument, or the intuition of an expert. When a proof of a conjecture is found, the conjecture becomes a theorem. Many times conjectures are shown to be false, so they are not theorems.

## Understanding How Theorems Are Stated

Extra
Examples

Before we introduce methods for proving theorems, we need to understand how many mathematical theorems are stated. Many theorems assert that a property holds for all elements in a domain, such as the integers or the real numbers. Although the precise statement of such theorems needs to include a universal quantifier, the standard convention in mathematics is to omit it. For example, the statement

"If $x > y$, where $x$ and $y$ are positive real numbers, then $x^2 > y^2$."

really means

"For all positive real numbers $x$ and $y$, if $x > y$, then $x^2 > y^2$."

Furthermore, when theorems of this type are proved, the first step of the proof usually involves selecting a general element of the domain. Subsequent steps show that this element has the property in question. Finally, universal generalization implies that the theorem holds for all members of the domain.

## Methods of Proving Theorems

Assessment

Proving mathematical theorems can be difficult. To construct proofs we need all available ammunition, including a powerful battery of different proof methods. These methods provide the overall approach and strategy of proofs. Understanding these methods is a key component of learning how to read and construct mathematical proofs. One we have chosen a proof method, we use axioms, definitions of terms, previously proved results, and rules of inference to complete the proof. Note that in this book we will always assume the axioms for real numbers found in Appendix 1. We will also assume the usual axioms whenever we prove a result about geometry. When you construct your own proofs, be careful not to use anything but these axioms, definitions, and previously proved results as facts!

To prove a theorem of the form $\forall x(P(x) \to Q(x))$, our goal is to show that $P(c) \to Q(c)$ is true, where $c$ is an arbitrary element of the domain, and then apply universal generalization. In this proof, we need to show that a conditional statement is true. Because of this, we now focus on methods that show that conditional statements are true. Recall that $p \to q$ is true unless $p$ is true but $q$ is false. Note that to prove the statement $p \to q$, we need only show that $q$ is true if $p$ is true. The following discussion will give the most common techniques for proving conditional statements. Later we will discuss methods for proving other types of statements. In this section, and in Section 1.8, we will develop a large arsenal of proof techniques that can be used to prove a wide variety of theorems.

When you read proofs, you will often find the words "obviously" or "clearly." These words indicate that steps have been omitted that the author expects the reader to be able to fill in. Unfortunately, this assumption is often not warranted and readers are not at all sure how to fill in the gaps. We will assiduously try to avoid using these words and try not to omit too many steps. However, if we included all steps in proofs, our proofs would often be excruciatingly long.

## Direct Proofs

A **direct proof** of a conditional statement $p \to q$ is constructed when the first step is the assumption that $p$ is true; subsequent steps are constructed using rules of inference, with the final step showing that $q$ must also be true. A direct proof shows that a conditional statement $p \to q$ is true by showing that if $p$ is true, then $q$ must also be true, so that the combination $p$ true and $q$ false never occurs. In a direct proof, we assume that $p$ is true and use axioms, definitions, and previously proven theorems, together with rules of inference, to show that $q$ must also be true. You will find that direct proofs of many results are quite straightforward, with a fairly obvious sequence of steps leading from the hypothesis to the conclusion. However, direct proofs sometimes require particular insights and can be quite tricky. The first direct proofs we present here are quite straightforward; later in the text you will see some that are less obvious.

We will provide examples of several different direct proofs. Before we give the first example, we need to define some terminology.

**DEFINITION 1**    The integer $n$ is *even* if there exists an integer $k$ such that $n = 2k$, and $n$ is *odd* if there exists an integer $k$ such that $n = 2k + 1$. (Note that every integer is either even or odd, and no integer is both even and odd.) Two integers have the *same parity* when both are even or both are odd; they have *opposite parity* when one is even and the other is odd.

**EXAMPLE 1**    Give a direct proof of the theorem "If $n$ is an odd integer, then $n^2$ is odd."

*Solution:* Note that this theorem states $\forall n\, P((n) \rightarrow Q(n))$, where $P(n)$ is "$n$ is an odd integer" and $Q(n)$ is "$n^2$ is odd." As we have said, we will follow the usual convention in mathematical proofs by showing that $P(n)$ implies $Q(n)$, and not explicitly using universal instantiation. To begin a direct proof of this theorem, we assume that the hypothesis of this conditional statement is true, namely, we assume that $n$ is odd. By the definition of an odd integer, it follows that $n = 2k + 1$, where $k$ is some integer. We want to show that $n^2$ is also odd. We can square both sides of the equation $n = 2k + 1$ to obtain a new equation that expresses $n^2$. When we do this, we find that $n^2 = (2k + 1)^2 = 4k^2 + 4k + 1 = 2(2k^2 + 2k) + 1$. By the definition of an odd integer, we can conclude that $n^2$ is an odd integer (it is one more than twice an integer). Consequently, we have proved that if $n$ is an odd integer, then $n^2$ is an odd integer. ◀

**EXAMPLE 2**    Give a direct proof that if $m$ and $n$ are both perfect squares, then $nm$ is also a perfect square. (An integer $a$ is a **perfect square** if there is an integer $b$ such that $a = b^2$.)

*Solution:* To produce a direct proof of this theorem, we assume that the hypothesis of this conditional statement is true, namely, we assume that $m$ and $n$ are both perfect squares. By the definition of a perfect square, it follows that there are integers $s$ and $t$ such that $m = s^2$ and $n = t^2$. The goal of the proof is to show that $mn$ must also be a perfect square when $m$ and $n$ are; looking ahead we see how we can show this by substituting $s^2$ for $m$ and $t^2$ for $n$ into $mn$. This tells us that $mn = s^2 t^2$. Hence, $mn = s^2 t^2 = (ss)(tt) = (st)(st) = (st)^2$, using commutativity and associativity of multiplication. By the definition of perfect square, it follows that $mn$ is also a perfect square, because it is the square of $st$, which is an integer. We have proved that if $m$ and $n$ are both perfect squares, then $mn$ is also a perfect square. ◀

## Proof by Contraposition

Direct proofs lead from the premises of a theorem to the conclusion. They begin with the premises, continue with a sequence of deductions, and end with the conclusion. However, we will see that attempts at direct proofs often reach dead ends. We need other methods of proving theorems of the form $\forall x (P(x) \rightarrow Q(x))$. Proofs of theorems of this type that are not direct proofs, that is, that do not start with the premises and end with the conclusion, are called **indirect proofs**.

An extremely useful type of indirect proof is known as **proof by contraposition**. Proofs by contraposition make use of the fact that the conditional statement $p \rightarrow q$ is equivalent to its contrapositive, $\neg q \rightarrow \neg p$. This means that the conditional statement $p \rightarrow q$ can be proved by showing that its contrapositive, $\neg q \rightarrow \neg p$, is true. In a proof by contraposition of $p \rightarrow q$, we take $\neg q$ as a premise, and using axioms, definitions, and previously proven theorems, together with rules of inference, we show that $\neg p$ must follow. We will illustrate proof by contraposition with two examples. These examples show that proof by contraposition can succeed when we cannot easily find a direct proof.

**EXAMPLE 3**    Prove that if $n$ is an integer and $3n + 2$ is odd, then $n$ is odd.

*Solution:* We first attempt a direct proof. To construct a direct proof, we first assume that $3n + 2$ is an odd integer. This means that $3n + 2 = 2k + 1$ for some integer $k$. Can we use this fact to show that $n$ is odd? We see that $3n + 1 = 2k$, but there does not seem to be any direct way to conclude that $n$ is odd. Because our attempt at a direct proof failed, we next try a proof by contraposition.

The first step in a proof by contraposition is to assume that the conclusion of the conditional statement "If $3n + 2$ is odd, then $n$ is odd" is false; namely, assume that $n$ is even. Then, by the definition of an even integer, $n = 2k$ for some integer $k$. Substituting $2k$ for $n$, we find that $3n + 2 = 3(2k) + 2 = 6k + 2 = 2(3k + 1)$. This tells us that $3n + 2$ is even (because it is a multiple of 2), and therefore not odd. This is the negation of the premise of the theorem. Because the negation of the conclusion of the conditional statement implies that the hypothesis is false, the original conditional statement is true. Our proof by contraposition succeeded; we have proved the theorem "If $3n + 2$ is odd, then $n$ is odd." ◄

**EXAMPLE 4**    Prove that if $n = ab$, where $a$ and $b$ are positive integers, then $a \leq \sqrt{n}$ or $b \leq \sqrt{n}$.

*Solution:* Because there is no obvious way of showing that $a \leq \sqrt{n}$ or $b \leq \sqrt{n}$ directly from the equation $n = ab$, where $a$ and $b$ are positive integers, we attempt a proof by contraposition.

The first step in a proof by contraposition is to assume that the conclusion of the conditional statement "If $n = ab$, where $a$ and $b$ are positive integers, then $a \leq \sqrt{n}$ or $b \leq \sqrt{n}$" is false. That is, we assume that the statement $(a \leq \sqrt{n}) \vee (b \leq \sqrt{n})$ is false. Using the meaning of disjunction together with De Morgan's law, we see that this implies that both $a \leq \sqrt{n}$ and $b \leq \sqrt{n}$ are false. This implies that $a > \sqrt{n}$ and $b > \sqrt{n}$. We can multiply these inequalities together (using the fact that if $0 < s < t$ and $0 < u < v$, then $su < tv$) to obtain $ab > \sqrt{n} \cdot \sqrt{n} = n$. This shows that $ab \neq n$, which contradicts the statement $n = ab$.

Because the negation of the conclusion of the conditional statement implies that the hypothesis is false, the original conditional statement is true. Our proof by contraposition succeeded; we have proved that if $n = ab$, where $a$ and $b$ are positive integers, then $a \leq \sqrt{n}$ or $b \leq \sqrt{n}$. ◄

VACUOUS AND TRIVIAL PROOFS    We can quickly prove that a conditional statement $p \rightarrow q$ is true when we know that $p$ is false, because $p \rightarrow q$ must be true when $p$ is false. Consequently, if we can show that $p$ is false, then we have a proof, called a **vacuous proof**, of the conditional statement $p \rightarrow q$. Vacuous proofs are often used to establish special cases of theorems that state that a conditional statement is true for all positive integers [i.e., a theorem of the kind $\forall n P(n)$, where $P(n)$ is a propositional function]. Proof techniques for theorems of this kind will be discussed in Section 5.1.

**EXAMPLE 5**    Show that the proposition $P(0)$ is true, where $P(n)$ is "If $n > 1$, then $n^2 > n$" and the domain consists of all integers.

*Solution:* Note that $P(0)$ is "If $0 > 1$, then $0^2 > 0$." We can show $P(0)$ using a vacuous proof. Indeed, the hypothesis $0 > 1$ is false. This tells us that $P(0)$ is automatically true. ◄

***Remark:*** The fact that the conclusion of this conditional statement, $0^2 > 0$, is false is irrelevant to the truth value of the conditional statement, because a conditional statement with a false hypothesis is guaranteed to be true.

We can also quickly prove a conditional statement $p \rightarrow q$ if we know that the conclusion $q$ is true. By showing that $q$ is true, it follows that $p \rightarrow q$ must also be true. A proof of $p \rightarrow q$ that uses the fact that $q$ is true is called a **trivial proof**. Trivial proofs are often important when special cases of theorems are proved (see the discussion of proof by cases in Section 1.8) and in mathematical induction, which is a proof technique discussed in Section 5.1.

**EXAMPLE 6**  Let $P(n)$ be "If $a$ and $b$ are positive integers with $a \geq b$, then $a^n \geq b^n$," where the domain consists of all nonnegative integers. Show that $P(0)$ is true.

*Solution:* The proposition $P(0)$ is "If $a \geq b$, then $a^0 \geq b^0$." Because $a^0 = b^0 = 1$, the conclusion of the conditional statement "If $a \geq b$, then $a^0 \geq b^0$" is true. Hence, this conditional statement, which is $P(0)$, is true. This is an example of a trivial proof. Note that the hypothesis, which is the statement "$a \geq b$," was not needed in this proof.  ◀

**A LITTLE PROOF STRATEGY**  We have described two important approaches for proving theorems of the form $\forall x(P(x) \rightarrow Q(x))$: direct proof and proof by contraposition. We have also given examples that show how each is used. However, when you are presented with a theorem of the form $\forall x(P(x) \rightarrow Q(x))$, which method should you use to attempt to prove it? We will provide a few rules of thumb here; in Section 1.8 we will discuss proof strategy at greater length. When you want to prove a statement of the form $\forall x(P(x) \rightarrow Q(x))$, first evaluate whether a direct proof looks promising. Begin by expanding the definitions in the hypotheses. Start to reason using these hypotheses, together with axioms and available theorems. If a direct proof does not seem to go anywhere, try the same thing with a proof by contraposition. Recall that in a proof by contraposition you assume that the conclusion of the conditional statement is false and use a direct proof to show this implies that the hypothesis must be false. We illustrate this strategy in Examples 7 and 8. Before we present our next example, we need a definition.

**DEFINITION 2**  The real number $r$ is *rational* if there exist integers $p$ and $q$ with $q \neq 0$ such that $r = p/q$. A real number that is not rational is called *irrational*.

**EXAMPLE 7**  Prove that the sum of two rational numbers is rational. (Note that if we include the implicit quantifiers here, the theorem we want to prove is "For every real number $r$ and every real number $s$, if $r$ and $s$ are rational numbers, then $r + s$ is rational.)

Extra Examples

*Solution:* We first attempt a direct proof. To begin, suppose that $r$ and $s$ are rational numbers. From the definition of a rational number, it follows that there are integers $p$ and $q$, with $q \neq 0$, such that $r = p/q$, and integers $t$ and $u$, with $u \neq 0$, such that $s = t/u$. Can we use this information to show that $r + s$ is rational? The obvious next step is to add $r = p/q$ and $s = t/u$, to obtain

$$r + s = \frac{p}{q} + \frac{t}{u} = \frac{pu + qt}{qu}.$$

Because $q \neq 0$ and $u \neq 0$, it follows that $qu \neq 0$. Consequently, we have expressed $r + s$ as the ratio of two integers, $pu + qt$ and $qu$, where $qu \neq 0$. This means that $r + s$ is rational. We have proved that the sum of two rational numbers is rational; our attempt to find a direct proof succeeded.  ◀

**EXAMPLE 8**  Prove that if $n$ is an integer and $n^2$ is odd, then $n$ is odd.

*Solution:* We first attempt a direct proof. Suppose that $n$ is an integer and $n^2$ is odd. Then, there exists an integer $k$ such that $n^2 = 2k + 1$. Can we use this information to show that $n$ is odd? There seems to be no obvious approach to show that $n$ is odd because solving for $n$ produces the equation $n = \pm\sqrt{2k + 1}$, which is not terribly useful.

Because this attempt to use a direct proof did not bear fruit, we next attempt a proof by contraposition. We take as our hypothesis the statement that $n$ is not odd. Because every integer is odd or even, this means that $n$ is even. This implies that there exists an integer $k$ such that $n = 2k$. To prove the theorem, we need to show that this hypothesis implies the conclusion that $n^2$ is not odd, that is, that $n^2$ is even. Can we use the equation $n = 2k$ to achieve this? By squaring both sides of this equation, we obtain $n^2 = 4k^2 = 2(2k^2)$, which implies that $n^2$ is also even because $n^2 = 2t$, where $t = 2k^2$. We have proved that if $n$ is an integer and $n^2$ is odd, then $n$ is odd. Our attempt to find a proof by contraposition succeeded.   ◄

## Proofs by Contradiction

Suppose we want to prove that a statement $p$ is true. Furthermore, suppose that we can find a contradiction $q$ such that $\neg p \rightarrow q$ is true. Because $q$ is false, but $\neg p \rightarrow q$ is true, we can conclude that $\neg p$ is false, which means that $p$ is true. How can we find a contradiction $q$ that might help us prove that $p$ is true in this way?

Because the statement $r \wedge \neg r$ is a contradiction whenever $r$ is a proposition, we can prove that $p$ is true if we can show that $\neg p \rightarrow (r \wedge \neg r)$ is true for some proposition $r$. Proofs of this type are called **proofs by contradiction**. Because a proof by contradiction does not prove a result directly, it is another type of indirect proof. We provide three examples of proof by contradiction. The first is an example of an application of the pigeonhole principle, a combinatorial technique that we will cover in depth in Section 6.2.

**EXAMPLE 9**    Show that at least four of any 22 days must fall on the same day of the week.

*Solution:* Let $p$ be the proposition "At least four of 22 chosen days fall on the same day of the week." Suppose that $\neg p$ is true. This means that at most three of the 22 days fall on the same day of the week. Because there are seven days of the week, this implies that at most 21 days could have been chosen, as for each of the days of the week, at most three of the chosen days could fall on that day. This contradicts the premise that we have 22 days under consideration. That is, if $r$ is the statement that 22 days are chosen, then we have shown that $\neg p \rightarrow (r \wedge \neg r)$. Consequently, we know that $p$ is true. We have proved that at least four of 22 chosen days fall on the same day of the week.   ◄

**EXAMPLE 10**    Prove that $\sqrt{2}$ is irrational by giving a proof by contradiction.

*Solution:* Let $p$ be the proposition "$\sqrt{2}$ is irrational." To start a proof by contradiction, we suppose that $\neg p$ is true. Note that $\neg p$ is the statement "It is not the case that $\sqrt{2}$ is irrational," which says that $\sqrt{2}$ is rational. We will show that assuming that $\neg p$ is true leads to a contradiction.

If $\sqrt{2}$ is rational, there exist integers $a$ and $b$ with $\sqrt{2} = a/b$, where $b \neq 0$ and $a$ and $b$ have no common factors (so that the fraction $a/b$ is in lowest terms.) (Here, we are using the fact that every rational number can be written in lowest terms.) Because $\sqrt{2} = a/b$, when both sides of this equation are squared, it follows that

$$2 = \frac{a^2}{b^2}.$$

Hence,

$$2b^2 = a^2.$$

By the definition of an even integer it follows that $a^2$ is even. We next use the fact that if $a^2$ is even, $a$ must also be even, which follows by Exercise 16. Furthermore, because $a$ is even, by the definition of an even integer, $a = 2c$ for some integer $c$. Thus,

$$2b^2 = 4c^2.$$

Dividing both sides of this equation by 2 gives

$$b^2 = 2c^2.$$

By the definition of even, this means that $b^2$ is even. Again using the fact that if the square of an integer is even, then the integer itself must be even, we conclude that $b$ must be even as well.

We have now shown that the assumption of $\neg p$ leads to the equation $\sqrt{2} = a/b$, where $a$ and $b$ have no common factors, but both $a$ and $b$ are even, that is, 2 divides both $a$ and $b$. Note that the statement that $\sqrt{2} = a/b$, where $a$ and $b$ have no common factors, means, in particular, that 2 does not divide both $a$ and $b$. Because our assumption of $\neg p$ leads to the contradiction that 2 divides both $a$ and $b$ and 2 does not divide both $a$ and $b$, $\neg p$ must be false. That is, the statement $p$, "$\sqrt{2}$ is irrational," is true. We have proved that $\sqrt{2}$ is irrational. ◄

Proof by contradiction can be used to prove conditional statements. In such proofs, we first assume the negation of the conclusion. We then use the premises of the theorem and the negation of the conclusion to arrive at a contradiction. (The reason that such proofs are valid rests on the logical equivalence of $p \to q$ and $(p \land \neg q) \to \mathbf{F}$. To see that these statements are equivalent, simply note that each is false in exactly one case, namely when $p$ is true and $q$ is false.)

Note that we can rewrite a proof by contraposition of a conditional statement as a proof by contradiction. In a proof of $p \to q$ by contraposition, we assume that $\neg q$ is true. We then show that $\neg p$ must also be true. To rewrite a proof by contraposition of $p \to q$ as a proof by contradiction, we suppose that both $p$ and $\neg q$ are true. Then, we use the steps from the proof of $\neg q \to \neg p$ to show that $\neg p$ is true. This leads to the contradiction $p \land \neg p$, completing the proof. Example 11 illustrates how a proof by contraposition of a conditional statement can be rewritten as a proof by contradiction.

**EXAMPLE 11**    Give a proof by contradiction of the theorem "If $3n + 2$ is odd, then $n$ is odd."

*Solution:* Let $p$ be "$3n + 2$ is odd" and $q$ be "$n$ is odd." To construct a proof by contradiction, assume that both $p$ and $\neg q$ are true. That is, assume that $3n + 2$ is odd and that $n$ is not odd. Because $n$ is not odd, we know that it is even. Because $n$ is even, there is an integer $k$ such that $n = 2k$. This implies that $3n + 2 = 3(2k) + 2 = 6k + 2 = 2(3k + 1)$. Because $3n + 2$ is $2t$, where $t = 3k + 1$, $3n + 2$ is even. Note that the statement "$3n + 2$ is even" is equivalent to the statement $\neg p$, because an integer is even if and only if it is not odd. Because both $p$ and $\neg p$ are true, we have a contradiction. This completes the proof by contradiction, proving that if $3n + 2$ is odd, then $n$ is odd. ◄

Note that we can also prove by contradiction that $p \to q$ is true by assuming that $p$ and $\neg q$ are true, and showing that $q$ must be also be true. This implies that $\neg q$ and $q$ are both true, a contradiction. This observation tells us that we can turn a direct proof into a proof by contradiction.

PROOFS OF EQUIVALENCE    To prove a theorem that is a biconditional statement, that is, a statement of the form $p \leftrightarrow q$, we show that $p \to q$ and $q \to p$ are both true. The validity of this approach is based on the tautology

$$(p \leftrightarrow q) \leftrightarrow (p \to q) \land (q \to p).$$

**EXAMPLE 12**    Prove the theorem "If $n$ is an integer, then $n$ is odd if and only if $n^2$ is odd."

*Solution:* This theorem has the form "$p$ if and only if $q$," where $p$ is "$n$ is odd" and $q$ is "$n^2$ is odd." (As usual, we do not explicitly deal with the universal quantification.) To prove this theorem, we need to show that $p \to q$ and $q \to p$ are true.

We have already shown (in Example 1) that $p \to q$ is true and (in Example 8) that $q \to p$ is true.

Because we have shown that both $p \to q$ and $q \to p$ are true, we have shown that the theorem is true. ◄

Sometimes a theorem states that several propositions are equivalent. Such a theorem states that propositions $p_1, p_2, p_3, \ldots, p_n$ are equivalent. This can be written as

$$p_1 \leftrightarrow p_2 \leftrightarrow \cdots \leftrightarrow p_n,$$

which states that all $n$ propositions have the same truth values, and consequently, that for all $i$ and $j$ with $1 \leq i \leq n$ and $1 \leq j \leq n$, $p_i$ and $p_j$ are equivalent. One way to prove these mutually equivalent is to use the tautology

$$p_1 \leftrightarrow p_2 \leftrightarrow \cdots \leftrightarrow p_n \leftrightarrow (p_1 \to p_2) \wedge (p_2 \to p_3) \wedge \cdots \wedge (p_n \to p_1).$$

This shows that if the $n$ conditional statements $p_1 \to p_2, p_2 \to p_3, \ldots, p_n \to p_1$ can be shown to be true, then the propositions $p_1, p_2, \ldots, p_n$ are all equivalent.

This is much more efficient than proving that $p_i \to p_j$ for all $i \neq j$ with $1 \leq i \leq n$ and $1 \leq j \leq n$. (Note that there are $n^2 - n$ such conditional statements.)

When we prove that a group of statements are equivalent, we can establish any chain of conditional statements we choose as long as it is possible to work through the chain to go from any one of these statements to any other statement. For example, we can show that $p_1, p_2,$ and $p_3$ are equivalent by showing that $p_1 \to p_3, p_3 \to p_2,$ and $p_2 \to p_1$.

**EXAMPLE 13**    Show that these statements about the integer $n$ are equivalent:

$p_1$:   $n$ is even.
$p_2$:   $n - 1$ is odd.
$p_3$:   $n^2$ is even.

*Solution:* We will show that these three statements are equivalent by showing that the conditional statements $p_1 \to p_2, p_2 \to p_3,$ and $p_3 \to p_1$ are true.

We use a direct proof to show that $p_1 \to p_2$. Suppose that $n$ is even. Then $n = 2k$ for some integer $k$. Consequently, $n - 1 = 2k - 1 = 2(k - 1) + 1$. This means that $n - 1$ is odd because it is of the form $2m + 1$, where $m$ is the integer $k - 1$.

We also use a direct proof to show that $p_2 \to p_3$. Now suppose $n - 1$ is odd. Then $n - 1 = 2k + 1$ for some integer $k$. Hence, $n = 2k + 2$ so that $n^2 = (2k + 2)^2 = 4k^2 + 8k + 4 = 2(2k^2 + 4k + 2)$. This means that $n^2$ is twice the integer $2k^2 + 4k + 2$, and hence is even.

To prove $p_3 \to p_1$, we use a proof by contraposition. That is, we prove that if $n$ is not even, then $n^2$ is not even. This is the same as proving that if $n$ is odd, then $n^2$ is odd, which we have already done in Example 1. This completes the proof.    ◄

COUNTEREXAMPLES    In Section 1.4 we stated that to show that a statement of the form $\forall x P(x)$ is false, we need only find a **counterexample**, that is, an example $x$ for which $P(x)$ is false. When presented with a statement of the form $\forall x P(x)$, which we believe to be false or which has resisted all proof attempts, we look for a counterexample. We illustrate the use of counterexamples in Example 14.

**EXAMPLE 14**    Show that the statement "Every positive integer is the sum of the squares of two integers" is false.

*Solution:* To show that this statement is false, we look for a counterexample, which is a particular integer that is not the sum of the squares of two integers. It does not take long to find a counterexample, because 3 cannot be written as the sum of the squares of two integers. To show this is the case, note that the only perfect squares not exceeding 3 are $0^2 = 0$ and $1^2 = 1$. Furthermore, there is no way to get 3 as the sum of two terms each of which is 0 or 1. Consequently, we have shown that "Every positive integer is the sum of the squares of two integers" is false.    ◄

## Mistakes in Proofs

There are many common errors made in constructing mathematical proofs. We will briefly describe some of these here. Among the most common errors are mistakes in arithmetic and basic algebra. Even professional mathematicians make such errors, especially when working with complicated formulae. Whenever you use such computations you should check them as carefully as possible. (You should also review any troublesome aspects of basic algebra, especially before you study Section 5.1.)

**Links**

Each step of a mathematical proof needs to be correct and the conclusion needs to follow logically from the steps that precede it. Many mistakes result from the introduction of steps that do not logically follow from those that precede it. This is illustrated in Examples 15–17.

**EXAMPLE 15**  What is wrong with this famous supposed "proof" that $1 = 2$?

*"Proof:"* We use these steps, where $a$ and $b$ are two equal positive integers.

| **Step** | **Reason** |
|---|---|
| 1. $a = b$ | Given |
| 2. $a^2 = ab$ | Multiply both sides of (1) by $a$ |
| 3. $a^2 - b^2 = ab - b^2$ | Subtract $b^2$ from both sides of (2) |
| 4. $(a - b)(a + b) = b(a - b)$ | Factor both sides of (3) |
| 5. $a + b = b$ | Divide both sides of (4) by $a - b$ |
| 6. $2b = b$ | Replace $a$ by $b$ in (5) because $a = b$ and simplify |
| 7. $2 = 1$ | Divide both sides of (6) by $b$ |

*Solution:* Every step is valid except for one, step 5 where we divided both sides by $a - b$. The error is that $a - b$ equals zero; division of both sides of an equation by the same quantity is valid as long as this quantity is not zero.    ◀

**EXAMPLE 16**  What is wrong with this "proof?"

"Theorem:" If $n^2$ is positive, then $n$ is positive.

*"Proof:"* Suppose that $n^2$ is positive. Because the conditional statement "If $n$ is positive, then $n^2$ is positive" is true, we can conclude that $n$ is positive.

*Solution:* Let $P(n)$ be "$n$ is positive" and $Q(n)$ be "$n^2$ is positive." Then our hypothesis is $Q(n)$. The statement "If $n$ is positive, then $n^2$ is positive" is the statement $\forall n(P(n) \to Q(n))$. From the hypothesis $Q(n)$ and the statement $\forall n(P(n) \to Q(n))$ we cannot conclude $P(n)$, because we are not using a valid rule of inference. Instead, this is an example of the fallacy of affirming the conclusion. A counterexample is supplied by $n = -1$ for which $n^2 = 1$ is positive, but $n$ is negative.    ◀

**EXAMPLE 17**  What is wrong with this "proof?"

"Theorem:" If $n$ is not positive, then $n^2$ is not positive. (This is the contrapositive of the "theorem" in Example 16.)

*"Proof:"* Suppose that $n$ is not positive. Because the conditional statement "If $n$ is positive, then $n^2$ is positive" is true, we can conclude that $n^2$ is not positive.

*Solution:* Let $P(n)$ and $Q(n)$ be as in the solution of Example 16. Then our hypothesis is $\neg P(n)$ and the statement "If $n$ is positive, then $n^2$ is positive" is the statement $\forall n(P(n) \to Q(n))$. From the hypothesis $\neg P(n)$ and the statement $\forall n(P(n) \to Q(n))$ we cannot conclude $\neg Q(n)$, because we are not using a valid rule of inference. Instead, this is an example of the fallacy of denying the hypothesis. A counterexample is supplied by $n = -1$, as in Example 16.    ◄

Finally, we briefly discuss a particularly nasty type of error. Many incorrect arguments are based on a fallacy called **begging the question**. This fallacy occurs when one or more steps of a proof are based on the truth of the statement being proved. In other words, this fallacy arises when a statement is proved using itself, or a statement equivalent to it. That is why this fallacy is also called **circular reasoning**.

**EXAMPLE 18**    Is the following argument correct? It supposedly shows that $n$ is an even integer whenever $n^2$ is an even integer.

Suppose that $n^2$ is even. Then $n^2 = 2k$ for some integer $k$. Let $n = 2l$ for some integer $l$. This shows that $n$ is even.

*Solution:* This argument is incorrect. The statement "let $n = 2l$ for some integer $l$" occurs in the proof. No argument has been given to show that $n$ can be written as $2l$ for some integer $l$. This is circular reasoning because this statement is equivalent to the statement being proved, namely, "$n$ is even." Of course, the result itself is correct; only the method of proof is wrong.◄

Making mistakes in proofs is part of the learning process. When you make a mistake that someone else finds, you should carefully analyze where you went wrong and make sure that you do not make the same mistake again. Even professional mathematicians make mistakes in proofs. More than a few incorrect proofs of important results have fooled people for many years before subtle errors in them were found.

## Just a Beginning

We have now developed a basic arsenal of proof methods. In the next section we will introduce other important proof methods. We will also introduce several important proof techniques in Chapter 5, including mathematical induction, which can be used to prove results that hold for all positive integers. In Chapter 6 we will introduce the notion of combinatorial proofs.

In this section we introduced several methods for proving theorems of the form $\forall x(P(x) \to Q(x))$, including direct proofs and proofs by contraposition. There are many theorems of this type whose proofs are easy to construct by directly working through the hypotheses and definitions of the terms of the theorem. However, it is often difficult to prove a theorem without resorting to a clever use of a proof by contraposition or a proof by contradiction, or some other proof technique. In Section 1.8 we will address proof strategy. We will describe various approaches that can be used to find proofs when straightforward approaches do not work. Constructing proofs is an art that can be learned only through experience, including writing proofs, having your proofs critiqued, and reading and analyzing other proofs.

# Exercises

1. Use a direct proof to show that the sum of two odd integers is even.

2. Use a direct proof to show that the sum of two even integers is even.

3. Show that the square of an even number is an even number using a direct proof.

4. Show that the additive inverse, or negative, of an even number is an even number using a direct proof.

5. Prove that if $m + n$ and $n + p$ are even integers, where $m$, $n$, and $p$ are integers, then $m + p$ is even. What kind of proof did you use?

6. Use a direct proof to show that the product of two odd numbers is odd.

7. Use a direct proof to show that every odd integer is the difference of two squares.

8. Prove that if $n$ is a perfect square, then $n + 2$ is not a perfect square.

9. Use a proof by contradiction to prove that the sum of an irrational number and a rational number is irrational.

10. Use a direct proof to show that the product of two rational numbers is rational.

11. Prove or disprove that the product of two irrational numbers is irrational.

12. Prove or disprove that the product of a nonzero rational number and an irrational number is irrational.

13. Prove that if $x$ is irrational, then $1/x$ is irrational.

14. Prove that if $x$ is rational and $x \neq 0$, then $1/x$ is rational.

15. Use a proof by contraposition to show that if $x + y \geq 2$, where $x$ and $y$ are real numbers, then $x \geq 1$ or $y \geq 1$.

16. Prove that if $m$ and $n$ are integers and $mn$ is even, then $m$ is even or $n$ is even.

17. Show that if $n$ is an integer and $n^3 + 5$ is odd, then $n$ is even using

    a) a proof by contraposition.
    b) a proof by contradiction.

18. Prove that if $n$ is an integer and $3n + 2$ is even, then $n$ is even using

    a) a proof by contraposition.
    b) a proof by contradiction.

19. Prove the proposition $P(0)$, where $P(n)$ is the proposition "If $n$ is a positive integer greater than 1, then $n^2 > n$." What kind of proof did you use?

20. Prove the proposition $P(1)$, where $P(n)$ is the proposition "If $n$ is a positive integer, then $n^2 \geq n$." What kind of proof did you use?

21. Let $P(n)$ be the proposition "If $a$ and $b$ are positive real numbers, then $(a + b)^n \geq a^n + b^n$." Prove that $P(1)$ is true. What kind of proof did you use?

22. Show that if you pick three socks from a drawer containing just blue socks and black socks, you must get either a pair of blue socks or a pair of black socks.

23. Show that at least ten of any 64 days chosen must fall on the same day of the week.

24. Show that at least three of any 25 days chosen must fall in the same month of the year.

25. Use a proof by contradiction to show that there is no rational number $r$ for which $r^3 + r + 1 = 0$. [*Hint:* Assume that $r = a/b$ is a root, where $a$ and $b$ are integers and $a/b$ is in lowest terms. Obtain an equation involving integers by multiplying by $b^3$. Then look at whether $a$ and $b$ are each odd or even.]

26. Prove that if $n$ is a positive integer, then $n$ is even if and only if $7n + 4$ is even.

27. Prove that if $n$ is a positive integer, then $n$ is odd if and only if $5n + 6$ is odd.

28. Prove that $m^2 = n^2$ if and only if $m = n$ or $m = -n$.

29. Prove or disprove that if $m$ and $n$ are integers such that $mn = 1$, then either $m = 1$ and $n = 1$, or else $m = -1$ and $n = -1$.

30. Show that these three statements are equivalent, where $a$ and $b$ are real numbers: (*i*) $a$ is less than $b$, (*ii*) the average of $a$ and $b$ is greater than $a$, and (*iii*) the average of $a$ and $b$ is less than $b$.

31. Show that these statements about the integer $x$ are equivalent: (*i*) $3x + 2$ is even, (*ii*) $x + 5$ is odd, (*iii*) $x^2$ is even.

32. Show that these statements about the real number $x$ are equivalent: (*i*) $x$ is rational, (*ii*) $x/2$ is rational, (*iii*) $3x - 1$ is rational.

33. Show that these statements about the real number $x$ are equivalent: (*i*) $x$ is irrational, (*ii*) $3x + 2$ is irrational, (*iii*) $x/2$ is irrational.

34. Is this reasoning for finding the solutions of the equation $\sqrt{2x^2 - 1} = x$ correct? (1) $\sqrt{2x^2 - 1} = x$ is given; (2) $2x^2 - 1 = x^2$, obtained by squaring both sides of (1); (3) $x^2 - 1 = 0$, obtained by subtracting $x^2$ from both sides of (2); (4) $(x - 1)(x + 1) = 0$, obtained by factoring the left-hand side of $x^2 - 1$; (5) $x = 1$ or $x = -1$, which follows because $ab = 0$ implies that $a = 0$ or $b = 0$.

35. Are these steps for finding the solutions of $\sqrt{x + 3} = 3 - x$ correct? (*1*) $\sqrt{x + 3} = 3 - x$ is given; (2) $x + 3 = x^2 - 6x + 9$, obtained by squaring both sides of (1); (3) $0 = x^2 - 7x + 6$, obtained by subtracting $x + 3$ from both sides of (2); (4) $0 = (x - 1)(x - 6)$, obtained by factoring the right-hand side of (3); (5) $x = 1$ or $x = 6$, which follows from (4) because $ab = 0$ implies that $a = 0$ or $b = 0$.

36. Show that the propositions $p_1$, $p_2$, $p_3$, and $p_4$ can be shown to be equivalent by showing that $p_1 \leftrightarrow p_4$, $p_2 \leftrightarrow p_3$, and $p_1 \leftrightarrow p_3$.

37. Show that the propositions $p_1$, $p_2$, $p_3$, $p_4$, and $p_5$ can be shown to be equivalent by proving that the conditional statements $p_1 \rightarrow p_4$, $p_3 \rightarrow p_1$, $p_4 \rightarrow p_2$, $p_2 \rightarrow p_5$, and $p_5 \rightarrow p_3$ are true.

**38.** Find a counterexample to the statement that every positive integer can be written as the sum of the squares of three integers.

**39.** Prove that at least one of the real numbers $a_1, a_2, \ldots, a_n$ is greater than or equal to the average of these numbers. What kind of proof did you use?

**40.** Use Exercise 39 to show that if the first 10 positive integers are placed around a circle, in any order, there exist

three integers in consecutive locations around the circle that have a sum greater than or equal to 17.

**41.** Prove that if $n$ is an integer, these four statements are equivalent: (*i*) $n$ is even, (*ii*) $n + 1$ is odd, (*iii*) $3n + 1$ is odd, (*iv*) $3n$ is even.

**42.** Prove that these four statements about the integer $n$ are equivalent: (*i*) $n^2$ is odd, (*ii*) $1 - n$ is even, (*iii*) $n^3$ is odd, (*iv*) $n^2 + 1$ is even.

# 1.8    Proof Methods and Strategy

## Introduction

Assessment

In Section 1.7 we introduced many methods of proof and illustrated how each method can be used. In this section we continue this effort. We will introduce several other commonly used proof methods, including the method of proving a theorem by considering different cases separately. We will also discuss proofs where we prove the existence of objects with desired properties.

In Section 1.7 we briefly discussed the strategy behind constructing proofs. This strategy includes selecting a proof method and then successfully constructing an argument step by step, based on this method. In this section, after we have developed a versatile arsenal of proof methods, we will study some aspects of the art and science of proofs. We will provide advice on how to find a proof of a theorem. We will describe some tricks of the trade, including how proofs can be found by working backward and by adapting existing proofs.

When mathematicians work, they formulate conjectures and attempt to prove or disprove them. We will briefly describe this process here by proving results about tiling checkerboards with dominoes and other types of pieces. Looking at tilings of this kind, we will be able to quickly formulate conjectures and prove theorems without first developing a theory.

We will conclude the section by discussing the role of open questions. In particular, we will discuss some interesting problems either that have been solved after remaining open for hundreds of years or that still remain open.

## Exhaustive Proof and Proof by Cases

Sometimes we cannot prove a theorem using a single argument that holds for all possible cases. We now introduce a method that can be used to prove a theorem, by considering different cases separately. This method is based on a rule of inference that we will now introduce. To prove a conditional statement of the form

$$(p_1 \lor p_2 \lor \cdots \lor p_n) \to q$$

the tautology

$$[(p_1 \lor p_2 \lor \cdots \lor p_n) \to q] \leftrightarrow [(p_1 \to q) \land (p_2 \to q) \land \cdots \land (p_n \to q)]$$

can be used as a rule of inference. This shows that the original conditional statement with a hypothesis made up of a disjunction of the propositions $p_1, p_2, \ldots, p_n$ can be proved by proving each of the $n$ conditional statements $p_i \to q$, $i = 1, 2, \ldots, n$, individually. Such an argument is called a **proof by cases**. Sometimes to prove that a conditional statement $p \to q$ is true, it is convenient to use a disjunction $p_1 \lor p_2 \lor \cdots \lor p_n$ instead of $p$ as the hypothesis of the conditional statement, where $p$ and $p_1 \lor p_2 \lor \cdots \lor p_n$ are equivalent.

**EXHAUSTIVE PROOF**    Some theorems can be proved by examining a relatively small number of examples. Such proofs are called **exhaustive proofs**, or **proofs by exhaustion** because these proofs proceed by exhausting all possibilities. An exhaustive proof is a special type of proof by cases where each case involves checking a single example. We now provide some illustrations of exhaustive proofs.

**EXAMPLE 1**    Prove that $(n + 1)^3 \geq 3^n$ if $n$ is a positive integer with $n \leq 4$.

*Solution:* We use a proof by exhaustion. We only need verify the inequality $(n + 1)^3 \geq 3^n$ when $n = 1, 2, 3$, and 4. For $n = 1$, we have $(n + 1)^3 = 2^3 = 8$ and $3^n = 3^1 = 3$; for $n = 2$, we have $(n + 1)^3 = 3^3 = 27$ and $3^n = 3^2 = 9$; for $n = 3$, we have $(n + 1)^3 = 4^3 = 64$ and $3^n = 3^3 = 27$; and for $n = 4$, we have $(n + 1)^3 = 5^3 = 125$ and $3^n = 3^4 = 81$. In each of these four cases, we see that $(n + 1)^3 \geq 3^n$. We have used the method of exhaustion to prove that $(n + 1)^3 \geq 3^n$ if $n$ is a positive integer with $n \leq 4$.    ◄

**EXAMPLE 2**    Prove that the only consecutive positive integers not exceeding 100 that are perfect powers are 8 and 9. (An integer is a **perfect power** if it equals $n^a$, where $a$ is an integer greater than 1.)

*Solution:* We use a proof by exhaustion. In particular, we can prove this fact by examining positive integers $n$ not exceeding 100, first checking whether $n$ is a perfect power, and if it is, checking whether $n + 1$ is also a perfect power. A quicker way to do this is simply to look at all perfect powers not exceeding 100 and checking whether the next largest integer is also a perfect power. The squares of positive integers not exceeding 100 are 1, 4, 9, 16, 25, 36, 49, 64, 81, and 100. The cubes of positive integers not exceeding 100 are 1, 8, 27, and 64. The fourth powers of positive integers not exceeding 100 are 1, 16, and 81. The fifth powers of positive integers not exceeding 100 are 1 and 32. The sixth powers of positive integers not exceeding 100 are 1 and 64. There are no powers of positive integers higher than the sixth power not exceeding 100, other than 1. Looking at this list of perfect powers not exceeding 100, we see that $n = 8$ is the only perfect power $n$ for which $n + 1$ is also a perfect power. That is, $2^3 = 8$ and $3^2 = 9$ are the only two consecutive perfect powers not exceeding 100.    ◄

Proofs by exhaustion can tire out people and computers when the number of cases challenges the available processing power!

   People can carry out exhaustive proofs when it is necessary to check only a relatively small number of instances of a statement. Computers do not complain when they are asked to check a much larger number of instances of a statement, but they still have limitations. Note that not even a computer can check all instances when it is impossible to list all instances to check.

**PROOF BY CASES**    A proof by cases must cover all possible cases that arise in a theorem. We illustrate proof by cases with a couple of examples. In each example, you should check that all possible cases are covered.

**EXAMPLE 3**    Prove that if $n$ is an integer, then $n^2 \geq n$.

*Solution:* We can prove that $n^2 \geq n$ for every integer by considering three cases, when $n = 0$, when $n \geq 1$, and when $n \leq -1$. We split the proof into three cases because it is straightforward to prove the result by considering zero, positive integers, and negative integers separately.

   *Case (i):* When $n = 0$, because $0^2 = 0$, we see that $0^2 \geq 0$. It follows that $n^2 \geq n$ is true in this case.

   *Case (ii):* When $n \geq 1$, when we multiply both sides of the inequality $n \geq 1$ by the positive integer $n$, we obtain $n \cdot n \geq n \cdot 1$. This implies that $n^2 \geq n$ for $n \geq 1$.

   *Case (iii):* In this case $n \leq -1$. However, $n^2 \geq 0$. It follows that $n^2 \geq n$.

Because the inequality $n^2 \geq n$ holds in all three cases, we can conclude that if $n$ is an integer, then $n^2 \geq n$.    ◄

**EXAMPLE 4**    Use a proof by cases to show that $|xy| = |x||y|$, where $x$ and $y$ are real numbers. (Recall that $|a|$, the absolute value of $a$, equals $a$ when $a \geq 0$ and equals $-a$ when $a \leq 0$.)

*Solution:* In our proof of this theorem, we remove absolute values using the fact that $|a| = a$ when $a \geq 0$ and $|a| = -a$ when $a < 0$. Because both $|x|$ and $|y|$ occur in our formula, we will need four cases: *(i)* $x$ and $y$ both nonnegative, *(ii)* $x$ nonnegative and $y$ is negative, *(iii)* $x$ negative and $y$ nonnegative, and *(iv)* $x$ negative and $y$ negative. We denote by $p_1$, $p_2$, $p_3$, and $p_4$, the proposition stating the assumption for each of these four cases, respectively.

(Note that we can remove the absolute value signs by making the appropriate choice of signs within each case.)

Case (i): We see that $p_1 \rightarrow q$ because $xy \geq 0$ when $x \geq 0$ and $y \geq 0$, so that $|xy| = xy = |x||y|$.

Case (ii): To see that $p_2 \rightarrow q$, note that if $x \geq 0$ and $y < 0$, then $xy \leq 0$, so that $|xy| = -xy = x(-y) = |x||y|$. (Here, because $y < 0$, we have $|y| = -y$.)

Case (iii): To see that $p_3 \rightarrow q$, we follow the same reasoning as the previous case with the roles of $x$ and $y$ reversed.

Case (iv): To see that $p_4 \rightarrow q$, note that when $x < 0$ and $y < 0$, it follows that $xy > 0$. Hence, $|xy| = xy = (-x)(-y) = |x||y|$.

Because $|xy| = |x||y|$ holds in each of the four cases and these cases exhaust all possibilities, we can conclude that $|xy| = |x||y|$, whenever $x$ and $y$ are real numbers.    ◀

**LEVERAGING PROOF BY CASES**    The examples we have presented illustrating proof by cases provide some insight into when to use this method of proof. In particular, when it is not possible to consider all cases of a proof at the same time, a proof by cases should be considered. When should you use such a proof? Generally, look for a proof by cases when there is no obvious way to begin a proof, but when extra information in each case helps move the proof forward. Example 5 illustrates how the method of proof by cases can be used effectively.

**EXAMPLE 5**    Formulate a conjecture about the final decimal digit of the square of an integer and prove your result.

*Solution:* The smallest perfect squares are $1, 4, 9, 16, 25, 36, 49, 64, 81, 100, 121, 144, 169, 196, 225$, and so on. We notice that the digits that occur as the final digit of a square are $0, 1, 4, 5, 6$, and $9$, with $2, 3, 7$, and $8$ never appearing as the final digit of a square. We conjecture this theorem: The final decimal digit of a perfect square is $0, 1, 4, 5, 6$ or $9$. How can we prove this theorem?

We first note that we can express an integer $n$ as $10a + b$, where $a$ and $b$ are positive integers and $b$ is $0, 1, 2, 3, 4, 5, 6, 7, 8$, or $9$. Here $a$ is the integer obtained by subtracting the final decimal digit of $n$ from $n$ and dividing by 10. Next, note that $(10a + b)^2 = 100a^2 + 20ab + b^2 = 10(10a^2 + 2b) + b^2$, so that the final decimal digit of $n^2$ is the same as the final decimal digit of $b^2$. Furthermore, note that the final decimal digit of $b^2$ is the same as the final decimal digit of $(10 - b)^2 = 100 - 20b + b^2$. Consequently, we can reduce our proof to the consideration of six cases.

Case (i): The final digit of $n$ is 1 or 9. Then the final decimal digit of $n^2$ is the final decimal digit of $1^2 = 1$ or $9^2 = 81$, namely 1.

Case (ii): The final digit of $n$ is 2 or 8. Then the final decimal digit of $n^2$ is the final decimal digit of $2^2 = 4$ or $8^2 = 64$, namely 4.

Case (iii): The final digit of $n$ is 3 or 7. Then the final decimal digit of $n^2$ is the final decimal digit of $3^2 = 9$ or $7^2 = 49$, namely 9.

Case (iv): The final digit of $n$ is 4 or 6. Then the final decimal digit of $n^2$ is the final decimal digit of $4^2 = 16$ or $6^2 = 36$, namely 6.

Case (v): The final decimal digit of $n$ is 5. Then the final decimal digit of $n^2$ is the final decimal digit of $5^2 = 25$, namely 5.

*Case (vi):* The final decimal digit of $n$ is 0. Then the final decimal digit of $n^2$ is the final decimal digit of $0^2 = 0$, namely 0.

Because we have considered all six cases, we can conclude that the final decimal digit of $n^2$, where $n$ is an integer is either 0, 1, 2, 4, 5, 6, or 9. ◀

Sometimes we can eliminate all but a few examples in a proof by cases, as Example 6 illustrates.

**EXAMPLE 6** Show that there are no solutions in integers $x$ and $y$ of $x^2 + 3y^2 = 8$.

*Solution:* We can quickly reduce a proof to checking just a few simple cases because $x^2 > 8$ when $|x| \geq 3$ and $3y^2 > 8$ when $|y| \geq 2$. This leaves the cases when $x$ equals $-2, -1, 0, 1$, or 2 and $y$ equals $-1, 0$, or 1. We can finish using an exhaustive proof. To dispense with the remaining cases, we note that possible values for $x^2$ are 0, 1, and 4, and possible values for $3y^2$ are 0 and 3, and the largest sum of possible values for $x^2$ and $3y^2$ is 7. Consequently, it is impossible for $x^2 + 3y^2 = 8$ to hold when $x$ and $y$ are integers. ◀

WITHOUT LOSS OF GENERALITY  In the proof in Example 4, we dismissed case (*iii*), where $x < 0$ and $y \geq 0$, because it is the same as case (*ii*), where $x \geq 0$ and $y < 0$, with the roles of $x$ and $y$ reversed. To shorten the proof, we could have proved cases (*ii*) and (*iii*) together by assuming, **without loss of generality**, that $x \geq 0$ and $y < 0$. Implicit in this statement is that we can complete the case with $x < 0$ and $y \geq 0$ using the same argument as we used for the case with $x \geq 0$ and $y < 0$, but with the obvious changes.

In a proof by cases be sure not to omit any cases and check that you have proved all cases correctly!

In general, when the phrase "without loss of generality" is used in a proof (often abbreviated as WLOG), we assert that by proving one case of a theorem, no additional argument is required to prove other specified cases. That is, other cases follow by making straightforward changes to the argument, or by filling in some straightforward initial step. Proofs by cases can often be made much more efficient when the notion of without loss of generality is employed. Of course, incorrect use of this principle can lead to unfortunate errors. Sometimes assumptions are made that lead to a loss in generality. Such assumptions can be made that do not take into account that one case may be substantially different from others. This can lead to an incomplete, and possibly unsalvageable, proof. In fact, many incorrect proofs of famous theorems turned out to rely on arguments that used the idea of "without loss of generality" to establish cases that could not be quickly proved from simpler cases.

We now illustrate a proof where without loss of generality is used effectively together with other proof techniques.

**EXAMPLE 7** Show that if $x$ and $y$ are integers and both $xy$ and $x + y$ are even, then both $x$ and $y$ are even.

*Solution:* We will use proof by contraposition, the notion of without loss of generality, and proof by cases. First, suppose that $x$ and $y$ are not both even. That is, assume that $x$ is odd or that $y$ is odd (or both). Without loss of generality, we assume that $x$ is odd, so that $x = 2m + 1$ for some integer $k$.

To complete the proof, we need to show that $xy$ is odd or $x + y$ is odd. Consider two cases: (i) $y$ even, and (ii) $y$ odd. In (i), $y = 2n$ for some integer $n$, so that $x + y = (2m + 1) + 2n = 2(m + n) + 1$ is odd. In (ii), $y = 2n + 1$ for some integer $n$, so that $xy = (2m + 1)(2n + 1) = 4mn + 2m + 2n + 1 = 2(2mn + m + n) + 1$ is odd. This completes the proof by contraposition. (Note that our use of without loss of generality within the proof is justified because the proof when $y$ is odd can be obtained by simply interchanging the roles of $x$ and $y$ in the proof we have given.) ◀

COMMON ERRORS WITH EXHAUSTIVE PROOF AND PROOF BY CASES  A common error of reasoning is to draw incorrect conclusions from examples. No matter how many separate examples are considered, a theorem is not proved by considering examples unless every possible case is covered. The problem of proving a theorem is analogous to showing that a computer program always produces the output desired. No matter how many input values are tested, unless all input values are tested, we cannot conclude that the program always produces the correct output.

**EXAMPLE 8**    Is it true that every positive integer is the sum of 18 fourth powers of integers?

*Solution:* To determine whether a positive integer $n$ can be written as the sum of 18 fourth powers of integers, we might begin by examining whether $n$ is the sum of 18 fourth powers of integers for the smallest positive integers. Because the fourth powers of integers are 0, 1, 16, 81, . . . , if we can select 18 terms from these numbers that add up to $n$, then $n$ is the sum of 18 fourth powers. We can show that all positive integers up to 78 can be written as the sum of 18 fourth powers. (The details are left to the reader.) However, if we decided this was enough checking, we would come to the wrong conclusion. It is not true that every positive integer is the sum of 18 fourth powers because 79 is not the sum of 18 fourth powers (as the reader can verify).    ◀

Another common error involves making unwarranted assumptions that lead to incorrect proofs by cases where not all cases are considered. This is illustrated in Example 9.

**EXAMPLE 9**    What is wrong with this "proof?"

"Theorem:"  If $x$ is a real number, then $x^2$ is a positive real number.

*"Proof:"* Let $p_1$ be "$x$ is positive," let $p_2$ be "$x$ is negative," and let $q$ be "$x^2$ is positive." To show that $p_1 \rightarrow q$ is true, note that when $x$ is positive, $x^2$ is positive because it is the product of two positive numbers, $x$ and $x$. To show that $p_2 \rightarrow q$, note that when $x$ is negative, $x^2$ is positive because it is the product of two negative numbers, $x$ and $x$. This completes the proof.

*Solution:* The problem with this "proof" is that we missed the case of $x = 0$. When $x = 0$, $x^2 = 0$ is not positive, so the supposed theorem is false. If $p$ is "$x$ is a real number," then we can prove results where $p$ is the hypothesis with three cases, $p_1$, $p_2$, and $p_3$, where $p_1$ is "$x$ is positive," $p_2$ is "$x$ is negative," and $p_3$ is "$x = 0$" because of the equivalence $p \leftrightarrow p_1 \vee p_2 \vee p_3$.    ◀

## Existence Proofs

Many theorems are assertions that objects of a particular type exist. A theorem of this type is a proposition of the form $\exists x P(x)$, where $P$ is a predicate. A proof of a proposition of the form $\exists x P(x)$ is called an **existence proof**. There are several ways to prove a theorem of this type. Sometimes an existence proof of $\exists x P(x)$ can be given by finding an element $a$, called a **witness**, such that $P(a)$ is true. This type of existence proof is called **constructive**. It is also possible to give an existence proof that is **nonconstructive**; that is, we do not find an element $a$ such that $P(a)$ is true, but rather prove that $\exists x P(x)$ is true in some other way. One common method of giving a nonconstructive existence proof is to use proof by contradiction and show that the negation of the existential quantification implies a contradiction. The concept of a constructive existence proof is illustrated by Example 10 and the concept of a nonconstructive existence proof is illustrated by Example 11.

**EXAMPLE 10**    **A Constructive Existence Proof**    Show that there is a positive integer that can be written as the sum of cubes of positive integers in two different ways.

*Solution:* After considerable computation (such as a computer search) we find that

$$1729 = 10^3 + 9^3 = 12^3 + 1^3.$$

Because we have displayed a positive integer that can be written as the sum of cubes in two different ways, we are done.

There is an interesting story pertaining to this example. The English mathematician G. H. Hardy, when visiting the ailing Indian prodigy Ramanujan in the hospital, remarked that 1729, the number of the cab he took, was rather dull. Ramanujan replied "No, it is a very interesting number; it is the smallest number expressible as the sum of cubes in two different ways." ◀

**EXAMPLE 11**   **A Nonconstructive Existence Proof**   Show that there exist irrational numbers $x$ and $y$ such that $x^y$ is rational.

*Solution:* By Example 10 in Section 1.7 we know that $\sqrt{2}$ is irrational. Consider the number $\sqrt{2}^{\sqrt{2}}$. If it is rational, we have two irrational numbers $x$ and $y$ with $x^y$ rational, namely, $x = \sqrt{2}$ and $y = \sqrt{2}$. On the other hand if $\sqrt{2}^{\sqrt{2}}$ is irrational, then we can let $x = \sqrt{2}^{\sqrt{2}}$ and $y = \sqrt{2}$ so that $x^y = (\sqrt{2}^{\sqrt{2}})^{\sqrt{2}} = \sqrt{2}^{(\sqrt{2} \cdot \sqrt{2})} = \sqrt{2}^2 = 2$.

This proof is an example of a nonconstructive existence proof because we have not found irrational numbers $x$ and $y$ such that $x^y$ is rational. Rather, we have shown that either the pair $x = \sqrt{2}$, $y = \sqrt{2}$ or the pair $x = \sqrt{2}^{\sqrt{2}}$, $y = \sqrt{2}$ have the desired property, but we do not know which of these two pairs works! ◀

GODFREY HAROLD HARDY (1877–1947)   Hardy, born in Cranleigh, Surrey, England, was the older of two children of Isaac Hardy and Sophia Hall Hardy. His father was the geography and drawing master at the Cranleigh School and also gave singing lessons and played soccer. His mother gave piano lessons and helped run a boardinghouse for young students. Hardy's parents were devoted to their children's education. Hardy demonstrated his numerical ability at the early age of two when he began writing down numbers into the millions. He had a private mathematics tutor rather than attending regular classes at the Cranleigh School. He moved to Winchester College, a private high school, when he was 13 and was awarded a scholarship. He excelled in his studies and demonstrated a strong interest in mathematics. He entered Trinity College, Cambridge, in 1896 on a scholarship and won several prizes during his time there, graduating in 1899.

Hardy held the position of lecturer in mathematics at Trinity College at Cambridge University from 1906 to 1919, when he was appointed to the Sullivan chair of geometry at Oxford. He had become unhappy with Cambridge over the dismissal of the famous philosopher and mathematician Bertrand Russell from Trinity for antiwar activities and did not like a heavy load of administrative duties. In 1931 he returned to Cambridge as the Sadleirian professor of pure mathematics, where he remained until his retirement in 1942. He was a pure mathematician and held an elitist view of mathematics, hoping that his research could never be applied. Ironically, he is perhaps best known as one of the developers of the Hardy–Weinberg law, which predicts patterns of inheritance. His work in this area appeared as a letter to the journal *Science* in which he used simple algebraic ideas to demonstrate errors in an article on genetics. Hardy worked primarily in number theory and function theory, exploring such topics as the Riemann zeta function, Fourier series, and the distribution of primes. He made many important contributions to many important problems, such as Waring's problem about representing positive integers as sums of $k$th powers and the problem of representing odd integers as sums of three primes. Hardy is also remembered for his collaborations with John E. Littlewood, a colleague at Cambridge, with whom he wrote more than 100 papers, and the famous Indian mathematical prodigy Srinivasa Ramanujan. His collaboration with Littlewood led to the joke that there were only three important English mathematicians at that time, Hardy, Littlewood, and Hardy–Littlewood, although some people thought that Hardy had invented a fictitious person, Littlewood, because Littlewood was seldom seen outside Cambridge. Hardy had the wisdom of recognizing Ramanujan's genius from unconventional but extremely creative writings Ramanujan sent him, while other mathematicians failed to see the genius. Hardy brought Ramanujan to Cambridge and collaborated on important joint papers, establishing new results on the number of partitions of an integer. Hardy was interested in mathematics education, and his book *A Course of Pure Mathematics* had a profound effect on undergraduate instruction in mathematics in the first half of the twentieth century. Hardy also wrote *A Mathematician's Apology*, in which he gives his answer to the question of whether it is worthwhile to devote one's life to the study of mathematics. It presents Hardy's view of what mathematics is and what a mathematician does.

Hardy had a strong interest in sports. He was an avid cricket fan and followed scores closely. One peculiar trait he had was that he did not like his picture taken (only five snapshots are known) and disliked mirrors, covering them with towels immediately upon entering a hotel room.

Nonconstructive existence proofs often are quite subtle, as Example 12 illustrates.

**EXAMPLE 12**

**Chomp** is a game played by two players. In this game, cookies are laid out on a rectangular grid. The cookie in the top left position is poisoned, as shown in Figure 1(a). The two players take turns making moves; at each move, a player is required to eat a remaining cookie, together with all cookies to the right and/or below it (see Figure 1(b), for example). The loser is the player who has no choice but to eat the poisoned cookie. We ask whether one of the two players has a winning strategy. That is, can one of the players always make moves that are guaranteed to lead to a win?

*Solution:* We will give a nonconstructive existence proof of a winning strategy for the first player. That is, we will show that the first player always has a winning strategy without explicitly describing the moves this player must follow.

First, note that the game ends and cannot finish in a draw because with each move at least one cookie is eaten, so after no more than $m \times n$ moves the game ends, where the initial grid is $m \times n$. Now, suppose that the first player begins the game by eating just the cookie in the bottom right corner. There are two possibilities, this is the first move of a winning strategy for the first player, or the second player can make a move that is the first move of a winning strategy for the second player. In this second case, instead of eating just the cookie in the bottom right corner, the first player could have made the same move that the second player made as the first

SRINIVASA RAMANUJAN (1887–1920)   The famous mathematical prodigy Ramanujan was born and raised in southern India near the city of Madras (now called Chennai). His father was a clerk in a cloth shop. His mother contributed to the family income by singing at a local temple. Ramanujan studied at the local English language school, displaying his talent and interest for mathematics. At the age of 13 he mastered a textbook used by college students. When he was 15, a university student lent him a copy of *Synopsis of Pure Mathematics*. Ramanujan decided to work out the over 6000 results in this book, stated without proof or explanation, writing on sheets later collected to form notebooks. He graduated from high school in 1904, winning a scholarship to the University of Madras. Enrolling in a fine arts curriculum, he neglected his subjects other than mathematics and lost his scholarship. He failed to pass examinations at the university four times from 1904 to 1907, doing well only in mathematics. During this time he filled his notebooks with original writings, sometimes rediscovering already published work and at other times making new discoveries.

Without a university degree, it was difficult for Ramanujan to find a decent job. To survive, he had to depend on the goodwill of his friends. He tutored students in mathematics, but his unconventional ways of thinking and failure to stick to the syllabus caused problems. He was married in 1909 in an arranged marriage to a young woman nine years his junior. Needing to support himself and his wife, he moved to Madras and sought a job. He showed his notebooks of mathematical writings to his potential employers, but the books bewildered them. However, a professor at the Presidency College recognized his genius and supported him, and in 1912 he found work as an accounts clerk, earning a small salary.

Ramanujan continued his mathematical work during this time and published his first paper in 1910 in an Indian journal. He realized that his work was beyond that of Indian mathematicians and decided to write to leading English mathematicians. The first mathematicians he wrote to turned down his request for help. But in January 1913 he wrote to G. H. Hardy, who was inclined to turn Ramanujan down, but the mathematical statements in the letter, although stated without proof, puzzled Hardy. He decided to examine them closely with the help of his colleague and collaborator J. E. Littlewood. They decided, after careful study, that Ramanujan was probably a genius, because his statements "could only be written down by a mathematician of the highest class; they must be true, because if they were not true, no one would have the imagination to invent them."

Hardy arranged a scholarship for Ramanujan, bringing him to England in 1914. Hardy personally tutored him in mathematical analysis, and they collaborated for five years, proving significant theorems about the number of partitions of integers. During this time, Ramanujan made important contributions to number theory and also worked on continued fractions, infinite series, and elliptic functions. Ramanujan had amazing insight involving certain types of functions and series, but his purported theorems on prime numbers were often wrong, illustrating his vague idea of what constitutes a correct proof. He was one of the youngest members ever appointed a Fellow of the Royal Society. Unfortunately, in 1917 Ramanujan became extremely ill. At the time, it was thought that he had trouble with the English climate and had contracted tuberculosis. It is now thought that he suffered from a vitamin deficiency, brought on by Ramanujan's strict vegetarianism and shortages in wartime England. He returned to India in 1919, continuing to do mathematics even when confined to his bed. He was religious and thought his mathematical talent came from his family deity, Namagiri. He considered mathematics and religion to be linked. He said that "an equation for me has no meaning unless it expresses a thought of God." His short life came to an end in April 1920, when he was 32 years old. Ramanujan left several notebooks of unpublished results. The writings in these notebooks illustrate Ramanujan's insights but are quite sketchy. Several mathematicians have devoted many years of study to explaining and justifying the results in these notebooks.

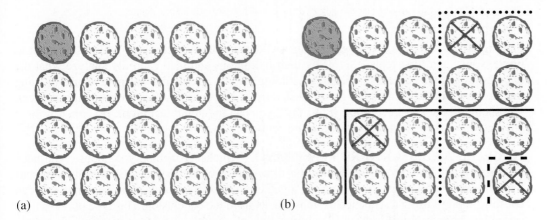

FIGURE 1    (a) Chomp (Top Left Cookie Poisoned).    (b) Three Possible Moves.

move of a winning strategy (and then continued to follow that winning strategy). This would guarantee a win for the first player.

Note that we showed that a winning strategy exists, but we did not specify an actual winning strategy. Consequently, the proof is a nonconstructive existence proof. In fact, no one has been able to describe a winning strategy for that Chomp that applies for all rectangular grids by describing the moves that the first player should follow. However, winning strategies can be described for certain special cases, such as when the grid is square and when the grid only has two rows of cookies (see Exercises 15 and 16 in Section 5.2).    ◀

## Uniqueness Proofs

Some theorems assert the existence of a unique element with a particular property. In other words, these theorems assert that there is exactly one element with this property. To prove a statement of this type we need to show that an element with this property exists and that no other element has this property. The two parts of a **uniqueness proof** are:

*Existence:*    We show that an element $x$ with the desired property exists.
*Uniqueness:*    We show that if $y \neq x$, then $y$ does not have the desired property.

Equivalently, we can show that if $x$ and $y$ both have the desired property, then $x = y$.

***Remark:*** Showing that there is a unique element $x$ such that $P(x)$ is the same as proving the statement $\exists x (P(x) \land \forall y (y \neq x \rightarrow \neg P(y)))$.

We illustrate the elements of a uniqueness proof in Example 13.

EXAMPLE 13    Show that if $a$ and $b$ are real numbers and $a \neq 0$, then there is a unique real number $r$ such that $ar + b = 0$.

*Solution:* First, note that the real number $r = -b/a$ is a solution of $ar + b = 0$ because $a(-b/a) + b = -b + b = 0$. Consequently, a real number $r$ exists for which $ar + b = 0$. This is the existence part of the proof.

Second, suppose that $s$ is a real number such that $as + b = 0$. Then $ar + b = as + b$, where $r = -b/a$. Subtracting $b$ from both sides, we find that $ar = as$. Dividing both sides of this last equation by $a$, which is nonzero, we see that $r = s$. This means that if $s \neq r$, then $as + b \neq 0$. This establishes the uniqueness part of the proof.    ◀

Extra
Examples

# Proof Strategies

Finding proofs can be a challenging business. When you are confronted with a statement to prove, you should first replace terms by their definitions and then carefully analyze what the hypotheses and the conclusion mean. After doing so, you can attempt to prove the result using one of the available methods of proof. Generally, if the statement is a conditional statement, you should first try a direct proof; if this fails, you can try an indirect proof. If neither of these approaches works, you might try a proof by contradiction.

FORWARD AND BACKWARD REASONING   Whichever method you choose, you need a starting point for your proof. To begin a direct proof of a conditional statement, you start with the premises. Using these premises, together with axioms and known theorems, you can construct a proof using a sequence of steps that leads to the conclusion. This type of reasoning, called *forward reasoning*, is the most common type of reasoning used to prove relatively simple results. Similarly, with indirect reasoning you can start with the negation of the conclusion and, using a sequence of steps, obtain the negation of the premises.

Unfortunately, forward reasoning is often difficult to use to prove more complicated results, because the reasoning needed to reach the desired conclusion may be far from obvious. In such cases it may be helpful to use *backward reasoning*. To reason backward to prove a statement $q$, we find a statement $p$ that we can prove with the property that $p \rightarrow q$. (Note that it is not helpful to find a statement $r$ that you can prove such that $q \rightarrow r$, because it is the fallacy of begging the question to conclude from $q \rightarrow r$ and $r$ that $q$ is true.) Backward reasoning is illustrated in Examples 14 and 15.

**EXAMPLE 14**    Given two positive real numbers $x$ and $y$, their **arithmetic mean** is $(x + y)/2$ and their **geometric mean** is $\sqrt{xy}$. When we compare the arithmetic and geometric means of pairs of distinct positive real numbers, we find that the arithmetic mean is always greater than the geometric mean. [For example, when $x = 4$ and $y = 6$, we have $5 = (4 + 6)/2 > \sqrt{4 \cdot 6} = \sqrt{24}$.] Can we prove that this inequality is always true?

*Solution:* To prove that $(x + y)/2 > \sqrt{xy}$ when $x$ and $y$ are distinct positive real numbers, we can work backward. We construct a sequence of equivalent inequalities. The equivalent inequalities are

$$(x + y)/2 > \sqrt{xy},$$
$$(x + y)^2/4 > xy,$$
$$(x + y)^2 > 4xy,$$
$$x^2 + 2xy + y^2 > 4xy,$$
$$x^2 - 2xy + y^2 > 0,$$
$$(x - y)^2 > 0.$$

Extra Examples

Because $(x - y)^2 > 0$ when $x \neq y$, it follows that the final inequality is true. Because all these inequalities are equivalent, it follows that $(x + y)/2 > \sqrt{xy}$ when $x \neq y$. Once we have carried out this backward reasoning, we can easily reverse the steps to construct a proof using forward reasoning. We now give this proof.

Suppose that $x$ and $y$ are distinct positive real numbers. Then $(x - y)^2 > 0$ because the square of a nonzero real number is positive (see Appendix 1). Because $(x - y)^2 = x^2 - 2xy + y^2$, this implies that $x^2 - 2xy + y^2 > 0$. Adding $4xy$ to both sides, we obtain $x^2 + 2xy + y^2 > 4xy$. Because $x^2 + 2xy + y^2 = (x + y)^2$, this means that $(x + y)^2 \geq 4xy$. Dividing both sides of this equation by 4, we see that $(x + y)^2/4 > xy$. Finally, taking square roots of both sides (which preserves the inequality because both sides are positive) yields

$(x + y)/2 > \sqrt{xy}$. We conclude that if $x$ and $y$ are distinct positive real numbers, then their arithmetic mean $(x + y)/2$ is greater than their geometric mean $\sqrt{xy}$.    ◀

**EXAMPLE 15**    Suppose that two people play a game taking turns removing one, two, or three stones at a time from a pile that begins with 15 stones. The person who removes the last stone wins the game. Show that the first player can win the game no matter what the second player does.

*Solution:* To prove that the first player can always win the game, we work backward. At the last step, the first player can win if this player is left with a pile containing one, two, or three stones. The second player will be forced to leave one, two, or three stones if this player has to remove stones from a pile containing four stones. Consequently, one way for the first person to win is to leave four stones for the second player on the next-to-last move. The first person can leave four stones when there are five, six, or seven stones left at the beginning of this player's move, which happens when the second player has to remove stones from a pile with eight stones. Consequently, to force the second player to leave five, six, or seven stones, the first player should leave eight stones for the second player at the second-to-last move for the first player. This means that there are nine, ten, or eleven stones when the first player makes this move. Similarly, the first player should leave twelve stones when this player makes the first move. We can reverse this argument to show that the first player can always make moves so that this player wins the game no matter what the second player does. These moves successively leave twelve, eight, and four stones for the second player.    ◀

ADAPTING EXISTING PROOFS    An excellent way to look for possible approaches that can be used to prove a statement is to take advantage of existing proofs of similar results. Often an existing proof can be adapted to prove other facts. Even when this is not the case, some of the ideas used in existing proofs may be helpful. Because existing proofs provide clues for new proofs, you should read and understand the proofs you encounter in your studies. This process is illustrated in Example 16.

**EXAMPLE 16**    In Example 10 of Section 1.7 we proved that $\sqrt{2}$ is irrational. We now conjecture that $\sqrt{3}$ is irrational. Can we adapt the proof in Example 10 in Section 1.7 to show that $\sqrt{3}$ is irrational?

Extra
Examples

*Solution:* To adapt the proof in Example 10 in Section 1.7, we begin by mimicking the steps in that proof, but with $\sqrt{2}$ replaced with $\sqrt{3}$. First, we suppose that $\sqrt{3} = d/c$ where the fraction $c/d$ is in lowest terms. Squaring both sides tells us that $3 = c^2/d^2$, so that $3d^2 = c^2$. Can we use this equation to show that 3 must be a factor of both $c$ and $d$, similar to how we used the equation $2b^2 = a^2$ in Example 10 in Section 1.7 to show that 2 must be a factor of both $a$ and $b$? (Recall that an integer $s$ is a factor of the integer $t$ if $t/s$ is an integer. An integer $n$ is even if and only if 2 is a factor of $n$.) In turns out that we can, but we need some ammunition from number theory, which we will develop in Chapter 4. We sketch out the remainder of the proof, but leave the justification of these steps until Chapter 4. Because 3 is a factor of $c^2$, it must also be a factor of $c$. Furthermore, because 3 is a factor of $c$, 9 is a factor of $c^2$, which means that 9 is a factor of $3d^2$. This implies that 3 is a factor of $d^2$, which means that 3 is a factor of that $d$. This makes 3 a factor of both $c$ and $d$, which contradicts the assumption that $c/d$ is in lowest terms. After we have filled in the justification for these steps, we will have shown that $\sqrt{3}$ is irrational by adapting the proof that $\sqrt{2}$ is irrational. Note that this proof can be extended to show that $\sqrt{n}$ is irrational whenever $n$ is a positive integer that is not a perfect square. We leave the details of this to Chapter 4.    ◀

A good tip is to look for existing proofs that you might adapt when you are confronted with proving a new theorem, particularly when the new theorem seems similar to one you have already proved.

## Looking for Counterexamples

In Section 1.7 we introduced the use of counterexamples to show that certain statements are false. When confronted with a conjecture, you might first try to prove this conjecture, and if your attempts are unsuccessful, you might try to find a counterexample, first by looking at the simplest, smallest examples. If you cannot find a counterexample, you might again try to prove the statement. In any case, looking for counterexamples is an extremely important pursuit, which often provides insights into problems. We will illustrate the role of counterexamples in Example 17.

**EXAMPLE 17**    In Example 14 in Section 1.7 we showed that the statement "Every positive integer is the sum of two squares of integers" is false by finding a counterexample. That is, there are positive integers that cannot be written as the sum of the squares of two integers. Although we cannot write every positive integer as the sum of the squares of two integers, maybe we can write every positive integer as the sum of the squares of three integers. That is, is the statement "Every positive integer is the sum of the squares of three integers" true or false?

Extra
Examples

*Solution:* Because we know that not every positive integer can be written as the sum of two squares of integers, we might initially be skeptical that every positive integer can be written as the sum of three squares of integers. So, we first look for a counterexample. That is, we can show that the statement "Every positive integer is the sum of three squares of integers" is false if we can find a particular integer that is not the sum of the squares of three integers. To look for a counterexample, we try to write successive positive integers as a sum of three squares. We find that $1 = 0^2 + 0^2 + 1^2$, $2 = 0^2 + 1^2 + 1^2$, $3 = 1^2 + 1^2 + 1^2$, $4 = 0^2 + 0^2 + 2^2$, $5 = 0^2 + 1^2 + 2^2$, $6 = 1^2 + 1^2 + 2^2$, but we cannot find a way to write 7 as the sum of three squares. To show that there are not three squares that add up to 7, we note that the only possible squares we can use are those not exceeding 7, namely, 0, 1, and 4. Because no three terms where each term is 0, 1, or 4 add up to 7, it follows that 7 is a counterexample. We conclude that the statement "Every positive integer is the sum of the squares of three integers" is false.

We have shown that not every positive integer is the sum of the squares of three integers. The next question to ask is whether every positive integer is the sum of the squares of four positive integers. Some experimentation provides evidence that the answer is yes. For example, $7 = 1^2 + 1^2 + 1^2 + 2^2$, $25 = 4^2 + 2^2 + 2^2 + 1^2$, and $87 = 9^2 + 2^2 + 1^2 + 1^2$. It turns out the conjecture "Every positive integer is the sum of the squares of four integers" is true. For a proof, see [Ro10].    ◀

## Proof Strategy in Action

Mathematics is generally taught as if mathematical facts were carved in stone. Mathematics texts (including the bulk of this book) formally present theorems and their proofs. Such presentations do not convey the discovery process in mathematics. This process begins with exploring concepts and examples, asking questions, formulating conjectures, and attempting to settle these conjectures either by proof or by counterexample. These are the day-to-day activities of mathematicians. Believe it or not, the material taught in textbooks was originally developed in this way.

Extra
Examples

People formulate conjectures on the basis of many types of possible evidence. The examination of special cases can lead to a conjecture, as can the identification of possible patterns. Altering the hypotheses and conclusions of known theorems also can lead to plausible conjectures. At other times, conjectures are made based on intuition or a belief that a result holds. No matter how a conjecture was made, once it has been formulated, the goal is to prove or disprove it. When mathematicians believe that a conjecture may be true, they try to find a proof. If they cannot find a proof, they may look for a counterexample. When they cannot find a counterexample, they may switch gears and once again try to prove the conjecture. Although many conjectures are quickly settled, a few conjectures resist attack for hundreds of years and lead to

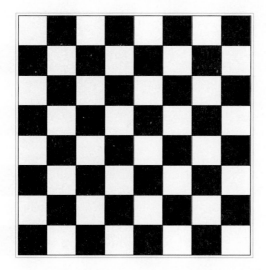

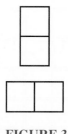

**FIGURE 3**
**Two Dominoes.**

**FIGURE 2    The Standard Checkerboard.**

the development of new parts of mathematics. We will mention a few famous conjectures later in this section.

## Tilings

Links

We can illustrate aspects of proof strategy through a brief study of tilings of checkerboards. Looking at tilings of checkerboards is a fruitful way to quickly discover many different results and construct their proofs using a variety of proof methods. There are almost an endless number of conjectures that can be made and studied in this area too. To begin, we need to define some terms. A **checkerboard** is a rectangle divided into squares of the same size by horizontal and vertical lines. The game of checkers is played on a board with 8 rows and 8 columns; this board is called the **standard checkerboard** and is shown in Figure 2. In this section we use the term **board** to refer to a checkerboard of any rectangular size as well as parts of checkerboards obtained by removing one or more squares. A **domino** is a rectangular piece that is one square by two squares, as shown in Figure 3. We say that a board is **tiled** by dominoes when all its squares are covered with no overlapping dominoes and no dominoes overhanging the board. We now develop some results about tiling boards using dominoes.

EXAMPLE 18    Can we tile the standard checkerboard using dominoes?

*Solution:* We can find many ways to tile the standard checkerboard using dominoes. For example, we can tile it by placing 32 dominoes horizontally, as shown in Figure 4. The existence of one such tiling completes a constructive existence proof. Of course, there are a large number of other ways to do this tiling. We can place 32 dominoes vertically on the board or we can place some tiles vertically and some horizontally. But for a constructive existence proof we needed to find just one such tiling.    ◄

EXAMPLE 19    Can we tile a board obtained by removing one of the four corner squares of a standard checkerboard?

Extra
Examples

*Solution:* To answer this question, note that a standard checkerboard has 64 squares, so removing a square produces a board with 63 squares. Now suppose that we could tile a board obtained from the standard checkerboard by removing a corner square. The board has an even number of

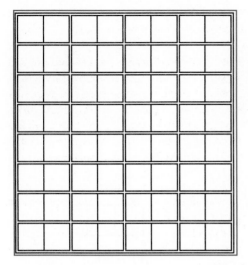

**FIGURE 4    Tiling the Standard Checkerboard.**

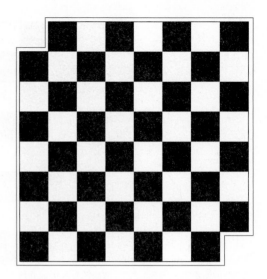

**FIGURE 5    The Standard Checkerboard with the Upper Left and Lower Right Squares Removed.**

squares because each domino covers two squares and no two dominoes overlap and no dominoes overhang the board. Consequently, we can prove by contradiction that a standard checkerboard with one square removed cannot be tiled using dominoes because such a board has an odd number of squares.    ◀

We now consider a trickier situation.

**EXAMPLE 20**    Can we tile the board obtained by deleting the upper left and lower right corner squares of a standard checkerboard, shown in Figure 5?

*Solution:* A board obtained by deleting two squares of a standard checkerboard contains $64 - 2 = 62$ squares. Because 62 is even, we cannot quickly rule out the existence of a tiling of the standard checkerboard with its upper left and lower right squares removed, unlike Example 19, where we ruled out the existence of a tiling of the standard checkerboard with one corner square removed. Trying to construct a tiling of this board by successively placing dominoes might be a first approach, as the reader should attempt. However, no matter how much we try, we cannot find such a tiling. Because our efforts do not produce a tiling, we are led to conjecture that no tiling exists.

We might try to prove that no tiling exists by showing that we reach a dead end however we successively place dominoes on the board. To construct such a proof, we would have to consider all possible cases that arise as we run through all possible choices of successively placing dominoes. For example, we have two choices for covering the square in the second column of the first row, next to the removed top left corner. We could cover it with a horizontally placed tile or a vertically placed tile. Each of these two choices leads to further choices, and so on. It does not take long to see that this is not a fruitful plan of attack for a person, although a computer could be used to complete such a proof by exhaustion. (Exercise 45 asks you to supply such a proof to show that a $4 \times 4$ checkerboard with opposite corners removed cannot be tiled.)

We need another approach. Perhaps there is an easier way to prove there is no tiling of a standard checkerboard with two opposite corners removed. As with many proofs, a key observation can help. We color the squares of this checkerboard using alternating white and black squares, as in Figure 2. Observe that a domino in a tiling of such a board covers one white square and one black square. Next, note that this board has unequal numbers of white square and black squares. We can use these observations to prove by contradiction that a standard checkerboard with opposite corners removed cannot be tiled using dominoes. We now present such a proof.

*Proof:* Suppose we can use dominoes to tile a standard checkerboard with opposite corners removed. Note that the standard checkerboard with opposite corners removed contains $64 - 2 = 62$ squares. The tiling would use $62/2 = 31$ dominoes. Note that each domino in this tiling covers one white and one black square. Consequently, the tiling covers 31 white squares and 31 black squares. However, when we remove two opposite corner squares, either 32 of the remaining squares are white and 30 are black or else 30 are white and 32 are black. This contradicts the assumption that we can use dominoes to cover a standard checkerboard with opposite corners removed, completing the proof. ◀

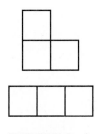

**FIGURE 6 A Right Triomino and a Straight Triomino.**

We can use other types of pieces besides dominoes in tilings. Instead of dominoes we can study tilings that use identically shaped pieces constructed from congruent squares that are connected along their edges. Such pieces are called **polyominoes**, a term coined in 1953 by the mathematician Solomon Golomb, the author of an entertaining book about them [Go94]. We will consider two polyominoes with the same number of squares the same if we can rotate and/or flip one of the polyominoes to get the other one. For example, there are two types of triominoes (see Figure 6), which are polyominoes made up of three squares connected by their sides. One type of triomino, the **straight triomino**, has three horizontally connected squares; the other type, **right triominoes**, resembles the letter L in shape, flipped and/or rotated, if necessary. We will study the tilings of a checkerboard by straight triominoes here; we will study tilings by right triominoes in Section 5.1.

**EXAMPLE 21**    Can you use straight triominoes to tile a standard checkerboard?

*Solution:* The standard checkerboard contains 64 squares and each triomino covers three squares. Consequently, if triominoes tile a board, the number of squares of the board must be a multiple of 3. Because 64 is not a multiple of 3, triominoes cannot be used to cover an $8 \times 8$ checkerboard. ◀

In Example 22, we consider the problem of using straight triominoes to tile a standard checkerboard with one corner missing.

**EXAMPLE 22**    Can we use straight triominoes to tile a standard checkerboard with one of its four corners removed? An $8 \times 8$ checkerboard with one corner removed contains $64 - 1 = 63$ squares. Any tiling by straight triominoes of one of these four boards uses $63/3 = 21$ triominoes. However, when we experiment, we cannot find a tiling of one of these boards using straight triominoes. A proof by exhaustion does not appear promising. Can we adapt our proof from Example 20 to prove that no such tiling exists?

*Solution:* We will color the squares of the checkerboard in an attempt to adapt the proof by contradiction we gave in Example 20 of the impossibility of using dominoes to tile a standard checkerboard with opposite corners removed. Because we are using straight triominoes rather than dominoes, we color the squares using three colors rather than two colors, as shown in Figure 7. Note that there are 21 blue squares, 21 black squares, and 22 white squares in this coloring. Next, we make the crucial observation that when a straight triomino covers three squares of the checkerboard, it covers one blue square, one black square, and one white square. Next, note that each of the three colors appears in a corner square. Thus without loss of generality, we may assume that we have rotated the coloring so that the missing square is colored blue. Therefore, we assume that the remaining board contains 20 blue squares, 21 black squares, and 22 white squares.

If we could tile this board using straight triominoes, then we would use $63/3 = 21$ straight triominoes. These triominoes would cover 21 blue squares, 21 black squares, and 21 white

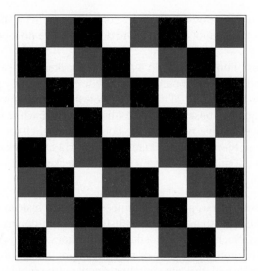

**FIGURE 7   Coloring the Squares of the Standard Checkerboard with Three Colors.**

squares. This contradicts the fact that this board contains 20 blue squares, 21 black squares, and 22 white squares. Therefore we cannot tile this board using straight triominoes.   ◀

## The Role of Open Problems

Many advances in mathematics have been made by people trying to solve famous unsolved problems. In the past 20 years, many unsolved problems have finally been resolved, such as the proof of a conjecture in number theory made more than 300 years ago. This conjecture asserts the truth of the statement known as **Fermat's last theorem**.

**THEOREM 1**   **FERMAT'S LAST THEOREM**   The equation

$$x^n + y^n = z^n$$

has no solutions in integers $x$, $y$, and $z$ with $xyz \neq 0$ whenever $n$ is an integer with $n > 2$.

Links

***Remark:*** The equation $x^2 + y^2 = z^2$ has infinitely many solutions in integers $x$, $y$, and $z$; these solutions are called Pythagorean triples and correspond to the lengths of the sides of right triangles with integer lengths. See Exercise 32.

This problem has a fascinating history. In the seventeenth century, Fermat jotted in the margin of his copy of the works of Diophantus that he had a "wondrous proof" that there are no integer solutions of $x^n + y^n = z^n$ when $n$ is an integer greater than 2 with $xyz \neq 0$. However, he never published a proof (Fermat published almost nothing), and no proof could be found in the papers he left when he died. Mathematicians looked for a proof for three centuries without success, although many people were convinced that a relatively simple proof could be found. (Proofs of special cases were found, such as the proof of the case when $n = 3$ by Euler and the proof of the $n = 4$ case by Fermat himself.) Over the years, several established mathematicians thought that they had proved this theorem. In the nineteenth century, one of these failed attempts led to the development of the part of number theory called algebraic number theory. A correct proof, requiring hundreds of pages of advanced mathematics, was not found until the 1990s, when Andrew Wiles used recently developed ideas from a sophisticated area of number theory called the theory of elliptic curves to prove Fermat's last theorem. Wiles's quest to find a proof of Fermat's last theorem using this powerful theory, described in a program in the *Nova* series on public television, took close to ten years! Moreover, his proof was based on major contributions of many mathematicians. (The interested reader should consult [Ro10] for more information about Fermat's last theorem and for additional references concerning this problem and its resolution.)

We now state an open problem that is simple to describe, but that seems quite difficult to resolve.

**EXAMPLE 23**

Links

**Watch out! Working on the $3x + 1$ problem can be addictive.**

***The $3x + 1$ Conjecture***   Let $T$ be the transformation that sends an even integer $x$ to $x/2$ and an odd integer $x$ to $3x + 1$. A famous conjecture, sometimes known as the **$3x + 1$ conjecture**, states that for all positive integers $x$, when we repeatedly apply the transformation $T$, we will eventually reach the integer 1. For example, starting with $x = 13$, we find $T(13) = 3 \cdot 13 + 1 = 40$, $T(40) = 40/2 = 20$, $T(20) = 20/2 = 10$, $T(10) = 10/2 = 5$, $T(5) = 3 \cdot 5 + 1 = 16$, $T(16) = 8$, $T(8) = 4$, $T(4) = 2$, and $T(2) = 1$. The $3x + 1$ conjecture has been verified using computers for all integers $x$ up to $5.6 \cdot 10^{13}$.

The $3x + 1$ conjecture has an interesting history and has attracted the attention of mathematicians since the 1950s. The conjecture has been raised many times and goes by many other names, including the Collatz problem, Hasse's algorithm, Ulam's problem, the Syracuse problem, and Kakutani's problem. Many mathematicians have been diverted from their work to spend time attacking this conjecture. This led to the joke that this problem was part of a conspiracy to slow down American mathematical research. See the article by Jeffrey Lagarias [La10] for a fascinating discussion of this problem and the results that have been found by mathematicians attacking it.   ◀

In Chapter 4 we will describe additional open questions about prime numbers. Students already familiar with the basic notions about primes might want to explore Section 4.3, where these open questions are discussed. We will mention other important open questions throughout the book.

## Additional Proof Methods

**Build up your arsenal of proof methods as you work through this book.**

In this chapter we introduced the basic methods used in proofs. We also described how to leverage these methods to prove a variety of results. We will use these proof methods in all subsequent chapters. In particular, we will use them in Chapters 2, 3, and 4 to prove results about sets, functions, algorithms, and number theory and in Chapters 9, 10, and 11 to prove results in graph theory. Among the theorems we will prove is the famous halting theorem which states that there is a problem that cannot be solved using any procedure. However, there are many important proof methods besides those we have covered. We will introduce some of these methods later in this book. In particular, in Section 5.1 we will discuss mathematical induction, which is an extremely useful method for proving statements of the form $\forall n P(n)$, where the domain consists of all positive integers. In Section 5.3 we will introduce structural induction, which can be used to prove results about recursively defined sets. We will use the Cantor diagonalization method, which can be used to prove results about the size of infinite sets, in Section 2.5. In Chapter 6 we will introduce the notion of combinatorial proofs, which can be used to prove results by counting arguments. The reader should note that entire books have been devoted to the activities discussed in this section, including many excellent works by George Pólya ([Po61], [Po71], [Po90]).

Finally, note that we have not given a procedure that can be used for proving theorems in mathematics. It is a deep theorem of mathematical logic that there is no such procedure.

# Exercises

**1.** Prove that $n^2 + 1 \geq 2^n$ when $n$ is a positive integer with $1 \leq n \leq 4$.

**2.** Prove that there are no positive perfect cubes less than 1000 that are the sum of the cubes of two positive integers.

**3.** Prove that if $x$ and $y$ are real numbers, then $\max(x, y) + \min(x, y) = x + y$. [*Hint:* Use a proof by cases, with the two cases corresponding to $x \geq y$ and $x < y$, respectively.]

**4.** Use a proof by cases to show that $\min(a, \min(b, c)) = \min(\min(a, b), c)$ whenever $a, b$, and $c$ are real numbers.

**5.** Prove using the notion of without loss of generality that $\min(x, y) = (x + y - |x - y|)/2$ and $\max(x, y) = (x + y + |x - y|)/2$ whenever $x$ and $y$ are real numbers.

**6.** Prove using the notion of without loss of generality that $5x + 5y$ is an odd integer when $x$ and $y$ are integers of opposite parity.

**7.** Prove the **triangle inequality**, which states that if $x$ and $y$ are real numbers, then $|x| + |y| \geq |x + y|$ (where $|x|$ represents the absolute value of $x$, which equals $x$ if $x \geq 0$ and equals $-x$ if $x < 0$).

**8.** Prove that there is a positive integer that equals the sum of the positive integers not exceeding it. Is your proof constructive or nonconstructive?

**9.** Prove that there are 100 consecutive positive integers that are not perfect squares. Is your proof constructive or nonconstructive?

**10.** Prove that either $2 \cdot 10^{500} + 15$ or $2 \cdot 10^{500} + 16$ is not a perfect square. Is your proof constructive or nonconstructive?

**11.** Prove that there exists a pair of consecutive integers such that one of these integers is a perfect square and the other is a perfect cube.

**12.** Show that the product of two of the numbers $65^{1000} - 8^{2001} + 3^{177}$, $79^{1212} - 9^{2399} + 2^{2001}$, and $24^{4493} - 5^{8192} + 7^{1777}$ is nonnegative. Is your proof constructive or nonconstructive? [*Hint:* Do not try to evaluate these numbers!]

**13.** Prove or disprove that there is a rational number $x$ and an irrational number $y$ such that $x^y$ is irrational.

**14.** Prove or disprove that if $a$ and $b$ are rational numbers, then $a^b$ is also rational.

**15.** Show that each of these statements can be used to express the fact that there is a unique element $x$ such that $P(x)$ is true. [Note that we can also write this statement as $\exists!x\, P(x)$.]
**a)** $\exists x \forall y (P(y) \leftrightarrow x = y)$
**b)** $\exists x P(x) \wedge \forall x \forall y (P(x) \wedge P(y) \rightarrow x = y)$
**c)** $\exists x (P(x) \wedge \forall y (P(y) \rightarrow x = y))$

**16.** Show that if $a, b$, and $c$ are real numbers and $a \neq 0$, then there is a unique solution of the equation $ax + b = c$.

**17.** Suppose that $a$ and $b$ are odd integers with $a \neq b$. Show there is a unique integer $c$ such that $|a - c| = |b - c|$.

**18.** Show that if $r$ is an irrational number, there is a unique integer $n$ such that the distance between $r$ and $n$ is less than $1/2$.

**19.** Show that if $n$ is an odd integer, then there is a unique integer $k$ such that $n$ is the sum of $k - 2$ and $k + 3$.

**20.** Prove that given a real number $x$ there exist unique numbers $n$ and $\epsilon$ such that $x = n + \epsilon$, $n$ is an integer, and $0 \leq \epsilon < 1$.

**21.** Prove that given a real number $x$ there exist unique numbers $n$ and $\epsilon$ such that $x = n - \epsilon$, $n$ is an integer, and $0 \leq \epsilon < 1$.

**22.** Use forward reasoning to show that if $x$ is a nonzero real number, then $x^2 + 1/x^2 \geq 2$. [*Hint:* Start with the inequality $(x - 1/x)^2 \geq 0$ which holds for all nonzero real numbers $x$.]

**23.** The **harmonic mean** of two real numbers $x$ and $y$ equals $2xy/(x + y)$. By computing the harmonic and geometric means of different pairs of positive real numbers, formulate a conjecture about their relative sizes and prove your conjecture.

**24.** The **quadratic mean** of two real numbers $x$ and $y$ equals $\sqrt{(x^2 + y^2)/2}$. By computing the arithmetic and quadratic means of different pairs of positive real numbers, formulate a conjecture about their relative sizes and prove your conjecture.

**∗25.** Write the numbers $1, 2, \ldots, 2n$ on a blackboard, where $n$ is an odd integer. Pick any two of the numbers, $j$ and $k$, write $|j - k|$ on the board and erase $j$ and $k$. Continue this process until only one integer is written on the board. Prove that this integer must be odd.

**∗26.** Suppose that five ones and four zeros are arranged around a circle. Between any two equal bits you insert a 0 and between any two unequal bits you insert a 1 to produce nine new bits. Then you erase the nine original bits. Show that when you iterate this procedure, you can never get nine zeros. [*Hint:* Work backward, assuming that you did end up with nine zeros.]

**27.** Formulate a conjecture about the decimal digits that appear as the final decimal digit of the fourth power of an integer. Prove your conjecture using a proof by cases.

**28.** Formulate a conjecture about the final two decimal digits of the square of an integer. Prove your conjecture using a proof by cases.

**29.** Prove that there is no positive integer $n$ such that $n^2 + n^3 = 100$.

**30.** Prove that there are no solutions in integers $x$ and $y$ to the equation $2x^2 + 5y^2 = 14$.

**31.** Prove that there are no solutions in positive integers $x$ and $y$ to the equation $x^4 + y^4 = 625$.

**32.** Prove that there are infinitely many solutions in positive integers $x, y$, and $z$ to the equation $x^2 + y^2 = z^2$. [*Hint:* Let $x = m^2 - n^2$, $y = 2mn$, and $z = m^2 + n^2$, where $m$ and $n$ are integers.]

33. Adapt the proof in Example 4 in Section 1.7 to prove that if $n = abc$, where $a, b$, and $c$ are positive integers, then $a \le \sqrt[3]{n}, b \le \sqrt[3]{n}$, or $c \le \sqrt[3]{n}$.

34. Prove that $\sqrt[3]{2}$ is irrational.

35. Prove that between every two rational numbers there is an irrational number.

36. Prove that between every rational number and every irrational number there is an irrational number.

*37. Let $S = x_1 y_1 + x_2 y_2 + \cdots + x_n y_n$, where $x_1, x_2, \ldots, x_n$ and $y_1, y_2, \ldots, y_n$ are orderings of two different sequences of positive real numbers, each containing $n$ elements.

   a) Show that $S$ takes its maximum value over all orderings of the two sequences when both sequences are sorted (so that the elements in each sequence are in nondecreasing order).

   b) Show that $S$ takes its minimum value over all orderings of the two sequences when one sequence is sorted into nondecreasing order and the other is sorted into nonincreasing order.

38. Prove or disprove that if you have an 8-gallon jug of water and two empty jugs with capacities of 5 gallons and 3 gallons, respectively, then you can measure 4 gallons by successively pouring some of or all of the water in a jug into another jug.

39. Verify the $3x + 1$ conjecture for these integers.

   a) 6     b) 7     c) 17     d) 21

40. Verify the $3x + 1$ conjecture for these integers.

   a) 16    b) 11    c) 35     d) 113

41. Prove or disprove that you can use dominoes to tile the standard checkerboard with two adjacent corners removed (that is, corners that are not opposite).

42. Prove or disprove that you can use dominoes to tile a standard checkerboard with all four corners removed.

43. Prove that you can use dominoes to tile a rectangular checkerboard with an even number of squares.

44. Prove or disprove that you can use dominoes to tile a $5 \times 5$ checkerboard with three corners removed.

45. Use a proof by exhaustion to show that a tiling using dominoes of a $4 \times 4$ checkerboard with opposite corners removed does not exist. [*Hint:* First show that you can assume that the squares in the upper left and lower right corners are removed. Number the squares of the original

checkerboard from 1 to 16, starting in the first row, moving right in this row, then starting in the leftmost square in the second row and moving right, and so on. Remove squares 1 and 16. To begin the proof, note that square 2 is covered either by a domino laid horizontally, which covers squares 2 and 3, or vertically, which covers squares 2 and 6. Consider each of these cases separately, and work through all the subcases that arise.]

*46. Prove that when a white square and a black square are removed from an $8 \times 8$ checkerboard (colored as in the text) you can tile the remaining squares of the checkerboard using dominoes. [*Hint:* Show that when one black and one white square are removed, each part of the partition of the remaining cells formed by inserting the barriers shown in the figure can be covered by dominoes.]

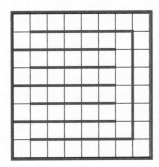

47. Show that by removing two white squares and two black squares from an $8 \times 8$ checkerboard (colored as in the text) you can make it impossible to tile the remaining squares using dominoes.

*48. Find all squares, if they exist, on an $8 \times 8$ checkerboard such that the board obtained by removing one of these square can be tiled using straight triominoes. [*Hint:* First use arguments based on coloring and rotations to eliminate as many squares as possible from consideration.]

*49. a) Draw each of the five different tetrominoes, where a tetromino is a polyomino consisting of four squares.

   b) For each of the five different tetrominoes, prove or disprove that you can tile a standard checkerboard using these tetrominoes.

*50. Prove or disprove that you can tile a $10 \times 10$ checkerboard using straight tetrominoes.

## Key Terms and Results

### TERMS

**proposition:** a statement that is true or false

**propositional variable:** a variable that represents a proposition

**truth value:** true or false

**$\neg p$ (negation of $p$):** the proposition with truth value opposite to the truth value of $p$

**logical operators:** operators used to combine propositions

**compound proposition:** a proposition constructed by combining propositions using logical operators

**truth table:** a table displaying all possible truth values of propositions

**$p \vee q$ (disjunction of $p$ and $q$):** the proposition "$p$ or $q$," which is true if and only if at least one of $p$ and $q$ is true

$p \wedge q$ **(conjunction of $p$ and $q$):** the proposition "$p$ and $q$," which is true if and only if both $p$ and $q$ are true

$p \oplus q$ **(exclusive or of $p$ and $q$):** the proposition "$p$ XOR $q$," which is true when exactly one of $p$ and $q$ is true

$p \rightarrow q$ **($p$ implies $q$):** the proposition "if $p$, then $q$," which is false if and only if $p$ is true and $q$ is false

**converse of $p \rightarrow q$:** the conditional statement $q \rightarrow p$

**contrapositive of $p \rightarrow q$:** the conditional statement $\neg q \rightarrow \neg p$

**inverse of $p \rightarrow q$:** the conditional statement $\neg p \rightarrow \neg q$

$p \leftrightarrow q$ **(biconditional):** the proposition "$p$ if and only if $q$," which is true if and only if $p$ and $q$ have the same truth value

**bit:** either a 0 or a 1

**Boolean variable:** a variable that has a value of 0 or 1

**bit operation:** an operation on a bit or bits

**bit string:** a list of bits

**bitwise operations:** operations on bit strings that operate on each bit in one string and the corresponding bit in the other string

**logic gate:** a logic element that performs a logical operation on one or more bits to produce an output bit

**logic circuit:** a switching circuit made up of logic gates that produces one or more output bits

**tautology:** a compound proposition that is always true

**contradiction:** a compound proposition that is always false

**contingency:** a compound proposition that is sometimes true and sometimes false

**consistent compound propositions:** compound propositions for which there is an assignment of truth values to the variables that makes all these propositions true

**satisfiable compound proposition:** a compound proposition for which there is an assignment of truth values to its variables that makes it true

**logically equivalent compound propositions:** compound propositions that always have the same truth values

**predicate:** part of a sentence that attributes a property to the subject

**propositional function:** a statement containing one or more variables that becomes a proposition when each of its variables is assigned a value or is bound by a quantifier

**domain (or universe) of discourse:** the values a variable in a propositional function may take

$\exists x\, P(x)$ **(existential quantification of $P(x)$):** the proposition that is true if and only if there exists an $x$ in the domain such that $P(x)$ is true

$\forall x P(x)$ **(universal quantification of $P(x)$):** the proposition that is true if and only if $P(x)$ is true for every $x$ in the domain

**logically equivalent expressions:** expressions that have the same truth value no matter which propositional functions and domains are used

**free variable:** a variable not bound in a propositional function

**bound variable:** a variable that is quantified

**scope of a quantifier:** portion of a statement where the quantifier binds its variable

**argument:** a sequence of statements

**argument form:** a sequence of compound propositions involving propositional variables

**premise:** a statement, in an argument, or argument form, other than the final one

**conclusion:** the final statement in an argument or argument form

**valid argument form:** a sequence of compound propositions involving propositional variables where the truth of all the premises implies the truth of the conclusion

**valid argument:** an argument with a valid argument form

**rule of inference:** a valid argument form that can be used in the demonstration that arguments are valid

**fallacy:** an invalid argument form often used incorrectly as a rule of inference (or sometimes, more generally, an incorrect argument)

**circular reasoning or begging the question:** reasoning where one or more steps are based on the truth of the statement being proved

**theorem:** a mathematical assertion that can be shown to be true

**conjecture:** a mathematical assertion proposed to be true, but that has not been proved

**proof:** a demonstration that a theorem is true

**axiom:** a statement that is assumed to be true and that can be used as a basis for proving theorems

**lemma:** a theorem used to prove other theorems

**corollary:** a proposition that can be proved as a consequence of a theorem that has just been proved

**vacuous proof:** a proof that $p \rightarrow q$ is true based on the fact that $p$ is false

**trivial proof:** a proof that $p \rightarrow q$ is true based on the fact that $q$ is true

**direct proof:** a proof that $p \rightarrow q$ is true that proceeds by showing that $q$ must be true when $p$ is true

**proof by contraposition:** a proof that $p \rightarrow q$ is true that proceeds by showing that $p$ must be false when $q$ is false

**proof by contradiction:** a proof that $p$ is true based on the truth of the conditional statement $\neg p \rightarrow q$, where $q$ is a contradiction

**exhaustive proof:** a proof that establishes a result by checking a list of all possible cases

**proof by cases:** a proof broken into separate cases, where these cases cover all possibilities

**without loss of generality:** an assumption in a proof that makes it possible to prove a theorem by reducing the number of cases to consider in the proof

**counterexample:** an element $x$ such that $P(x)$ is false

**constructive existence proof:** a proof that an element with a specified property exists that explicitly finds such an element

**nonconstructive existence proof:** a proof that an element with a specified property exists that does not explicitly find such an element

**rational number:** a number that can be expressed as the ratio of two integers $p$ and $q$ such that $q \neq 0$

**uniqueness proof:** a proof that there is exactly one element satisfying a specified property

## RESULTS

The logical equivalences given in Tables 6, 7, and 8 in Section 1.3.

De Morgan's laws for quantifiers.
Rules of inference for propositional calculus.
Rules of inference for quantified statements.

# Review Questions

**1. a)** Define the negation of a proposition.

**b)** What is the negation of "This is a boring course"?

**2. a)** Define (using truth tables) the disjunction, conjunction, exclusive or, conditional, and biconditional of the propositions $p$ and $q$.

**b)** What are the disjunction, conjunction, exclusive or, conditional, and biconditional of the propositions "I'll go to the movies tonight" and "I'll finish my discrete mathematics homework"?

**3. a)** Describe at least five different ways to write the conditional statement $p \rightarrow q$ in English.

**b)** Define the converse and contrapositive of a conditional statement.

**c)** State the converse and the contrapositive of the conditional statement "If it is sunny tomorrow, then I will go for a walk in the woods."

**4. a)** What does it mean for two propositions to be logically equivalent?

**b)** Describe the different ways to show that two compound propositions are logically equivalent.

**c)** Show in at least two different ways that the compound propositions $\neg p \vee (r \rightarrow \neg q)$ and $\neg p \vee \neg q \vee \neg r$ are equivalent.

**5.** *(Depends on the Exercise Set in Section 1.3)*

**a)** Given a truth table, explain how to use disjunctive normal form to construct a compound proposition with this truth table.

**b)** Explain why part (a) shows that the operators $\wedge$, $\vee$, and $\neg$ are functionally complete.

**c)** Is there an operator such that the set containing just this operator is functionally complete?

**6.** What are the universal and existential quantifications of a predicate $P(x)$? What are their negations?

**7. a)** What is the difference between the quantification $\exists x \forall y P(x, y)$ and $\forall y \exists x P(x, y)$, where $P(x, y)$ is a predicate?

**b)** Give an example of a predicate $P(x, y)$ such that $\exists x \forall y P(x, y)$ and $\forall y \exists x P(x, y)$ have different truth values.

**8.** Describe what is meant by a valid argument in propositional logic and show that the argument "If the earth is flat, then you can sail off the edge of the earth," "You cannot sail off the edge of the earth," therefore, "The earth is not flat" is a valid argument.

**9.** Use rules of inference to show that if the premises "All zebras have stripes" and "Mark is a zebra" are true, then the conclusion "Mark has stripes" is true.

**10. a)** Describe what is meant by a direct proof, a proof by contraposition, and a proof by contradiction of a conditional statement $p \rightarrow q$.

**b)** Give a direct proof, a proof by contraposition and a proof by contradiction of the statement: "If $n$ is even, then $n + 4$ is even."

**11. a)** Describe a way to prove the biconditional $p \leftrightarrow q$.

**b)** Prove the statement: "The integer $3n + 2$ is odd if and only if the integer $9n + 5$ is even, where $n$ is an integer."

**12.** To prove that the statements $p_1$, $p_2$, $p_3$, and $p_4$ are equivalent, is it sufficient to show that the conditional statements $p_4 \rightarrow p_2$, $p_3 \rightarrow p_1$, and $p_1 \rightarrow p_2$ are valid? If not, provide another collection of conditional statements that can be used to show that the four statements are equivalent.

**13. a)** Suppose that a statement of the form $\forall x P(x)$ is false. How can this be proved?

**b)** Show that the statement "For every positive integer $n$, $n^2 \geq 2n$" is false.

**14.** What is the difference between a constructive and nonconstructive existence proof? Give an example of each.

**15.** What are the elements of a proof that there is a unique element $x$ such that $P(x)$, where $P(x)$ is a propositional function?

**16.** Explain how a proof by cases can be used to prove a result about absolute values, such as the fact that $|xy| = |x||y|$ for all real numbers $x$ and $y$.

# Supplementary Exercises

**1.** Let $p$ be the proposition "I will do every exercise in this book" and $q$ be the proposition "I will get an "A" in this course." Express each of these as a combination of $p$ and $q$.

**a)** I will get an "A" in this course only if I do every exercise in this book.

**b)** I will get an "A" in this course and I will do every exercise in this book.

**c)** Either I will not get an "A" in this course or I will not do every exercise in this book.

**d)** For me to get an "A" in this course it is necessary and sufficient that I do every exercise in this book.

2. Find the truth table of the compound proposition $(p \vee q) \rightarrow (p \wedge \neg r)$.

3. Show that these compound propositions are tautologies.
   a) $(\neg q \wedge (p \rightarrow q)) \rightarrow \neg p$
   b) $((p \vee q) \wedge \neg p) \rightarrow q$

4. Give the converse, the contrapositive, and the inverse of these conditional statements.
   a) If it rains today, then I will drive to work.
   b) If $|x| = x$, then $x \geq 0$.
   c) If $n$ is greater than 3, then $n^2$ is greater than 9.

5. Given a conditional statement $p \rightarrow q$, find the converse of its inverse, the converse of its converse, and the converse of its contrapositive.

6. Given a conditional statement $p \rightarrow q$, find the inverse of its inverse, the inverse of its converse, and the inverse of its contrapositive.

7. Find a compound proposition involving the propositional variables $p, q, r$, and $s$ that is true when exactly three of these propositional variables are true and is false otherwise.

8. Show that these statements are inconsistent: "If Sergei takes the job offer then he will get a signing bonus." "If Sergei takes the job offer, then he will receive a higher salary." "If Sergei gets a signing bonus, then he will not receive a higher salary." "Sergei takes the job offer."

9. Show that these statements are inconsistent: "If Miranda does not take a course in discrete mathematics, then she will not graduate." "If Miranda does not graduate, then she is not qualified for the job." "If Miranda reads this book, then she is qualified for the job." "Miranda does not take a course in discrete mathematics but she reads this book."

Teachers in the Middle Ages supposedly tested the realtime propositional logic ability of a student via a technique known as an **obligato game**. In an obligato game, a number of rounds is set and in each round the teacher gives the student successive assertions that the student must either accept or reject as they are given. When the student accepts an assertion, it is added as a commitment; when the student rejects an assertion its negation is added as a commitment. The student passes the test if the consistency of all commitments is maintained throughout the test.

10. Suppose that in a three-round obligato game, the teacher first gives the student the proposition $p \rightarrow q$, then the proposition $\neg(p \vee r) \vee q$, and finally the proposition $q$. For which of the eight possible sequences of three answers will the student pass the test?

11. Suppose that in a four-round obligato game, the teacher first gives the student the proposition $\neg(p \rightarrow (q \wedge r))$, then the proposition $p \vee \neg q$, then the proposition $\neg r$, and finally, the proposition $(p \wedge r) \vee (q \rightarrow p)$. For which of the 16 possible sequences of four answers will the student pass the test?

12. Explain why every obligato game has a winning strategy.

Exercises 13 and 14 are set on the island of knights and knaves described in Example 7 in Section 1.2.

13. Suppose that you meet three people Aaron, Bohan, and Crystal. Can you determine what Aaron, Bohan, and Crystal are if Aaron says "All of us are knaves" and Bohan says "Exactly one of us is a knave."?

14. Suppose that you meet three people, Anita, Boris, and Carmen. What are Anita, Boris, and Carmen if Anita says "I am a knave and Boris is a knight" and Boris says "Exactly one of the three of us is a knight"?

15. (Adapted from [Sm78]) Suppose that on an island there are three types of people, knights, knaves, and normals (also known as spies). Knights always tell the truth, knaves always lie, and normals sometimes lie and sometimes tell the truth. Detectives questioned three inhabitants of the island—Amy, Brenda, and Claire—as part of the investigation of a crime. The detectives knew that one of the three committed the crime, but not which one. They also knew that the criminal was a knight, and that the other two were not. Additionally, the detectives recorded these statements: Amy: "I am innocent." Brenda: "What Amy says is true." Claire: "Brenda is not a normal." After analyzing their information, the detectives positively identified the guilty party. Who was it?

16. Show that if $S$ is a proposition, where $S$ is the conditional statement "If $S$ is true, then unicorns live," then "Unicorns live" is true. Show that it follows that $S$ cannot be a proposition. (This paradox is known as *Löb's paradox*.)

17. Show that the argument with premises "The tooth fairy is a real person" and "The tooth fairy is not a real person" and conclusion "You can find gold at the end of the rainbow" is a valid argument. Does this show that the conclusion is true?

18. Suppose that the truth value of the proposition $p_i$ is **T** whenever $i$ is an odd positive integer and is **F** whenever $i$ is an even positive integer. Find the truth values of $\bigvee_{i=1}^{100}(p_i \wedge p_{i+1})$ and $\bigwedge_{i=1}^{100}(p_i \vee p_{i+1})$.

*19. Model $16 \times 16$ Sudoku puzzles (with $4 \times 4$ blocks) as satisfiability problems.

20. Let $P(x)$ be the statement "Student $x$ knows calculus" and let $Q(y)$ be the statement "Class $y$ contains a student who knows calculus." Express each of these as quantifications of $P(x)$ and $Q(y)$.
    a) Some students know calculus.
    b) Not every student knows calculus.
    c) Every class has a student in it who knows calculus.
    d) Every student in every class knows calculus.
    e) There is at least one class with no students who know calculus.

21. Let $P(m, n)$ be the statement "$m$ divides $n$," where the domain for both variables consists of all positive integers. (By "$m$ divides $n$" we mean that $n = km$ for some integer $k$.) Determine the truth values of each of these statements.
    a) $P(4, 5)$          b) $P(2, 4)$
    c) $\forall m \, \forall n \, P(m, n)$     d) $\exists m \, \forall n \, P(m, n)$
    e) $\exists n \, \forall m \, P(m, n)$     f) $\forall n \, P(1, n)$

22. Find a domain for the quantifiers in $\exists x \exists y (x \neq y \wedge \forall z((z = x) \vee (z = y)))$ such that this statement is true.

23. Find a domain for the quantifiers in $\exists x \exists y (x \neq y \wedge \forall z((z = x) \vee (z = y)))$ such that this statement is false.

24. Use existential and universal quantifiers to express the statement "No one has more than three grandmothers" using the propositional function $G(x, y)$, which represents "$x$ is the grandmother of $y$."

25. Use existential and universal quantifiers to express the statement "Everyone has exactly two biological parents" using the propositional function $P(x, y)$, which represents "$x$ is the biological parent of $y$."

26. The quantifier $\exists_n$ denotes "there exists exactly $n$," so that $\exists_n x P(x)$ means there exist exactly $n$ values in the domain such that $P(x)$ is true. Determine the true value of these statements where the domain consists of all real numbers.

   **a)** $\exists_0 x (x^2 = -1)$   **b)** $\exists_1 x (|x| = 0)$
   **c)** $\exists_2 x (x^2 = 2)$   **d)** $\exists_3 x (x = |x|)$

27. Express each of these statements using existential and universal quantifiers and propositional logic where $\exists_n$ is defined in Exercise 26.

   **a)** $\exists_0 x P(x)$   **b)** $\exists_1 x P(x)$
   **c)** $\exists_2 x P(x)$   **d)** $\exists_3 x P(x)$

28. Let $P(x, y)$ be a propositional function. Show that $\exists x \forall y\, P(x, y) \to \forall y \exists x\, P(x, y)$ is a tautology.

29. Let $P(x)$ and $Q(x)$ be propositional functions. Show that $\exists x\,(P(x) \to Q(x))$ and $\forall x\, P(x) \to \exists x\, Q(x)$ always have the same truth value.

30. If $\forall y \exists x\, P(x, y)$ is true, does it necessarily follow that $\exists x \forall y\, P(x, y)$ is true?

31. If $\forall x \exists y\, P(x, y)$ is true, does it necessarily follow that $\exists x \forall y\, P(x, y)$ is true?

32. Find the negations of these statements.

   **a)** If it snows today, then I will go skiing tomorrow.
   **b)** Every person in this class understands mathematical induction.
   **c)** Some students in this class do not like discrete mathematics.
   **d)** In every mathematics class there is some student who falls asleep during lectures.

33. Express this statement using quantifiers: "Every student in this class has taken some course in every department in the school of mathematical sciences."

34. Express this statement using quantifiers: "There is a building on the campus of some college in the United States in which every room is painted white."

35. Express the statement "There is exactly one student in this class who has taken exactly one mathematics class at this school" using the uniqueness quantifier. Then express this statement using quantifiers, without using the uniqueness quantifier.

36. Describe a rule of inference that can be used to prove that there are exactly two elements $x$ and $y$ in a domain such that $P(x)$ and $P(y)$ are true. Express this rule of inference as a statement in English.

37. Use rules of inference to show that if the premises $\forall x(P(x) \to Q(x))$, $\forall x(Q(x) \to R(x))$, and $\neg R(a)$, where $a$ is in the domain, are true, then the conclusion $\neg P(a)$ is true.

38. Prove that if $x^3$ is irrational, then $x$ is irrational.

39. Prove that if $x$ is irrational and $x \geq 0$, then $\sqrt{x}$ is irrational.

40. Prove that given a nonnegative integer $n$, there is a unique nonnegative integer $m$ such that $m^2 \leq n < (m + 1)^2$.

41. Prove that there exists an integer $m$ such that $m^2 > 10^{1000}$. Is your proof constructive or nonconstructive?

42. Prove that there is a positive integer that can be written as the sum of squares of positive integers in two different ways. (Use a computer or calculator to speed up your work.)

43. Disprove the statement that every positive integer is the sum of the cubes of eight nonnegative integers.

44. Disprove the statement that every positive integer is the sum of at most two squares and a cube of nonnegative integers.

45. Disprove the statement that every positive integer is the sum of 36 fifth powers of nonnegative integers.

46. Assuming the truth of the theorem that states that $\sqrt{n}$ is irrational whenever $n$ is a positive integer that is not a perfect square, prove that $\sqrt{2} + \sqrt{3}$ is irrational.

# Computer Projects

**Write programs with the specified input and output.**

1. Given the truth values of the propositions $p$ and $q$, find the truth values of the conjunction, disjunction, exclusive or, conditional statement, and biconditional of these propositions.

2. Given two bit strings of length $n$, find the bitwise *AND*, bitwise *OR*, and bitwise *XOR* of these strings.

**∗3.** Give a compound proposition, determine whether it is satisfiable by checking its truth value for all positive assignments of truth values to its propositional variables.

4. Given the truth values of the propositions $p$ and $q$ in fuzzy logic, find the truth value of the disjunction and the conjunction of $p$ and $q$ (see Exercises 46 and 47 of Section 1.1).

**∗5.** Given positive integers $m$ and $n$, interactively play the game of Chomp.

**∗6.** Given a portion of a checkerboard, look for tilings of this checkerboard with various types of polyominoes, including dominoes, the two types of triominoes, and larger polyominoes.

# Computations and Explorations

**Use a computational program or programs you have written to do these exercises.**

1. Look for positive integers that are not the sum of the cubes of nine different positive integers.

2. Look for positive integers greater than 79 that are not the sum of the fourth powers of 18 positive integers.

3. Find as many positive integers as you can that can be written as the sum of cubes of positive integers, in two different ways, sharing this property with 1729.

**\*4.** Try to find winning strategies for the game of Chomp for different initial configurations of cookies.

5. Construct the 12 different pentominoes, where a pentomino is a polyomino consisting of five squares.

6. Find all the rectangles of 60 squares that can be tiled using every one of the 12 different pentominoes.

# Writing Projects

**Respond to these with essays using outside sources.**

1. Discuss logical paradoxes, including the paradox of Epimenides the Cretan, Jourdain's card paradox, and the barber paradox, and how they are resolved.

2. Describe how fuzzy logic is being applied to practical applications. Consult one or more of the recent books on fuzzy logic written for general audiences.

3. Describe some of the practical problems that can be modeled as satisfiability problems.

4. Describe some of the techniques that have been devised to help people solve Sudoku puzzles without the use of a computer.

5. Describe the basic rules of *WFF'N PROOF, The Game of Modern Logic*, developed by Layman Allen. Give examples of some of the games included in *WFF'N PROOF*.

6. Read some of the writings of Lewis Carroll on symbolic logic. Describe in detail some of the models he used to represent logical arguments and the rules of inference he used in these arguments.

7. Extend the discussion of Prolog given in Section 1.4, explaining in more depth how Prolog employs resolution.

8. Discuss some of the techniques used in computational logic, including Skolem's rule.

9. "Automated theorem proving" is the task of using computers to mechanically prove theorems. Discuss the goals and applications of automated theorem proving and the progress made in developing automated theorem provers.

10. Describe how DNA computing has been used to solve instances of the satisfiability problem.

11. Look up some of the incorrect proofs of famous open questions and open questions that were solved since 1970 and describe the type of error made in each proof.

12. Discuss what is known about winning strategies in the game of Chomp.

13. Describe various aspects of proof strategy discussed by George Pólya in his writings on reasoning, including [Po62], [Po71], and [Po90].

14. Describe a few problems and results about tilings with polyominoes, as described in [Go94] and [Ma91], for example.

# 2 Basic Structures: Sets, Functions, Sequences, Sums, and Matrices

**M**uch of discrete mathematics is devoted to the study of discrete structures, used to represent discrete objects. Many important discrete structures are built using sets, which are collections of objects. Among the discrete structures built from sets are combinations, unordered collections of objects used extensively in counting; relations, sets of ordered pairs that represent relationships between objects; graphs, sets of vertices and edges that connect vertices; and finite state machines, used to model computing machines. These are some of the topics we will study in later chapters.

The concept of a function is extremely important in discrete mathematics. A function assigns to each element of a first set exactly one element of a second set, where the two sets are not necessarily distinct. Functions play important roles throughout discrete mathematics. They are used to represent the computational complexity of algorithms, to study the size of sets, to count objects, and in a myriad of other ways. Useful structures such as sequences and strings are special types of functions. In this chapter, we will introduce the notion of a sequence, which represents ordered lists of elements. Furthermore, we will introduce some important types of sequences and we will show how to define the terms of a sequence using earlier terms. We will also address the problem of identifying a sequence from its first few terms.

In our study of discrete mathematics, we will often add consecutive terms of a sequence of numbers. Because adding terms from a sequence, as well as other indexed sets of numbers, is such a common occurrence, a special notation has been developed for adding such terms. In this chapter, we will introduce the notation used to express summations. We will develop formulae for certain types of summations that appear throughout the study of discrete mathematics. For instance, we will encounter such summations in the analysis of the number of steps used by an algorithm to sort a list of numbers so that its terms are in increasing order.

The relative sizes of infinite sets can be studied by introducing the notion of the size, or cardinality, of a set. We say that a set is countable when it is finite or has the same size as the set of positive integers. In this chapter we will establish the surprising result that the set of rational numbers is countable, while the set of real numbers is not. We will also show how the concepts we discuss can be used to show that there are functions that cannot be computed using a computer program in any programming language.

Matrices are used in discrete mathematics to represent a variety of discrete structures. We will review the basic material about matrices and matrix arithmetic needed to represent relations and graphs. The matrix arithmetic we study will be used to solve a variety of problems involving these structures.

## 2.1 Sets

### Introduction

In this section, we study the fundamental discrete structure on which all other discrete structures are built, namely, the set. Sets are used to group objects together. Often, but not always, the objects in a set have similar properties. For instance, all the students who are currently enrolled in your school make up a set. Likewise, all the students currently taking a course in discrete mathematics at any school make up a set. In addition, those students enrolled in your school who are taking a course in discrete mathematics form a set that can be obtained by taking the elements common to the first two collections. The language of sets is a means to study such collections in an organized fashion. We now provide a definition of a set. This definition is an intuitive definition, which is not part of a formal theory of sets.

**DEFINITION 1**

A *set* is an unordered collection of objects, called *elements* or *members* of the set. A set is said to *contain* its elements. We write $a \in A$ to denote that $a$ is an element of the set $A$. The notation $a \notin A$ denotes that $a$ is not an element of the set $A$.

It is common for sets to be denoted using uppercase letters. Lowercase letters are usually used to denote elements of sets.

There are several ways to describe a set. One way is to list all the members of a set, when this is possible. We use a notation where all members of the set are listed between braces. For example, the notation $\{a, b, c, d\}$ represents the set with the four elements $a, b, c,$ and $d$. This way of describing a set is known as the **roster method**.

**EXAMPLE 1**  The set $V$ of all vowels in the English alphabet can be written as $V = \{a, e, i, o, u\}$.  ◄

**EXAMPLE 2**  The set $O$ of odd positive integers less than 10 can be expressed by $O = \{1, 3, 5, 7, 9\}$.  ◄

**EXAMPLE 3**  Although sets are usually used to group together elements with common properties, there is nothing that prevents a set from having seemingly unrelated elements. For instance, $\{a, 2, \text{Fred}, \text{New Jersey}\}$ is the set containing the four elements $a, 2, \text{Fred}, $ and New Jersey.  ◄

Sometimes the roster method is used to describe a set without listing all its members. Some members of the set are listed, and then *ellipses* (...) are used when the general pattern of the elements is obvious.

**EXAMPLE 4**  The set of positive integers less than 100 can be denoted by $\{1, 2, 3, \ldots, 99\}$.  ◄

Extra
Examples

Another way to describe a set is to use **set builder** notation. We characterize all those elements in the set by stating the property or properties they must have to be members. For instance, the set $O$ of all odd positive integers less than 10 can be written as

$$O = \{x \mid x \text{ is an odd positive integer less than } 10\},$$

or, specifying the universe as the set of positive integers, as

$$O = \{x \in \mathbf{Z}^+ \mid x \text{ is odd and } x < 10\}.$$

We often use this type of notation to describe sets when it is impossible to list all the elements of the set. For instance, the set $\mathbf{Q}^+$ of all positive rational numbers can be written as

$$\mathbf{Q}^+ = \{x \in \mathbf{R} \mid x = \tfrac{p}{q}, \text{ for some positive integers } p \text{ and } q\}.$$

Beware that mathematicians disagree whether 0 is a natural number. We consider it quite natural.

These sets, each denoted using a boldface letter, play an important role in discrete mathematics:

$\mathbf{N} = \{0, 1, 2, 3, \ldots\}$, the set of **natural numbers**
$\mathbf{Z} = \{\ldots, -2, -1, 0, 1, 2, \ldots\}$, the set of **integers**
$\mathbf{Z}^+ = \{1, 2, 3, \ldots\}$, the set of **positive integers**
$\mathbf{Q} = \{p/q \mid p \in \mathbf{Z}, q \in \mathbf{Z}, \text{and } q \neq 0\}$, the set of **rational numbers**
$\mathbf{R}$, the set of **real numbers**
$\mathbf{R}^+$, the set of **positive real numbers**
$\mathbf{C}$, the set of **complex numbers**.

(Note that some people do not consider 0 a natural number, so be careful to check how the term *natural numbers* is used when you read other books.)

Recall the notation for **intervals** of real numbers. When $a$ and $b$ are real numbers with $a < b$, we write

$$[a, b] = \{x \mid a \leq x \leq b\}$$
$$[a, b) = \{x \mid a \leq x < b\}$$
$$(a, b] = \{x \mid a < x \leq b\}$$
$$(a, b) = \{x \mid a < x < b\}$$

Note that $[a, b]$ is called the **closed interval** from $a$ to $b$ and $(a, b)$ is called the **open interval** from $a$ to $b$.

Sets can have other sets as members, as Example 5 illustrates.

**EXAMPLE 5**    The set $\{\mathbf{N}, \mathbf{Z}, \mathbf{Q}, \mathbf{R}\}$ is a set containing four elements, each of which is a set. The four elements of this set are $\mathbf{N}$, the set of natural numbers; $\mathbf{Z}$, the set of integers; $\mathbf{Q}$, the set of rational numbers; and $\mathbf{R}$, the set of real numbers. ◀

*Remark:* Note that the concept of a datatype, or type, in computer science is built upon the concept of a set. In particular, a **datatype** or **type** is the name of a set, together with a set of operations that can be performed on objects from that set. For example, *boolean* is the name of the set $\{0, 1\}$ together with operators on one or more elements of this set, such as AND, OR, and NOT.

Because many mathematical statements assert that two differently specified collections of objects are really the same set, we need to understand what it means for two sets to be equal.

**DEFINITION 2**    Two sets are *equal* if and only if they have the same elements. Therefore, if $A$ and $B$ are sets, then $A$ and $B$ are equal if and only if $\forall x(x \in A \leftrightarrow x \in B)$. We write $A = B$ if $A$ and $B$ are equal sets.

**EXAMPLE 6**    The sets $\{1, 3, 5\}$ and $\{3, 5, 1\}$ are equal, because they have the same elements. Note that the order in which the elements of a set are listed does not matter. Note also that it does not matter if an element of a set is listed more than once, so $\{1, 3, 3, 3, 5, 5, 5, 5\}$ is the same as the set $\{1, 3, 5\}$ because they have the same elements. ◀

GEORG CANTOR (1845–1918)    Georg Cantor was born in St. Petersburg, Russia, where his father was a successful merchant. Cantor developed his interest in mathematics in his teens. He began his university studies in Zurich in 1862, but when his father died he left Zurich. He continued his university studies at the University of Berlin in 1863, where he studied under the eminent mathematicians Weierstrass, Kummer, and Kronecker. He received his doctor's degree in 1867, after having written a dissertation on number theory. Cantor assumed a position at the University of Halle in 1869, where he continued working until his death.

Cantor is considered the founder of set theory. His contributions in this area include the discovery that the set of real numbers is uncountable. He is also noted for his many important contributions to analysis. Cantor also was interested in philosophy and wrote papers relating his theory of sets with metaphysics.

Cantor married in 1874 and had five children. His melancholy temperament was balanced by his wife's happy disposition. Although he received a large inheritance from his father, he was poorly paid as a professor. To mitigate this, he tried to obtain a better-paying position at the University of Berlin. His appointment there was blocked by Kronecker, who did not agree with Cantor's views on set theory. Cantor suffered from mental illness throughout the later years of his life. He died in 1918 from a heart attack.

THE EMPTY SET    There is a special set that has no elements. This set is called the **empty set**, or **null set**, and is denoted by ∅. The empty set can also be denoted by { } (that is, we represent the empty set with a pair of braces that encloses all the elements in this set). Often, a set of elements with certain properties turns out to be the null set. For instance, the set of all positive integers that are greater than their squares is the null set.

A set with one element is called a **singleton set**. A common error is to confuse the empty set ∅ with the set {∅}, which is a singleton set. The single element of the set {∅} is the empty set itself! A useful analogy for remembering this difference is to think of folders in a computer file system. The empty set can be thought of as an empty folder and the set consisting of just the empty set can be thought of as a folder with exactly one folder inside, namely, the empty folder.

{∅} has one more element than ∅.

NAIVE SET THEORY    Note that the term *object* has been used in the definition of a set, Definition 1, without specifying what an object is. This description of a set as a collection of objects, based on the intuitive notion of an object, was first stated in 1895 by the German mathematician Georg Cantor. The theory that results from this intuitive definition of a set, and the use of the intuitive notion that for any property whatever, there is a set consisting of exactly the objects with this property, leads to **paradoxes**, or logical inconsistencies. This was shown by the English philosopher Bertrand Russell in 1902 (see Exercise 46 for a description of one of these paradoxes). These logical inconsistencies can be avoided by building set theory beginning with axioms. However, we will use Cantor's original version of set theory, known as **naive set theory**, in this book because all sets considered in this book can be treated consistently using Cantor's original theory. Students will find familiarity with naive set theory helpful if they go on to learn about axiomatic set theory. They will also find the development of axiomatic set theory much more abstract than the material in this text. We refer the interested reader to [Su72] to learn more about axiomatic set theory.

Links

## Venn Diagrams

Sets can be represented graphically using Venn diagrams, named after the English mathematician John Venn, who introduced their use in 1881. In Venn diagrams the **universal set** $U$, which contains all the objects under consideration, is represented by a rectangle. (Note that the universal set varies depending on which objects are of interest.) Inside this rectangle, circles or other geometrical figures are used to represent sets. Sometimes points are used to represent the particular elements of the set. Venn diagrams are often used to indicate the relationships between sets. We show how a Venn diagram can be used in Example 7.

Assessment

EXAMPLE 7    Draw a Venn diagram that represents $V$, the set of vowels in the English alphabet.

*Solution:* We draw a rectangle to indicate the universal set $U$, which is the set of the 26 letters of the English alphabet. Inside this rectangle we draw a circle to represent $V$. Inside this circle we indicate the elements of $V$ with points (see Figure 1).    ◀

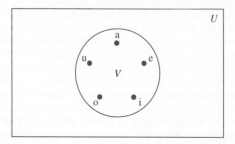

**FIGURE 1    Venn Diagram for the Set of Vowels.**

## Subsets

It is common to encounter situations where the elements of one set are also the elements of a second set. We now introduce some terminology and notation to express such relationships between sets.

**DEFINITION 3**

The set $A$ is a *subset* of $B$ if and only if every element of $A$ is also an element of $B$. We use the notation $A \subseteq B$ to indicate that $A$ is a subset of the set $B$.

We see that $A \subseteq B$ if and only if the quantification

$$\forall x (x \in A \rightarrow x \in B)$$

is true. Note that to show that $A$ is not a subset of $B$ we need only find one element $x \in A$ with $x \notin B$. Such an $x$ is a counterexample to the claim that $x \in A$ implies $x \in B$.

We have these useful rules for determining whether one set is a subset of another:

*Showing that A is a Subset of B*  To show that $A \subseteq B$, show that if $x$ belongs to $A$ then $x$ also belongs to $B$.

*Showing that A is Not a Subset of B*  To show that $A \nsubseteq B$, find a single $x \in A$ such that $x \notin B$.

**EXAMPLE 8**

The set of all odd positive integers less than 10 is a subset of the set of all positive integers less than 10, the set of rational numbers is a subset of the set of real numbers, the set of all computer science majors at your school is a subset of the set of all students at your school, and the set of all people in China is a subset of the set of all people in China (that is, it is a subset of itself). Each of these facts follows immediately by noting that an element that belongs to the first set in each pair of sets also belongs to the second set in that pair.  ◀

**EXAMPLE 9**

The set of integers with squares less than 100 is not a subset of the set of nonnegative integers because $-1$ is in the former set [as $(-1)^2 < 100$], but not the later set. The set of people who have taken discrete mathematics at your school is not a subset of the set of all computer science majors at your school if there is at least one student who has taken discrete mathematics who is not a computer science major.  ◀

BERTRAND RUSSELL (1872–1970)   Bertrand Russell  was born into a prominent English family active in the progressive movement and having a strong commitment to liberty. He became an orphan at an early age and was placed in the care of his father's parents, who had him educated at home. He entered Trinity College, Cambridge, in 1890, where he excelled in mathematics and in moral science. He won a fellowship on the basis of his work on the foundations of geometry. In 1910 Trinity College appointed him to a lectureship in logic and the philosophy of mathematics.

Russell fought for progressive causes throughout his life. He held strong pacifist views, and his protests against World War I led to dismissal from his position at Trinity College. He was imprisoned for 6 months in 1918 because of an article he wrote that was branded as seditious. Russell fought for women's suffrage in Great Britain. In 1961, at the age of 89, he was imprisoned for the second time for his protests advocating nuclear disarmament.

Russell's greatest work was in his development of principles that could be used as a foundation for all of mathematics. His most famous work is *Principia Mathematica,* written with Alfred North Whitehead, which attempts to deduce all of mathematics using a set of primitive axioms. He wrote many books on philosophy, physics, and his political ideas. Russell won the Nobel Prize for literature in 1950.

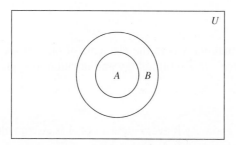

**FIGURE 2    Venn Diagram Showing that $A$ Is a Subset of $B$.**

Theorem 1 shows that every nonempty set $S$ is guaranteed to have at least two subsets, the empty set and the set $S$ itself, that is, $\emptyset \subseteq S$ and $S \subseteq S$.

**THEOREM 1**    For every set $S$, $(i)\,\emptyset \subseteq S$    and    $(ii)\,S \subseteq S$.

*Proof:* We will prove $(i)$ and leave the proof of $(ii)$ as an exercise.

Let $S$ be a set. To show that $\emptyset \subseteq S$, we must show that $\forall x(x \in \emptyset \rightarrow x \in S)$ is true. Because the empty set contains no elements, it follows that $x \in \emptyset$ is always false. It follows that the conditional statement $x \in \emptyset \rightarrow x \in S$ is always true, because its hypothesis is always false and a conditional statement with a false hypothesis is true. Therefore, $\forall x(x \in \emptyset \rightarrow x \in S)$ is true. This completes the proof of $(i)$. Note that this is an example of a vacuous proof.    ◁

When we wish to emphasize that a set $A$ is a subset of a set $B$ but that $A \neq B$, we write $A \subset B$ and say that $A$ is a **proper subset** of $B$. For $A \subset B$ to be true, it must be the case that $A \subseteq B$ and there must exist an element $x$ of $B$ that is not an element of $A$. That is, $A$ is a proper subset of $B$ if and only if

$$\forall x(x \in A \rightarrow x \in B) \wedge \exists x(x \in B \wedge x \notin A)$$

is true. Venn diagrams can be used to illustrate that a set $A$ is a subset of a set $B$. We draw the universal set $U$ as a rectangle. Within this rectangle we draw a circle for $B$. Because $A$ is a subset of $B$, we draw the circle for $A$ within the circle for $B$. This relationship is shown in Figure 2.

A useful way to show that two sets have the same elements is to show that each set is a subset of the other. In other words, we can show that if $A$ and $B$ are sets with $A \subseteq B$ and $B \subseteq A$, then $A = B$. That is, $A = B$ if and only if $\forall x(x \in A \rightarrow x \in B)$ and $\forall x(x \in B \rightarrow x \in A)$ or equivalently if and only if $\forall x(x \in A \leftrightarrow x \in B)$, which is what it means for the $A$ and $B$ to be equal. Because this method of showing two sets are equal is so useful, we highlight it here.

JOHN VENN (1834–1923)    John Venn was born into a London suburban family noted for its philanthropy. He attended London schools and got his mathematics degree from Caius College, Cambridge, in 1857. He was elected a fellow of this college and held his fellowship there until his death. He took holy orders in 1859 and, after a brief stint of religious work, returned to Cambridge, where he developed programs in the moral sciences. Besides his mathematical work, Venn had an interest in history and wrote extensively about his college and family.

Venn's book *Symbolic Logic* clarifies ideas originally presented by Boole. In this book, Venn presents a systematic development of a method that uses geometric figures, known now as *Venn diagrams*. Today these diagrams are primarily used to analyze logical arguments and to illustrate relationships between sets. In addition to his work on symbolic logic, Venn made contributions to probability theory described in his widely used textbook on that subject.

*Showing Two Sets are Equal*  To show that two sets $A$ and $B$ are equal, show that $A \subseteq B$ and $B \subseteq A$.

Sets may have other sets as members. For instance, we have the sets

$$A = \{\emptyset, \{a\}, \{b\}, \{a, b\}\} \qquad \text{and} \qquad B = \{x \mid x \text{ is a subset of the set } \{a, b\}\}.$$

Note that these two sets are equal, that is, $A = B$. Also note that $\{a\} \in A$, but $a \notin A$.

## The Size of a Set

Sets are used extensively in counting problems, and for such applications we need to discuss the sizes of sets.

**DEFINITION 4**  Let $S$ be a set. If there are exactly $n$ distinct elements in $S$ where $n$ is a nonnegative integer, we say that $S$ is a *finite set* and that $n$ is the *cardinality* of $S$. The cardinality of $S$ is denoted by $|S|$.

**Remark:** The term *cardinality* comes from the common usage of the term *cardinal number* as the size of a finite set.

**EXAMPLE 10**  Let $A$ be the set of odd positive integers less than 10. Then $|A| = 5$.  ◀

**EXAMPLE 11**  Let $S$ be the set of letters in the English alphabet. Then $|S| = 26$.  ◀

**EXAMPLE 12**  Because the null set has no elements, it follows that $|\emptyset| = 0$.  ◀

We will also be interested in sets that are not finite.

**DEFINITION 5**  A set is said to be *infinite* if it is not finite.

**EXAMPLE 13**  The set of positive integers is infinite.  ◀

We will extend the notion of cardinality to infinite sets in Section 2.5, a challenging topic full of surprising results.

## Power Sets

Many problems involve testing all combinations of elements of a set to see if they satisfy some property. To consider all such combinations of elements of a set $S$, we build a new set that has as its members all the subsets of $S$.

**DEFINITION 6**  Given a set $S$, the *power set* of $S$ is the set of all subsets of the set $S$. The power set of $S$ is denoted by $\mathcal{P}(S)$.

**EXAMPLE 14**    What is the power set of the set $\{0, 1, 2\}$?

*Solution:* The power set $\mathcal{P}(\{0, 1, 2\})$ is the set of all subsets of $\{0, 1, 2\}$. Hence,

$$\mathcal{P}(\{0, 1, 2\}) = \{\emptyset, \{0\}, \{1\}, \{2\}, \{0, 1\}, \{0, 2\}, \{1, 2\}, \{0, 1, 2\}\}.$$

Note that the empty set and the set itself are members of this set of subsets.    ◀

**EXAMPLE 15**    What is the power set of the empty set? What is the power set of the set $\{\emptyset\}$?

*Solution:* The empty set has exactly one subset, namely, itself. Consequently,

$$\mathcal{P}(\emptyset) = \{\emptyset\}.$$

The set $\{\emptyset\}$ has exactly two subsets, namely, $\emptyset$ and the set $\{\emptyset\}$ itself. Therefore,

$$\mathcal{P}(\{\emptyset\}) = \{\emptyset, \{\emptyset\}\}.$$    ◀

If a set has $n$ elements, then its power set has $2^n$ elements. We will demonstrate this fact in several ways in subsequent sections of the text.

## Cartesian Products

The order of elements in a collection is often important. Because sets are unordered, a different structure is needed to represent ordered collections. This is provided by **ordered $n$-tuples**.

**DEFINITION 7**    The *ordered n-tuple* $(a_1, a_2, \ldots, a_n)$ is the ordered collection that has $a_1$ as its first element, $a_2$ as its second element, $\ldots$, and $a_n$ as its $n$th element.

We say that two ordered $n$-tuples are equal if and only if each corresponding pair of their elements is equal. In other words, $(a_1, a_2, \ldots, a_n) = (b_1, b_2, \ldots, b_n)$ if and only if $a_i = b_i$, for $i = 1, 2, \ldots, n$. In particular, ordered 2-tuples are called **ordered pairs**. The ordered pairs $(a, b)$ and $(c, d)$ are equal if and only if $a = c$ and $b = d$. Note that $(a, b)$ and $(b, a)$ are not equal unless $a = b$.

RENÉ DESCARTES (1596–1650)    René Descartes was born into a noble family near Tours, France, about 200 miles southwest of Paris. He was the third child of his father's first wife; she died several days after his birth. Because of René's poor health, his father, a provincial judge, let his son's formal lessons slide until, at the age of 8, René entered the Jesuit college at La Flèche. The rector of the school took a liking to him and permitted him to stay in bed until late in the morning because of his frail health. From then on, Descartes spent his mornings in bed; he considered these times his most productive hours for thinking.

Descartes left school in 1612, moving to Paris, where he spent 2 years studying mathematics. He earned a law degree in 1616 from the University of Poitiers. At 18 Descartes became disgusted with studying and decided to see the world. He moved to Paris and became a successful gambler. However, he grew tired of bawdy living and moved to the suburb of Saint-Germain, where he devoted himself to mathematical study. When his gambling friends found him, he decided to leave France and undertake a military career. However, he never did any fighting. One day, while escaping the cold in an overheated room at a military encampment, he had several feverish dreams, which revealed his future career as a mathematician and philosopher.

After ending his military career, he traveled throughout Europe. He then spent several years in Paris, where he studied mathematics and philosophy and constructed optical instruments. Descartes decided to move to Holland, where he spent 20 years wandering around the country, accomplishing his most important work. During this time he wrote several books, including the *Discours,* which contains his contributions to analytic geometry, for which he is best known. He also made fundamental contributions to philosophy.

In 1649 Descartes was invited by Queen Christina to visit her court in Sweden to tutor her in philosophy. Although he was reluctant to live in what he called "the land of bears amongst rocks and ice," he finally accepted the invitation and moved to Sweden. Unfortunately, the winter of 1649–1650 was extremely bitter. Descartes caught pneumonia and died in mid-February.

Many of the discrete structures we will study in later chapters are based on the notion of the *Cartesian product* of sets (named after René Descartes). We first define the Cartesian product of two sets.

**DEFINITION 8**

Let $A$ and $B$ be sets. The *Cartesian product* of $A$ and $B$, denoted by $A \times B$, is the set of all ordered pairs $(a, b)$, where $a \in A$ and $b \in B$. Hence,

$$A \times B = \{(a, b) \mid a \in A \land b \in B\}.$$

**EXAMPLE 16**

Let $A$ represent the set of all students at a university, and let $B$ represent the set of all courses offered at the university. What is the Cartesian product $A \times B$ and how can it be used?

*Solution:* The Cartesian product $A \times B$ consists of all the ordered pairs of the form $(a, b)$, where $a$ is a student at the university and $b$ is a course offered at the university. One way to use the set $A \times B$ is to represent all possible enrollments of students in courses at the university.  ◄

**EXAMPLE 17**

What is the Cartesian product of $A = \{1, 2\}$ and $B = \{a, b, c\}$?

*Solution:* The Cartesian product $A \times B$ is

$$A \times B = \{(1, a), (1, b), (1, c), (2, a), (2, b), (2, c)\}.$$  ◄

Note that the Cartesian products $A \times B$ and $B \times A$ are not equal, unless $A = \emptyset$ or $B = \emptyset$ (so that $A \times B = \emptyset$) or $A = B$ (see Exercises 31 and 38). This is illustrated in Example 18.

**EXAMPLE 18**

Show that the Cartesian product $B \times A$ is not equal to the Cartesian product $A \times B$, where $A$ and $B$ are as in Example 17.

*Solution:* The Cartesian product $B \times A$ is

$$B \times A = \{(a, 1), (a, 2), (b, 1), (b, 2), (c, 1), (c, 2)\}.$$

This is not equal to $A \times B$, which was found in Example 17.  ◄

The Cartesian product of more than two sets can also be defined.

**DEFINITION 9**

The *Cartesian product* of the sets $A_1, A_2, \ldots, A_n$, denoted by $A_1 \times A_2 \times \cdots \times A_n$, is the set of ordered $n$-tuples $(a_1, a_2, \ldots, a_n)$, where $a_i$ belongs to $A_i$ for $i = 1, 2, \ldots, n$. In other words,

$$A_1 \times A_2 \times \cdots \times A_n = \{(a_1, a_2, \ldots, a_n) \mid a_i \in A_i \text{ for } i = 1, 2, \ldots, n\}.$$

**EXAMPLE 19**   What is the Cartesian product $A \times B \times C$, where $A = \{0, 1\}$, $B = \{1, 2\}$, and $C = \{0, 1, 2\}$?

*Solution:* The Cartesian product $A \times B \times C$ consists of all ordered triples $(a, b, c)$, where $a \in A$, $b \in B$, and $c \in C$. Hence,

$$A \times B \times C = \{(0, 1, 0), (0, 1, 1), (0, 1, 2), (0, 2, 0), (0, 2, 1), (0, 2, 2),$$
$$(1, 1, 0), (1, 1, 1), (1, 1, 2), (1, 2, 0), (1, 2, 1), (1, 2, 2)\}. \qquad \blacktriangleleft$$

*Remark:* Note that when $A$, $B$, and $C$ are sets, $(A \times B) \times C$ is not the same as $A \times B \times C$ (see Exercise 39).

We use the notation $A^2$ to denote $A \times A$, the Cartesian product of the set $A$ with itself. Similarly, $A^3 = A \times A \times A$, $A^4 = A \times A \times A \times A$, and so on. More generally,

$$A^n = \{(a_1, a_2, \dots, a_n) \mid a_i \in A \text{ for } i = 1, 2, \dots, n\}.$$

**EXAMPLE 20**   Suppose that $A = \{1, 2\}$. It follows that $A^2 = \{(1, 1), (1, 2), (2, 1), (2, 2)\}$ and $A^3 = \{(1, 1, 1), (1, 1, 2), (1, 2, 1), (1, 2, 2), (2, 1, 1), (2, 1, 2), (2, 2, 1), (2, 2, 2)\}$. $\qquad \blacktriangleleft$

A subset $R$ of the Cartesian product $A \times B$ is called a **relation** from the set $A$ to the set $B$. The elements of $R$ are ordered pairs, where the first element belongs to $A$ and the second to $B$. For example, $R = \{(a, 0), (a, 1), (a, 3), (b, 1), (b, 2), (c, 0), (c, 3)\}$ is a relation from the set $\{a, b, c\}$ to the set $\{0, 1, 2, 3\}$. A relation from a set $A$ to itself is called a relation on $A$.

**EXAMPLE 21**   What are the ordered pairs in the less than or equal to relation, which contains $(a, b)$ if $a \leq b$, on the set $\{0, 1, 2, 3\}$?

*Solution:* The ordered pair $(a, b)$ belongs to $R$ if and only if both $a$ and $b$ belong to $\{0, 1, 2, 3\}$ and $a \leq b$. Consequently, the ordered pairs in $R$ are (0,0), (0,1), (0,2), (0,3), (1,1), (1,2), (1,3), (2,2), (2, 3), and (3, 3). $\qquad \blacktriangleleft$

We will study relations and their properties at length in Chapter 9.

## Using Set Notation with Quantifiers

Sometimes we restrict the domain of a quantified statement explicitly by making use of a particular notation. For example, $\forall x \in S(P(x))$ denotes the universal quantification of $P(x)$ over all elements in the set $S$. In other words, $\forall x \in S(P(x))$ is shorthand for $\forall x (x \in S \to P(x))$. Similarly, $\exists x \in S(P(x))$ denotes the existential quantification of $P(x)$ over all elements in $S$. That is, $\exists x \in S(P(x))$ is shorthand for $\exists x (x \in S \land P(x))$.

**EXAMPLE 22**   What do the statements $\forall x \in \mathbf{R} \, (x^2 \geq 0)$ and $\exists x \in \mathbf{Z} \, (x^2 = 1)$ mean?

*Solution:* The statement $\forall x \in \mathbf{R}(x^2 \geq 0)$ states that for every real number $x$, $x^2 \geq 0$. This statement can be expressed as "The square of every real number is nonnegative." This is a true statement.

The statement $\exists x \in \mathbf{Z}(x^2 = 1)$ states that there exists an integer $x$ such that $x^2 = 1$. This statement can be expressed as "There is an integer whose square is 1." This is also a true statement because $x = 1$ is such an integer (as is $-1$). $\qquad \blacktriangleleft$

## Truth Sets and Quantifiers

We will now tie together concepts from set theory and from predicate logic. Given a predicate $P$, and a domain $D$, we define the **truth set** of $P$ to be the set of elements $x$ in $D$ for which $P(x)$ is true. The truth set of $P(x)$ is denoted by $\{x \in D \mid P(x)\}$.

**EXAMPLE 23**    What are the truth sets of the predicates $P(x)$, $Q(x)$, and $R(x)$, where the domain is the set of integers and $P(x)$ is "$|x| = 1$," $Q(x)$ is "$x^2 = 2$," and $R(x)$ is "$|x| = x$."

*Solution:* The truth set of $P$, $\{x \in \mathbf{Z} \mid |x| = 1\}$, is the set of integers for which $|x| = 1$. Because $|x| = 1$ when $x = 1$ or $x = -1$, and for no other integers $x$, we see that the truth set of $P$ is the set $\{-1, 1\}$.

The truth set of $Q$, $\{x \in \mathbf{Z} \mid x^2 = 2\}$, is the set of integers for which $x^2 = 2$. This is the empty set because there are no integers $x$ for which $x^2 = 2$.

The truth set of $R$, $\{x \in \mathbf{Z} \mid |x| = x\}$, is the set of integers for which $|x| = x$. Because $|x| = x$ if and only if $x \geq 0$, it follows that the truth set of $R$ is $\mathbf{N}$, the set of nonnegative integers.    ◀

Note that $\forall x P(x)$ is true over the domain $U$ if and only if the truth set of $P$ is the set $U$. Likewise, $\exists x P(x)$ is true over the domain $U$ if and only if the truth set of $P$ is nonempty.

# Exercises

**1.** List the members of these sets.

   **a)** $\{x \mid x$ is a real number such that $x^2 = 1\}$

   **b)** $\{x \mid x$ is a positive integer less than 12$\}$

   **c)** $\{x \mid x$ is the square of an integer and $x < 100\}$

   **d)** $\{x \mid x$ is an integer such that $x^2 = 2\}$

**2.** Use set builder notation to give a description of each of these sets.

   **a)** $\{0, 3, 6, 9, 12\}$

   **b)** $\{-3, -2, -1, 0, 1, 2, 3\}$

   **c)** $\{m, n, o, p\}$

**3.** For each of these pairs of sets, determine whether the first is a subset of the second, the second is a subset of the first, or neither is a subset of the other.

   **a)** the set of airline flights from New York to New Delhi, the set of nonstop airline flights from New York to New Delhi

   **b)** the set of people who speak English, the set of people who speak Chinese

   **c)** the set of flying squirrels, the set of living creatures that can fly

**4.** For each of these pairs of sets, determine whether the first is a subset of the second, the second is a subset of the first, or neither is a subset of the other.

   **a)** the set of people who speak English, the set of people who speak English with an Australian accent

   **b)** the set of fruits, the set of citrus fruits

   **c)** the set of students studying discrete mathematics, the set of students studying data structures

**5.** Determine whether each of these pairs of sets are equal.

   **a)** $\{1, 3, 3, 3, 5, 5, 5, 5, 5\}$, $\{5, 3, 1\}$

   **b)** $\{\{1\}\}$, $\{1, \{1\}\}$        **c)** $\emptyset$, $\{\emptyset\}$

**6.** Suppose that $A = \{2, 4, 6\}$, $B = \{2, 6\}$, $C = \{4, 6\}$, and $D = \{4, 6, 8\}$. Determine which of these sets are subsets of which other of these sets.

**7.** For each of the following sets, determine whether 2 is an element of that set.

   **a)** $\{x \in \mathbf{R} \mid x$ is an integer greater than 1$\}$

   **b)** $\{x \in \mathbf{R} \mid x$ is the square of an integer$\}$

   **c)** $\{2, \{2\}\}$        **d)** $\{\{2\}, \{\{2\}\}\}$

   **e)** $\{\{2\}, \{2, \{2\}\}\}$        **f)** $\{\{\{2\}\}\}$

**8.** For each of the sets in Exercise 7, determine whether $\{2\}$ is an element of that set.

**9.** Determine whether each of these statements is true or false.

   **a)** $0 \in \emptyset$        **b)** $\emptyset \in \{0\}$

   **c)** $\{0\} \subset \emptyset$        **d)** $\emptyset \subset \{0\}$

   **e)** $\{0\} \in \{0\}$        **f)** $\{0\} \subset \{0\}$

   **g)** $\{\emptyset\} \subseteq \{\emptyset\}$

**10.** Determine whether these statements are true or false.

   **a)** $\emptyset \in \{\emptyset\}$        **b)** $\emptyset \in \{\emptyset, \{\emptyset\}\}$

   **c)** $\{\emptyset\} \in \{\emptyset\}$        **d)** $\{\emptyset\} \in \{\{\emptyset\}\}$

   **e)** $\{\emptyset\} \subset \{\emptyset, \{\emptyset\}\}$        **f)** $\{\{\emptyset\}\} \subset \{\emptyset, \{\emptyset\}\}$

   **g)** $\{\{\emptyset\}\} \subset \{\{\emptyset\}, \{\emptyset\}\}$

**11.** Determine whether each of these statements is true or false.

   **a)** $x \in \{x\}$        **b)** $\{x\} \subseteq \{x\}$        **c)** $\{x\} \in \{x\}$

   **d)** $\{x\} \in \{\{x\}\}$        **e)** $\emptyset \subseteq \{x\}$        **f)** $\emptyset \in \{x\}$

**12.** Use a Venn diagram to illustrate the subset of odd integers in the set of all positive integers not exceeding 10.

**13.** Use a Venn diagram to illustrate the set of all months of the year whose names do not contain the letter $R$ in the set of all months of the year.

**14.** Use a Venn diagram to illustrate the relationship $A \subseteq B$ and $B \subseteq C$.

**15.** Use a Venn diagram to illustrate the relationships $A \subset B$ and $B \subset C$.

**16.** Use a Venn diagram to illustrate the relationships $A \subset B$ and $A \subset C$.

**17.** Suppose that $A$, $B$, and $C$ are sets such that $A \subseteq B$ and $B \subseteq C$. Show that $A \subseteq C$.

**18.** Find two sets $A$ and $B$ such that $A \in B$ and $A \subseteq B$.

**19.** What is the cardinality of each of these sets?
  **a)** $\{a\}$
  **b)** $\{\{a\}\}$
  **c)** $\{a, \{a\}\}$
  **d)** $\{a, \{a\}, \{a, \{a\}\}\}$

**20.** What is the cardinality of each of these sets?
  **a)** $\emptyset$
  **b)** $\{\emptyset\}$
  **c)** $\{\emptyset, \{\emptyset\}\}$
  **d)** $\{\emptyset, \{\emptyset\}, \{\emptyset, \{\emptyset\}\}\}$

**21.** Find the power set of each of these sets, where $a$ and $b$ are distinct elements.
  **a)** $\{a\}$
  **b)** $\{a, b\}$
  **c)** $\{\emptyset, \{\emptyset\}\}$

**22.** Can you conclude that $A = B$ if $A$ and $B$ are two sets with the same power set?

**23.** How many elements does each of these sets have where $a$ and $b$ are distinct elements?
  **a)** $\mathcal{P}(\{a, b, \{a, b\}\})$
  **b)** $\mathcal{P}(\{\emptyset, a, \{a\}, \{\{a\}\}\})$
  **c)** $\mathcal{P}(\mathcal{P}(\emptyset))$

**24.** Determine whether each of these sets is the power set of a set, where $a$ and $b$ are distinct elements.
  **a)** $\emptyset$
  **b)** $\{\emptyset, \{a\}\}$
  **c)** $\{\emptyset, \{a\}, \{\emptyset, a\}\}$
  **d)** $\{\emptyset, \{a\}, \{b\}, \{a, b\}\}$

**25.** Prove that $\mathcal{P}(A) \subseteq \mathcal{P}(B)$ if and only if $A \subseteq B$.

**26.** Show that if $A \subseteq C$ and $B \subseteq D$, then $A \times B \subseteq C \times D$

**27.** Let $A = \{a, b, c, d\}$ and $B = \{y, z\}$. Find
  **a)** $A \times B$.
  **b)** $B \times A$.

**28.** What is the Cartesian product $A \times B$, where $A$ is the set of courses offered by the mathematics department at a university and $B$ is the set of mathematics professors at this university? Give an example of how this Cartesian product can be used.

**29.** What is the Cartesian product $A \times B \times C$, where $A$ is the set of all airlines and $B$ and $C$ are both the set of all cities in the United States? Give an example of how this Cartesian product can be used.

**30.** Suppose that $A \times B = \emptyset$, where $A$ and $B$ are sets. What can you conclude?

**31.** Let $A$ be a set. Show that $\emptyset \times A = A \times \emptyset = \emptyset$.

**32.** Let $A = \{a, b, c\}$, $B = \{x, y\}$, and $C = \{0, 1\}$. Find
  **a)** $A \times B \times C$.
  **b)** $C \times B \times A$.
  **c)** $C \times A \times B$.
  **d)** $B \times B \times B$.

**33.** Find $A^2$ if
  **a)** $A = \{0, 1, 3\}$.
  **b)** $A = \{1, 2, a, b\}$.

**34.** Find $A^3$ if
  **a)** $A = \{a\}$.
  **b)** $A = \{0, a\}$.

**35.** How many different elements does $A \times B$ have if $A$ has $m$ elements and $B$ has $n$ elements?

**36.** How many different elements does $A \times B \times C$ have if $A$ has $m$ elements, $B$ has $n$ elements, and $C$ has $p$ elements?

**37.** How many different elements does $A^n$ have when $A$ has $m$ elements and $n$ is a positive integer?

**38.** Show that $A \times B \neq B \times A$, when $A$ and $B$ are nonempty, unless $A = B$.

**39.** Explain why $A \times B \times C$ and $(A \times B) \times C$ are not the same.

**40.** Explain why $(A \times B) \times (C \times D)$ and $A \times (B \times C) \times D$ are not the same.

**41.** Translate each of these quantifications into English and determine its truth value.
  **a)** $\forall x \in \mathbf{R}\ (x^2 \neq -1)$
  **b)** $\exists x \in \mathbf{Z}\ (x^2 = 2)$
  **c)** $\forall x \in \mathbf{Z}\ (x^2 > 0)$
  **d)** $\exists x \in \mathbf{R}\ (x^2 = x)$

**42.** Translate each of these quantifications into English and determine its truth value.
  **a)** $\exists x \in \mathbf{R}\ (x^3 = -1)$
  **b)** $\exists x \in \mathbf{Z}\ (x + 1 > x)$
  **c)** $\forall x \in \mathbf{Z}\ (x - 1 \in \mathbf{Z})$
  **d)** $\forall x \in \mathbf{Z}\ (x^2 \in \mathbf{Z})$

**43.** Find the truth set of each of these predicates where the domain is the set of integers.
  **a)** $P(x)$: $x^2 < 3$
  **b)** $Q(x)$: $x^2 > x$
  **c)** $R(x)$: $2x + 1 = 0$

**44.** Find the truth set of each of these predicates where the domain is the set of integers.
  **a)** $P(x)$: $x^3 \geq 1$
  **b)** $Q(x)$: $x^2 = 2$
  **c)** $R(x)$: $x < x^2$

**\*45.** The defining property of an ordered pair is that two ordered pairs are equal if and only if their first elements are equal and their second elements are equal. Surprisingly, instead of taking the ordered pair as a primitive concept, we can construct ordered pairs using basic notions from set theory. Show that if we define the ordered pair $(a, b)$ to be $\{\{a\}, \{a, b\}\}$, then $(a, b) = (c, d)$ if and only if $a = c$ and $b = d$. [*Hint:* First show that $\{\{a\}, \{a, b\}\} = \{\{c\}, \{c, d\}\}$ if and only if $a = c$ and $b = d$.]

**\*46.** This exercise presents **Russell's paradox**. Let $S$ be the set that contains a set $x$ if the set $x$ does not belong to itself, so that $S = \{x \mid x \notin x\}$.
  **a)** Show the assumption that $S$ is a member of $S$ leads to a contradiction.
  **b)** Show the assumption that $S$ is not a member of $S$ leads to a contradiction.

By parts (a) and (b) it follows that the set $S$ cannot be defined as it was. This paradox can be avoided by restricting the types of elements that sets can have.

**\*47.** Describe a procedure for listing all the subsets of a finite set.

# 2.2  Set Operations

## Introduction

Two, or more, sets can be combined in many different ways. For instance, starting with the set of mathematics majors at your school and the set of computer science majors at your school, we can form the set of students who are mathematics majors or computer science majors, the set of students who are joint majors in mathematics and computer science, the set of all students not majoring in mathematics, and so on.

Links

**DEFINITION 1**  Let $A$ and $B$ be sets. The *union* of the sets $A$ and $B$, denoted by $A \cup B$, is the set that contains those elements that are either in $A$ or in $B$, or in both.

An element $x$ belongs to the union of the sets $A$ and $B$ if and only if $x$ belongs to $A$ or $x$ belongs to $B$. This tells us that

$$A \cup B = \{x \mid x \in A \lor x \in B\}.$$

The Venn diagram shown in Figure 1 represents the union of two sets $A$ and $B$. The area that represents $A \cup B$ is the shaded area within either the circle representing $A$ or the circle representing $B$.

We will give some examples of the union of sets.

**EXAMPLE 1**  The union of the sets $\{1, 3, 5\}$ and $\{1, 2, 3\}$ is the set $\{1, 2, 3, 5\}$; that is, $\{1, 3, 5\} \cup \{1, 2, 3\} = \{1, 2, 3, 5\}$. ◀

**EXAMPLE 2**  The union of the set of all computer science majors at your school and the set of all mathematics majors at your school is the set of students at your school who are majoring either in mathematics or in computer science (or in both). ◀

**DEFINITION 2**  Let $A$ and $B$ be sets. The *intersection* of the sets $A$ and $B$, denoted by $A \cap B$, is the set containing those elements in both $A$ and $B$.

An element $x$ belongs to the intersection of the sets $A$ and $B$ if and only if $x$ belongs to $A$ and $x$ belongs to $B$. This tells us that

$$A \cap B = \{x \mid x \in A \land x \in B\}.$$

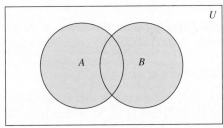

$A \cup B$ is shaded.

**FIGURE 1  Venn Diagram of the Union of $A$ and $B$.**

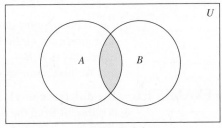

$A \cap B$ is shaded.

**FIGURE 2  Venn Diagram of the Intersection of $A$ and $B$.**

The Venn diagram shown in Figure 2 represents the intersection of two sets $A$ and $B$. The shaded area that is within both the circles representing the sets $A$ and $B$ is the area that represents the intersection of $A$ and $B$.

We give some examples of the intersection of sets.

**EXAMPLE 3**    The intersection of the sets $\{1, 3, 5\}$ and $\{1, 2, 3\}$ is the set $\{1, 3\}$; that is, $\{1, 3, 5\} \cap \{1, 2, 3\} = \{1, 3\}$. ◄

**EXAMPLE 4**    The intersection of the set of all computer science majors at your school and the set of all mathematics majors is the set of all students who are joint majors in mathematics and computer science. ◄

**DEFINITION 3**    Two sets are called *disjoint* if their intersection is the empty set.

**EXAMPLE 5**    Let $A = \{1, 3, 5, 7, 9\}$ and $B = \{2, 4, 6, 8, 10\}$. Because $A \cap B = \emptyset$, $A$ and $B$ are disjoint. ◄

Be careful not to overcount!

We are often interested in finding the cardinality of a union of two finite sets $A$ and $B$. Note that $|A| + |B|$ counts each element that is in $A$ but not in $B$ or in $B$ but not in $A$ exactly once, and each element that is in both $A$ and $B$ exactly twice. Thus, if the number of elements that are in both $A$ and $B$ is subtracted from $|A| + |B|$, elements in $A \cap B$ will be counted only once. Hence,

$$|A \cup B| = |A| + |B| - |A \cap B|.$$

The generalization of this result to unions of an arbitrary number of sets is called the **principle of inclusion–exclusion**. The principle of inclusion–exclusion is an important technique used in enumeration. We will discuss this principle and other counting techniques in detail in Chapters 6 and 8.

There are other important ways to combine sets.

**DEFINITION 4**    Let $A$ and $B$ be sets. The *difference* of $A$ and $B$, denoted by $A - B$, is the set containing those elements that are in $A$ but not in $B$. The difference of $A$ and $B$ is also called the *complement of B with respect to A*.

*Remark:* The difference of sets $A$ and $B$ is sometimes denoted by $A \backslash B$.

An element $x$ belongs to the difference of $A$ and $B$ if and only if $x \in A$ and $x \notin B$. This tells us that

$$A - B = \{x \mid x \in A \land x \notin B\}.$$

The Venn diagram shown in Figure 3 represents the difference of the sets $A$ and $B$. The shaded area inside the circle that represents $A$ and outside the circle that represents $B$ is the area that represents $A - B$.

We give some examples of differences of sets.

**EXAMPLE 6**    The difference of $\{1, 3, 5\}$ and $\{1, 2, 3\}$ is the set $\{5\}$; that is, $\{1, 3, 5\} - \{1, 2, 3\} = \{5\}$. This is different from the difference of $\{1, 2, 3\}$ and $\{1, 3, 5\}$, which is the set $\{2\}$. ◄

**EXAMPLE 7**    The difference of the set of computer science majors at your school and the set of mathematics majors at your school is the set of all computer science majors at your school who are not also mathematics majors. ◄

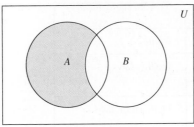

$A - B$ is shaded.

**FIGURE 3    Venn Diagram for
the Difference of $A$ and $B$.**

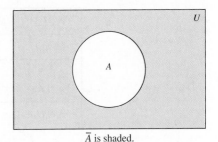

$\overline{A}$ is shaded.

**FIGURE 4    Venn Diagram for
the Complement of the Set $A$.**

Once the universal set $U$ has been specified, the **complement** of a set can be defined.

**DEFINITION 5**    Let $U$ be the universal set. The *complement* of the set $A$, denoted by $\overline{A}$, is the complement of $A$ with respect to $U$. Therefore, the complement of the set $A$ is $U - A$.

An element belongs to $\overline{A}$ if and only if $x \notin A$. This tells us that

$$\overline{A} = \{x \in U \mid x \notin A\}.$$

In Figure 4 the shaded area outside the circle representing $A$ is the area representing $\overline{A}$.
We give some examples of the complement of a set.

**EXAMPLE 8**    Let $A = \{a, e, i, o, u\}$ (where the universal set is the set of letters of the English alphabet). Then $\overline{A} = \{b, c, d, f, g, h, j, k, l, m, n, p, q, r, s, t, v, w, x, y, z\}$.    ◀

**EXAMPLE 9**    Let $A$ be the set of positive integers greater than 10 (with universal set the set of all positive integers). Then $\overline{A} = \{1, 2, 3, 4, 5, 6, 7, 8, 9, 10\}$.    ◀

It is left to the reader (Exercise 19) to show that we can express the difference of $A$ and $B$ as the intersection of $A$ and the complement of $B$. That is,

$$A - B = A \cap \overline{B}.$$

## Set Identities

Table 1 lists the most important set identities. We will prove several of these identities here, using three different methods. These methods are presented to illustrate that there are often many different approaches to the solution of a problem. The proofs of the remaining identities will be left as exercises. The reader should note the similarity between these set identities and the logical equivalences discussed in Section 1.3. (Compare Table 6 of Section 1.6 and Table 1.) In fact, the set identities given can be proved directly from the corresponding logical equivalences. Furthermore, both are special cases of identities that hold for Boolean algebra (discussed in Chapter 12).

*Set identities and propositional equivalences are just special cases of identities for Boolean algebra.*

One way to show that two sets are equal is to show that each is a subset of the other. Recall that to show that one set is a subset of a second set, we can show that if an element belongs to the first set, then it must also belong to the second set. We generally use a direct proof to do this. We illustrate this type of proof by establishing the first of De Morgan's laws.

| TABLE 1  Set Identities. | |
|---|---|
| **Identity** | **Name** |
| $A \cap U = A$ <br> $A \cup \emptyset = A$ | Identity laws |
| $A \cup U = U$ <br> $A \cap \emptyset = \emptyset$ | Domination laws |
| $A \cup A = A$ <br> $A \cap A = A$ | Idempotent laws |
| $\overline{(\overline{A})} = A$ | Complementation law |
| $A \cup B = B \cup A$ <br> $A \cap B = B \cap A$ | Commutative laws |
| $A \cup (B \cup C) = (A \cup B) \cup C$ <br> $A \cap (B \cap C) = (A \cap B) \cap C$ | Associative laws |
| $A \cup (B \cap C) = (A \cup B) \cap (A \cup C)$ <br> $A \cap (B \cup C) = (A \cap B) \cup (A \cap C)$ | Distributive laws |
| $\overline{A \cap B} = \overline{A} \cup \overline{B}$ <br> $\overline{A \cup B} = \overline{A} \cap \overline{B}$ | De Morgan's laws |
| $A \cup (A \cap B) = A$ <br> $A \cap (A \cup B) = A$ | Absorption laws |
| $A \cup \overline{A} = U$ <br> $A \cap \overline{A} = \emptyset$ | Complement laws |

**EXAMPLE 10**   Prove that $\overline{A \cap B} = \overline{A} \cup \overline{B}$.

*This identity says that the complement of the intersection of two sets is the union of their complements.*

*Solution:* We will prove that the two sets $\overline{A \cap B}$ and $\overline{A} \cup \overline{B}$ are equal by showing that each set is a subset of the other.

First, we will show that $\overline{A \cap B} \subseteq \overline{A} \cup \overline{B}$. We do this by showing that if $x$ is in $\overline{A \cap B}$, then it must also be in $\overline{A} \cup \overline{B}$. Now suppose that $x \in \overline{A \cap B}$. By the definition of complement, $x \notin A \cap B$. Using the definition of intersection, we see that the proposition $\neg((x \in A) \wedge (x \in B))$ is true.

By applying De Morgan's law for propositions, we see that $\neg(x \in A)$ or $\neg(x \in B)$. Using the definition of negation of propositions, we have $x \notin A$ or $x \notin B$. Using the definition of the complement of a set, we see that this implies that $x \in \overline{A}$ or $x \in \overline{B}$. Consequently, by the definition of union, we see that $x \in \overline{A} \cup \overline{B}$. We have now shown that $\overline{A \cap B} \subseteq \overline{A} \cup \overline{B}$.

**Extra Examples**

Next, we will show that $\overline{A} \cup \overline{B} \subseteq \overline{A \cap B}$. We do this by showing that if $x$ is in $\overline{A} \cup \overline{B}$, then it must also be in $\overline{A \cap B}$. Now suppose that $x \in \overline{A} \cup \overline{B}$. By the definition of union, we know that $x \in \overline{A}$ or $x \in \overline{B}$. Using the definition of complement, we see that $x \notin A$ or $x \notin B$. Consequently, the proposition $\neg(x \in A) \vee \neg(x \in B)$ is true.

By De Morgan's law for propositions, we conclude that $\neg((x \in A) \wedge (x \in B))$ is true. By the definition of intersection, it follows that $\neg(x \in A \cap B)$. We now use the definition of complement to conclude that $x \in \overline{A \cap B}$. This shows that $\overline{A} \cup \overline{B} \subseteq \overline{A \cap B}$.

Because we have shown that each set is a subset of the other, the two sets are equal, and the identity is proved.    ◀

We can more succinctly express the reasoning used in Example 10 using set builder notation, as Example 11 illustrates.

**EXAMPLE 11**    Use set builder notation and logical equivalences to establish the first De Morgan law $\overline{A \cap B} = \overline{A} \cup \overline{B}$.

*Solution:* We can prove this identity with the following steps.

$$
\begin{aligned}
\overline{A \cap B} &= \{x \mid x \notin A \cap B\} && \text{by definition of complement} \\
&= \{x \mid \neg(x \in (A \cap B))\} && \text{by definition of does not belong symbol} \\
&= \{x \mid \neg(x \in A \wedge x \in B)\} && \text{by definition of intersection} \\
&= \{x \mid \neg(x \in A) \vee \neg(x \in B)\} && \text{by the first De Morgan law for logical equivalences} \\
&= \{x \mid x \notin A \vee x \notin B\} && \text{by definition of does not belong symbol} \\
&= \{x \mid x \in \overline{A} \vee x \in \overline{B}\} && \text{by definition of complement} \\
&= \{x \mid x \in \overline{A} \cup \overline{B}\} && \text{by definition of union} \\
&= \overline{A} \cup \overline{B} && \text{by meaning of set builder notation}
\end{aligned}
$$

Note that besides the definitions of complement, union, set membership, and set builder notation, this proof uses the second De Morgan law for logical equivalences. ◄

Proving a set identity involving more than two sets by showing each side of the identity is a subset of the other often requires that we keep track of different cases, as illustrated by the proof in Example 12 of one of the distributive laws for sets.

**EXAMPLE 12**    Prove the second distributive law from Table 1, which states that $A \cap (B \cup C) = (A \cap B) \cup (A \cap C)$ for all sets $A$, $B$, and $C$.

*Solution:* We will prove this identity by showing that each side is a subset of the other side.

Suppose that $x \in A \cap (B \cup C)$. Then $x \in A$ and $x \in B \cup C$. By the definition of union, it follows that $x \in A$, and $x \in B$ or $x \in C$ (or both). In other words, we know that the compound proposition $(x \in A) \wedge ((x \in B) \vee (x \in C))$ is true. By the distributive law for conjunction over disjunction, it follows that $((x \in A) \wedge (x \in B)) \vee ((x \in A) \wedge (x \in C))$. We conclude that either $x \in A$ and $x \in B$, or $x \in A$ and $x \in C$. By the definition of intersection, it follows that $x \in A \cap B$ or $x \in A \cap C$. Using the definition of union, we conclude that $x \in (A \cap B) \cup (A \cap C)$. We conclude that $A \cap (B \cup C) \subseteq (A \cap B) \cup (A \cap C)$.

Now suppose that $x \in (A \cap B) \cup (A \cap C)$. Then, by the definition of union, $x \in A \cap B$ or $x \in A \cap C$. By the definition of intersection, it follows that $x \in A$ and $x \in B$ or that $x \in A$ and $x \in C$. From this we see that $x \in A$, and $x \in B$ or $x \in C$. Consequently, by the definition of union we see that $x \in A$ and $x \in B \cup C$. Furthermore, by the definition of intersection, it follows that $x \in A \cap (B \cup C)$. We conclude that $(A \cap B) \cup (A \cap C) \subseteq A \cap (B \cup C)$. This completes the proof of the identity. ◄

Set identities can also be proved using **membership tables**. We consider each combination of sets that an element can belong to and verify that elements in the same combinations of sets belong to both the sets in the identity. To indicate that an element is in a set, a 1 is used; to indicate that an element is not in a set, a 0 is used. (The reader should note the similarity between membership tables and truth tables.)

**EXAMPLE 13**    Use a membership table to show that $A \cap (B \cup C) = (A \cap B) \cup (A \cap C)$.

*Solution:* The membership table for these combinations of sets is shown in Table 2. This table has eight rows. Because the columns for $A \cap (B \cup C)$ and $(A \cap B) \cup (A \cap C)$ are the same, the identity is valid. ◄

Additional set identities can be established using those that we have already proved. Consider Example 14.

| TABLE 2  A Membership Table for the Distributive Property. | | | | | | | |
|---|---|---|---|---|---|---|---|
| $A$ | $B$ | $C$ | $B \cup C$ | $A \cap (B \cup C)$ | $A \cap B$ | $A \cap C$ | $(A \cap B) \cup (A \cap C)$ |
| 1 | 1 | 1 | 1 | 1 | 1 | 1 | 1 |
| 1 | 1 | 0 | 1 | 1 | 1 | 0 | 1 |
| 1 | 0 | 1 | 1 | 1 | 0 | 1 | 1 |
| 1 | 0 | 0 | 0 | 0 | 0 | 0 | 0 |
| 0 | 1 | 1 | 1 | 0 | 0 | 0 | 0 |
| 0 | 1 | 0 | 1 | 0 | 0 | 0 | 0 |
| 0 | 0 | 1 | 1 | 0 | 0 | 0 | 0 |
| 0 | 0 | 0 | 0 | 0 | 0 | 0 | 0 |

**EXAMPLE 14**   Let $A$, $B$, and $C$ be sets. Show that

$$\overline{A \cup (B \cap C)} = (\overline{C} \cup \overline{B}) \cap \overline{A}.$$

*Solution:* We have

$$
\begin{aligned}
\overline{A \cup (B \cap C)} &= \overline{A} \cap \overline{(B \cap C)} && \text{by the first De Morgan law} \\
&= \overline{A} \cap (\overline{B} \cup \overline{C}) && \text{by the second De Morgan law} \\
&= (\overline{B} \cup \overline{C}) \cap \overline{A} && \text{by the commutative law for intersections} \\
&= (\overline{C} \cup \overline{B}) \cap \overline{A} && \text{by the commutative law for unions.}
\end{aligned}
$$

◄

## Generalized Unions and Intersections

Because unions and intersections of sets satisfy associative laws, the sets $A \cup B \cup C$ and $A \cap B \cap C$ are well defined; that is, the meaning of this notation is unambiguous when $A$, $B$, and $C$ are sets. That is, we do not have to use parentheses to indicate which operation comes first because $A \cup (B \cup C) = (A \cup B) \cup C$ and $A \cap (B \cap C) = (A \cap B) \cap C$. Note that $A \cup B \cup C$ contains those elements that are in at least one of the sets $A$, $B$, and $C$, and that $A \cap B \cap C$ contains those elements that are in all of $A$, $B$, and $C$. These combinations of the three sets, $A$, $B$, and $C$, are shown in Figure 5.

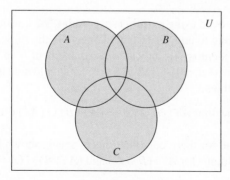

(a) $A \cup B \cup C$ is shaded.

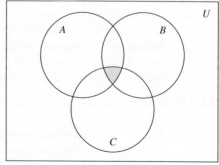

(b) $A \cap B \cap C$ is shaded.

**FIGURE 5**   The Union and Intersection of $A$, $B$, and $C$.

**EXAMPLE 15** Let $A = \{0, 2, 4, 6, 8\}$, $B = \{0, 1, 2, 3, 4\}$, and $C = \{0, 3, 6, 9\}$. What are $A \cup B \cup C$ and $A \cap B \cap C$?

*Solution:* The set $A \cup B \cup C$ contains those elements in at least one of $A$, $B$, and $C$. Hence,

$$A \cup B \cup C = \{0, 1, 2, 3, 4, 6, 8, 9\}.$$

The set $A \cap B \cap C$ contains those elements in all three of $A$, $B$, and $C$. Thus,

$$A \cap B \cap C = \{0\}. \qquad \blacktriangleleft$$

We can also consider unions and intersections of an arbitrary number of sets. We introduce these definitions.

**DEFINITION 6** The *union* of a collection of sets is the set that contains those elements that are members of at least one set in the collection.

We use the notation

$$A_1 \cup A_2 \cup \cdots \cup A_n = \bigcup_{i=1}^{n} A_i$$

to denote the union of the sets $A_1, A_2, \ldots, A_n$.

**DEFINITION 7** The *intersection* of a collection of sets is the set that contains those elements that are members of all the sets in the collection.

We use the notation

$$A_1 \cap A_2 \cap \cdots \cap A_n = \bigcap_{i=1}^{n} A_i$$

to denote the intersection of the sets $A_1, A_2, \ldots, A_n$. We illustrate generalized unions and intersections with Example 16.

**EXAMPLE 16** For $i = 1, 2, \ldots$, let $A_i = \{i, i + 1, i + 2, \ldots\}$. Then,

$$\bigcup_{i=1}^{n} A_i = \bigcup_{i=1}^{n} \{i, i + 1, i + 2, \ldots\} = \{1, 2, 3, \ldots\},$$

and

$$\bigcap_{i=1}^{n} A_i = \bigcap_{i=1}^{n} \{i, i + 1, i + 2, \ldots\} = \{n, n + 1, n + 2, \ldots\} = A_n. \qquad \blacktriangleleft$$

We can extend the notation we have introduced for unions and intersections to other families of sets. In particular, we use the notation

$$A_1 \cup A_2 \cup \cdots \cup A_n \cup \cdots = \bigcup_{i=1}^{\infty} A_i$$

to denote the union of the sets $A_1, A_2, \ldots, A_n, \ldots$. Similarly, the intersection of these sets is denoted by

$$A_1 \cap A_2 \cap \cdots \cap A_n \cap \cdots = \bigcap_{i=1}^{\infty} A_i.$$

More generally, when $I$ is a set, the notations $\bigcap_{i \in I} A_i$ and $\bigcup_{i \in I} A_i$ are used to denote the intersection and union of the sets $A_i$ for $i \in I$, respectively. Note that we have $\bigcap_{i \in I} A_i = \{x \mid \forall i \in I \ (x \in A_i)\}$ and $\bigcup_{i \in I} A_i = \{x \mid \exists i \in I \ (x \in A_i)\}$.

**EXAMPLE 17**   Suppose that $A_i = \{1, 2, 3, \ldots, i\}$ for $i = 1, 2, 3, \ldots$. Then,

$$\bigcup_{i=1}^{\infty} A_i = \bigcup_{i=1}^{\infty} \{1, 2, 3, \ldots, i\} = \{1, 2, 3, \ldots\} = \mathbf{Z}^+$$

and

$$\bigcap_{i=1}^{\infty} A_i = \bigcap_{i=1}^{\infty} \{1, 2, 3, \ldots, i\} = \{1\}.$$

To see that the union of these sets is the set of positive integers, note that every positive integer $n$ is in at least one of the sets, because it belongs to $A_n = \{1, 2, \ldots, n\}$, and every element of the sets in the union is a positive integer. To see that the intersection of these sets is the set $\{1\}$, note that the only element that belongs to all the sets $A_1, A_2, \ldots$ is 1. To see this note that $A_1 = \{1\}$ and $1 \in A_i$ for $i = 1, 2, \ldots$.   ◀

## Computer Representation of Sets

There are various ways to represent sets using a computer. One method is to store the elements of the set in an unordered fashion. However, if this is done, the operations of computing the union, intersection, or difference of two sets would be time-consuming, because each of these operations would require a large amount of searching for elements. We will present a method for storing elements using an arbitrary ordering of the elements of the universal set. This method of representing sets makes computing combinations of sets easy.

Assume that the universal set $U$ is finite (and of reasonable size so that the number of elements of $U$ is not larger than the memory size of the computer being used). First, specify an arbitrary ordering of the elements of $U$, for instance $a_1, a_2, \ldots, a_n$. Represent a subset $A$ of $U$ with the bit string of length $n$, where the $i$th bit in this string is 1 if $a_i$ belongs to $A$ and is 0 if $a_i$ does not belong to $A$. Example 18 illustrates this technique.

**EXAMPLE 18**   Let $U = \{1, 2, 3, 4, 5, 6, 7, 8, 9, 10\}$, and the ordering of elements of $U$ has the elements in increasing order; that is, $a_i = i$. What bit strings represent the subset of all odd integers in $U$, the subset of all even integers in $U$, and the subset of integers not exceeding 5 in $U$?

*Solution:* The bit string that represents the set of odd integers in $U$, namely, $\{1, 3, 5, 7, 9\}$, has a one bit in the first, third, fifth, seventh, and ninth positions, and a zero elsewhere. It is

10 1010 1010.

(We have split this bit string of length ten into blocks of length four for easy reading.) Similarly, we represent the subset of all even integers in $U$, namely, $\{2, 4, 6, 8, 10\}$, by the string

01 0101 0101.

The set of all integers in $U$ that do not exceed 5, namely, $\{1, 2, 3, 4, 5\}$, is represented by the string

11 1110 0000.    ◄

Using bit strings to represent sets, it is easy to find complements of sets and unions, intersections, and differences of sets. To find the bit string for the complement of a set from the bit string for that set, we simply change each 1 to a 0 and each 0 to 1, because $x \in A$ if and only if $x \notin \overline{A}$. Note that this operation corresponds to taking the negation of each bit when we associate a bit with a truth value—with 1 representing true and 0 representing false.

**EXAMPLE 19**   We have seen that the bit string for the set $\{1, 3, 5, 7, 9\}$ (with universal set $\{1, 2, 3, 4, 5, 6, 7, 8, 9, 10\}$) is

10 1010 1010.

What is the bit string for the complement of this set?

*Solution:* The bit string for the complement of this set is obtained by replacing 0s with 1s and vice versa. This yields the string

01 0101 0101,

which corresponds to the set $\{2, 4, 6, 8, 10\}$.    ◄

To obtain the bit string for the union and intersection of two sets we perform bitwise Boolean operations on the bit strings representing the two sets. The bit in the $i$th position of the bit string of the union is 1 if either of the bits in the $i$th position in the two strings is 1 (or both are 1), and is 0 when both bits are 0. Hence, the bit string for the union is the bitwise *OR* of the bit strings for the two sets. The bit in the $i$th position of the bit string of the intersection is 1 when the bits in the corresponding position in the two strings are both 1, and is 0 when either of the two bits is 0 (or both are). Hence, the bit string for the intersection is the bitwise *AND* of the bit strings for the two sets.

**EXAMPLE 20**   The bit strings for the sets $\{1, 2, 3, 4, 5\}$ and $\{1, 3, 5, 7, 9\}$ are 11 1110 0000 and 10 1010 1010, respectively. Use bit strings to find the union and intersection of these sets.

*Solution:* The bit string for the union of these sets is

11 1110 0000 $\vee$ 10 1010 1010 = 11 1110 1010,

which corresponds to the set $\{1, 2, 3, 4, 5, 7, 9\}$. The bit string for the intersection of these sets is

11 1110 0000 $\wedge$ 10 1010 1010 = 10 1010 0000,

which corresponds to the set $\{1, 3, 5\}$.    ◄

# Exercises

1. Let $A$ be the set of students who live within one mile of school and let $B$ be the set of students who walk to classes. Describe the students in each of these sets.
   a) $A \cap B$
   b) $A \cup B$
   c) $A - B$
   d) $B - A$

2. Suppose that $A$ is the set of sophomores at your school and $B$ is the set of students in discrete mathematics at your school. Express each of these sets in terms of $A$ and $B$.
   a) the set of sophomores taking discrete mathematics in your school
   b) the set of sophomores at your school who are not taking discrete mathematics
   c) the set of students at your school who either are sophomores or are taking discrete mathematics
   d) the set of students at your school who either are not sophomores or are not taking discrete mathematics

3. Let $A = \{1, 2, 3, 4, 5\}$ and $B = \{0, 3, 6\}$. Find
   a) $A \cup B$.
   b) $A \cap B$.
   c) $A - B$.
   d) $B - A$.

4. Let $A = \{a, b, c, d, e\}$ and $B = \{a, b, c, d, e, f, g, h\}$. Find
   a) $A \cup B$.
   b) $A \cap B$.
   c) $A - B$.
   d) $B - A$.

In Exercises 5–10 assume that $A$ is a subset of some underlying universal set $U$.

5. Prove the complementation law in Table 1 by showing that $\overline{\overline{A}} = A$.

6. Prove the identity laws in Table 1 by showing that
   a) $A \cup \emptyset = A$.
   b) $A \cap U = A$.

7. Prove the domination laws in Table 1 by showing that
   a) $A \cup U = U$.
   b) $A \cap \emptyset = \emptyset$.

8. Prove the idempotent laws in Table 1 by showing that
   a) $A \cup A = A$.
   b) $A \cap A = A$.

9. Prove the complement laws in Table 1 by showing that
   a) $A \cup \overline{A} = U$.
   b) $A \cap \overline{A} = \emptyset$.

10. Show that
    a) $A - \emptyset = A$.
    b) $\emptyset - A = \emptyset$.

11. Let $A$ and $B$ be sets. Prove the commutative laws from Table 1 by showing that
    a) $A \cup B = B \cup A$.
    b) $A \cap B = B \cap A$.

12. Prove the first absorption law from Table 1 by showing that if $A$ and $B$ are sets, then $A \cup (A \cap B) = A$.

13. Prove the second absorption law from Table 1 by showing that if $A$ and $B$ are sets, then $A \cap (A \cup B) = A$.

14. Find the sets $A$ and $B$ if $A - B = \{1, 5, 7, 8\}$, $B - A = \{2, 10\}$, and $A \cap B = \{3, 6, 9\}$.

15. Prove the second De Morgan law in Table 1 by showing that if $A$ and $B$ are sets, then $\overline{A \cup B} = \overline{A} \cap \overline{B}$
    a) by showing each side is a subset of the other side.
    b) using a membership table.

16. Let $A$ and $B$ be sets. Show that
    a) $(A \cap B) \subseteq A$.
    b) $A \subseteq (A \cup B)$.
    c) $A - B \subseteq A$.
    d) $A \cap (B - A) = \emptyset$.
    e) $A \cup (B - A) = A \cup B$.

17. Show that if $A$, $B$, and $C$ are sets, then $\overline{A \cap B \cap C} = \overline{A} \cup \overline{B} \cup \overline{C}$
    a) by showing each side is a subset of the other side.
    b) using a membership table.

18. Let $A$, $B$, and $C$ be sets. Show that
    a) $(A \cup B) \subseteq (A \cup B \cup C)$.
    b) $(A \cap B \cap C) \subseteq (A \cap B)$.
    c) $(A - B) - C \subseteq A - C$.
    d) $(A - C) \cap (C - B) = \emptyset$.
    e) $(B - A) \cup (C - A) = (B \cup C) - A$.

19. Show that if $A$ and $B$ are sets, then
    a) $A - B = A \cap \overline{B}$.
    b) $(A \cap B) \cup (A \cap \overline{B}) = A$.

20. Show that if $A$ and $B$ are sets with $A \subseteq B$, then
    a) $A \cup B = B$.
    b) $A \cap B = A$.

21. Prove the first associative law from Table 1 by showing that if $A$, $B$, and $C$ are sets, then $A \cup (B \cup C) = (A \cup B) \cup C$.

22. Prove the second associative law from Table 1 by showing that if $A$, $B$, and $C$ are sets, then $A \cap (B \cap C) = (A \cap B) \cap C$.

23. Prove the first distributive law from Table 1 by showing that if $A$, $B$, and $C$ are sets, then $A \cup (B \cap C) = (A \cup B) \cap (A \cup C)$.

24. Let $A$, $B$, and $C$ be sets. Show that $(A - B) - C = (A - C) - (B - C)$.

25. Let $A = \{0, 2, 4, 6, 8, 10\}$, $B = \{0, 1, 2, 3, 4, 5, 6\}$, and $C = \{4, 5, 6, 7, 8, 9, 10\}$. Find
    a) $A \cap B \cap C$.
    b) $A \cup B \cup C$.
    c) $(A \cup B) \cap C$.
    d) $(A \cap B) \cup C$.

26. Draw the Venn diagrams for each of these combinations of the sets $A$, $B$, and $C$.
    a) $A \cap (B \cup C)$
    b) $\overline{A} \cap \overline{B} \cap \overline{C}$
    c) $(A - B) \cup (A - C) \cup (B - C)$

27. Draw the Venn diagrams for each of these combinations of the sets $A$, $B$, and $C$.
    a) $A \cap (B - C)$
    b) $(A \cap B) \cup (A \cap C)$
    c) $(A \cap \overline{B}) \cup (A \cap \overline{C})$

28. Draw the Venn diagrams for each of these combinations of the sets $A$, $B$, $C$, and $D$.
    a) $(A \cap B) \cup (C \cap D)$
    b) $\overline{A} \cup \overline{B} \cup \overline{C} \cup \overline{D}$
    c) $A - (B \cap C \cap D)$

29. What can you say about the sets $A$ and $B$ if we know that
    a) $A \cup B = A$?
    b) $A \cap B = A$?
    c) $A - B = A$?
    d) $A \cap B = B \cap A$?
    e) $A - B = B - A$?

**30.** Can you conclude that $A = B$ if $A$, $B$, and $C$ are sets such that
   **a)** $A \cup C = B \cup C$?       **b)** $A \cap C = B \cap C$?
   **c)** $A \cup C = B \cup C$ and $A \cap C = B \cap C$?

**31.** Let $A$ and $B$ be subsets of a universal set $U$. Show that $A \subseteq B$ if and only if $\overline{B} \subseteq \overline{A}$.

The **symmetric difference** of $A$ and $B$, denoted by $A \oplus B$, is the set containing those elements in either $A$ or $B$, but not in both $A$ and $B$.

**32.** Find the symmetric difference of $\{1, 3, 5\}$ and $\{1, 2, 3\}$.

**33.** Find the symmetric difference of the set of computer science majors at a school and the set of mathematics majors at this school.

**34.** Draw a Venn diagram for the symmetric difference of the sets $A$ and $B$.

**35.** Show that $A \oplus B = (A \cup B) - (A \cap B)$.

**36.** Show that $A \oplus B = (A - B) \cup (B - A)$.

**37.** Show that if $A$ is a subset of a universal set $U$, then
   **a)** $A \oplus A = \emptyset$.       **b)** $A \oplus \emptyset = A$.
   **c)** $A \oplus U = \overline{A}$.       **d)** $A \oplus \overline{A} = U$.

**38.** Show that if $A$ and $B$ are sets, then
   **a)** $A \oplus B = B \oplus A$.       **b)** $(A \oplus B) \oplus B = A$.

**39.** What can you say about the sets $A$ and $B$ if $A \oplus B = A$?

**∗40.** Determine whether the symmetric difference is associative; that is, if $A$, $B$, and $C$ are sets, does it follow that $A \oplus (B \oplus C) = (A \oplus B) \oplus C$?

**∗41.** Suppose that $A$, $B$, and $C$ are sets such that $A \oplus C = B \oplus C$. Must it be the case that $A = B$?

**42.** If $A$, $B$, $C$, and $D$ are sets, does it follow that $(A \oplus B) \oplus (C \oplus D) = (A \oplus C) \oplus (B \oplus D)$?

**43.** If $A$, $B$, $C$, and $D$ are sets, does it follow that $(A \oplus B) \oplus (C \oplus D) = (A \oplus D) \oplus (B \oplus C)$?

**44.** Show that if $A$ and $B$ are finite sets, then $A \cup B$ is a finite set.

**45.** Show that if $A$ is an infinite set, then whenever $B$ is a set, $A \cup B$ is also an infinite set.

**∗46.** Show that if $A$, $B$, and $C$ are sets, then

$$|A \cup B \cup C| = |A| + |B| + |C| - |A \cap B|$$
$$- |A \cap C| - |B \cap C| + |A \cap B \cap C|.$$

(This is a special case of the inclusion–exclusion principle, which will be studied in Chapter 8.)

**47.** Let $A_i = \{1, 2, 3, \ldots, i\}$ for $i = 1, 2, 3, \ldots$. Find
   **a)** $\displaystyle\bigcup_{i=1}^{n} A_i$.       **b)** $\displaystyle\bigcap_{i=1}^{n} A_i$.

**48.** Let $A_i = \{\ldots, -2, -1, 0, 1, \ldots, i\}$. Find
   **a)** $\displaystyle\bigcup_{i=1}^{n} A_i$.       **b)** $\displaystyle\bigcap_{i=1}^{n} A_i$.

**49.** Let $A_i$ be the set of all nonempty bit strings (that is, bit strings of length at least one) of length not exceeding $i$. Find
   **a)** $\displaystyle\bigcup_{i=1}^{n} A_i$.       **b)** $\displaystyle\bigcap_{i=1}^{n} A_i$.

**50.** Find $\bigcup_{i=1}^{\infty} A_i$ and $\bigcap_{i=1}^{\infty} A_i$ if for every positive integer $i$,
   **a)** $A_i = \{i, i + 1, i + 2, \ldots\}$.
   **b)** $A_i = \{0, i\}$.
   **c)** $A_i = (0, i)$, that is, the set of real numbers $x$ with $0 < x < i$.
   **d)** $A_i = (i, \infty)$, that is, the set of real numbers $x$ with $x > i$.

**51.** Find $\bigcup_{i=1}^{\infty} A_i$ and $\bigcap_{i=1}^{\infty} A_i$ if for every positive integer $i$,
   **a)** $A_i = \{-i, -i + 1, \ldots, -1, 0, 1, \ldots, i - 1, i\}$.
   **b)** $A_i = \{-i, i\}$.
   **c)** $A_i = [-i, i]$, that is, the set of real numbers $x$ with $-i \leq x \leq i$.
   **d)** $A_i = [i, \infty)$, that is, the set of real numbers $x$ with $x \geq i$.

**52.** Suppose that the universal set is $U = \{1, 2, 3, 4, 5, 6, 7, 8, 9, 10\}$. Express each of these sets with bit strings where the $i$th bit in the string is 1 if $i$ is in the set and 0 otherwise.
   **a)** $\{3, 4, 5\}$
   **b)** $\{1, 3, 6, 10\}$
   **c)** $\{2, 3, 4, 7, 8, 9\}$

**53.** Using the same universal set as in the last problem, find the set specified by each of these bit strings.
   **a)** 11 1100 1111
   **b)** 01 0111 1000
   **c)** 10 0000 0001

**54.** What subsets of a finite universal set do these bit strings represent?
   **a)** the string with all zeros
   **b)** the string with all ones

**55.** What is the bit string corresponding to the difference of two sets?

**56.** What is the bit string corresponding to the symmetric difference of two sets?

**57.** Show how bitwise operations on bit strings can be used to find these combinations of $A = \{a, b, c, d, e\}$, $B = \{b, c, d, g, p, t, v\}$, $C = \{c, e, i, o, u, x, y, z\}$, and $D = \{d, e, h, i, n, o, t, u, x, y\}$.
   **a)** $A \cup B$       **b)** $A \cap B$
   **c)** $(A \cup D) \cap (B \cup C)$       **d)** $A \cup B \cup C \cup D$

**58.** How can the union and intersection of $n$ sets that all are subsets of the universal set $U$ be found using bit strings?

The **successor** of the set $A$ is the set $A \cup \{A\}$.

**59.** Find the successors of the following sets.
   **a)** $\{1, 2, 3\}$       **b)** $\emptyset$
   **c)** $\{\emptyset\}$       **d)** $\{\emptyset, \{\emptyset\}\}$

**60.** How many elements does the successor of a set with $n$ elements have?

Sometimes the number of times that an element occurs in an unordered collection matters. **Multisets** are unordered collections of elements where an element can occur as a member more than once. The notation $\{m_1 \cdot a_1, m_2 \cdot a_2, \ldots, m_r \cdot a_r\}$ denotes the multiset with element $a_1$ occurring $m_1$ times, element $a_2$ occurring $m_2$ times, and so on. The numbers $m_i$, $i = 1, 2, \ldots, r$ are called the **multiplicities** of the elements $a_i, i = 1, 2, \ldots, r$.

Let $P$ and $Q$ be multisets. The **union** of the multisets $P$ and $Q$ is the multiset where the multiplicity of an element is the maximum of its multiplicities in $P$ and $Q$. The **intersection** of $P$ and $Q$ is the multiset where the multiplicity of an element is the minimum of its multiplicities in $P$ and $Q$. The **difference** of $P$ and $Q$ is the multiset where the multiplicity of an element is the multiplicity of the element in $P$ less its multiplicity in $Q$ unless this difference is negative, in which case the multiplicity is 0. The **sum** of $P$ and $Q$ is the multiset where the multiplicity of an element is the sum of multiplicities in $P$ and $Q$. The union, intersection, and difference of $P$ and $Q$ are denoted by $P \cup Q$, $P \cap Q$, and $P - Q$, respectively (where these operations should not be confused with the analogous operations for sets). The sum of $P$ and $Q$ is denoted by $P + Q$.

**61.** Let $A$ and $B$ be the multisets $\{3 \cdot a, 2 \cdot b, 1 \cdot c\}$ and $\{2 \cdot a, 3 \cdot b, 4 \cdot d\}$, respectively. Find

    **a)** $A \cup B$.     **b)** $A \cap B$.     **c)** $A - B$.

    **d)** $B - A$.     **e)** $A + B$.

**62.** Suppose that $A$ is the multiset that has as its elements the types of computer equipment needed by one department of a university and the multiplicities are the number of pieces of each type needed, and $B$ is the analogous multiset for a second department of the university. For instance, $A$ could be the multiset $\{107 \cdot \text{personal computers}, 44 \cdot \text{routers}, 6 \cdot \text{servers}\}$ and $B$ could be the multiset $\{14 \cdot \text{personal computers}, 6 \cdot \text{routers}, 2 \cdot \text{mainframes}\}$.

    **a)** What combination of $A$ and $B$ represents the equipment the university should buy assuming both departments use the same equipment?

    **b)** What combination of $A$ and $B$ represents the equipment that will be used by both departments if both departments use the same equipment?

    **c)** What combination of $A$ and $B$ represents the equipment that the second department uses, but the first department does not, if both departments use the same equipment?

    **d)** What combination of $A$ and $B$ represents the equipment that the university should purchase if the departments do not share equipment?

**Fuzzy sets** are used in artificial intelligence. Each element in the universal set $U$ has a **degree of membership**, which is a real number between 0 and 1 (including 0 and 1), in a fuzzy set $S$. The fuzzy set $S$ is denoted by listing the elements with their degrees of membership (elements with 0 degree of membership are not listed). For instance, we write $\{0.6 \text{ Alice}, 0.9 \text{ Brian}, 0.4 \text{ Fred}, 0.1 \text{ Oscar}, 0.5 \text{ Rita}\}$ for the set $F$ (of famous people) to indicate that Alice has a 0.6 degree of membership in $F$, Brian has a 0.9 degree of membership in $F$, Fred has a 0.4 degree of membership in $F$, Oscar has a 0.1 degree of membership in $F$, and Rita has a 0.5 degree of membership in $F$ (so that Brian is the most famous and Oscar is the least famous of these people). Also suppose that $R$ is the set of rich people with $R = \{0.4 \text{ Alice}, 0.8 \text{ Brian}, 0.2 \text{ Fred}, 0.9 \text{ Oscar}, 0.7 \text{ Rita}\}$.

**63.** The **complement** of a fuzzy set $S$ is the set $\overline{S}$, with the degree of the membership of an element in $\overline{S}$ equal to 1 minus the degree of membership of this element in $S$. Find $\overline{F}$ (the fuzzy set of people who are not famous) and $\overline{R}$ (the fuzzy set of people who are not rich).

**64.** The **union** of two fuzzy sets $S$ and $T$ is the fuzzy set $S \cup T$, where the degree of membership of an element in $S \cup T$ is the maximum of the degrees of membership of this element in $S$ and in $T$. Find the fuzzy set $F \cup R$ of rich or famous people.

**65.** The **intersection** of two fuzzy sets $S$ and $T$ is the fuzzy set $S \cap T$, where the degree of membership of an element in $S \cap T$ is the minimum of the degrees of membership of this element in $S$ and in $T$. Find the fuzzy set $F \cap R$ of rich and famous people.

# 2.3    Functions

## Introduction

In many instances we assign to each element of a set a particular element of a second set (which may be the same as the first). For example, suppose that each student in a discrete mathematics class is assigned a letter grade from the set $\{A, B, C, D, F\}$. And suppose that the grades are $A$ for Adams, $C$ for Chou, $B$ for Goodfriend, $A$ for Rodriguez, and $F$ for Stevens. This assignment of grades is illustrated in Figure 1.

This assignment is an example of a function. The concept of a function is extremely important in mathematics and computer science. For example, in discrete mathematics functions are used in the definition of such discrete structures as sequences and strings. Functions are also used to represent how long it takes a computer to solve problems of a given size. Many computer programs and subroutines are designed to calculate values of functions. Recursive functions,

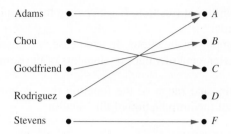

**FIGURE 1    Assignment of Grades in a Discrete Mathematics Class.**

which are functions defined in terms of themselves, are used throughout computer science; they will be studied in Chapter 5. This section reviews the basic concepts involving functions needed in discrete mathematics.

**DEFINITION 1**

Let $A$ and $B$ be nonempty sets. A *function* $f$ from $A$ to $B$ is an assignment of exactly one element of $B$ to each element of $A$. We write $f(a) = b$ if $b$ is the unique element of $B$ assigned by the function $f$ to the element $a$ of $A$. If $f$ is a function from $A$ to $B$, we write $f : A \rightarrow B$.

*Remark:* Functions are sometimes also called **mappings** or **transformations**.

**Assessment**

Functions are specified in many different ways. Sometimes we explicitly state the assignments, as in Figure 1. Often we give a formula, such as $f(x) = x + 1$, to define a function. Other times we use a computer program to specify a function.

A function $f : A \rightarrow B$ can also be defined in terms of a relation from $A$ to $B$. Recall from Section 2.1 that a relation from $A$ to $B$ is just a subset of $A \times B$. A relation from $A$ to $B$ that contains one, and only one, ordered pair $(a, b)$ for every element $a \in A$, defines a function $f$ from $A$ to $B$. This function is defined by the assignment $f(a) = b$, where $(a, b)$ is the unique ordered pair in the relation that has $a$ as its first element.

**DEFINITION 2**

If $f$ is a function from $A$ to $B$, we say that $A$ is the *domain* of $f$ and $B$ is the *codomain* of $f$. If $f(a) = b$, we say that $b$ is the *image* of $a$ and $a$ is a *preimage* of $b$. The *range*, or *image*, of $f$ is the set of all images of elements of $A$. Also, if $f$ is a function from $A$ to $B$, we say that $f$ *maps* $A$ to $B$.

Figure 2 represents a function $f$ from $A$ to $B$.

When we define a function we specify its domain, its codomain, and the mapping of elements of the domain to elements in the codomain. Two functions are **equal** when they have the same domain, have the same codomain, and map each element of their common domain to the same element in their common codomain. Note that if we change either the domain or the codomain

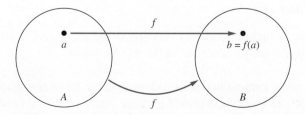

**FIGURE 2    The Function $f$ Maps $A$ to $B$.**

of a function, then we obtain a different function. If we change the mapping of elements, then we also obtain a different function.

Examples 1–5 provide examples of functions. In each case, we describe the domain, the codomain, the range, and the assignment of values to elements of the domain.

**EXAMPLE 1**   What are the domain, codomain, and range of the function that assigns grades to students described in the first paragraph of the introduction of this section?

*Solution:* Let $G$ be the function that assigns a grade to a student in our discrete mathematics class. Note that $G$(Adams) $= A$, for instance. The domain of $G$ is the set {Adams, Chou, Goodfriend, Rodriguez, Stevens}, and the codomain is the set $\{A, B, C, D, F\}$. The range of $G$ is the set $\{A, B, C, F\}$, because each grade except $D$ is assigned to some student.  ◀

**EXAMPLE 2**   Let $R$ be the relation with ordered pairs (Abdul, 22), (Brenda, 24), (Carla, 21), (Desire, 22), (Eddie, 24), and (Felicia, 22). Here each pair consists of a graduate student and this student's age. Specify a function determined by this relation.

*Solution:* If $f$ is a function specified by $R$, then $f$(Abdul) $= 22$, $f$(Brenda) $= 24$, $f$(Carla) $= 21$, $f$(Desire) $= 22$, $f$(Eddie) $= 24$, and $f$(Felicia) $= 22$. (Here, $f(x)$ is the age of $x$, where $x$ is a student.) For the domain, we take the set {Abdul, Brenda, Carla, Desire, Eddie, Felicia}. We also need to specify a codomain, which needs to contain all possible ages of students. Because it is highly likely that all students are less than 100 years old, we can take the set of positive integers less than 100 as the codomain. (Note that we could choose a different codomain, such as the set of all positive integers or the set of positive integers between 10 and 90, but that would change the function. Using this codomain will also allow us to extend the function by adding the names and ages of more students later.) The range of the function we have specified is the set of different ages of these students, which is the set $\{21, 22, 24\}$.  ◀

**EXAMPLE 3**   Let $f$ be the function that assigns the last two bits of a bit string of length 2 or greater to that
*Extra* string. For example, $f(11010) = 10$. Then, the domain of $f$ is the set of all bit strings of length
*Examples* 2 or greater, and both the codomain and range are the set $\{00, 01, 10, 11\}$.  ◀

**EXAMPLE 4**   Let $f : \mathbf{Z} \to \mathbf{Z}$ assign the square of an integer to this integer. Then, $f(x) = x^2$, where the domain of $f$ is the set of all integers, the codomain of $f$ is the set of all integers, and the range of $f$ is the set of all integers that are perfect squares, namely, $\{0, 1, 4, 9, \ldots\}$.  ◀

**EXAMPLE 5**   The domain and codomain of functions are often specified in programming languages. For instance, the Java statement

    int **floor**(float real){...}

and the C++ function statement

    int **function** (float $x$){...}

both tell us that the domain of the floor function is the set of real numbers (represented by floating point numbers) and its codomain is the set of integers.  ◀

A function is called **real-valued** if its codomain is the set of real numbers, and it is called **integer-valued** if its codomain is the set of integers. Two real-valued functions or two integer-valued functions with the same domain can be added, as well as multiplied.

**DEFINITION 3**    Let $f_1$ and $f_2$ be functions from $A$ to $\mathbf{R}$. Then $f_1 + f_2$ and $f_1 f_2$ are also functions from $A$ to $\mathbf{R}$ defined for all $x \in A$ by

$$(f_1 + f_2)(x) = f_1(x) + f_2(x),$$
$$(f_1 f_2)(x) = f_1(x) f_2(x).$$

Note that the functions $f_1 + f_2$ and $f_1 f_2$ have been defined by specifying their values at $x$ in terms of the values of $f_1$ and $f_2$ at $x$.

**EXAMPLE 6**    Let $f_1$ and $f_2$ be functions from $\mathbf{R}$ to $\mathbf{R}$ such that $f_1(x) = x^2$ and $f_2(x) = x - x^2$. What are the functions $f_1 + f_2$ and $f_1 f_2$?

*Solution:* From the definition of the sum and product of functions, it follows that

$$(f_1 + f_2)(x) = f_1(x) + f_2(x) = x^2 + (x - x^2) = x$$

and

$$(f_1 f_2)(x) = x^2(x - x^2) = x^3 - x^4. \qquad \blacktriangleleft$$

When $f$ is a function from $A$ to $B$, the image of a subset of $A$ can also be defined.

**DEFINITION 4**    Let $f$ be a function from $A$ to $B$ and let $S$ be a subset of $A$. The *image* of $S$ under the function $f$ is the subset of $B$ that consists of the images of the elements of $S$. We denote the image of $S$ by $f(S)$, so

$$f(S) = \{t \mid \exists s \in S \ (t = f(s))\}.$$

We also use the shorthand $\{f(s) \mid s \in S\}$ to denote this set.

***Remark:*** The notation $f(S)$ for the image of the set $S$ under the function $f$ is potentially ambiguous. Here, $f(S)$ denotes a set, and not the value of the function $f$ for the set $S$.

**EXAMPLE 7**    Let $A = \{a, b, c, d, e\}$ and $B = \{1, 2, 3, 4\}$ with $f(a) = 2$, $f(b) = 1$, $f(c) = 4$, $f(d) = 1$, and $f(e) = 1$. The image of the subset $S = \{b, c, d\}$ is the set $f(S) = \{1, 4\}$.    $\blacktriangleleft$

## One-to-One and Onto Functions

Some functions never assign the same value to two different domain elements. These functions are said to be **one-to-one**.

**DEFINITION 5**    A function $f$ is said to be *one-to-one*, or an *injunction*, if and only if $f(a) = f(b)$ implies that $a = b$ for all $a$ and $b$ in the domain of $f$. A function is said to be *injective* if it is one-to-one.

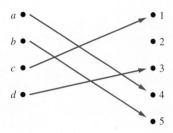

**FIGURE 3    A One-to-One Function.**

Note that a function $f$ is one-to-one if and only if $f(a) \neq f(b)$ whenever $a \neq b$. This way of expressing that $f$ is one-to-one is obtained by taking the contrapositive of the implication in the definition.

***Remark:*** We can express that $f$ is one-to-one using quantifiers as $\forall a \forall b (f(a) = f(b) \rightarrow a = b)$ or equivalently $\forall a \forall b (a \neq b \rightarrow f(a) \neq f(b))$, where the universe of discourse is the domain of the function.

**Assessment**

We illustrate this concept by giving examples of functions that are one-to-one and other functions that are not one-to-one.

**EXAMPLE 8**    Determine whether the function $f$ from $\{a, b, c, d\}$ to $\{1, 2, 3, 4, 5\}$ with $f(a) = 4$, $f(b) = 5$, $f(c) = 1$, and $f(d) = 3$ is one-to-one.

**Extra Examples**

*Solution:* The function $f$ is one-to-one because $f$ takes on different values at the four elements of its domain. This is illustrated in Figure 3.    ◄

**EXAMPLE 9**    Determine whether the function $f(x) = x^2$ from the set of integers to the set of integers is one-to-one.

*Solution:* The function $f(x) = x^2$ is not one-to-one because, for instance, $f(1) = f(-1) = 1$, but $1 \neq -1$.

Note that the function $f(x) = x^2$ with its domain restricted to $\mathbf{Z}^+$ is one-to-one. (Technically, when we restrict the domain of a function, we obtain a new function whose values agree with those of the original function for the elements of the restricted domain. The restricted function is not defined for elements of the original domain outside of the restricted domain.)    ◄

**EXAMPLE 10**    Determine whether the function $f(x) = x + 1$ from the set of real numbers to itself is one-to-one.

*Solution:* The function $f(x) = x + 1$ is a one-to-one function. To demonstrate this, note that $x + 1 \neq y + 1$ when $x \neq y$.    ◄

**EXAMPLE 11**    Suppose that each worker in a group of employees is assigned a job from a set of possible jobs, each to be done by a single worker. In this situation, the function $f$ that assigns a job to each worker is one-to-one. To see this, note that if $x$ and $y$ are two different workers, then $f(x) \neq f(y)$ because the two workers $x$ and $y$ must be assigned different jobs.    ◄

We now give some conditions that guarantee that a function is one-to-one.

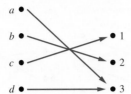

**FIGURE 4    An Onto Function.**

**DEFINITION 6**

A function $f$ whose domain and codomain are subsets of the set of real numbers is called *increasing* if $f(x) \leq f(y)$, and *strictly increasing* if $f(x) < f(y)$, whenever $x < y$ and $x$ and $y$ are in the domain of $f$. Similarly, $f$ is called *decreasing* if $f(x) \geq f(y)$, and *strictly decreasing* if $f(x) > f(y)$, whenever $x < y$ and $x$ and $y$ are in the domain of $f$. (The word *strictly* in this definition indicates a strict inequality.)

*Remark:* A function $f$ is increasing if $\forall x \forall y (x < y \rightarrow f(x) \leq f(y))$, strictly increasing if $\forall x \forall y (x < y \rightarrow f(x) < f(y))$, decreasing if $\forall x \forall y (x < y \rightarrow f(x) \geq f(y))$, and strictly decreasing if $\forall x \forall y (x < y \rightarrow f(x) > f(y))$, where the universe of discourse is the domain of $f$.

From these definitions, it can be shown (see Exercises 26 and 27) that a function that is either strictly increasing or strictly decreasing must be one-to-one. However, a function that is increasing, but not strictly increasing, or decreasing, but not strictly decreasing, is not one-to-one.

For some functions the range and the codomain are equal. That is, every member of the codomain is the image of some element of the domain. Functions with this property are called **onto** functions.

**DEFINITION 7**

A function $f$ from $A$ to $B$ is called *onto,* or a *surjection,* if and only if for every element $b \in B$ there is an element $a \in A$ with $f(a) = b$. A function $f$ is called *surjective* if it is onto.

*Remark:* A function $f$ is onto if $\forall y \exists x (f(x) = y)$, where the domain for $x$ is the domain of the function and the domain for $y$ is the codomain of the function.

We now give examples of onto functions and functions that are not onto.

**EXAMPLE 12**

Let $f$ be the function from $\{a, b, c, d\}$ to $\{1, 2, 3\}$ defined by $f(a) = 3$, $f(b) = 2$, $f(c) = 1$, and $f(d) = 3$. Is $f$ an onto function?

Extra Examples

*Solution:* Because all three elements of the codomain are images of elements in the domain, we see that $f$ is onto. This is illustrated in Figure 4. Note that if the codomain were $\{1, 2, 3, 4\}$, then $f$ would not be onto. ◀

**EXAMPLE 13**

Is the function $f(x) = x^2$ from the set of integers to the set of integers onto?

*Solution:* The function $f$ is not onto because there is no integer $x$ with $x^2 = -1$, for instance. ◀

**EXAMPLE 14**

Is the function $f(x) = x + 1$ from the set of integers to the set of integers onto?

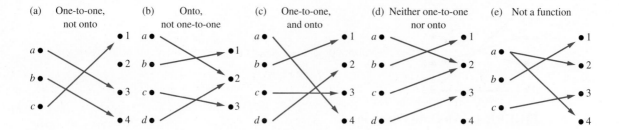

FIGURE 5    **Examples of Different Types of Correspondences.**

*Solution:* This function is onto, because for every integer $y$ there is an integer $x$ such that $f(x) = y$. To see this, note that $f(x) = y$ if and only if $x + 1 = y$, which holds if and only if $x = y - 1$.    ◀

**EXAMPLE 15**    Consider the function $f$ in Example 11 that assigns jobs to workers. The function $f$ is onto if for every job there is a worker assigned this job. The function $f$ is not onto when there is at least one job that has no worker assigned it.    ◀

**DEFINITION 8**    The function $f$ is a *one-to-one correspondence,* or a *bijection,* if it is both one-to-one and onto. We also say that such a function is *bijective.*

Examples 16 and 17 illustrate the concept of a bijection.

**EXAMPLE 16**    Let $f$ be the function from $\{a, b, c, d\}$ to $\{1, 2, 3, 4\}$ with $f(a) = 4$, $f(b) = 2$, $f(c) = 1$, and $f(d) = 3$. Is $f$ a bijection?

*Solution:* The function $f$ is one-to-one and onto. It is one-to-one because no two values in the domain are assigned the same function value. It is onto because all four elements of the codomain are images of elements in the domain. Hence, $f$ is a bijection.    ◀

Figure 5 displays four functions where the first is one-to-one but not onto, the second is onto but not one-to-one, the third is both one-to-one and onto, and the fourth is neither one-to-one nor onto. The fifth correspondence in Figure 5 is not a function, because it sends an element to two different elements.

Suppose that $f$ is a function from a set $A$ to itself. If $A$ is finite, then $f$ is one-to-one if and only if it is onto. (This follows from the result in Exercise 72.) This is not necessarily the case if $A$ is infinite (as will be shown in Section 2.5).

**EXAMPLE 17**    Let $A$ be a set. The *identity function* on $A$ is the function $\iota_A : A \to A$, where

$$\iota_A(x) = x$$

for all $x \in A$. In other words, the identity function $\iota_A$ is the function that assigns each element to itself. The function $\iota_A$ is one-to-one and onto, so it is a bijection. (Note that $\iota$ is the Greek letter iota.)    ◀

For future reference, we summarize what needs be to shown to establish whether a function is one-to-one and whether it is onto. It is instructive to review Examples 8–17 in light of this summary.

Suppose that $f : A \rightarrow B$.

*To show that $f$ is injective* Show that if $f(x) = f(y)$ for arbitrary $x, y \in A$ with $x \neq y$, then $x = y$.

*To show that $f$ is not injective* Find particular elements $x, y \in A$ such that $x \neq y$ and $f(x) = f(y)$.

*To show that $f$ is surjective* Consider an arbitrary element $y \in B$ and find an element $x \in A$ such that $f(x) = y$.

*To show that $f$ is not surjective* Find a particular $y \in B$ such that $f(x) \neq y$ for all $x \in A$.

## Inverse Functions and Compositions of Functions

Now consider a one-to-one correspondence $f$ from the set $A$ to the set $B$. Because $f$ is an onto function, every element of $B$ is the image of some element in $A$. Furthermore, because $f$ is also a one-to-one function, every element of $B$ is the image of a *unique* element of $A$. Consequently, we can define a new function from $B$ to $A$ that reverses the correspondence given by $f$. This leads to Definition 9.

**DEFINITION 9**    Let $f$ be a one-to-one correspondence from the set $A$ to the set $B$. The *inverse function* of $f$ is the function that assigns to an element $b$ belonging to $B$ the unique element $a$ in $A$ such that $f(a) = b$. The inverse function of $f$ is denoted by $f^{-1}$. Hence, $f^{-1}(b) = a$ when $f(a) = b$.

***Remark:*** Be sure not to confuse the function $f^{-1}$ with the function $1/f$, which is the function that assigns to each $x$ in the domain the value $1/f(x)$. Notice that the latter makes sense only when $f(x)$ is a non-zero real number.

Figure 6 illustrates the concept of an inverse function.

If a function $f$ is not a one-to-one correspondence, we cannot define an inverse function of $f$. When $f$ is not a one-to-one correspondence, either it is not one-to-one or it is not onto. If $f$ is not one-to-one, some element $b$ in the codomain is the image of more than one element in the domain. If $f$ is not onto, for some element $b$ in the codomain, no element $a$ in the domain exists for which $f(a) = b$. Consequently, if $f$ is not a one-to-one correspondence, we cannot assign to each element $b$ in the codomain a unique element $a$ in the domain such that $f(a) = b$ (because for some $b$ there is either more than one such $a$ or no such $a$).

A one-to-one correspondence is called **invertible** because we can define an inverse of this function. A function is **not invertible** if it is not a one-to-one correspondence, because the inverse of such a function does not exist.

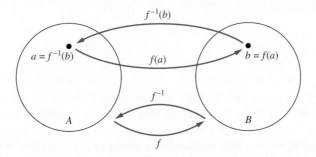

**FIGURE 6    The Function $f^{-1}$ Is the Inverse of Function $f$.**

**EXAMPLE 18**    Let $f$ be the function from $\{a, b, c\}$ to $\{1, 2, 3\}$ such that $f(a) = 2$, $f(b) = 3$, and $f(c) = 1$. Is $f$ invertible, and if it is, what is its inverse?

*Solution:* The function $f$ is invertible because it is a one-to-one correspondence. The inverse function $f^{-1}$ reverses the correspondence given by $f$, so $f^{-1}(1) = c$, $f^{-1}(2) = a$, and $f^{-1}(3) = b$.    ◄

**EXAMPLE 19**    Let $f : \mathbf{Z} \to \mathbf{Z}$ be such that $f(x) = x + 1$. Is $f$ invertible, and if it is, what is its inverse?

*Solution:* The function $f$ has an inverse because it is a one-to-one correspondence, as follows from Examples 10 and 14. To reverse the correspondence, suppose that $y$ is the image of $x$, so that $y = x + 1$. Then $x = y - 1$. This means that $y - 1$ is the unique element of $\mathbf{Z}$ that is sent to $y$ by $f$. Consequently, $f^{-1}(y) = y - 1$.    ◄

**EXAMPLE 20**    Let $f$ be the function from $\mathbf{R}$ to $\mathbf{R}$ with $f(x) = x^2$. Is $f$ invertible?

*Solution:* Because $f(-2) = f(2) = 4$, $f$ is not one-to-one. If an inverse function were defined, it would have to assign two elements to 4. Hence, $f$ is not invertible. (Note we can also show that $f$ is not invertible because it is not onto.)    ◄

Sometimes we can restrict the domain or the codomain of a function, or both, to obtain an invertible function, as Example 21 illustrates.

**EXAMPLE 21**    Show that if we restrict the function $f(x) = x^2$ in Example 20 to a function from the set of all nonnegative real numbers to the set of all nonnegative real numbers, then $f$ is invertible.

*Solution:* The function $f(x) = x^2$ from the set of nonnegative real numbers to the set of nonnegative real numbers is one-to-one. To see this, note that if $f(x) = f(y)$, then $x^2 = y^2$, so $x^2 - y^2 = (x + y)(x - y) = 0$. This means that $x + y = 0$ or $x - y = 0$, so $x = -y$ or $x = y$. Because both $x$ and $y$ are nonnegative, we must have $x = y$. So, this function is one-to-one. Furthermore, $f(x) = x^2$ is onto when the codomain is the set of all nonnegative real numbers, because each nonnegative real number has a square root. That is, if $y$ is a nonnegative real number, there exists a nonnegative real number $x$ such that $x = \sqrt{y}$, which means that $x^2 = y$. Because the function $f(x) = x^2$ from the set of nonnegative real numbers to the set of nonnegative real numbers is one-to-one and onto, it is invertible. Its inverse is given by the rule $f^{-1}(y) = \sqrt{y}$.    ◄

**DEFINITION 10**    Let $g$ be a function from the set $A$ to the set $B$ and let $f$ be a function from the set $B$ to the set $C$. The *composition* of the functions $f$ and $g$, denoted for all $a \in A$ by $f \circ g$, is defined by

$$(f \circ g)(a) = f(g(a)).$$

In other words, $f \circ g$ is the function that assigns to the element $a$ of $A$ the element assigned by $f$ to $g(a)$. That is, to find $(f \circ g)(a)$ we first apply the function $g$ to $a$ to obtain $g(a)$ and then we apply the function $f$ to the result $g(a)$ to obtain $(f \circ g)(a) = f(g(a))$. Note that the composition $f \circ g$ cannot be defined unless the range of $g$ is a subset of the domain of $f$. In Figure 7 the composition of functions is shown.

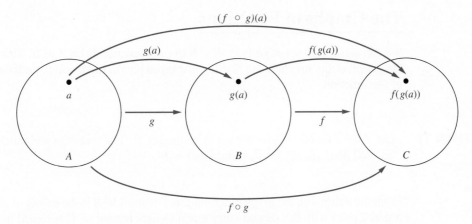

**FIGURE 7    The Composition of the Functions $f$ and $g$.**

**EXAMPLE 22**    Let $g$ be the function from the set $\{a, b, c\}$ to itself such that $g(a) = b$, $g(b) = c$, and $g(c) = a$. Let $f$ be the function from the set $\{a, b, c\}$ to the set $\{1, 2, 3\}$ such that $f(a) = 3$, $f(b) = 2$, and $f(c) = 1$. What is the composition of $f$ and $g$, and what is the composition of $g$ and $f$?

*Solution:* The composition $f \circ g$ is defined by $(f \circ g)(a) = f(g(a)) = f(b) = 2$, $(f \circ g)(b) = f(g(b)) = f(c) = 1$, and $(f \circ g)(c) = f(g(c)) = f(a) = 3$.

Note that $g \circ f$ is not defined, because the range of $f$ is not a subset of the domain of $g$. ◀

**EXAMPLE 23**    Let $f$ and $g$ be the functions from the set of integers to the set of integers defined by $f(x) = 2x + 3$ and $g(x) = 3x + 2$. What is the composition of $f$ and $g$? What is the composition of $g$ and $f$?

*Solution:* Both the compositions $f \circ g$ and $g \circ f$ are defined. Moreover,

$$(f \circ g)(x) = f(g(x)) = f(3x + 2) = 2(3x + 2) + 3 = 6x + 7$$

and

$$(g \circ f)(x) = g(f(x)) = g(2x + 3) = 3(2x + 3) + 2 = 6x + 11. \qquad ◀$$

***Remark:*** Note that even though $f \circ g$ and $g \circ f$ are defined for the functions $f$ and $g$ in Example 23, $f \circ g$ and $g \circ f$ are not equal. In other words, the commutative law does not hold for the composition of functions.

When the composition of a function and its inverse is formed, in either order, an identity function is obtained. To see this, suppose that $f$ is a one-to-one correspondence from the set $A$ to the set $B$. Then the inverse function $f^{-1}$ exists and is a one-to-one correspondence from $B$ to $A$. The inverse function reverses the correspondence of the original function, so $f^{-1}(b) = a$ when $f(a) = b$, and $f(a) = b$ when $f^{-1}(b) = a$. Hence,

$$(f^{-1} \circ f)(a) = f^{-1}(f(a)) = f^{-1}(b) = a,$$

and

$$(f \circ f^{-1})(b) = f(f^{-1}(b)) = f(a) = b.$$

Consequently $f^{-1} \circ f = \iota_A$ and $f \circ f^{-1} = \iota_B$, where $\iota_A$ and $\iota_B$ are the identity functions on the sets $A$ and $B$, respectively. That is, $(f^{-1})^{-1} = f$.

## The Graphs of Functions

We can associate a set of pairs in $A \times B$ to each function from $A$ to $B$. This set of pairs is called the **graph** of the function and is often displayed pictorially to aid in understanding the behavior of the function.

**DEFINITION 11**    Let $f$ be a function from the set $A$ to the set $B$. The *graph* of the function $f$ is the set of ordered pairs $\{(a, b) \mid a \in A \text{ and } f(a) = b\}$.

From the definition, the graph of a function $f$ from $A$ to $B$ is the subset of $A \times B$ containing the ordered pairs with the second entry equal to the element of $B$ assigned by $f$ to the first entry. Also, note that the graph of a function $f$ from $A$ to $B$ is the same as the relation from $A$ to $B$ determined by the function $f$, as described on page 139.

**EXAMPLE 24**    Display the graph of the function $f(n) = 2n + 1$ from the set of integers to the set of integers.

*Solution:* The graph of $f$ is the set of ordered pairs of the form $(n, 2n + 1)$, where $n$ is an integer. This graph is displayed in Figure 8.    ◄

**EXAMPLE 25**    Display the graph of the function $f(x) = x^2$ from the set of integers to the set of integers.

*Solution:* The graph of $f$ is the set of ordered pairs of the form $(x, f(x)) = (x, x^2)$, where $x$ is an integer. This graph is displayed in Figure 9.    ◄

## Some Important Functions

Next, we introduce two important functions in discrete mathematics, namely, the floor and ceiling functions. Let $x$ be a real number. The floor function rounds $x$ down to the closest integer less than or equal to $x$, and the ceiling function rounds $x$ up to the closest integer greater than or equal to $x$. These functions are often used when objects are counted. They play an important role in the analysis of the number of steps used by procedures to solve problems of a particular size.

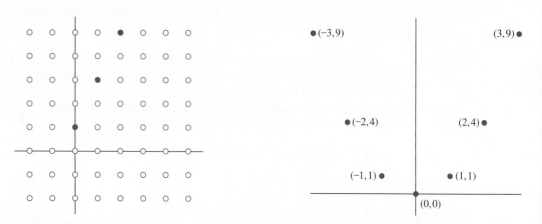

**FIGURE 8    The Graph of**
$f(n) = 2n + 1$ **from Z to Z.**

**FIGURE 9    The Graph of**
$f(x) = x^2$ **from Z to Z.**

**DEFINITION 12**  The *floor function* assigns to the real number $x$ the largest integer that is less than or equal to $x$. The value of the floor function at $x$ is denoted by $\lfloor x \rfloor$. The *ceiling function* assigns to the real number $x$ the smallest integer that is greater than or equal to $x$. The value of the ceiling function at $x$ is denoted by $\lceil x \rceil$.

*Remark:* The floor function is often also called the *greatest integer function*. It is often denoted by $[x]$.

**EXAMPLE 26**  These are some values of the floor and ceiling functions:

$$\lfloor \tfrac{1}{2} \rfloor = 0, \lceil \tfrac{1}{2} \rceil = 1, \lfloor -\tfrac{1}{2} \rfloor = -1, \lceil -\tfrac{1}{2} \rceil = 0, \lfloor 3.1 \rfloor = 3, \lceil 3.1 \rceil = 4, \lfloor 7 \rfloor = 7, \lceil 7 \rceil = 7. \quad \blacktriangleleft$$

We display the graphs of the floor and ceiling functions in Figure 10. In Figure 10(a) we display the graph of the floor function $\lfloor x \rfloor$. Note that this function has the same value throughout the interval $[n, n + 1)$, namely $n$, and then it jumps up to $n + 1$ when $x = n + 1$. In Figure 10(b) we display the graph of the ceiling function $\lceil x \rceil$. Note that this function has the same value throughout the interval $(n, n + 1]$, namely $n + 1$, and then jumps to $n + 2$ when $x$ is a little larger than $n + 1$.

**Links**

The floor and ceiling functions are useful in a wide variety of applications, including those involving data storage and data transmission. Consider Examples 27 and 28, typical of basic calculations done when database and data communications problems are studied.

**EXAMPLE 27**  Data stored on a computer disk or transmitted over a data network are usually represented as a string of bytes. Each byte is made up of 8 bits. How many bytes are required to encode 100 bits of data?

*Solution:* To determine the number of bytes needed, we determine the smallest integer that is at least as large as the quotient when 100 is divided by 8, the number of bits in a byte. Consequently, $\lceil 100/8 \rceil = \lceil 12.5 \rceil = 13$ bytes are required. $\quad \blacktriangleleft$

**EXAMPLE 28**  In asynchronous transfer mode (ATM) (a communications protocol used on backbone networks), data are organized into cells of 53 bytes. How many ATM cells can be transmitted in 1 minute over a connection that transmits data at the rate of 500 kilobits per second?

*Solution:* In 1 minute, this connection can transmit $500{,}000 \cdot 60 = 30{,}000{,}000$ bits. Each ATM cell is 53 bytes long, which means that it is $53 \cdot 8 = 424$ bits long. To determine the number

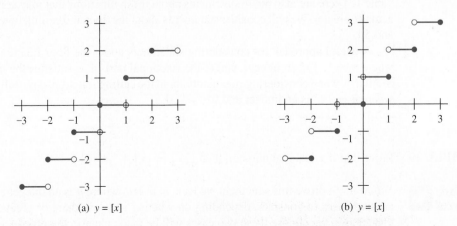

(a) $y = \lfloor x \rfloor$       (b) $y = \lceil x \rceil$

**FIGURE 10**  **Graphs of the (a) Floor and (b) Ceiling Functions.**

**TABLE 1  Useful Properties of the Floor and Ceiling Functions.**
($n$ is an integer, $x$ is a real number)

(1a)  $\lfloor x \rfloor = n$ if and only if $n \leq x < n + 1$
(1b)  $\lceil x \rceil = n$ if and only if $n - 1 < x \leq n$
(1c)  $\lfloor x \rfloor = n$ if and only if $x - 1 < n \leq x$
(1d)  $\lceil x \rceil = n$ if and only if $x \leq n < x + 1$

(2)    $x - 1 < \lfloor x \rfloor \leq x \leq \lceil x \rceil < x + 1$

(3a)  $\lfloor -x \rfloor = -\lceil x \rceil$
(3b)  $\lceil -x \rceil = -\lfloor x \rfloor$

(4a)  $\lfloor x + n \rfloor = \lfloor x \rfloor + n$
(4b)  $\lceil x + n \rceil = \lceil x \rceil + n$

of cells that can be transmitted in 1 minute, we determine the largest integer not exceeding the quotient when 30,000,000 is divided by 424. Consequently, $\lfloor 30{,}000{,}000/424 \rfloor = 70{,}754$ ATM cells can be transmitted in 1 minute over a 500 kilobit per second connection.  ◀

Table 1, with $x$ denoting a real number, displays some simple but important properties of the floor and ceiling functions. Because these functions appear so frequently in discrete mathematics, it is useful to look over these identities. Each property in this table can be established using the definitions of the floor and ceiling functions. Properties (1a), (1b), (1c), and (1d) follow directly from these definitions. For example, (1a) states that $\lfloor x \rfloor = n$ if and only if the integer $n$ is less than or equal to $x$ and $n + 1$ is larger than $x$. This is precisely what it means for $n$ to be the greatest integer not exceeding $x$, which is the definition of $\lfloor x \rfloor = n$. Properties (1b), (1c), and (1d) can be established similarly. We will prove property (4a) using a direct proof.

*Proof:* Suppose that $\lfloor x \rfloor = m$, where $m$ is a positive integer. By property (1a), it follows that $m \leq x < m + 1$. Adding $n$ to all three quantities in this chain of two inequalities shows that $m + n \leq x + n < m + n + 1$. Using property (1a) again, we see that $\lfloor x + n \rfloor = m + n = \lfloor x \rfloor + n$. This completes the proof. Proofs of the other properties are left as exercises.  ◁

The floor and ceiling functions enjoy many other useful properties besides those displayed in Table 1. There are also many statements about these functions that may appear to be correct, but actually are not. We will consider statements about the floor and ceiling functions in Examples 29 and 30.

A useful approach for considering statements about the floor function is to let $x = n + \epsilon$, where $n = \lfloor x \rfloor$ is an integer, and $\epsilon$, the fractional part of $x$, satisfies the inequality $0 \leq \epsilon < 1$. Similarly, when considering statements about the ceiling function, it is useful to write $x = n - \epsilon$, where $n = \lceil x \rceil$ is an integer and $0 \leq \epsilon < 1$.

**EXAMPLE 29**    Prove that if $x$ is a real number, then $\lfloor 2x \rfloor = \lfloor x \rfloor + \lfloor x + \frac{1}{2} \rfloor$.

*Solution:* To prove this statement we let $x = n + \epsilon$, where $n$ is an integer and $0 \leq \epsilon < 1$. There are two cases to consider, depending on whether $\epsilon$ is less than, or greater than or equal to $\frac{1}{2}$. (The reason we choose these two cases will be made clear in the proof.)

We first consider the case when $0 \le \epsilon < \frac{1}{2}$. In this case, $2x = 2n + 2\epsilon$ and $\lfloor 2x \rfloor = 2n$ because $0 \le 2\epsilon < 1$. Similarly, $x + \frac{1}{2} = n + (\frac{1}{2} + \epsilon)$, so $\lfloor x + \frac{1}{2} \rfloor = n$, because $0 < \frac{1}{2} + \epsilon < 1$. Consequently, $\lfloor 2x \rfloor = 2n$ and $\lfloor x \rfloor + \lfloor x + \frac{1}{2} \rfloor = n + n = 2n$.

Next, we consider the case when $\frac{1}{2} \le \epsilon < 1$. In this case, $2x = 2n + 2\epsilon = (2n + 1) + (2\epsilon - 1)$. Because $0 \le 2\epsilon - 1 < 1$, it follows that $\lfloor 2x \rfloor = 2n + 1$. Because $\lfloor x + \frac{1}{2} \rfloor = \lfloor n + (\frac{1}{2} + \epsilon) \rfloor = \lfloor n + 1 + (\epsilon - \frac{1}{2}) \rfloor$ and $0 \le \epsilon - \frac{1}{2} < 1$, it follows that $\lfloor x + \frac{1}{2} \rfloor = n + 1$. Consequently, $\lfloor 2x \rfloor = 2n + 1$ and $\lfloor x \rfloor + \lfloor x + \frac{1}{2} \rfloor = n + (n + 1) = 2n + 1$. This concludes the proof. ◄

**EXAMPLE 30**    Prove or disprove that $\lceil x + y \rceil = \lceil x \rceil + \lceil y \rceil$ for all real numbers $x$ and $y$.

*Solution:* Although this statement may appear reasonable, it is false. A counterexample is supplied by $x = \frac{1}{2}$ and $y = \frac{1}{2}$. With these values we find that $\lceil x + y \rceil = \lceil \frac{1}{2} + \frac{1}{2} \rceil = \lceil 1 \rceil = 1$, but $\lceil x \rceil + \lceil y \rceil = \lceil \frac{1}{2} \rceil + \lceil \frac{1}{2} \rceil = 1 + 1 = 2$. ◄

There are certain types of functions that will be used throughout the text. These include polynomial, logarithmic, and exponential functions. A brief review of the properties of these functions needed in this text is given in Appendix 2. In this book the notation $\log x$ will be used to denote the logarithm to the base 2 of $x$, because 2 is the base that we will usually use for logarithms. We will denote logarithms to the base $b$, where $b$ is any real number greater than 1, by $\log_b x$, and the natural logarithm by $\ln x$.

Another function we will use throughout this text is the **factorial function** $f : \mathbf{N} \to \mathbf{Z}^+$, denoted by $f(n) = n!$. The value of $f(n) = n!$ is the product of the first $n$ positive integers, so $f(n) = 1 \cdot 2 \cdots (n - 1) \cdot n$ [and $f(0) = 0! = 1$].

**EXAMPLE 31**    We have $f(1) = 1! = 1$, $f(2) = 2! = 1 \cdot 2 = 2$, $f(6) = 6! = 1 \cdot 2 \cdot 3 \cdot 4 \cdot 5 \cdot 6 = 720$, and $f(20) = 1 \cdot 2 \cdot 3 \cdot 4 \cdot 5 \cdot 6 \cdot 7 \cdot 8 \cdot 9 \cdot 10 \cdot 11 \cdot 12 \cdot 13 \cdot 14 \cdot 15 \cdot 16 \cdot 17 \cdot 18 \cdot 19 \cdot 20 = 2,432,902,008,176,640,000$. ◄

Example 31 illustrates that the factorial function grows extremely rapidly as $n$ grows. The rapid growth of the factorial function is made clearer by Stirling's formula, a result from higher mathematics that tell us that $n! \sim \sqrt{2\pi n}(n/e)^n$. Here, we have used the notation $f(n) \sim g(n)$, which means that the ratio $f(n)/g(n)$ approaches 1 as $n$ grows without bound (that is, $\lim_{n \to \infty} f(n)/g(n) = 1$). The symbol $\sim$ is read "is asymptotic to." Stirling's formula is named after James Stirling, a Scottish mathematician of the eighteenth century.

Links

---

## Partial Functions

A program designed to evaluate a function may not produce the correct value of the function for all elements in the domain of this function. For example, a program may not produce a correct value because evaluating the function may lead to an infinite loop or an overflow. Similarly, in abstract mathematics, we often want to discuss functions that are defined only for a subset of the real numbers, such as $1/x$, $\sqrt{x}$, and arcsin $(x)$. Also, we may want to use such notions as the "youngest child" function, which is undefined for a couple having no children, or the "time of sunrise," which is undefined for some days above the Arctic Circle. To study such situations, we use the concept of a partial function.

**DEFINITION 13**    A *partial function* $f$ from a set $A$ to a set $B$ is an assignment to each element $a$ in a subset of $A$, called the *domain of definition* of $f$, of a unique element $b$ in $B$. The sets $A$ and $B$ are called the *domain* and *codomain* of $f$, respectively. We say that $f$ is *undefined* for elements in $A$ that are not in the domain of definition of $f$. When the domain of definition of $f$ equals $A$, we say that $f$ is a *total function*.

**Remark:** We write $f : A \to B$ to denote that $f$ is a partial function from $A$ to $B$. Note that this is the same notation as is used for functions. The context in which the notation is used determines whether $f$ is a partial function or a total function.

**EXAMPLE 32**    The function $f : \mathbf{Z} \to \mathbf{R}$ where $f(n) = \sqrt{n}$ is a partial function from $\mathbf{Z}$ to $\mathbf{R}$ where the domain of definition is the set of nonnegative integers. Note that $f$ is undefined for negative integers.  ◀

## Exercises

**1.** Why is $f$ not a function from $\mathbf{R}$ to $\mathbf{R}$ if
   **a)** $f(x) = 1/x$?
   **b)** $f(x) = \sqrt{x}$?
   **c)** $f(x) = \pm\sqrt{(x^2 + 1)}$?

**2.** Determine whether $f$ is a function from $\mathbf{Z}$ to $\mathbf{R}$ if
   **a)** $f(n) = \pm n$.
   **b)** $f(n) = \sqrt{n^2 + 1}$.
   **c)** $f(n) = 1/(n^2 - 4)$.

**3.** Determine whether $f$ is a function from the set of all bit strings to the set of integers if
   **a)** $f(S)$ is the position of a 0 bit in $S$.
   **b)** $f(S)$ is the number of 1 bits in $S$.
   **c)** $f(S)$ is the smallest integer $i$ such that the $i$th bit of $S$ is 1 and $f(S) = 0$ when $S$ is the empty string, the string with no bits.

**4.** Find the domain and range of these functions. Note that in each case, to find the domain, determine the set of elements assigned values by the function.
   **a)** the function that assigns to each nonnegative integer its last digit
   **b)** the function that assigns the next largest integer to a positive integer
   **c)** the function that assigns to a bit string the number of one bits in the string
   **d)** the function that assigns to a bit string the number of bits in the string

**5.** Find the domain and range of these functions. Note that in each case, to find the domain, determine the set of elements assigned values by the function.
   **a)** the function that assigns to each bit string the number of ones in the string minus the number of zeros in the string
   **b)** the function that assigns to each bit string twice the number of zeros in that string
   **c)** the function that assigns the number of bits left over when a bit string is split into bytes (which are blocks of 8 bits)
   **d)** the function that assigns to each positive integer the largest perfect square not exceeding this integer

**6.** Find the domain and range of these functions.
   **a)** the function that assigns to each pair of positive integers the first integer of the pair
   **b)** the function that assigns to each positive integer its largest decimal digit
   **c)** the function that assigns to a bit string the number of ones minus the number of zeros in the string
   **d)** the function that assigns to each positive integer the largest integer not exceeding the square root of the integer
   **e)** the function that assigns to a bit string the longest string of ones in the string

7. Find the domain and range of these functions.
   a) the function that assigns to each pair of positive integers the maximum of these two integers
   b) the function that assigns to each positive integer the number of the digits 0, 1, 2, 3, 4, 5, 6, 7, 8, 9 that do not appear as decimal digits of the integer
   c) the function that assigns to a bit string the number of times the block 11 appears
   d) the function that assigns to a bit string the numerical position of the first 1 in the string and that assigns the value 0 to a bit string consisting of all 0s

8. Find these values.
   a) $\lfloor 1.1 \rfloor$
   b) $\lceil 1.1 \rceil$
   c) $\lfloor -0.1 \rfloor$
   d) $\lceil -0.1 \rceil$
   e) $\lceil 2.99 \rceil$
   f) $\lceil -2.99 \rceil$
   g) $\lfloor \frac{1}{2} + \lceil \frac{1}{2} \rceil \rfloor$
   h) $\lceil \lfloor \frac{1}{2} \rfloor + \lceil \frac{1}{2} \rceil + \frac{1}{2} \rceil$

9. Find these values.
   a) $\lceil \frac{3}{4} \rceil$
   b) $\lfloor \frac{7}{8} \rfloor$
   c) $\lceil -\frac{3}{4} \rceil$
   d) $\lfloor -\frac{7}{8} \rfloor$
   e) $\lceil 3 \rceil$
   f) $\lfloor -1 \rfloor$
   g) $\lfloor \frac{1}{2} + \lceil \frac{3}{2} \rceil \rfloor$
   h) $\lfloor \frac{1}{2} \cdot \lfloor \frac{5}{2} \rfloor \rfloor$

10. Determine whether each of these functions from $\{a, b, c, d\}$ to itself is one-to-one.
    a) $f(a) = b, f(b) = a, f(c) = c, f(d) = d$
    b) $f(a) = b, f(b) = b, f(c) = d, f(d) = c$
    c) $f(a) = d, f(b) = b, f(c) = c, f(d) = d$

11. Which functions in Exercise 10 are onto?

12. Determine whether each of these functions from $\mathbf{Z}$ to $\mathbf{Z}$ is one-to-one.
    a) $f(n) = n - 1$
    b) $f(n) = n^2 + 1$
    c) $f(n) = n^3$
    d) $f(n) = \lceil n/2 \rceil$

13. Which functions in Exercise 12 are onto?

14. Determine whether $f : \mathbf{Z} \times \mathbf{Z} \to \mathbf{Z}$ is onto if
    a) $f(m, n) = 2m - n$.
    b) $f(m, n) = m^2 - n^2$.
    c) $f(m, n) = m + n + 1$.
    d) $f(m, n) = |m| - |n|$.
    e) $f(m, n) = m^2 - 4$.

15. Determine whether the function $f : \mathbf{Z} \times \mathbf{Z} \to \mathbf{Z}$ is onto if
    a) $f(m, n) = m + n$.
    b) $f(m, n) = m^2 + n^2$.
    c) $f(m, n) = m$.
    d) $f(m, n) = |n|$.
    e) $f(m, n) = m - n$.

16. Consider these functions from the set of students in a discrete mathematics class. Under what conditions is the function one-to-one if it assigns to a student his or her
    a) mobile phone number.
    b) student identification number.
    c) final grade in the class.
    d) home town.

17. Consider these functions from the set of teachers in a school. Under what conditions is the function one-to-one if it assigns to a teacher his or her

    a) office.
    b) assigned bus to chaperone in a group of buses taking students on a field trip.
    c) salary.
    d) social security number.

18. Specify a codomain for each of the functions in Exercise 16. Under what conditions is each of these functions with the codomain you specified onto?

19. Specify a codomain for each of the functions in Exercise 17. Under what conditions is each of the functions with the codomain you specified onto?

20. Give an example of a function from $\mathbf{N}$ to $\mathbf{N}$ that is
    a) one-to-one but not onto.
    b) onto but not one-to-one.
    c) both onto and one-to-one (but different from the identity function).
    d) neither one-to-one nor onto.

21. Give an explicit formula for a function from the set of integers to the set of positive integers that is
    a) one-to-one, but not onto.
    b) onto, but not one-to-one.
    c) one-to-one and onto.
    d) neither one-to-one nor onto.

22. Determine whether each of these functions is a bijection from $\mathbf{R}$ to $\mathbf{R}$.
    a) $f(x) = -3x + 4$
    b) $f(x) = -3x^2 + 7$
    c) $f(x) = (x + 1)/(x + 2)$
    d) $f(x) = x^5 + 1$

23. Determine whether each of these functions is a bijection from $\mathbf{R}$ to $\mathbf{R}$.
    a) $f(x) = 2x + 1$
    b) $f(x) = x^2 + 1$
    c) $f(x) = x^3$
    d) $f(x) = (x^2 + 1)/(x^2 + 2)$

24. Let $f : \mathbf{R} \to \mathbf{R}$ and let $f(x) > 0$ for all $x \in \mathbf{R}$. Show that $f(x)$ is strictly increasing if and only if the function $g(x) = 1/f(x)$ is strictly decreasing.

25. Let $f : \mathbf{R} \to \mathbf{R}$ and let $f(x) > 0$ for all $x \in \mathbf{R}$. Show that $f(x)$ is strictly decreasing if and only if the function $g(x) = 1/f(x)$ is strictly increasing.

26. a) Prove that a strictly increasing function from $\mathbf{R}$ to itself is one-to-one.
    b) Give an example of an increasing function from $\mathbf{R}$ to itself that is not one-to-one.

27. a) Prove that a strictly decreasing function from $\mathbf{R}$ to itself is one-to-one.
    b) Give an example of a decreasing function from $\mathbf{R}$ to itself that is not one-to-one.

28. Show that the function $f(x) = e^x$ from the set of real numbers to the set of real numbers is not invertible, but if the codomain is restricted to the set of positive real numbers, the resulting function is invertible.

**29.** Show that the function $f(x) = |x|$ from the set of real numbers to the set of nonnegative real numbers is not invertible, but if the domain is restricted to the set of non-negative real numbers, the resulting function is invertible.

**30.** Let $S = \{-1, 0, 2, 4, 7\}$. Find $f(S)$ if

**a)** $f(x) = 1$.                **b)** $f(x) = 2x + 1$.

**c)** $f(x) = \lceil x/5 \rceil$.       **d)** $f(x) = \lfloor (x^2 + 1)/3 \rfloor$.

**31.** Let $f(x) = \lfloor x^2/3 \rfloor$. Find $f(S)$ if

**a)** $S = \{-2, -1, 0, 1, 2, 3\}$.

**b)** $S = \{0, 1, 2, 3, 4, 5\}$.

**c)** $S = \{1, 5, 7, 11\}$.

**d)** $S = \{2, 6, 10, 14\}$.

**32.** Let $f(x) = 2x$ where the domain is the set of real numbers. What is

**a)** $f(\mathbf{Z})$?       **b)** $f(\mathbf{N})$?       **c)** $f(\mathbf{R})$?

**33.** Suppose that $g$ is a function from $A$ to $B$ and $f$ is a function from $B$ to $C$.

**a)** Show that if both $f$ and $g$ are one-to-one functions, then $f \circ g$ is also one-to-one.

**b)** Show that if both $f$ and $g$ are onto functions, then $f \circ g$ is also onto.

**\*34.** If $f$ and $f \circ g$ are one-to-one, does it follow that $g$ is one-to-one? Justify your answer.

**\*35.** If $f$ and $f \circ g$ are onto, does it follow that $g$ is onto? Justify your answer.

**36.** Find $f \circ g$ and $g \circ f$, where $f(x) = x^2 + 1$ and $g(x) = x + 2$, are functions from $\mathbf{R}$ to $\mathbf{R}$.

**37.** Find $f + g$ and $fg$ for the functions $f$ and $g$ given in Exercise 36.

**38.** Let $f(x) = ax + b$ and $g(x) = cx + d$, where $a, b, c$, and $d$ are constants. Determine necessary and sufficient conditions on the constants $a, b, c$, and $d$ so that $f \circ g = g \circ f$.

**39.** Show that the function $f(x) = ax + b$ from $\mathbf{R}$ to $\mathbf{R}$ is invertible, where $a$ and $b$ are constants, with $a \neq 0$, and find the inverse of $f$.

**40.** Let $f$ be a function from the set $A$ to the set $B$. Let $S$ and $T$ be subsets of $A$. Show that

**a)** $f(S \cup T) = f(S) \cup f(T)$.

**b)** $f(S \cap T) \subseteq f(S) \cap f(T)$.

**41. a)** Give an example to show that the inclusion in part (b) in Exercise 40 may be proper.

**b)** Show that if $f$ is one-to-one, the inclusion in part (b) in Exercise 40 is an equality.

Let $f$ be a function from the set $A$ to the set $B$. Let $S$ be a subset of $B$. We define the **inverse image** of $S$ to be the subset of $A$ whose elements are precisely all pre-images of all elements of $S$. We denote the inverse image of $S$ by $f^{-1}(S)$, so $f^{-1}(S) = \{a \in A \mid f(a) \in S\}$. (*Beware:* The notation $f^{-1}$ is used in two different ways. Do not confuse the notation introduced here with the notation $f^{-1}(y)$ for the value at $y$ of the inverse of the invertible function $f$. Notice also that $f^{-1}(S)$, the inverse image of the set $S$, makes sense for all functions $f$, not just invertible functions.)

**42.** Let $f$ be the function from $\mathbf{R}$ to $\mathbf{R}$ defined by $f(x) = x^2$. Find

**a)** $f^{-1}(\{1\})$.                **b)** $f^{-1}(\{x \mid 0 < x < 1\})$.

**c)** $f^{-1}(\{x \mid x > 4\})$.

**43.** Let $g(x) = \lfloor x \rfloor$. Find

**a)** $g^{-1}(\{0\})$.                **b)** $g^{-1}(\{-1, 0, 1\})$.

**c)** $g^{-1}(\{x \mid 0 < x < 1\})$.

**44.** Let $f$ be a function from $A$ to $B$. Let $S$ and $T$ be subsets of $B$. Show that

**a)** $f^{-1}(S \cup T) = f^{-1}(S) \cup f^{-1}(T)$.

**b)** $f^{-1}(S \cap T) = f^{-1}(S) \cap f^{-1}(T)$.

**45.** Let $f$ be a function from $A$ to $B$. Let $S$ be a subset of $B$. Show that $f^{-1}(\overline{S}) = \overline{f^{-1}(S)}$.

**46.** Show that $\lfloor x + \frac{1}{2} \rfloor$ is the closest integer to the number $x$, except when $x$ is midway between two integers, when it is the larger of these two integers.

**47.** Show that $\lceil x - \frac{1}{2} \rceil$ is the closest integer to the number $x$, except when $x$ is midway between two integers, when it is the smaller of these two integers.

**48.** Show that if $x$ is a real number, then $\lceil x \rceil - \lfloor x \rfloor = 1$ if $x$ is not an integer and $\lceil x \rceil - \lfloor x \rfloor = 0$ if $x$ is an integer.

**49.** Show that if $x$ is a real number, then $x - 1 < \lfloor x \rfloor \leq x \leq \lceil x \rceil < x + 1$.

**50.** Show that if $x$ is a real number and $m$ is an integer, then $\lceil x + m \rceil = \lceil x \rceil + m$.

**51.** Show that if $x$ is a real number and $n$ is an integer, then

**a)** $x < n$ if and only if $\lfloor x \rfloor < n$.

**b)** $n < x$ if and only if $n < \lceil x \rceil$.

**52.** Show that if $x$ is a real number and $n$ is an integer, then

**a)** $x \leq n$ if and only if $\lceil x \rceil \leq n$.

**b)** $n \leq x$ if and only if $n \leq \lfloor x \rfloor$.

**53.** Prove that if $n$ is an integer, then $\lfloor n/2 \rfloor = n/2$ if $n$ is even and $(n-1)/2$ if $n$ is odd.

**54.** Prove that if $x$ is a real number, then $\lfloor -x \rfloor = -\lceil x \rceil$ and $\lceil -x \rceil = -\lfloor x \rfloor$.

**55.** The function INT is found on some calculators, where $\text{INT}(x) = \lfloor x \rfloor$ when $x$ is a nonnegative real number and $\text{INT}(x) = \lceil x \rceil$ when $x$ is a negative real number. Show that this INT function satisfies the identity $\text{INT}(-x) = -\text{INT}(x)$.

**56.** Let $a$ and $b$ be real numbers with $a < b$. Use the floor and/or ceiling functions to express the number of integers $n$ that satisfy the inequality $a \leq n \leq b$.

**57.** Let $a$ and $b$ be real numbers with $a < b$. Use the floor and/or ceiling functions to express the number of integers $n$ that satisfy the inequality $a < n < b$.

**58.** How many bytes are required to encode $n$ bits of data where $n$ equals

**a)** 4?       **b)** 10?       **c)** 500?       **d)** 3000?

**59.** How many bytes are required to encode $n$ bits of data where $n$ equals

    **a)** 7?      **b)** 17?      **c)** 1001?      **d)** 28,800?

**60.** How many ATM cells (described in Example 28) can be transmitted in 10 seconds over a link operating at the following rates?

    **a)** 128 kilobits per second (1 kilobit = 1000 bits)
    **b)** 300 kilobits per second
    **c)** 1 megabit per second (1 megabit = 1,000,000 bits)

**61.** Data are transmitted over a particular Ethernet network in blocks of 1500 octets (blocks of 8 bits). How many blocks are required to transmit the following amounts of data over this Ethernet network? (Note that a byte is a synonym for an octet, a kilobyte is 1000 bytes, and a megabyte is 1,000,000 bytes.)

    **a)** 150 kilobytes of data
    **b)** 384 kilobytes of data
    **c)** 1.544 megabytes of data
    **d)** 45.3 megabytes of data

**62.** Draw the graph of the function $f(n) = 1 - n^2$ from $\mathbf{Z}$ to $\mathbf{Z}$.

**63.** Draw the graph of the function $f(x) = \lfloor 2x \rfloor$ from $\mathbf{R}$ to $\mathbf{R}$.

**64.** Draw the graph of the function $f(x) = \lfloor x/2 \rfloor$ from $\mathbf{R}$ to $\mathbf{R}$.

**65.** Draw the graph of the function $f(x) = \lfloor x \rfloor + \lfloor x/2 \rfloor$ from $\mathbf{R}$ to $\mathbf{R}$.

**66.** Draw the graph of the function $f(x) = \lceil x \rceil + \lfloor x/2 \rfloor$ from $\mathbf{R}$ to $\mathbf{R}$.

**67.** Draw graphs of each of these functions.

    **a)** $f(x) = \lfloor x + \frac{1}{2} \rfloor$      **b)** $f(x) = \lfloor 2x + 1 \rfloor$
    **c)** $f(x) = \lceil x/3 \rceil$      **d)** $f(x) = \lceil 1/x \rceil$
    **e)** $f(x) = \lceil x - 2 \rceil + \lfloor x + 2 \rfloor$
    **f)** $f(x) = \lfloor 2x \rfloor \lceil x/2 \rceil$      **g)** $f(x) = \lceil \lfloor x - \frac{1}{2} \rfloor + \frac{1}{2} \rceil$

**68.** Draw graphs of each of these functions.

    **a)** $f(x) = \lceil 3x - 2 \rceil$      **b)** $f(x) = \lceil 0.2x \rceil$
    **c)** $f(x) = \lfloor -1/x \rfloor$      **d)** $f(x) = \lfloor x^2 \rfloor$
    **e)** $f(x) = \lceil x/2 \rceil \lfloor x/2 \rfloor$      **f)** $f(x) = \lfloor x/2 \rfloor + \lceil x/2 \rceil$
    **g)** $f(x) = \lfloor 2 \lceil x/2 \rceil + \frac{1}{2} \rfloor$

**69.** Find the inverse function of $f(x) = x^3 + 1$.

**70.** Suppose that $f$ is an invertible function from $Y$ to $Z$ and $g$ is an invertible function from $X$ to $Y$. Show that the inverse of the composition $f \circ g$ is given by $(f \circ g)^{-1} = g^{-1} \circ f^{-1}$.

**71.** Let $S$ be a subset of a universal set $U$. The **characteristic function** $f_S$ of $S$ is the function from $U$ to the set $\{0, 1\}$ such that $f_S(x) = 1$ if $x$ belongs to $S$ and $f_S(x) = 0$ if $x$ does not belong to $S$. Let $A$ and $B$ be sets. Show that for all $x \in U$,

    **a)** $f_{A \cap B}(x) = f_A(x) \cdot f_B(x)$
    **b)** $f_{A \cup B}(x) = f_A(x) + f_B(x) - f_A(x) \cdot f_B(x)$
    **c)** $f_{\overline{A}}(x) = 1 - f_A(x)$
    **d)** $f_{A \oplus B}(x) = f_A(x) + f_B(x) - 2f_A(x)f_B(x)$

**72.** Suppose that $f$ is a function from $A$ to $B$, where $A$ and $B$ are finite sets with $|A| = |B|$. Show that $f$ is one-to-one if and only if it is onto.

**73.** Prove or disprove each of these statements about the floor and ceiling functions.

    **a)** $\lceil \lfloor x \rfloor \rceil = \lfloor x \rfloor$ for all real numbers $x$.
    **b)** $\lfloor 2x \rfloor = 2 \lfloor x \rfloor$ whenever $x$ is a real number.
    **c)** $\lceil x \rceil + \lceil y \rceil - \lceil x + y \rceil = 0$ or 1 whenever $x$ and $y$ are real numbers.
    **d)** $\lceil xy \rceil = \lceil x \rceil \lceil y \rceil$ for all real numbers $x$ and $y$.
    **e)** $\left\lceil \dfrac{x}{2} \right\rceil = \left\lfloor \dfrac{x+1}{2} \right\rfloor$ for all real numbers $x$.

**74.** Prove or disprove each of these statements about the floor and ceiling functions.

    **a)** $\lfloor \lceil x \rceil \rfloor = \lceil x \rceil$ for all real numbers $x$.
    **b)** $\lfloor x + y \rfloor = \lfloor x \rfloor + \lfloor y \rfloor$ for all real numbers $x$ and $y$.
    **c)** $\lceil \lceil x/2 \rceil /2 \rceil = \lceil x/4 \rceil$ for all real numbers $x$.
    **d)** $\lfloor \sqrt{\lceil x \rceil} \rfloor = \lfloor \sqrt{x} \rfloor$ for all positive real numbers $x$.
    **e)** $\lfloor x \rfloor + \lfloor y \rfloor + \lfloor x + y \rfloor \le \lfloor 2x \rfloor + \lfloor 2y \rfloor$ for all real numbers $x$ and $y$.

**75.** Prove that if $x$ is a positive real number, then

    **a)** $\lfloor \sqrt{\lfloor x \rfloor} \rfloor = \lfloor \sqrt{x} \rfloor$.
    **b)** $\lceil \sqrt{\lceil x \rceil} \rceil = \lceil \sqrt{x} \rceil$.

**76.** Let $x$ be a real number. Show that $\lfloor 3x \rfloor = \lfloor x \rfloor + \lfloor x + \frac{1}{3} \rfloor + \lfloor x + \frac{2}{3} \rfloor$.

**77.** For each of these partial functions, determine its domain, codomain, domain of definition, and the set of values for which it is undefined. Also, determine whether it is a total function.

    **a)** $f : \mathbf{Z} \to \mathbf{R}$, $f(n) = 1/n$
    **b)** $f : \mathbf{Z} \to \mathbf{Z}$, $f(n) = \lceil n/2 \rceil$
    **c)** $f : \mathbf{Z} \times \mathbf{Z} \to \mathbf{Q}$, $f(m, n) = m/n$
    **d)** $f : \mathbf{Z} \times \mathbf{Z} \to \mathbf{Z}$, $f(m, n) = mn$
    **e)** $f : \mathbf{Z} \times \mathbf{Z} \to \mathbf{Z}$, $f(m, n) = m - n$ if $m > n$

**78. a)** Show that a partial function from $A$ to $B$ can be viewed as a function $f^*$ from $A$ to $B \cup \{u\}$, where $u$ is not an element of $B$ and

$$f^*(a) = \begin{cases} f(a) & \text{if } a \text{ belongs to the domain} \\ & \text{of definition of } f \\ u & \text{if } f \text{ is undefined at } a. \end{cases}$$

    **b)** Using the construction in (a), find the function $f^*$ corresponding to each partial function in Exercise 77.

**79. a)** Show that if a set $S$ has cardinality $m$, where $m$ is a positive integer, then there is a one-to-one correspondence between $S$ and the set $\{1, 2, \ldots, m\}$.

    **b)** Show that if $S$ and $T$ are two sets each with $m$ elements, where $m$ is a positive integer, then there is a one-to-one correspondence between $S$ and $T$.

**\*80.** Show that a set $S$ is infinite if and only if there is a proper subset $A$ of $S$ such that there is a one-to-one correspondence between $A$ and $S$.

# 2.4    Sequences and Summations

## Introduction

Sequences are ordered lists of elements, used in discrete mathematics in many ways. For example, they can be used to represent solutions to certain counting problems, as we will see in Chapter 8. They are also an important data structure in computer science. We will often need to work with sums of terms of sequences in our study of discrete mathematics. This section reviews the use of summation notation, basic properties of summations, and formulas for the sums of terms of some particular types of sequences.

The terms of a sequence can be specified by providing a formula for each term of the sequence. In this section we describe another way to specify the terms of a sequence using a recurrence relation, which expresses each term as a combination of the previous terms. We will introduce one method, known as iteration, for finding a closed formula for the terms of a sequence specified via a recurrence relation. Identifying a sequence when the first few terms are provided is a useful skill when solving problems in discrete mathematics. We will provide some tips, including a useful tool on the Web, for doing so.

## Sequences

A sequence is a discrete structure used to represent an ordered list. For example, 1, 2, 3, 5, 8 is a sequence with five terms and $1, 3, 9, 27, 81, \ldots, 3^n, \ldots$ is an infinite sequence.

**DEFINITION 1**    A *sequence* is a function from a subset of the set of integers (usually either the set $\{0, 1, 2, \ldots\}$ or the set $\{1, 2, 3, \ldots\}$) to a set $S$. We use the notation $a_n$ to denote the image of the integer $n$. We call $a_n$ a *term* of the sequence.

We use the notation $\{a_n\}$ to describe the sequence. (Note that $a_n$ represents an individual term of the sequence $\{a_n\}$. Be aware that the notation $\{a_n\}$ for a sequence conflicts with the notation for a set. However, the context in which we use this notation will always make it clear when we are dealing with sets and when we are dealing with sequences. Moreover, although we have used the letter $a$ in the notation for a sequence, other letters or expressions may be used depending on the sequence under consideration. That is, the choice of the letter $a$ is arbitrary.)

We describe sequences by listing the terms of the sequence in order of increasing subscripts.

**EXAMPLE 1**    Consider the sequence $\{a_n\}$, where

$$a_n = \frac{1}{n}.$$

The list of the terms of this sequence, beginning with $a_1$, namely,

$$a_1, a_2, a_3, a_4, \ldots,$$

starts with

$$1, \frac{1}{2}, \frac{1}{3}, \frac{1}{4}, \ldots. \qquad \blacktriangleleft$$

# 4

# Number Theory and Cryptography

The part of mathematics devoted to the study of the set of integers and their properties is known as number theory. In this chapter we will develop some of the important concepts of number theory including many of those used in computer science. As we develop number theory, we will use the proof methods developed in Chapter 1 to prove many theorems.

We will first introduce the notion of divisibility of integers, which we use to introduce modular, or clock, arithmetic. Modular arithmetic operates with the remainders of integers when they are divided by a fixed positive integer, called the modulus. We will prove many important results about modular arithmetic which we will use extensively in this chapter.

Integers can be represented with any positive integer $b$ greater than 1 as a base. In this chapter we discuss base $b$ representations of integers and give an algorithm for finding them. In particular, we will discuss binary, octal, and hexadecimal (base 2, 8, and 16) representations. We will describe algorithms for carrying out arithmetic using these representations and study their complexity. These algorithms were the first procedures called algorithms.

We will discuss prime numbers, the positive integers that have only 1 and themselves as positive divisors. We will prove that there are infinitely many primes; the proof we give is considered to be one of the most beautiful proofs in mathematics. We will discuss the distribution of primes and many famous open questions concerning primes. We will introduce the concept of greatest common divisors and study the Euclidean algorithm for computing them. This algorithm was first described thousands of years ago. We will introduce the fundamental theorem of arithmetic, a key result which tells us that every positive integer has a unique factorization into primes.

We will explain how to solve linear congruences, as well as systems of linear congruences, which we solve using the famous Chinese remainder theorem. We will introduce the notion of pseudoprimes, which are composite integers masquerading as primes, and show how this notion can help us rapidly generate prime numbers.

This chapter introduces several important applications of number theory. In particular, we will use number theory to generate pseudorandom numbers, to assign memory locations to computer files, and to find check digits used to detect errors in various kinds of identification numbers. We also introduce the subject of cryptography. Number theory plays an essential role both in classical cryptography, first used thousands of years ago, and modern cryptography, which plays an essential role in electronic communication. We will show how the ideas we develop can be used in cryptographical protocols, introducing protocols for sharing keys and for sending signed messages. Number theory, once considered the purest of subjects, has become an essential tool in providing computer and Internet security.

## 4.1 Divisibility and Modular Arithmetic

### Introduction

The ideas that we will develop in this section are based on the notion of divisibility. Division of an integer by a positive integer produces a quotient and a remainder. Working with these remainders leads to modular arithmetic, which plays an important role in mathematics and which is used throughout computer science. We will discuss some important applications of modular arithmetic later in this chapter, including generating pseudorandom numbers, assigning computer memory locations to files, constructing check digits, and encrypting messages.

## Division

When one integer is divided by a second nonzero integer, the quotient may or may not be an integer. For example, $12/3 = 4$ is an integer, whereas $11/4 = 2.75$ is not. This leads to Definition 1.

**DEFINITION 1**

If $a$ and $b$ are integers with $a \neq 0$, we say that $a$ *divides* $b$ if there is an integer $c$ such that $b = ac$, or equivalently, if $\frac{b}{a}$ is an integer. When $a$ divides $b$ we say that $a$ is a *factor* or *divisor* of $b$, and that $b$ is a *multiple* of $a$. The notation $a \mid b$ denotes that $a$ divides $b$. We write $a \nmid b$ when $a$ does not divide $b$.

*Remark:* We can express $a \mid b$ using quantifiers as $\exists c (ac = b)$, where the universe of discourse is the set of integers.

In Figure 1 a number line indicates which integers are divisible by the positive integer $d$.

**EXAMPLE 1**    Determine whether $3 \mid 7$ and whether $3 \mid 12$.

*Solution:* We see that $3 \nmid 7$, because $7/3$ is not an integer. On the other hand, $3 \mid 12$ because $12/3 = 4$.    ◀

**EXAMPLE 2**    Let $n$ and $d$ be positive integers. How many positive integers not exceeding $n$ are divisible by $d$?

*Solution:* The positive integers divisible by $d$ are all the integers of the form $dk$, where $k$ is a positive integer. Hence, the number of positive integers divisible by $d$ that do not exceed $n$ equals the number of integers $k$ with $0 < dk \leq n$, or with $0 < k \leq n/d$. Therefore, there are $\lfloor n/d \rfloor$ positive integers not exceeding $n$ that are divisible by $d$.    ◀

Some of the basic properties of divisibility of integers are given in Theorem 1.

**THEOREM 1**

Let $a$, $b$, and $c$ be integers, where $a \neq 0$. Then

($i$) if $a \mid b$ and $a \mid c$, then $a \mid (b + c)$;
($ii$) if $a \mid b$, then $a \mid bc$ for all integers $c$;
($iii$) if $a \mid b$ and $b \mid c$, then $a \mid c$.

*Proof:* We will give a direct proof of ($i$). Suppose that $a \mid b$ and $a \mid c$. Then, from the definition of divisibility, it follows that there are integers $s$ and $t$ with $b = as$ and $c = at$. Hence,

$$b + c = as + at = a(s + t).$$

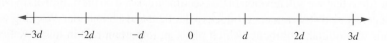

**FIGURE 1**    **Integers Divisible by the Positive Integer $d$.**

Therefore, $a$ divides $b + c$. This establishes part ($i$) of the theorem. The proofs of parts ($ii$) and ($iii$) are left as Exercises 3 and 4.    ◁

Theorem 1 has this useful consequence.

**COROLLARY 1**    If $a$, $b$, and $c$ are integers, where $a \neq 0$, such that $a \mid b$ and $a \mid c$, then $a \mid mb + nc$ whenever $m$ and $n$ are integers.

*Proof:* We will give a direct proof. By part ($ii$) of Theorem 1 we see that $a \mid mb$ and $a \mid nc$ whenever $m$ and $n$ are integers. By part ($i$) of Theorem 1 it follows that $a \mid mb + nc$.    ◁

## The Division Algorithm

When an integer is divided by a positive integer, there is a quotient and a remainder, as the division algorithm shows.

**THEOREM 2**    **THE DIVISION ALGORITHM**    Let $a$ be an integer and $d$ a positive integer. Then there are unique integers $q$ and $r$, with $0 \leq r < d$, such that $a = dq + r$.

We defer the proof of the division algorithm to Section 5.2. (See Example 5 and Exercise 37.)

*Remark:* Theorem 2 is not really an algorithm. (Why not?) Nevertheless, we use its traditional name.

**DEFINITION 2**    In the equality given in the division algorithm, $d$ is called the *divisor*, $a$ is called the *dividend*, $q$ is called the *quotient*, and $r$ is called the *remainder*. This notation is used to express the quotient and remainder:

$$q = a \textbf{ div } d, \quad r = a \textbf{ mod } d.$$

*Remark:* Note that both $a$ **div** $d$ and $a$ **mod** $d$ for a fixed $d$ are functions on the set of integers. Furthermore, when $a$ is an integer and $d$ is a positive integer, we have $a$ **div** $d = \lfloor a/d \rfloor$ and $a$ **mod** $d = a - d$. (See exercise 18.)

Examples 3 and 4 illustrate the division algorithm.

**EXAMPLE 3**    What are the quotient and remainder when 101 is divided by 11?

*Solution:* We have

$$101 = 11 \cdot 9 + 2.$$

Hence, the quotient when 101 is divided by 11 is $9 = 101$ **div** 11, and the remainder is $2 = 101$ **mod** 11.    ◀

**EXAMPLE 4**    What are the quotient and remainder when $-11$ is divided by 3?

*Solution:* We have

$$-11 = 3(-4) + 1.$$

 Hence, the quotient when $-11$ is divided by 3 is $-4 = -11$ **div** 3, and the remainder is $1 = -11 \bmod 3$.

Note that the remainder cannot be negative. Consequently, the remainder is *not* $-2$, even though

$$-11 = 3(-3) - 2,$$

because $r = -2$ does not satisfy $0 \le r < 3$.                                        ◀

Note that the integer $a$ is divisible by the integer $d$ if and only if the remainder is zero when $a$ is divided by $d$.

***Remark:*** A programming language may have one, or possibly two, operators for modular arithmetic, denoted by mod (in BASIC, Maple, Mathematica, EXCEL, and SQL), % (in C, C++, Java, and Python), rem (in Ada and Lisp), or something else. Be careful when using them, because for $a < 0$, some of these operators return $a - m\lceil a/m \rceil$ instead of $a \bmod m = a - m\lfloor a/m \rfloor$ (as shown in Exercise 18). Also, unlike $a \bmod m$, some of these operators are defined when $m < 0$, and even when $m = 0$.

## Modular Arithmetic

In some situations we care only about the remainder of an integer when it is divided by some specified positive integer. For instance, when we ask what time it will be (on a 24-hour clock) 50 hours from now, we care only about the remainder when 50 plus the current hour is divided by 24. Because we are often interested only in remainders, we have special notations for them. We have already introduced the notation $a \bmod m$ to represent the remainder when an integer $a$ is divided by the positive integer $m$. We now introduce a different, but related, notation that indicates that two integers have the same remainder when they are divided by the positive integer $m$.

**DEFINITION 3**    If $a$ and $b$ are integers and $m$ is a positive integer, then $a$ is *congruent to $b$ modulo $m$* if $m$ divides $a - b$. We use the notation $a \equiv b \pmod{m}$ to indicate that $a$ is congruent to $b$ modulo $m$. We say that $a \equiv b \pmod{m}$ is a **congruence** and that $m$ is its **modulus** (plural **moduli**). If $a$ and $b$ are not congruent modulo $m$, we write $a \not\equiv b \pmod{m}$.

Although both notations $a \equiv b \pmod{m}$ and $a \bmod m = b$ include "mod," they represent fundamentally different concepts. The first represents a relation on the set of integers, whereas the second represents a function. However, the relation $a \equiv b \pmod{m}$ and the **mod** $m$ function are closely related, as described in Theorem 3.

**THEOREM 3**   Let $a$ and $b$ be integers, and let $m$ be a positive integer. Then $a \equiv b \pmod{m}$ if and only if $a \bmod m = b \bmod m$.

The proof of Theorem 3 is left as Exercises 15 and 16. Recall that $a \bmod m$ and $b \bmod m$ are the remainders when $a$ and $b$ are divided by $m$, respectively. Consequently, Theorem 3 also says that $a \equiv b \pmod{m}$ if and only if $a$ and $b$ have the same remainder when divided by $m$.

**EXAMPLE 5**   Determine whether 17 is congruent to 5 modulo 6 and whether 24 and 14 are congruent modulo 6.

*Solution:* Because 6 divides $17 - 5 = 12$, we see that $17 \equiv 5 \pmod{6}$. However, because $24 - 14 = 10$ is not divisible by 6, we see that $24 \not\equiv 14 \pmod{6}$. ◀

The great German mathematician Karl Friedrich Gauss developed the concept of congruences at the end of the eighteenth century. The notion of congruences has played an important role in the development of number theory.

Theorem 4 provides a useful way to work with congruences.

**THEOREM 4**   Let $m$ be a positive integer. The integers $a$ and $b$ are congruent modulo $m$ if and only if there is an integer $k$ such that $a = b + km$.

*Proof:* If $a \equiv b \pmod{m}$, by the definition of congruence (Definition 3), we know that $m \mid (a - b)$. This means that there is an integer $k$ such that $a - b = km$, so that $a = b + km$. Conversely, if there is an integer $k$ such that $a = b + km$, then $km = a - b$. Hence, $m$ divides $a - b$, so that $a \equiv b \pmod{m}$. ◁

The set of all integers congruent to an integer $a$ modulo $m$ is called the **congruence class** of $a$ modulo $m$. In Chapter 9 we will show that there are $m$ pairwise disjoint equivalence classes modulo $m$ and that the union of these equivalence classes is the set of integers.

Theorem 5 shows that additions and multiplications preserve congruences.

Links

KARL FRIEDRICH GAUSS (1777–1855)   Karl Friedrich Gauss, the son of a bricklayer, was a child prodigy. He demonstrated his potential at the age of 10, when he quickly solved a problem assigned by a teacher to keep the class busy. The teacher asked the students to find the sum of the first 100 positive integers. Gauss realized that this sum could be found by forming 50 pairs, each with the sum 101: $1 + 100, 2 + 99, \ldots, 50 + 51$. This brilliance attracted the sponsorship of patrons, including Duke Ferdinand of Brunswick, who made it possible for Gauss to attend Caroline College and the University of Göttingen. While a student, he invented the method of least squares, which is used to estimate the most likely value of a variable from experimental results. In 1796 Gauss made a fundamental discovery in geometry, advancing a subject that had not advanced since ancient times. He showed that a 17-sided regular polygon could be drawn using just a ruler and compass.

In 1799 Gauss presented the first rigorous proof of the fundamental theorem of algebra, which states that a polynomial of degree $n$ has exactly $n$ roots (counting multiplicities). Gauss achieved worldwide fame when he successfully calculated the orbit of the first asteroid discovered, Ceres, using scanty data.

Gauss was called the Prince of Mathematics by his contemporary mathematicians. Although Gauss is noted for his many discoveries in geometry, algebra, analysis, astronomy, and physics, he had a special interest in number theory, which can be seen from his statement "Mathematics is the queen of the sciences, and the theory of numbers is the queen of mathematics." Gauss laid the foundations for modern number theory with the publication of his book *Disquisitiones Arithmeticae* in 1801.

**THEOREM 5**    Let $m$ be a positive integer. If $a \equiv b \pmod{m}$ and $c \equiv d \pmod{m}$, then

$$a + c \equiv b + d \pmod{m} \qquad \text{and} \qquad ac \equiv bd \pmod{m}.$$

*Proof:* We use a direct proof. Because $a \equiv b \pmod{m}$ and $c \equiv d \pmod{m}$, by Theorem 4 there are integers $s$ and $t$ with $b = a + sm$ and $d = c + tm$. Hence,

$$b + d = (a + sm) + (c + tm) = (a + c) + m(s + t)$$

and

$$bd = (a + sm)(c + tm) = ac + m(at + cs + stm).$$

Hence,

$$a + c \equiv b + d \pmod{m} \qquad \text{and} \qquad ac \equiv bd \pmod{m}. \qquad \triangleleft$$

**EXAMPLE 6**    Because $7 \equiv 2 \pmod 5$ and $11 \equiv 1 \pmod 5$, it follows from Theorem 5 that

$$18 = 7 + 11 \equiv 2 + 1 = 3 \pmod 5$$

and that

$$77 = 7 \cdot 11 \equiv 2 \cdot 1 = 2 \pmod 5. \qquad \blacktriangleleft$$

You cannot always divide both sides of a congruence by the same number!

We must be careful working with congruences. Some properties we may expect to be true are not valid. For example, if $ac \equiv bc \pmod{m}$, the congruence $a \equiv b \pmod{m}$ may be false. Similarly, if $a \equiv b \pmod{m}$ and $c \equiv d \pmod{m}$, the congruence $a^c \equiv b^d \pmod{m}$ may be false. (See Exercise 37.)

Corollary 2 shows how to find the values of the **mod** $m$ function at the sum and product of two integers using the values of this function at each of these integers. We will use this result in Section 5.4.

**COROLLARY 2**    Let $m$ be a positive integer and let $a$ and $b$ be integers. Then

$$(a + b) \bmod m = ((a \bmod m) + (b \bmod m)) \bmod m$$

and

$$ab \bmod m = ((a \bmod m)(b \bmod m)) \bmod m.$$

*Proof:*    By the definitions of **mod** $m$ and of congruence modulo $m$, we know that $a \equiv (a \bmod m) \pmod{m}$ and $b \equiv (b \bmod m) \pmod{m}$. Hence, Theorem 5 tells us that

$$a + b \equiv (a \bmod m) + (b \bmod m) \pmod{m}$$

and

$$ab \equiv (a \bmod m)(b \bmod m) \pmod{m}.$$

The equalities in this corollary follow from these last two congruences by Theorem 3.    $\triangleleft$

## Arithmetic Modulo $m$

We can define arithmetic operations on $\mathbf{Z}_m$, the set of nonnegative integers less than $m$, that is, the set $\{0, 1, \ldots, m - 1\}$. In particular, we define addition of these integers, denoted by $+_m$ by

$$a +_m b = (a + b) \bmod m,$$

where the addition on the right-hand side of this equation is the ordinary addition of integers, and we define multiplication of these integers, denoted by $\cdot_m$ by

$$a \cdot_m b = (a \cdot b) \bmod m,$$

where the multiplication on the right-hand side of this equation is the ordinary multiplication of integers. The operations $+_m$ and $\cdot_m$ are called addition and multiplication modulo $m$ and when we use these operations, we are said to be doing **arithmetic modulo** $m$.

**EXAMPLE 7**  Use the definition of addition and multiplication in $\mathbf{Z}_m$ to find $7 +_{11} 9$ and $7 \cdot_{11} 9$.

*Solution:* Using the definition of addition modulo 11, we find that

$$7 +_{11} 9 = (7 + 9) \bmod 11 = 16 \bmod 11 = 5,$$

and

$$7 \cdot_{11} 9 = (7 \cdot 9) \bmod 11 = 63 \bmod 11 = 8.$$

Hence $7 +_{11} 9 = 5$ and $7 \cdot_{11} 9 = 8$.  ◀

The operations $+_m$ and $\cdot_m$ satisfy many of the same properties of ordinary addition and multiplication of integers. In particular, they satisfy these properties:

**Closure** If $a$ and $b$ belong to $\mathbf{Z}_m$, then $a +_m b$ and $a \cdot_m b$ belong to $\mathbf{Z}_m$.

**Associativity** If $a$, $b$, and $c$ belong to $\mathbf{Z}_m$, then $(a +_m b) +_m c = a +_m (b +_m c)$ and $(a \cdot_m b) \cdot_m c = a \cdot_m (b \cdot_m c)$.

**Commutativity** If $a$ and $b$ belong to $\mathbf{Z}_m$, then $a +_m b = b +_m a$ and $a \cdot_m b = b \cdot_m a$.

**Identity elements** The elements 0 and 1 are identity elements for addition and multiplication modulo $m$, respectively. That is, if $a$ belongs to $\mathbf{Z}_m$, then $a +_m 0 = 0 +_m a = a$ and $a \cdot_m 1 = 1 \cdot_m a = a$.

**Additive inverses** If $a \neq 0$ belongs to $\mathbf{Z}_m$, then $m - a$ is an additive inverse of $a$ modulo $m$ and 0 is its own additive inverse. That is $a +_m (m - a) = 0$ and $0 +_m 0 = 0$.

**Distributivity** If $a$, $b$, and $c$ belong to $\mathbf{Z}_m$, then $a \cdot_m (b +_m c) = (a \cdot_m b) +_m (a \cdot_m c)$ and $(a +_m b) \cdot_m c = (a \cdot_m c) +_m (b \cdot_m c)$.

These properties follow from the properties we have developed for congruences and remainders modulo $m$, together with the properties of integers; we leave their proofs as Exercises 42–44. Note that we have listed the property that every element of $\mathbf{Z}_m$ has an additive inverse, but no analogous property for multiplicative inverses has been included. This is because multiplicative inverses do not always exists modulo $m$. For instance, there is no multiplicative inverse of 2 modulo 6, as the reader can verify. We will return to the question of when an integer has a multiplicative inverse modulo $m$ later in this chapter.

*Remark:* Because $\mathbf{Z}_m$ with the operations of addition and multiplication modulo $m$ satisfies the properties listed, $\mathbf{Z}_m$ with modular addition is said to be a **commutative group** and $\mathbf{Z}_m$ with both of these operations is said to be a **commutative ring**. Note that the set of integers with ordinary addition and multiplication also forms a commutative ring. Groups and rings are studied in courses that cover abstract algebra.

*Remark:* In Exercise 30, and in later sections, we will use the notations $+$ and $\cdot$ for $+_m$ and $\cdot_m$ without the subscript $m$ on the symbol for the operator whenever we work with $\mathbf{Z}_m$.

## Exercises

**1.** Does 17 divide each of these numbers?
   **a)** 68     **b)** 84     **c)** 357     **d)** 1001

**2.** Prove that if $a$ is an integer other than 0, then
   **a)** 1 divides $a$.     **b)** $a$ divides 0.

**3.** Prove that part (*ii*) of Theorem 1 is true.

**4.** Prove that part (*iii*) of Theorem 1 is true.

**5.** Show that if $a \mid b$ and $b \mid a$, where $a$ and $b$ are integers, then $a = b$ or $a = -b$.

**6.** Show that if $a, b, c$, and $d$ are integers, where $a \neq 0$, such that $a \mid c$ and $b \mid d$, then $ab \mid cd$.

**7.** Show that if $a$, $b$, and $c$ are integers, where $a \neq 0$ and $c \neq 0$, such that $ac \mid bc$, then $a \mid b$.

**8.** Prove or disprove that if $a \mid bc$, where $a, b$, and $c$ are positive integers and $a \neq 0$, then $a \mid b$ or $a \mid c$.

**9.** What are the quotient and remainder when
   **a)** 19 is divided by 7?
   **b)** $-111$ is divided by 11?
   **c)** 789 is divided by 23?
   **d)** 1001 is divided by 13?
   **e)** 0 is divided by 19?
   **f)** 3 is divided by 5?
   **g)** $-1$ is divided by 3?
   **h)** 4 is divided by 1?

**10.** What are the quotient and remainder when
   **a)** 44 is divided by 8?
   **b)** 777 is divided by 21?
   **c)** $-123$ is divided by 19?
   **d)** $-1$ is divided by 23?
   **e)** $-2002$ is divided by 87?
   **f)** 0 is divided by 17?
   **g)** 1,234,567 is divided by 1001?
   **h)** $-100$ is divided by 101?

**11.** What time does a 12-hour clock read
   **a)** 80 hours after it reads 11:00?
   **b)** 40 hours before it reads 12:00?
   **c)** 100 hours after it reads 6:00?

**12.** What time does a 24-hour clock read
   **a)** 100 hours after it reads 2:00?
   **b)** 45 hours before it reads 12:00?
   **c)** 168 hours after it reads 19:00?

**13.** Suppose that $a$ and $b$ are integers, $a \equiv 4 \pmod{13}$, and $b \equiv 9 \pmod{13}$. Find the integer $c$ with $0 \leq c \leq 12$ such that
   **a)** $c \equiv 9a \pmod{13}$.
   **b)** $c \equiv 11b \pmod{13}$.
   **c)** $c \equiv a + b \pmod{13}$.
   **d)** $c \equiv 2a + 3b \pmod{13}$.
   **e)** $c \equiv a^2 + b^2 \pmod{13}$.
   **f)** $c \equiv a^3 - b^3 \pmod{13}$.

**14.** Suppose that $a$ and $b$ are integers, $a \equiv 11 \pmod{19}$, and $b \equiv 3 \pmod{19}$. Find the integer $c$ with $0 \leq c \leq 18$ such that
   **a)** $c \equiv 13a \pmod{19}$.
   **b)** $c \equiv 8b \pmod{19}$.
   **c)** $c \equiv a - b \pmod{19}$.
   **d)** $c \equiv 7a + 3b \pmod{19}$.
   **e)** $c \equiv 2a^2 + 3b^2 \pmod{19}$.
   **f)** $c \equiv a^3 + 4b^3 \pmod{19}$.

**15.** Let $m$ be a positive integer. Show that $a \equiv b \pmod{m}$ if $a \bmod m = b \bmod m$.

**16.** Let $m$ be a positive integer. Show that $a \bmod m = b \bmod m$ if $a \equiv b \pmod{m}$.

**17.** Show that if $n$ and $k$ are positive integers, then $\lceil n/k \rceil = \lfloor (n-1)/k \rfloor + 1$.

**18.** Show that if $a$ is an integer and $d$ is an integer greater than 1, then the quotient and remainder obtained when $a$ is divided by $d$ are $\lfloor a/d \rfloor$ and $a - d\lfloor a/d \rfloor$, respectively.

**19.** Find a formula for the integer with smallest absolute value that is congruent to an integer $a$ modulo $m$, where $m$ is a positive integer.

**20.** Evaluate these quantities.
   **a)** $-17 \bmod 2$          **b)** $144 \bmod 7$
   **c)** $-101 \bmod 13$        **d)** $199 \bmod 19$

**21.** Evaluate these quantities.
   **a)** $13 \bmod 3$           **b)** $-97 \bmod 11$
   **c)** $155 \bmod 19$         **d)** $-221 \bmod 23$

**22.** Find $a$ **div** $m$ and $a$ **mod** $m$ when
   **a)** $a = -111, m = 99$.
   **b)** $a = -9999, m = 101$.
   **c)** $a = 10299, m = 999$.
   **d)** $a = 123456, m = 1001$.

**23.** Find $a$ **div** $m$ and $a$ **mod** $m$ when
   **a)** $a = 228$, $m = 119$.
   **b)** $a = 9009$, $m = 223$.
   **c)** $a = -10101$, $m = 333$.
   **d)** $a = -765432$, $m = 38271$.

**24.** Find the integer $a$ such that
   **a)** $a \equiv 43 \pmod{23}$ and $-22 \leq a \leq 0$.
   **b)** $a \equiv 17 \pmod{29}$ and $-14 \leq a \leq 14$.
   **c)** $a \equiv -11 \pmod{21}$ and $90 \leq a \leq 110$.

**25.** Find the integer $a$ such that
   **a)** $a \equiv -15 \pmod{27}$ and $-26 \leq a \leq 0$.
   **b)** $a \equiv 24 \pmod{31}$ and $-15 \leq a \leq 15$.
   **c)** $a \equiv 99 \pmod{41}$ and $100 \leq a \leq 140$.

**26.** List five integers that are congruent to 4 modulo 12.

**27.** List all integers between $-100$ and $100$ that are congruent to $-1$ modulo 25.

**28.** Decide whether each of these integers is congruent to 3 modulo 7.
   **a)** 37          **b)** 66
   **c)** $-17$       **d)** $-67$

**29.** Decide whether each of these integers is congruent to 5 modulo 17.
   **a)** 80          **b)** 103
   **c)** $-29$       **d)** $-122$

**30.** Find each of these values.
   **a)** $(177 \bmod 31 + 270 \bmod 31) \bmod 31$
   **b)** $(177 \bmod 31 \cdot 270 \bmod 31) \bmod 31$

**31.** Find each of these values.
   **a)** $(-133 \bmod 23 + 261 \bmod 23) \bmod 23$
   **b)** $(457 \bmod 23 \cdot 182 \bmod 23) \bmod 23$

**32.** Find each of these values.
   **a)** $(19^2 \bmod 41) \bmod 9$
   **b)** $(32^3 \bmod 13)^2 \bmod 11$
   **c)** $(7^3 \bmod 23)^2 \bmod 31$
   **d)** $(21^2 \bmod 15)^3 \bmod 22$

**33.** Find each of these values.
   **a)** $(99^2 \bmod 32)^3 \bmod 15$
   **b)** $(3^4 \bmod 17)^2 \bmod 11$
   **c)** $(19^3 \bmod 23)^2 \bmod 31$
   **d)** $(89^3 \bmod 79)^4 \bmod 26$

**34.** Show that if $a \equiv b \pmod{m}$ and $c \equiv d \pmod{m}$, where $a, b, c, d,$ and $m$ are integers with $m \geq 2$, then $a - c \equiv b - d \pmod{m}$.

**35.** Show that if $n \mid m$, where $n$ and $m$ are integers greater than 1, and if $a \equiv b \pmod{m}$, where $a$ and $b$ are integers, then $a \equiv b \pmod{n}$.

**36.** Show that if $a, b, c,$ and $m$ are integers such that $m \geq 2$, $c > 0$, and $a \equiv b \pmod{m}$, then $ac \equiv bc \pmod{mc}$.

**37.** Find counterexamples to each of these statements about congruences.
   **a)** If $ac \equiv bc \pmod{m}$, where $a, b, c,$ and $m$ are integers with $m \geq 2$, then $a \equiv b \pmod{m}$.
   **b)** If $a \equiv b \pmod{m}$ and $c \equiv d \pmod{m}$, where $a, b, c, d,$ and $m$ are integers with $c$ and $d$ positive and $m \geq 2$, then $a^c \equiv b^d \pmod{m}$.

**38.** Show that if $n$ is an integer then $n^2 \equiv 0$ or $1 \pmod{4}$.

**39.** Use Exercise 38 to show that if $m$ is a positive integer of the form $4k + 3$ for some nonnegative integer $k$, then $m$ is not the sum of the squares of two integers.

**40.** Prove that if $n$ is an odd positive integer, then $n^2 \equiv 1 \pmod{8}$.

**41.** Show that if $a, b, k,$ and $m$ are integers such that $k \geq 1$, $m \geq 2$, and $a \equiv b \pmod{m}$, then $a^k \equiv b^k \pmod{m}$.

**42.** Show that $\mathbf{Z}_m$ with addition modulo $m$, where $m \geq 2$ is an integer, satisfies the closure, associative, and commutative properties, 0 is an additive identity, and for every nonzero $a \in \mathbf{Z}_m$, $m - a$ is an inverse of $a$ modulo $m$.

**43.** Show that $\mathbf{Z}_m$ with multiplication modulo $m$, where $m \geq 2$ is an integer, satisfies the closure, associative, and commutativity properties, and 1 is a multiplicative identity.

**44.** Show that the distributive property of multiplication over addition holds for $\mathbf{Z}_m$, where $m \geq 2$ is an integer.

**45.** Write out the addition and multiplication tables for $\mathbf{Z}_5$ (where by addition and multiplication we mean $+_5$ and $\cdot_5$).

**46.** Write out the addition and multiplication tables for $\mathbf{Z}_6$ (where by addition and multiplication we mean $+_6$ and $\cdot_6$).

**47.** Determine whether each of the functions $f(a) = a$ **div** $d$ and $g(a) = a$ **mod** $d$, where $d$ is a fixed positive integer, from the set of integers to the set of integers, is one-to-one, and determine whether each of these functions is onto.

## 4.2   Integer Representations and Algorithms

### Introduction

Integers can be expressed using any integer greater than one as a base, as we will show in this section. Although we commonly use decimal (base 10), representations, binary (base 2), octal (base 8), and hexadecimal (base 16) representations are often used, especially in computer science. Given a base $b$ and an integer $n$, we will show how to construct the base $b$ representation of this integer. We will also explain how to quickly covert between binary and octal and between binary and hexadecimal notations.

As mentioned in Section 3.1, the term *algorithm* originally referred to procedures for performing arithmetic operations using the decimal representations of integers. These algorithms, adapted for use with binary representations, are the basis for computer arithmetic. They provide good illustrations of the concept of an algorithm and the complexity of algorithms. For these reasons, they will be discussed in this section.

We will also introduce an algorithm for finding $a$ **div** $d$ and $a$ **mod** $d$ where $a$ and $d$ are integers with $d > 1$. Finally, we will describe an efficient algorithm for modular exponentiation, which is a particularly important algorithm for cryptography, as we will see in Section 4.6.

## Representations of Integers

In everyday life we use decimal notation to express integers. For example, 965 is used to denote $9 \cdot 10^2 + 6 \cdot 10 + 5$. However, it is often convenient to use bases other than 10. In particular, computers usually use binary notation (with 2 as the base) when carrying out arithmetic, and octal (base 8) or hexadecimal (base 16) notation when expressing characters, such as letters or digits. In fact, we can use any integer greater than 1 as the base when expressing integers. This is stated in Theorem 1.

**THEOREM 1**    Let $b$ be an integer greater than 1. Then if $n$ is a positive integer, it can be expressed uniquely in the form

$$n = a_k b^k + a_{k-1} b^{k-1} + \cdots + a_1 b + a_0,$$

where $k$ is a nonnegative integer, $a_0, a_1, \ldots, a_k$ are nonnegative integers less than $b$, and $a_k \neq 0$.

A proof of this theorem can be constructed using mathematical induction, a proof method that is discussed in Section 5.1. It can also be found in [Ro10]. The representation of $n$ given in Theorem 1 is called the **base $b$ expansion of $n$**. The base $b$ expansion of $n$ is denoted by $(a_k a_{k-1} \ldots a_1 a_0)_b$. For instance, $(245)_8$ represents $2 \cdot 8^2 + 4 \cdot 8 + 5 = 165$. Typically, the subscript 10 is omitted for base 10 expansions of integers because base 10, or **decimal expansions**, are commonly used to represent integers.

BINARY EXPANSIONS    Choosing 2 as the base gives **binary expansions** of integers. In binary notation each digit is either a 0 or a 1. In other words, the binary expansion of an integer is just a bit string. Binary expansions (and related expansions that are variants of binary expansions) are used by computers to represent and do arithmetic with integers.

**EXAMPLE 1**    What is the decimal expansion of the integer that has $(1\ 0101\ 1111)_2$ as its binary expansion?

*Solution:* We have

$$(1\ 0101\ 1111)_2 = 1 \cdot 2^8 + 0 \cdot 2^7 + 1 \cdot 2^6 + 0 \cdot 2^5 + 1 \cdot 2^4$$
$$+ 1 \cdot 2^3 + 1 \cdot 2^2 + 1 \cdot 2^1 + 1 \cdot 2^0 = 351.$$    ◀

OCTAL AND HEXADECIMAL EXPANSIONS    Among the most important bases in computer science are base 2, base 8, and base 16. Base 8 expansions are called **octal** expansions and base 16 expansions are **hexadecimal** expansions.

**EXAMPLE 2** What is the decimal expansion of the number with octal expansion $(7016)_8$?

*Solution:* Using the definition of a base $b$ expansion with $b = 8$ tells us that

$$(7016)_8 = 7 \cdot 8^3 + 0 \cdot 8^2 + 1 \cdot 8 + 6 = 3598.$$ ◄

Sixteen different digits are required for hexadecimal expansions. Usually, the hexadecimal digits used are 0, 1, 2, 3, 4, 5, 6, 7, 8, 9, A, B, C, D, E, and F, where the letters A through F represent the digits corresponding to the numbers 10 through 15 (in decimal notation).

**EXAMPLE 3** What is the decimal expansion of the number with hexadecimal expansion $(2AE0B)_{16}$?

*Solution:* Using the definition of a base $b$ expansion with $b = 16$ tells us that

$$(2AE0B)_{16} = 2 \cdot 16^4 + 10 \cdot 16^3 + 14 \cdot 16^2 + 0 \cdot 16 + 11 = 175627.$$ ◄

Each hexadecimal digit can be represented using four bits. For instance, we see that $(1110\ 0101)_2 = (E5)_{16}$ because $(1110)_2 = (E)_{16}$ and $(0101)_2 = (5)_{16}$. **Bytes**, which are bit strings of length eight, can be represented by two hexadecimal digits.

BASE CONVERSION   We will now describe an algorithm for constructing the base $b$ expansion of an integer $n$. First, divide $n$ by $b$ to obtain a quotient and remainder, that is,

$$n = bq_0 + a_0, \qquad 0 \le a_0 < b.$$

The remainder, $a_0$, is the rightmost digit in the base $b$ expansion of $n$. Next, divide $q_0$ by $b$ to obtain

$$q_0 = bq_1 + a_1, \qquad 0 \le a_1 < b.$$

We see that $a_1$ is the second digit from the right in the base $b$ expansion of $n$. Continue this process, successively dividing the quotients by $b$, obtaining additional base $b$ digits as the remainders. This process terminates when we obtain a quotient equal to zero. It produces the base $b$ digits of $n$ from the right to the left.

**EXAMPLE 4** Find the octal expansion of $(12345)_{10}$.

Extra
Examples

*Solution:* First, divide 12345 by 8 to obtain

$$12345 = 8 \cdot 1543 + 1.$$

Successively dividing quotients by 8 gives

$$1543 = 8 \cdot 192 + 7,$$
$$192 = 8 \cdot 24 + 0,$$
$$24 = 8 \cdot 3 + 0,$$
$$3 = 8 \cdot 0 + 3.$$

The successive remainders that we have found, 1, 7, 0, 0, and 3, are the digits from the right to the left of 12345 in base 8. Hence,

$$(12345)_{10} = (30071)_8.$$ ◄

**EXAMPLE 5**    Find the hexadecimal expansion of $(177130)_{10}$.

*Solution:* First divide 177130 by 16 to obtain

$$177130 = 16 \cdot 11070 + 10.$$

Successively dividing quotients by 16 gives

$$11070 = 16 \cdot 691 + 14,$$
$$691 = 16 \cdot 43 + 3,$$
$$43 = 16 \cdot 2 + 11,$$
$$2 = 16 \cdot 0 + 2.$$

The successive remainders that we have found, 10, 14, 3, 11, 2, give us the digits from the right to the left of 177130 in the hexadecimal (base 16) expansion of $(177130)_{10}$. It follows that

$$(177130)_{10} = (2B3EA)_{16}.$$

(Recall that the integers 10, 11, and 14 correspond to the hexadecimal digits A, B, and E, respectively.)    ◄

**EXAMPLE 6**    Find the binary expansion of $(241)_{10}$.

*Solution:* First divide 241 by 2 to obtain

$$241 = 2 \cdot 120 + 1.$$

Successively dividing quotients by 2 gives

$$120 = 2 \cdot 60 + 0,$$
$$60 = 2 \cdot 30 + 0,$$
$$30 = 2 \cdot 15 + 0,$$
$$15 = 2 \cdot 7 + 1,$$
$$7 = 2 \cdot 3 + 1,$$
$$3 = 2 \cdot 1 + 1,$$
$$1 = 2 \cdot 0 + 1.$$

The successive remainders that we have found, 1, 0, 0, 0, 1, 1, 1, 1, are the digits from the right to the left in the binary (base 2) expansion of $(241)_{10}$. Hence,

$$(241)_{10} = (1111\ 0001)_{2}.$$    ◄

The pseudocode given in Algorithm 1 finds the base $b$ expansion $(a_{k-1} \ldots a_1 a_0)_b$ of the integer $n$.

**TABLE 1  Hexadecimal, Octal, and Binary Representation of the Integers 0 through 15.**

| Decimal | 0 | 1 | 2 | 3 | 4 | 5 | 6 | 7 | 8 | 9 | 10 | 11 | 12 | 13 | 14 | 15 |
|---|---|---|---|---|---|---|---|---|---|---|---|---|---|---|---|---|
| Hexadecimal | 0 | 1 | 2 | 3 | 4 | 5 | 6 | 7 | 8 | 9 | A | B | C | D | E | F |
| Octal | 0 | 1 | 2 | 3 | 4 | 5 | 6 | 7 | 10 | 11 | 12 | 13 | 14 | 15 | 16 | 17 |
| Binary | 0 | 1 | 10 | 11 | 100 | 101 | 110 | 111 | 1000 | 1001 | 1010 | 1011 | 1100 | 1101 | 1110 | 1111 |

---

**ALGORITHM 1  Constructing Base $b$ Expansions.**

**procedure** *base $b$ expansion*($n, b$: positive integers with $b > 1$)
$q := n$
$k := 0$
**while** $q \neq 0$
$\quad a_k := q \bmod b$
$\quad q := q \mathbf{\ div\ } b$
$\quad k := k + 1$
**return** $(a_{k-1}, \ldots, a_1, a_0)$ {$(a_{k-1} \ldots a_1 a_0)_b$ is the base $b$ expansion of $n$}

---

In Algorithm 1, $q$ represents the quotient obtained by successive divisions by $b$, starting with $q = n$. The digits in the base $b$ expansion are the remainders of these divisions and are given by $q \bmod b$. The algorithm terminates when a quotient $q = 0$ is reached.

*Remark:* Note that Algorithm 1 can be thought of as a greedy algorithm, as the base $b$ digits are taken as large as possible in each step.

**CONVERSION BETWEEN BINARY, OCTAL, AND HEXADECIMAL EXPANSIONS**
Conversion between binary and octal and between binary and hexadecimal expansions is extremely easy because each octal digit corresponds to a block of three binary digits and each hexadecimal digit corresponds to a block of four binary digits, with these correspondences shown in Table 1 without initial 0s shown. (We leave it as Exercises 13–16 to show that this is the case.) This conversion is illustrated in Example 7.

**EXAMPLE 7**  Find the octal and hexadecimal expansions of $(11\ 1110\ 1011\ 1100)_2$ and the binary expansions of $(765)_8$ and $(A8D)_{16}$.

*Solution:* To convert $(11\ 1110\ 1011\ 1100)_2$ into octal notation we group the binary digits into blocks of three, adding initial zeros at the start of the leftmost block if necessary. These blocks, from left to right, are 011, 111, 010, 111, and 100, corresponding to 3, 7, 2, 7, and 4, respectively. Consequently, $(11\ 1110\ 1011\ 1100)_2 = (37274)_8$. To convert $(11\ 1110\ 1011\ 1100)_2$ into hexadecimal notation we group the binary digits into blocks of four, adding initial zeros at the start of the leftmost block if necessary. These blocks, from left to right, are 0011, 1110, 1011, and 1100, corresponding to the hexadecimal digits 3, E, B, and C, respectively. Consequently, $(11\ 1110\ 1011\ 1100)_2 = (3EBC)_{16}$.

To convert $(765)_8$ into binary notation, we replace each octal digit by a block of three binary digits. These blocks are 111, 110, and 101. Hence, $(765)_8 = (1\ 1111\ 0101)_2$. To convert $(A8D)_{16}$ into binary notation, we replace each hexadecimal digit by a block of four binary digits. These blocks are 1010, 1000, and 1101. Hence, $(A8D)_{16} = (1010\ 1000\ 1101)_2$. ◄

# Algorithms for Integer Operations

The algorithms for performing operations with integers using their binary expansions are extremely important in computer arithmetic. We will describe algorithms for the addition and the multiplication of two integers expressed in binary notation. We will also analyze the computational complexity of these algorithms, in terms of the actual number of bit operations used. Throughout this discussion, suppose that the binary expansions of $a$ and $b$ are

$$a = (a_{n-1}a_{n-2}\ldots a_1a_0)_2, \ b = (b_{n-1}b_{n-2}\ldots b_1b_0)_2,$$

so that $a$ and $b$ each have $n$ bits (putting bits equal to 0 at the beginning of one of these expansions if necessary).

We will measure the complexity of algorithms for integer arithmetic in terms of the number of bits in these numbers.

ADDITION ALGORITHM   Consider the problem of adding two integers in binary notation. A procedure to perform addition can be based on the usual method for adding numbers with pencil and paper. This method proceeds by adding pairs of binary digits together with carries, when they occur, to compute the sum of two integers. This procedure will now be specified in detail.

To add $a$ and $b$, first add their rightmost bits. This gives

$$a_0 + b_0 = c_0 \cdot 2 + s_0,$$

where $s_0$ is the rightmost bit in the binary expansion of $a + b$ and $c_0$ is the **carry**, which is either 0 or 1. Then add the next pair of bits and the carry,

$$a_1 + b_1 + c_0 = c_1 \cdot 2 + s_1,$$

where $s_1$ is the next bit (from the right) in the binary expansion of $a + b$, and $c_1$ is the carry. Continue this process, adding the corresponding bits in the two binary expansions and the carry, to determine the next bit from the right in the binary expansion of $a + b$. At the last stage, add $a_{n-1}, b_{n-1}$, and $c_{n-2}$ to obtain $c_{n-1} \cdot 2 + s_{n-1}$. The leading bit of the sum is $s_n = c_{n-1}$. This procedure produces the binary expansion of the sum, namely, $a + b = (s_n s_{n-1} s_{n-2} \ldots s_1 s_0)_2$.

**EXAMPLE 8**   Add $a = (1110)_2$ and $b = (1011)_2$.

*Solution:* Following the procedure specified in the algorithm, first note that

$$a_0 + b_0 = 0 + 1 = 0 \cdot 2 + 1,$$

so that $c_0 = 0$ and $s_0 = 1$. Then, because

$$a_1 + b_1 + c_0 = 1 + 1 + 0 = 1 \cdot 2 + 0,$$

it follows that $c_1 = 1$ and $s_1 = 0$. Continuing,

$$a_2 + b_2 + c_1 = 1 + 0 + 1 = 1 \cdot 2 + 0,$$

so that $c_2 = 1$ and $s_2 = 0$. Finally, because

$$a_3 + b_3 + c_2 = 1 + 1 + 1 = 1 \cdot 2 + 1,$$

follows that $c_3 = 1$ and $s_3 = 1$. This means that $s_4 = c_3 = 1$. Therefore, $s = a + b = (1\,1001)_2$. This addition is displayed in Figure 1, where carries are shown in blue. ◀

```
  1 1 1
    1 1 1 0
+ 1 0 1 1
-----------
  1 1 0 0 1
```

**FIGURE 1**
**Adding $(1110)_2$**
**and $(1011)_2$.**

The algorithm for addition can be described using pseudocode as follows.

---

**ALGORITHM 2  Addition of Integers.**

**procedure** $add(a, b$: positive integers)
{the binary expansions of $a$ and $b$ are $(a_{n-1}a_{n-2} \ldots a_1 a_0)_2$
  and $(b_{n-1}b_{n-2} \ldots b_1 b_0)_2$, respectively}
$c := 0$
**for** $j := 0$ **to** $n - 1$
  $d := \lfloor (a_j + b_j + c)/2 \rfloor$
  $s_j := a_j + b_j + c - 2d$
  $c := d$
$s_n := c$
**return** $(s_0, s_1, \ldots, s_n)$ {the binary expansion of the sum is $(s_n s_{n-1} \ldots s_0)_2$}

---

Next, the number of additions of bits used by Algorithm 2 will be analyzed.

**EXAMPLE 9**    How many additions of bits are required to use Algorithm 2 to add two integers with $n$ bits (or less) in their binary representations?

*Solution:* Two integers are added by successively adding pairs of bits and, when it occurs, a carry. Adding each pair of bits and the carry requires two additions of bits. Thus, the total number of additions of bits used is less than twice the number of bits in the expansion. Hence, the number of additions of bits used by Algorithm 2 to add two $n$-bit integers is $O(n)$. ◀

MULTIPLICATION ALGORITHM    Next, consider the multiplication of two $n$-bit integers $a$ and $b$. The conventional algorithm (used when multiplying with pencil and paper) works as follows. Using the distributive law, we see that

$$\begin{aligned} ab &= a(b_0 2^0 + b_1 2^1 + \cdots + b_{n-1} 2^{n-1}) \\ &= a(b_0 2^0) + a(b_1 2^1) + \cdots + a(b_{n-1} 2^{n-1}). \end{aligned}$$

We can compute $ab$ using this equation. We first note that $ab_j = a$ if $b_j = 1$ and $ab_j = 0$ if $b_j = 0$. Each time we multiply a term by 2, we shift its binary expansion one place to the left and add a zero at the tail end of the expansion. Consequently, we can obtain $(ab_j)2^j$ by **shifting** the binary expansion of $ab_j$ $j$ places to the left, adding $j$ zero bits at the tail end of this binary expansion. Finally, we obtain $ab$ by adding the $n$ integers $ab_j 2^j$, $j = 0, 1, 2, \ldots, n - 1$.

Algorithm 3 displays this procedure for multiplication.

---

**ALGORITHM 3  Multiplication of Integers.**

---

**procedure** *multiply*(*a*, *b*: positive integers)
{the binary expansions of *a* and *b* are $(a_{n-1}a_{n-2} \ldots a_1a_0)_2$
   and $(b_{n-1}b_{n-2} \ldots b_1b_0)_2$, respectively}
**for** $j := 0$ **to** $n - 1$
    **if** $b_j = 1$ **then** $c_j := a$ shifted $j$ places
    **else** $c_j := 0$
{$c_0, c_1, \ldots, c_{n-1}$ are the partial products}
$p := 0$
**for** $j := 0$ **to** $n - 1$
    $p := p + c_j$
**return** $p$ {$p$ is the value of $ab$}

---

Example 10 illustrates the use of this algorithm.

**EXAMPLE 10**  Find the product of $a = (110)_2$ and $b = (101)_2$.

*Solution:* First note that

$$ab_0 \cdot 2^0 = (110)_2 \cdot 1 \cdot 2^0 = (110)_2,$$

$$ab_1 \cdot 2^1 = (110)_2 \cdot 0 \cdot 2^1 = (0000)_2,$$

and

$$ab_2 \cdot 2^2 = (110)_2 \cdot 1 \cdot 2^2 = (11000)_2.$$

```
      1 1 0
   ×  1 0 1
   ─────────
      1 1 0
    0 0 0
  1 1 0
  ─────────
  1 1 1 1 0
```

**FIGURE 2**
**Multiplying**
$(110)_2$ **and** $(101)_2$.

To find the product, add $(110)_2$, $(0000)_2$, and $(11000)_2$. Carrying out these additions (using Algorithm 2, including initial zero bits when necessary) shows that $ab = (1\ 1110)_2$. This multiplication is displayed in Figure 2. ◄

Next, we determine the number of additions of bits and shifts of bits used by Algorithm 3 to multiply two integers.

**EXAMPLE 11**  How many additions of bits and shifts of bits are used to multiply $a$ and $b$ using Algorithm 3?

*Solution:* Algorithm 3 computes the products of $a$ and $b$ by adding the partial products $c_0, c_1, c_2, \ldots$, and $c_{n-1}$. When $b_j = 1$, we compute the partial product $c_j$ by shifting the binary expansion of $a$ by $j$ bits. When $b_j = 0$, no shifts are required because $c_j = 0$. Hence, to find all $n$ of the integers $ab_j2^j$, $j = 0, 1, \ldots, n - 1$, requires at most

$$0 + 1 + 2 + \cdots + n - 1$$

shifts. Hence, by Example 5 in Section 3.2 the number of shifts required is $O(n^2)$.

To add the integers $ab_j$ from $j = 0$ to $j = n - 1$ requires the addition of an $n$-bit integer, an $(n + 1)$-bit integer, $\ldots$, and a $(2n)$-bit integer. We know from Example 9 that each of these additions requires $O(n)$ additions of bits. Consequently, a total of $O(n^2)$ additions of bits are required for all $n$ additions. ◄

Surprisingly, there are more efficient algorithms than the conventional algorithm for multiplying integers. One such algorithm, which uses $O(n^{1.585})$ bit operations to multiply $n$-bit numbers, will be described in Section 8.3.

ALGORITHM FOR div AND mod   Given integers $a$ and $d$, $d > 0$, we can find $q = a$ **div** $d$ and $r = a$ **mod** $d$ using Algorithm 4. In this brute-force algorithm, when $a$ is positive we subtract $d$ from $a$ as many times as necessary until what is left is less than $d$. The number of times we perform this subtraction is the quotient and what is left over after all these subtractions is the remainder. Algorithm 4 also covers the case where $a$ is negative. This algorithm finds the quotient $q$ and remainder $r$ when $|a|$ is divided by $d$. Then, when $a < 0$ and $r > 0$, it uses these to find the quotient $-(q + 1)$ and remainder $d - r$ when $a$ is divided by $d$. We leave it to the reader (Exercise 59) to show that, assuming that $a > d$, this algorithm uses $O(q \log a)$ bit operations.

---

**ALGORITHM 4** **Computing div and mod.**

**procedure** *division algorithm*($a$: integer, $d$: positive integer)
$q := 0$
$r := |a|$
**while** $r \geq d$
    $r := r - d$
    $q := q + 1$
**if** $a < 0$ and $r > 0$ **then**
    $r := d - r$
    $q := -(q + 1)$
**return** $(q, r)$ {$q = a$ **div** $d$ is the quotient, $r = a$ **mod** $d$ is the remainder}

---

There are more efficient algorithms than Algorithm 4 for determining the quotient $q = a$ **div** $d$ and the remainder $r = a$ **mod** $d$ when a positive integer $a$ is divided by a positive integer $d$ (see [Kn98] for details). These algorithms require $O(\log a \cdot \log d)$ bit operations. If both of the binary expansions of $a$ and $d$ contain $n$ or fewer bits, then we can replace $\log a \cdot \log d$ by $n^2$. This means that we need $O(n^2)$ bit operations to find the quotient and remainder when $a$ is divided by $d$.

## Modular Exponentiation

In cryptography it is important to be able to find $b^n$ **mod** $m$ efficiently, where $b$, $n$, and $m$ are large integers. It is impractical to first compute $b^n$ and then find its remainder when divided by $m$ because $b^n$ will be a huge number. Instead, we can use an algorithm that employs the binary expansion of the exponent $n$.

Before we present this algorithm, we illustrate its basic idea. We will explain how to use the binary expansion of $n$, say $n = (a_{k-1} \ldots a_1 a_0)_2$, to compute $b^n$. First, note that

$$b^n = b^{a_{k-1} \cdot 2^{k-1} + \cdots + a_1 \cdot 2 + a_0} = b^{a_{k-1} \cdot 2^{k-1}} \cdots b^{a_1 \cdot 2} \cdot b^{a_0}.$$

This shows that to compute $b^n$, we need only compute the values of $b$, $b^2$, $(b^2)^2 = b^4$, $(b^4)^2 = b^8, \ldots, b^{2^k}$. Once we have these values, we multiply the terms $b^{2^j}$ in this list, where $a_j = 1$. (For efficiency, after multiplying by each term, we reduce the result modulo $m$.) This gives us $b^n$. For example, to compute $3^{11}$ we first note that $11 = (1011)_2$, so that $3^{11} = 3^8 3^2 3^1$. By successively squaring, we find that $3^2 = 9$, $3^4 = 9^2 = 81$, and $3^8 = (81)^2 = 6561$. Consequently, $3^{11} = 3^8 3^2 3^1 = 6561 \cdot 9 \cdot 3 = 177{,}147$.

The algorithm successively finds $b$ **mod** $m$, $b^2$ **mod** $m$, $b^4$ **mod** $m, \ldots, b^{2^{k-1}}$ **mod** $m$ and multiplies together those terms $b^{2^j}$ **mod** $m$ where $a_j = 1$, finding the remainder of the product when divided by $m$ after each multiplication. Pseudocode for this algorithm is shown in Algorithm 5. Note that in Algorithm 5 we can use the most efficient algorithm available to compute values of the **mod** function, not necessarily Algorithm 4.

Be sure to reduce modulo $m$ after each multiplication!

---

**ALGORITHM 5** Modular Exponentiation.

---

**procedure** *modular exponentiation*($b$: integer, $n = (a_{k-1}a_{k-2} \ldots a_1a_0)_2$,
        $m$: positive integers)
$x := 1$
*power* $:= b$ **mod** $m$
**for** $i := 0$ **to** $k - 1$
        **if** $a_i = 1$ **then** $x := (x \cdot power)$ **mod** $m$
        *power* $:= (power \cdot power)$ **mod** $m$
**return** $x$ {$x$ equals $b^n$ **mod** $m$}

---

We illustrate how Algorithm 5 works in Example 12.

**EXAMPLE 12** Use Algorithm 5 to find $3^{644}$ **mod** 645.

*Solution:* Algorithm 5 initially sets $x = 1$ and *power* $= 3$ **mod** $645 = 3$. In the computation of $3^{644}$ **mod** 645, this algorithm determines $3^{2^j}$ **mod** 645 for $j = 1, 2, \ldots, 9$ by successively squaring and reducing modulo 645. If $a_j = 1$ (where $a_j$ is the bit in the $j$th position in the binary expansion of 644, which is $(1010000100)_2$), it multiplies the current value of $x$ by $3^{2^j}$ **mod** 645 and reduces the result modulo 645. Here are the steps used:

---

$i = 0$: Because $a_0 = 0$, we have $x = 1$ and *power* $= 3^2$ **mod** $645 = 9$ **mod** $645 = 9$;

$i = 1$: Because $a_1 = 0$, we have $x = 1$ and *power* $= 9^2$ **mod** $645 = 81$ **mod** $645 = 81$;

$i = 2$: Because $a_2 = 1$, we have $x = 1 \cdot 81$ **mod** $645 = 81$ and *power* $= 81^2$ **mod** $645 = 6561$ **mod** $645 = 111$;

$i = 3$: Because $a_3 = 0$, we have $x = 81$ and *power* $= 111^2$ **mod** $645 = 12{,}321$ **mod** $645 = 66$;

$i = 4$: Because $a_4 = 0$, we have $x = 81$ and *power* $= 66^2$ **mod** $645 = 4356$ **mod** $645 = 486$;

$i = 5$: Because $a_5 = 0$, we have $x = 81$ and *power* $= 486^2$ **mod** $645 = 236{,}196$ **mod** $645 = 126$;

$i = 6$: Because $a_6 = 0$, we have $x = 81$ and *power* $= 126^2$ **mod** $645 = 15{,}876$ **mod** $645 = 396$;

$i = 7$: Because $a_7 = 1$, we find that $x = (81 \cdot 396)$ **mod** $645 = 471$ and *power* $= 396^2$ **mod** $645 = 156{,}816$ **mod** $645 = 81$;

$i = 8$: Because $a_8 = 0$, we have $x = 471$ and *power* $= 81^2$ **mod** $645 = 6561$ **mod** $645 = 111$;

$i = 9$: Because $a_9 = 1$, we find that $x = (471 \cdot 111)$ **mod** $645 = 36$.

---

This shows that following the steps of Algorithm 5 produces the result $3^{644}$ **mod** $645 = 36$. ◀

Algorithm 5 is quite efficient; it uses $O((\log m)^2 \log n)$ bit operations to find $b^n$ **mod** $m$ (see Exercise 58).

# Exercises

1. Convert the decimal expansion of each of these integers to a binary expansion.
   a) 231    b) 4532    c) 97644

2. Convert the decimal expansion of each of these integers to a binary expansion.
   a) 321    b) 1023    c) 100632

3. Convert the binary expansion of each of these integers to a decimal expansion.
   a) $(1\ 1111)_2$
   b) $(10\ 0000\ 0001)_2$
   c) $(1\ 0101\ 0101)_2$
   d) $(110\ 1001\ 0001\ 0000)_2$

4. Convert the binary expansion of each of these integers to a decimal expansion.
   a) $(1\ 1011)_2$
   b) $(10\ 1011\ 0101)_2$
   c) $(11\ 1011\ 1110)_2$
   d) $(111\ 1100\ 0001\ 1111)_2$

5. Convert the octal expansion of each of these integers to a binary expansion.
   a) $(572)_8$
   b) $(1604)_8$
   c) $(423)_8$
   d) $(2417)_8$

6. Convert the binary expansion of each of these integers to an octal expansion.
   a) $(1111\ 0111)_2$
   b) $(1010\ 1010\ 1010)_2$
   c) $(111\ 0111\ 0111\ 0111)_2$
   d) $(101\ 0101\ 0101\ 0101)_2$

7. Convert the hexadecimal expansion of each of these integers to a binary expansion.
   a) $(80E)_{16}$
   b) $(135AB)_{16}$
   c) $(ABBA)_{16}$
   d) $(DEFACED)_{16}$

8. Convert $(BADFACED)_{16}$ from its hexadecimal expansion to its binary expansion.

9. Convert $(ABCDEF)_{16}$ from its hexadecimal expansion to its binary expansion.

10. Convert each of the integers in Exercise 6 from a binary expansion to a hexadecimal expansion.

11. Convert $(1011\ 0111\ 1011)_2$ from its binary expansion to its hexadecimal expansion.

12. Convert $(1\ 1000\ 0110\ 0011)_2$ from its binary expansion to its hexadecimal expansion.

13. Show that the hexadecimal expansion of a positive integer can be obtained from its binary expansion by grouping together blocks of four binary digits, adding initial zeros if necessary, and translating each block of four binary digits into a single hexadecimal digit.

14. Show that the binary expansion of a positive integer can be obtained from its hexadecimal expansion by translating each hexadecimal digit into a block of four binary digits.

15. Show that the octal expansion of a positive integer can be obtained from its binary expansion by grouping together blocks of three binary digits, adding initial zeros if nec-

essary, and translating each block of three binary digits into a single octal digit.

16. Show that the binary expansion of a positive integer can be obtained from its octal expansion by translating each octal digit into a block of three binary digits.

17. Convert $(7345321)_8$ to its binary expansion and $(10\ 1011\ 1011)_2$ to its octal expansion.

18. Give a procedure for converting from the hexadecimal expansion of an integer to its octal expansion using binary notation as an intermediate step.

19. Give a procedure for converting from the octal expansion of an integer to its hexadecimal expansion using binary notation as an intermediate step.

20. Explain how to convert from binary to base 64 expansions and from base 64 expansions to binary expansions and from octal to base 64 expansions and from base 64 expansions to octal expansions.

21. Find the sum and the product of each of these pairs of numbers. Express your answers as a binary expansion.
    a) $(100\ 0111)_2, (111\ 0111)_2$
    b) $(1110\ 1111)_2, (1011\ 1101)_2$
    c) $(10\ 1010\ 1010)_2, (1\ 1111\ 0000)_2$
    d) $(10\ 0000\ 0001)_2, (11\ 1111\ 1111)_2$

22. Find the sum and product of each of these pairs of numbers. Express your answers as a base 3 expansion.
    a) $(112)_3, (210)_3$
    b) $(2112)_3, (12021)_3$
    c) $(20001)_3, (1111)_3$
    d) $(120021)_3, (2002)_3$

23. Find the sum and product of each of these pairs of numbers. Express your answers as an octal expansion.
    a) $(763)_8, (147)_8$
    b) $(6001)_8, (272)_8$
    c) $(1111)_8, (777)_8$
    d) $(54321)_8, (3456)_8$

24. Find the sum and product of each of these pairs of numbers. Express your answers as a hexadecimal expansion.
    a) $(1AE)_{16}, (BBC)_{16}$
    b) $(20CBA)_{16}, (A01)_{16}$
    c) $(ABCDE)_{16}, (1111)_{16}$
    d) $(E0000E)_{16}, (BAAA)_{16}$

25. Use Algorithm 5 to find $7^{644} \bmod 645$.

26. Use Algorithm 5 to find $11^{644} \bmod 645$.

27. Use Algorithm 5 to find $3^{2003} \bmod 99$.

28. Use Algorithm 5 to find $123^{1001} \bmod 101$.

29. Show that every positive integer can be represented uniquely as the sum of distinct powers of 2. [*Hint:* Consider binary expansions of integers.]

**30.** It can be shown that every integer can be uniquely represented in the form

$$e_k 3^k + e_{k-1} 3^{k-1} + \cdots + e_1 3 + e_0,$$

where $e_j = -1, 0,$ or $1$ for $j = 0, 1, 2, \ldots, k$. Expansions of this type are called **balanced ternary expansions**. Find the balanced ternary expansions of

**a)** 5.    **b)** 13.    **c)** 37.    **d)** 79.

**31.** Show that a positive integer is divisible by 3 if and only if the sum of its decimal digits is divisible by 3.

**32.** Show that a positive integer is divisible by 11 if and only if the difference of the sum of its decimal digits in even-numbered positions and the sum of its decimal digits in odd-numbered positions is divisible by 11.

**33.** Show that a positive integer is divisible by 3 if and only if the difference of the sum of its binary digits in even-numbered positions and the sum of its binary digits in odd-numbered positions is divisible by 3.

**One's complement** representations of integers are used to simplify computer arithmetic. To represent positive and negative integers with absolute value less than $2^{n-1}$, a total of $n$ bits is used. The leftmost bit is used to represent the sign. A 0 bit in this position is used for positive integers, and a 1 bit in this position is used for negative integers. For positive integers, the remaining bits are identical to the binary expansion of the integer. For negative integers, the remaining bits are obtained by first finding the binary expansion of the absolute value of the integer, and then taking the complement of each of these bits, where the complement of a 1 is a 0 and the complement of a 0 is a 1.

**34.** Find the one's complement representations, using bit strings of length six, of the following integers.

**a)** 22    **b)** 31    **c)** −7    **d)** −19

**35.** What integer does each of the following one's complement representations of length five represent?

**a)** 11001    **b)** 01101

**c)** 10001    **d)** 11111

**36.** If $m$ is a positive integer less than $2^{n-1}$, how is the one's complement representation of $-m$ obtained from the one's complement of $m$, when bit strings of length $n$ are used?

**37.** How is the one's complement representation of the sum of two integers obtained from the one's complement representations of these integers?

**38.** How is the one's complement representation of the difference of two integers obtained from the one's complement representations of these integers?

**39.** Show that the integer $m$ with one's complement representation $(a_{n-1} a_{n-2} \ldots a_1 a_0)$ can be found using the equation $m = -a_{n-1}(2^{n-1} - 1) + a_{n-2} 2^{n-2} + \cdots + a_1 \cdot 2 + a_0$.

**Two's complement** representations of integers are also used to simplify computer arithmetic and are used more commonly than one's complement representations. To represent an integer $x$ with $-2^{n-1} \le x \le 2^{n-1} - 1$ for a specified positive integer $n$, a total of $n$ bits is used. The leftmost bit is used to represent the sign. A 0 bit in this position is used for positive integers, and a 1 bit in this position is used for negative integers, just as in one's complement expansions. For a positive integer, the remaining bits are identical to the binary expansion of the integer. For a negative integer, the remaining bits are the bits of the binary expansion of $2^{n-1} - |x|$. Two's complement expansions of integers are often used by computers because addition and subtraction of integers can be performed easily using these expansions, where these integers can be either positive or negative.

**40.** Answer Exercise 34, but this time find the two's complement expansion using bit strings of length six.

**41.** Answer Exercise 35 if each expansion is a two's complement expansion of length five.

**42.** Answer Exercise 36 for two's complement expansions.

**43.** Answer Exercise 37 for two's complement expansions.

**44.** Answer Exercise 38 for two's complement expansions.

**45.** Show that the integer $m$ with two's complement representation $(a_{n-1} a_{n-2} \ldots a_1 a_0)$ can be found using the equation $m = -a_{n-1} \cdot 2^{n-1} + a_{n-2} 2^{n-2} + \cdots + a_1 \cdot 2 + a_0$.

**46.** Give a simple algorithm for forming the two's complement representation of an integer from its one's complement representation.

**47.** Sometimes integers are encoded by using four-digit binary expansions to represent each decimal digit. This produces the **binary coded decimal** form of the integer. For instance, 791 is encoded in this way by 011110010001. How many bits are required to represent a number with $n$ decimal digits using this type of encoding?

A **Cantor expansion** is a sum of the form

$$a_n n! + a_{n-1}(n-1)! + \cdots + a_2 2! + a_1 1!,$$

where $a_i$ is an integer with $0 \le a_i \le i$ for $i = 1, 2, \ldots, n$.

**48.** Find the Cantor expansions of

**a)** 2.    **b)** 7.

**c)** 19.    **d)** 87.

**e)** 1000.    **f)** 1,000,000.

**\*49.** Describe an algorithm that finds the Cantor expansion of an integer.

**\*50.** Describe an algorithm to add two integers from their Cantor expansions.

**51.** Add $(10111)_2$ and $(11010)_2$ by working through each step of the algorithm for addition given in the text.

**52.** Multiply $(1110)_2$ and $(1010)_2$ by working through each step of the algorithm for multiplication given in the text.

**53.** Describe an algorithm for finding the difference of two binary expansions.

**54.** Estimate the number of bit operations used to subtract two binary expansions.

**55.** Devise an algorithm that, given the binary expansions of the integers $a$ and $b$, determines whether $a > b$, $a = b$, or $a < b$.

**56.** How many bit operations does the comparison algorithm from Exercise 55 use when the larger of $a$ and $b$ has $n$ bits in its binary expansion?

**57.** Estimate the complexity of Algorithm 1 for finding the base $b$ expansion of an integer $n$ in terms of the number of divisions used.

**∗58.** Show that Algorithm 5 uses $O((\log m)^2 \log n)$ bit operations to find $b^n \bmod m$.

**59.** Show that Algorithm 4 uses $O(q \log a)$ bit operations, assuming that $a > d$.

# 4.3    Primes and Greatest Common Divisors

## Introduction

In Section 4.1 we studied the concept of divisibility of integers. One important concept based on divisibility is that of a prime number. A prime is an integer greater than 1 that is divisible by no positive integers other than 1 and itself. The study of prime numbers goes back to ancient times. Thousands of years ago it was known that there are infinitely many primes; the proof of this fact, found in the works of Euclid, is famous for its elegance and beauty.

We will discuss the distribution of primes among the integers. We will describe some of the results about primes found by mathematicians in the last 400 years. In particular, we will introduce an important theorem, the fundamental theorem of arithmetic. This theorem, which asserts that every positive integer can be written uniquely as the product of primes in nondecreasing order, has many interesting consequences. We will also discuss some of the many old conjectures about primes that remain unsettled today.

Primes have become essential in modern cryptographic systems, and we will develop some of their properties important in cryptography. For example, finding large primes is essential in modern cryptography. The length of time required to factor large integers into their prime factors is the basis for the strength of some important modern cryptographic systems.

In this section we will also study the greatest common divisor of two integers, as well as the least common multiple of two integers. We will develop an important algorithm for computing greatest common divisors, called the Euclidean algorithm.

## Primes

Every integer greater than 1 is divisible by at least two integers, because a positive integer is divisible by 1 and by itself. Positive integers that have exactly two different positive integer factors are called **primes**.

**DEFINITION 1**    An integer $p$ greater than 1 is called *prime* if the only positive factors of $p$ are 1 and $p$. A positive integer that is greater than 1 and is not prime is called *composite*.

*Remark:* The integer $n$ is composite if and only if there exists an integer $a$ such that $a \mid n$ and $1 < a < n$.

**EXAMPLE 1**    The integer 7 is prime because its only positive factors are 1 and 7, whereas the integer 9 is composite because it is divisible by 3.    ◀

The primes are the building blocks of positive integers, as the fundamental theorem of arithmetic shows. The proof will be given in Section 5.2.

**THEOREM 1**   **THE FUNDAMENTAL THEOREM OF ARITHMETIC**   Every integer greater than 1 can be written uniquely as a prime or as the product of two or more primes where the prime factors are written in order of nondecreasing size.

Example 2 gives some prime factorizations of integers.

**EXAMPLE 2**   The prime factorizations of 100, 641, 999, and 1024 are given by

$$100 = 2 \cdot 2 \cdot 5 \cdot 5 = 2^2 5^2,$$
$$641 = 641,$$
$$999 = 3 \cdot 3 \cdot 3 \cdot 37 = 3^3 \cdot 37,$$
$$1024 = 2 \cdot 2 \cdot 2 \cdot 2 \cdot 2 \cdot 2 \cdot 2 \cdot 2 \cdot 2 \cdot 2 = 2^{10}.$$

◄

## Trial Division

It is often important to show that a given integer is prime. For instance, in cryptology, large primes are used in some methods for making messages secret. One procedure for showing that an integer is prime is based on the following observation.

**THEOREM 2**   If $n$ is a composite integer, then $n$ has a prime divisor less than or equal to $\sqrt{n}$.

*Proof:* If $n$ is composite, by the definition of a composite integer, we know that it has a factor $a$ with $1 < a < n$. Hence, by the definition of a factor of a positive integer, we have $n = ab$, where $b$ is a positive integer greater than 1. We will show that $a \leq \sqrt{n}$ or $b \leq \sqrt{n}$. If $a > \sqrt{n}$ and $b > \sqrt{n}$, then $ab > \sqrt{n} \cdot \sqrt{n} = n$, which is a contradiction. Consequently, $a \leq \sqrt{n}$ or $b \leq \sqrt{n}$. Because both $a$ and $b$ are divisors of $n$, we see that $n$ has a positive divisor not exceeding $\sqrt{n}$. This divisor is either prime or, by the fundamental theorem of arithmetic, has a prime divisor less than itself. In either case, $n$ has a prime divisor less than or equal to $\sqrt{n}$.   ◁

From Theorem 2, it follows that an integer is prime if it is not divisible by any prime less than or equal to its square root. This leads to the brute-force algorithm known as **trial division**. To use trial division we divide $n$ by all primes not exceeding $\sqrt{n}$ and conclude that $n$ is prime if it is not divisible by any of these primes. In Example 3 we use trial division to show that 101 is prime.

**EXAMPLE 3**   Show that 101 is prime.

*Solution:* The only primes not exceeding $\sqrt{101}$ are 2, 3, 5, and 7. Because 101 is not divisible by 2, 3, 5, or 7 (the quotient of 101 and each of these integers is not an integer), it follows that 101 is prime.   ◄

Because every integer has a prime factorization, it would be useful to have a procedure for finding this prime factorization. Consider the problem of finding the prime factorization of $n$. Begin by dividing $n$ by successive primes, starting with the smallest prime, 2. If $n$ has a prime factor, then by Theorem 3 a prime factor $p$ not exceeding $\sqrt{n}$ will be found. So, if no prime factor not exceeding $\sqrt{n}$ is found, then $n$ is prime. Otherwise, if a prime factor $p$ is found, continue by factoring $n/p$. Note that $n/p$ has no prime factors less than $p$. Again, if $n/p$ has no prime factor greater than or equal to $p$ and not exceeding its square root, then it is prime. Otherwise, if it has a prime factor $q$, continue by factoring $n/(pq)$. This procedure is continued until the factorization has been reduced to a prime. This procedure is illustrated in Example 4.

**EXAMPLE 4**    Find the prime factorization of 7007.

*Solution:* To find the prime factorization of 7007, first perform divisions of 7007 by successive primes, beginning with 2. None of the primes 2, 3, and 5 divides 7007. However, 7 divides 7007, with $7007/7 = 1001$. Next, divide 1001 by successive primes, beginning with 7. It is immediately seen that 7 also divides 1001, because $1001/7 = 143$. Continue by dividing 143 by successive primes, beginning with 7. Although 7 does not divide 143, 11 does divide 143, and $143/11 = 13$. Because 13 is prime, the procedure is completed. It follows that $7007 = 7 \cdot 1001 = 7 \cdot 7 \cdot 143 = 7 \cdot 7 \cdot 11 \cdot 13$. Consequently, the prime factorization of 7007 is $7 \cdot 7 \cdot 11 \cdot 13 = 7^2 \cdot 11 \cdot 13$.    ◀

**Links**

Prime numbers were studied in ancient times for philosophical reasons. Today, there are highly practical reasons for their study. In particular, large primes play a crucial role in cryptography, as we will see in Section 4.6.

## The Sieve of Eratosthenes

Note that composite integers not exceeding 100 must have a prime factor not exceeding 10. Because the only primes less than 10 are 2, 3, 5, and 7, the primes not exceeding 100 are these four primes and those positive integers greater than 1 and not exceeding 100 that are divisible by none of 2, 3, 5, or 7.

**Links**

The **sieve of Eratosthenes** is used to find all primes not exceeding a specified positive integer. For instance, the following procedure is used to find the primes not exceeding 100. We begin with the list of all integers between 1 and 100. To begin the sieving process, the integers that are divisible by 2, other than 2, are deleted. Because 3 is the first integer greater than 2 that is left, all those integers divisible by 3, other than 3, are deleted. Because 5 is the next integer left after 3, those integers divisible by 5, other than 5, are deleted. The next integer left is 7, so those integers divisible by 7, other than 7, are deleted. Because all composite integers not exceeding 100 are divisible by 2, 3, 5, or 7, all remaining integers except 1 are prime. In Table 1, the panels display those integers deleted at each stage, where each integer divisible by 2, other than 2, is underlined in the first panel, each integer divisible by 3, other than 3, is underlined in the second panel, each integer divisible by 5, other than 5, is underlined in the third panel, and each integer divisible by 7, other than 7, is underlined in the fourth panel. The integers not underlined are the primes not exceeding 100. We conclude that the primes less than 100 are 2, 3, 5, 7, 11, 13, 17, 19, 23, 29, 31, 37, 41, 43, 47, 53, 59, 61, 67, 71, 73, 79, 83, 89, and 97.

THE INFINITUDE OF PRIMES    It has long been known that there are infinitely many primes. This means that whenever $p_1, p_2, \ldots, p_n$ are the $n$ smallest primes, we know there is a larger

**Links**

ERATOSTHENES (276 B.C.E.–194 B.C.E.)    It is known that Eratosthenes was born in Cyrene, a Greek colony west of Egypt, and spent time studying at Plato's Academy in Athens. We also know that King Ptolemy II invited Eratosthenes to Alexandria to tutor his son and that later Eratosthenes became chief librarian at the famous library at Alexandria, a central repository of ancient wisdom. Eratosthenes was an extremely versatile scholar, writing on mathematics, geography, astronomy, history, philosophy, and literary criticism. Besides his work in mathematics, he is most noted for his chronology of ancient history and for his famous measurement of the size of the earth.

**TABLE 1   The Sieve of Eratosthenes.**

| Integers divisible by 2 other than 2 receive an underline. | | | | | | | | | | Integers divisible by 3 other than 3 receive an underline. | | | | | | | | | |
|---|---|---|---|---|---|---|---|---|---|---|---|---|---|---|---|---|---|---|---|
| 1 | 2 | 3 | 4 | 5 | 6 | 7 | 8 | 9 | 10 | 1 | 2 | 3 | 4 | 5 | 6 | 7 | 8 | 9 | 10 |
| 11 | 12 | 13 | 14 | 15 | 16 | 17 | 18 | 19 | 20 | 11 | 12 | 13 | 14 | 15 | 16 | 17 | 18 | 19 | 20 |
| 21 | 22 | 23 | 24 | 25 | 26 | 27 | 28 | 29 | 30 | 21 | 22 | 23 | 24 | 25 | 26 | 27 | 28 | 29 | 30 |
| 31 | 32 | 33 | 34 | 35 | 36 | 37 | 38 | 39 | 40 | 31 | 32 | 33 | 34 | 35 | 36 | 37 | 38 | 39 | 40 |
| 41 | 42 | 43 | 44 | 45 | 46 | 47 | 48 | 49 | 50 | 41 | 42 | 43 | 44 | 45 | 46 | 47 | 48 | 49 | 50 |
| 51 | 52 | 53 | 54 | 55 | 56 | 57 | 58 | 59 | 60 | 51 | 52 | 53 | 54 | 55 | 56 | 57 | 58 | 59 | 60 |
| 61 | 62 | 63 | 64 | 65 | 66 | 67 | 68 | 69 | 70 | 61 | 62 | 63 | 64 | 65 | 66 | 67 | 68 | 69 | 70 |
| 71 | 72 | 73 | 74 | 75 | 76 | 77 | 78 | 79 | 80 | 71 | 72 | 73 | 74 | 75 | 76 | 77 | 78 | 79 | 80 |
| 81 | 82 | 83 | 84 | 85 | 86 | 87 | 88 | 89 | 90 | 81 | 82 | 83 | 84 | 85 | 86 | 87 | 88 | 89 | 90 |
| 91 | 92 | 93 | 94 | 95 | 96 | 97 | 98 | 99 | 100 | 91 | 92 | 93 | 94 | 95 | 96 | 97 | 98 | 99 | 100 |

| Integers divisible by 5 other than 5 receive an underline. | | | | | | | | | | Integers divisible by 7 other than 7 receive an underline; integers in color are prime. | | | | | | | | | |
|---|---|---|---|---|---|---|---|---|---|---|---|---|---|---|---|---|---|---|---|
| 1 | 2 | 3 | 4 | 5 | 6 | 7 | 8 | 9 | 10 | 1 | 2 | 3 | 4 | 5 | 6 | 7 | 8 | 9 | 10 |
| 11 | 12 | 13 | 14 | 15 | 16 | 17 | 18 | 19 | 20 | 11 | 12 | 13 | 14 | 15 | 16 | 17 | 18 | 19 | 20 |
| 21 | 22 | 23 | 24 | 25 | 26 | 27 | 28 | 29 | 30 | 21 | 22 | 23 | 24 | 25 | 26 | 27 | 28 | 29 | 30 |
| 31 | 32 | 33 | 34 | 35 | 36 | 37 | 38 | 39 | 40 | 31 | 32 | 33 | 34 | 35 | 36 | 37 | 38 | 39 | 40 |
| 41 | 42 | 43 | 44 | 45 | 46 | 47 | 48 | 49 | 50 | 41 | 42 | 43 | 44 | 45 | 46 | 47 | 48 | 49 | 50 |
| 51 | 52 | 53 | 54 | 55 | 56 | 57 | 58 | 59 | 60 | 51 | 52 | 53 | 54 | 55 | 56 | 57 | 58 | 59 | 60 |
| 61 | 62 | 63 | 64 | 65 | 66 | 67 | 68 | 69 | 70 | 61 | 62 | 63 | 64 | 65 | 66 | 67 | 68 | 69 | 70 |
| 71 | 72 | 73 | 74 | 75 | 76 | 77 | 78 | 79 | 80 | 71 | 72 | 73 | 74 | 75 | 76 | 77 | 78 | 79 | 80 |
| 81 | 82 | 83 | 84 | 85 | 86 | 87 | 88 | 89 | 90 | 81 | 82 | 83 | 84 | 85 | 86 | 87 | 88 | 89 | 90 |
| 91 | 92 | 93 | 94 | 95 | 96 | 97 | 98 | 99 | 100 | 91 | 92 | 93 | 94 | 95 | 96 | 97 | 98 | 99 | 100 |

prime not listed. We will prove this fact using a proof given by Euclid in his famous mathematics text, *The Elements*. This simple, yet elegant, proof is considered by many mathematicians to be among the most beautiful proofs in mathematics. It is the first proof presented in the book *Proofs from THE BOOK* [AiZi10], where THE BOOK refers to the imagined collection of perfect proofs that the famous mathematician Paul Erdős claimed is maintained by God. By the way, there are a vast number of different proofs than there are an infinitude of primes, and new ones are published surprisingly frequently.

**THEOREM 3**   There are infinitely many primes.

*Proof:* We will prove this theorem using a proof by contradiction. We assume that there are only finitely many primes, $p_1, p_2, \ldots, p_n$. Let

$$Q = p_1 p_2 \cdots p_n + 1.$$

By the fundamental theorem of arithmetic, $Q$ is prime or else it can be written as the product of two or more primes. However, none of the primes $p_j$ divides $Q$, for if $p_j \mid Q$, then $p_j$ divides

$Q - p_1 p_2 \cdots p_n = 1$. Hence, there is a prime not in the list $p_1, p_2, \ldots, p_n$. This prime is either $Q$, if it is prime, or a prime factor of $Q$. This is a contradiction because we assumed that we have listed all the primes. Consequently, there are infinitely many primes.  ◁

***Remark:*** Note that in this proof we do *not* state that $Q$ is prime! Furthermore, in this proof, we have given a nonconstructive existence proof that given any $n$ primes, there is a prime not in this list. For this proof to be constructive, we would have had to explicitly give a prime not in our original list of $n$ primes.

Because there are infinitely many primes, given any positive integer there are primes greater than this integer. There is an ongoing quest to discover larger and larger prime numbers; for almost all the last 300 years, the largest prime known has been an integer of the special form $2^p - 1$, where $p$ is also prime. (Note that $2^n - 1$ cannot be prime when $n$ is not prime; see Exercise 9.) Such primes are called **Mersenne primes**, after the French monk Marin Mersenne, who studied them in the seventeenth century. The reason that the largest known prime has usually been a Mersenne prime is that there is an extremely efficient test, known as the Lucas–Lehmer test, for determining whether $2^p - 1$ is prime. Furthermore, it is not currently possible to test numbers not of this or certain other special forms anywhere near as quickly to determine whether they are prime.

**EXAMPLE 5**    The numbers $2^2 - 1 = 3$, $2^3 - 1 = 7$, $2^5 - 1 = 31$ and $2^7 - 1 = 127$ are Mersenne primes, while $2^{11} - 1 = 2047$ is not a Mersenne prime because $2047 = 23 \cdot 89$.  ◀

**Links**

Progress in finding Mersenne primes has been steady since computers were invented. As of early 2011, 47 Mersenne primes were known, with 16 found since 1990. The largest Mersenne prime known (again as of early 2011) is $2^{43,112,609} - 1$, a number with nearly 13 million decimal digits, which was shown to be prime in 2008. A communal effort, the Great Internet Mersenne Prime Search (GIMPS), is devoted to the search for new Mersenne primes. You can join this search, and if you are lucky, find a new Mersenne prime and possibly even win a cash prize. By the way, even the search for Mersenne primes has practical implications. One quality control test for supercomputers has been to replicate the Lucas–Lehmer test that establishes the primality of a large Mersenne prime. (See [Ro10] for more information about the quest for finding Mersenne primes.)

THE DISTRIBUTION OF PRIMES    Theorem 3 tells us that there are infinitely many primes. However, how many primes are less than a positive number $x$? This question interested mathematicians for many years; in the late eighteenth century, mathematicians produced large tables

**Links**

MARIN MERSENNE (1588–1648)    Mersenne was born in Maine, France, into a family of laborers and attended the College of Mans and the Jesuit College at La Flèche. He continued his education at the Sorbonne, studying theology from 1609 to 1611. He joined the religious order of the Minims in 1611, a group whose name comes from the word *minimi* (the members of this group were extremely humble; they considered themselves the least of all religious orders). Besides prayer, the members of this group devoted their energy to scholarship and study. In 1612 he became a priest at the Place Royale in Paris; between 1614 and 1618 he taught philosophy at the Minim Convent at Nevers. He returned to Paris in 1619, where his cell in the Minims de l'Annociade became a place for meetings of French scientists, philosophers, and mathematicians, including Fermat and Pascal. Mersenne corresponded extensively with scholars throughout Europe, serving as a clearinghouse for mathematical and scientific knowledge, a function later served by mathematical journals (and today also by the Internet). Mersenne wrote books covering mechanics, mathematical physics, mathematics, music, and acoustics. He studied prime numbers and tried unsuccessfully to construct a formula representing all primes. In 1644 Mersenne claimed that $2^p - 1$ is prime for $p = 2, 3, 5, 7, 13, 17, 19, 31, 67, 127, 257$ but is composite for all other primes less than 257. It took over 300 years to determine that Mersenne's claim was wrong five times. Specifically, $2^p - 1$ is not prime for $p = 67$ and $p = 257$ but is prime for $p = 61$, $p = 87$, and $p = 107$. It is also noteworthy that Mersenne defended two of the most famous men of his time, Descartes and Galileo, from religious critics. He also helped expose alchemists and astrologers as frauds.

of prime numbers to gather evidence concerning the distribution of primes. Using this evidence, the great mathematicians of the day, including Gauss and Legendre, conjectured, but did not prove, Theorem 4.

**THEOREM 4**

**THE PRIME NUMBER THEOREM**   The ratio of the number of primes not exceeding $x$ and $x/\ln x$ approaches 1 as $x$ grows without bound. (Here $\ln x$ is the natural logarithm of $x$.)

The prime number theorem was first proved in 1896 by the French mathematician Jacques Hadamard and the Belgian mathematician Charles-Jean-Gustave-Nicholas de la Vallée-Poussin using the theory of complex variables. Although proofs not using complex variables have been found, all known proofs of the prime number theorem are quite complicated.

We can use the prime number theorem to estimate the odds that a randomly chosen number is prime. The prime number theorem tells us that the number of primes not exceeding $x$ can be approximated by $x/\ln x$. Consequently, the odds that a randomly selected positive integer less than $n$ is prime are approximately $(n/\ln n)/n = 1/\ln n$. Sometimes we need to find a prime with a particular number of digits. We would like an estimate of how many integers with a particular number of digits we need to select before we encounter a prime. Using the prime number theorem and calculus, it can be shown that the probability that an integer $n$ is prime is also approximately $1/\ln n$. For example, the odds that an integer near $10^{1000}$ is prime are approximately $1/\ln 10^{1000}$, which is approximately $1/2300$. (Of course, by choosing only odd numbers, we double our chances of finding a prime.)

Using trial division with Theorem 2 gives procedures for factoring and for primality testing. However, these procedures are not efficient algorithms; many much more practical and efficient algorithms for these tasks have been developed. Factoring and primality testing have become important in the applications of number theory to cryptography. This has led to a great interest in developing efficient algorithms for both tasks. Clever procedures have been devised in the last 30 years for efficiently generating large primes. Moreover, in 2002, an important theoretical discovery was made by Manindra Agrawal, Neeraj Kayal, and Nitin Saxena. They showed there is a polynomial-time algorithm in the number of bits in the binary expansion of an integer for determining whether a positive integer is prime. Algorithms based on their work use $O((\log n)^6)$ bit operations to determine whether a positive integer $n$ is prime.

However, even though powerful new factorization methods have been developed in the same time frame, factoring large numbers remains extraordinarily more time-consuming than primality testing. No polynomial-time algorithm for factoring integers is known. Nevertheless, the challenge of factoring large numbers interests many people. There is a communal effort on the Internet to factor large numbers, especially those of the special form $k^n \pm 1$, where $k$ is a small positive integer and $n$ is a large positive integer (such numbers are called *Cunningham numbers*). At any given time, there is a list of the "Ten Most Wanted" large numbers of this type awaiting factorization.

PRIMES AND ARITHMETIC PROGRESSIONS   Every odd integer is in one of the two arithmetic progressions $4k + 1$ or $4k + 3$, $k = 1, 2, \ldots$. Because we know that there are infinitely many primes, we can ask whether there are infinitely many primes in both of these arithmetic progressions. The primes $5, 13, 17, 29, 37, 41, \ldots$ are in the arithmetic progression $4k + 1$; the primes $3, 7, 11, 19, 23, 31, 43, \ldots$ are in the arithmetic progression $4k + 3$. Looking at the evidence hints that there may be infinitely many primes in both progressions. What about other arithmetic progressions $ak + b$, $k = 1, 2, \ldots$, where no integer greater than one divides both $a$ and $b$? Do they contain infinitely many primes? The answer was provided by the German mathematician G. Lejeune Dirichlet, who proved that every such arithmetic progression contains infinitely many primes. His proof, and all proofs found later, are beyond the scope of this book.

However, it is possible to prove special cases of Dirichlet's theorem using the ideas developed in this book. For example, Exercises 54 and 55 ask for proofs that there are infinitely many primes in the arithmetic progressions $3k + 2$ and $4k + 3$, where $k$ is a positive integer. (The hint for each of these exercises supplies the basic idea needed for the proof.)

We have explained that every arithmetic progression $ak + b$, $k = 1, 2, \ldots$, where $a$ and $b$ have no common factor greater than one, contains infinitely many primes. But are there long arithmetic progressions made up of just primes? For example, some exploration shows that 5, 11, 17, 23, 29 is an arithmetic progression of five primes and 199, 409, 619, 829, 1039, 1249, 1459, 1669, 1879, 2089 is an arithmetic progression of ten primes. In the 1930s, the famous mathematician Paul Erdős conjectured that for every positive integer $n$ greater than two, there is an arithmetic progression of length $n$ made up entirely of primes. In 2006, Ben Green and Terence Tao were able to prove this conjecture. Their proof, considered to be a mathematical tour de force, is a nonconstructive proof that combines powerful ideas from several advanced areas of mathematics.

## Conjectures and Open Problems About Primes

Number theory is noted as a subject for which it is easy to formulate conjectures, some of which are difficult to prove and others that remained open problems for many years. We will describe some conjectures in number theory and discuss their status in Examples 6–9.

**EXAMPLE 6**

It would be useful to have a function $f(n)$ such that $f(n)$ is prime for all positive integers $n$. If we had such a function, we could find large primes for use in cryptography and other applications. Looking for such a function, we might check out different polynomial functions, as some mathematicians did several hundred years ago. After a lot of computation we may encounter the polynomial $f(n) = n^2 - n + 41$. This polynomial has the interesting property that $f(n)$ is prime for all positive integers $n$ not exceeding 40. [We have $f(1) = 41$, $f(2) = 43$, $f(3) = 47$, $f(4) = 53$, and so on.] This can lead us to the conjecture that $f(n)$ is prime for all positive integers $n$. Can we settle this conjecture?

*Solution:* Perhaps not surprisingly, this conjecture turns out to be false; we do not have to look far to find a positive integer $n$ for which $f(n)$ is composite, because $f(41) = 41^2 - 41 + 41 = 41^2$. Because $f(n) = n^2 - n + 41$ is prime for all positive integers $n$ with $1 \leq n \leq 40$, we might

---

TERENCE TAO (BORN 1975)   Tao was born in Australia. His father is a pediatrician and his mother taught mathematics at a Hong Kong secondary school. Tao was a child prodigy, teaching himself arithmetic at the age of two. At 10, he became the youngest contestant at the International Mathematical Olympiad (IMO); he won an IMO gold medal at 13. Tao received his bachelors and masters degrees when he was 17, and began graduate studies at Princeton, receiving his Ph.D. in three years. In 1996 he became a faculty member at UCLA, where he continues to work.

Tao is extremely versatile; he enjoys working on problems in diverse areas, including harmonic analysis, partial differential equations, number theory, and combinatorics. You can follow his work by reading his blog where he discusses progress on various problems. His most famous result is the Green-Tao theorem, which says that there are arbitrarily long arithmetic progressions of primes. Tao has made important contributions to the applications of mathematics, such as developing a method for reconstructing digital images using the least possible amount of information.

Tao has an amazing reputation among mathematicians; he has become a Mr. Fix-It for researchers in mathematics. The well-known mathematician Charles Fefferman, himself a child prodigy, has said that "if you're stuck on a problem, then one way out is to interest Terence Tao." In 2006 Tao was awarded a Fields Medal, the most prestigious award for mathematicians under the age of 40. He was also awarded a MacArthur Fellowship in 2006, and in 2008, he received the Allan T. Waterman award, which came with a $500,000 cash prize to support research work of scientists early in their career. Tao's wife Laura is an engineer at the Jet Propulsion Laboratory.

be tempted to find a different polynomial with the property that $f(n)$ is prime for *all* positive integers $n$. However, there is no such polynomial. It can be shown that for every polynomial $f(n)$ with integer coefficients, there is a positive integer $y$ such that $f(y)$ is composite. (See Exercise 23 in the Supplementary Exercises.) ◀

Many famous problems about primes still await ultimate resolution by clever people. We describe a few of the most accessible and better known of these open problems in Examples 7–9. Number theory is noted for its wealth of easy-to-understand conjectures that resist attack by all but the most sophisticated techniques, or simply resist all attacks. We present these conjectures to show that many questions that seem relatively simple remain unsettled even in the twenty-first century.

**EXAMPLE 7**    **Goldbach's Conjecture**    In 1742, Christian Goldbach, in a letter to Leonhard Euler, conjectured that every odd integer $n, n > 5$, is the sum of three primes. Euler replied that this conjecture is equivalent to the conjecture that every even integer $n, n > 2$, is the sum of two primes (see Exercise 21 in the Supplementary Exercises). The conjecture that every even integer $n, n > 2$, is the sum of two primes is now called **Goldbach's conjecture**. We can check this conjecture for small even numbers. For example, $4 = 2 + 2, 6 = 3 + 3, 8 = 5 + 3, 10 = 7 + 3, 12 = 7 + 5$, and so on. Goldbach's conjecture was verified by hand calculations for numbers up to the millions prior to the advent of computers. With computers it can be checked for extremely large numbers. As of mid 2011, the conjecture has been checked for all positive even integers up to $1.6 \cdot 10^{18}$.

Although no proof of Goldbach's conjecture has been found, most mathematicians believe it is true. Several theorems have been proved, using complicated methods from analytic number theory far beyond the scope of this book, establishing results weaker than Goldbach's conjecture. Among these are the result that every even integer greater than 2 is the sum of at most six primes (proved in 1995 by O. Ramaré) and that every sufficiently large positive integer is the sum of a prime and a number that is either prime or the product of two primes (proved in 1966 by J. R. Chen). Perhaps Goldbach's conjecture will be settled in the not too distant future. ◀

**EXAMPLE 8**    There are many conjectures asserting that there are infinitely many primes of certain special forms. A conjecture of this sort is the conjecture that there are infinitely many primes of the form $n^2 + 1$, where $n$ is a positive integer. For example, $5 = 2^2 + 1, 17 = 4^2 + 1, 37 = 6^2 + 1$, and so on. The best result currently known is that there are infinitely many positive integers $n$ such that $n^2 + 1$ is prime or the product of at most two primes (proved by Henryk Iwaniec in 1973 using advanced techniques from analytic number theory, far beyond the scope of this book). ◀

**EXAMPLE 9**    **The Twin Prime Conjecture**    **Twin primes** are pairs of primes that differ by 2, such as 3 and 5, 5 and 7, 11 and 13, 17 and 19, and 4967 and 4969. The twin prime conjecture asserts that there are infinitely many twin primes. The strongest result proved concerning twin primes is that there are infinitely many pairs $p$ and $p + 2$, where $p$ is prime and $p + 2$ is prime or the product of two primes (proved by J. R. Chen in 1966). The world's record for twin primes, as of mid 2011, consists of the numbers $65,516,468,355 \cdot 2^{333,333} \pm 1$, which have 100,355 decimal digits. ◀

CHRISTIAN GOLDBACH (1690–1764)    Christian Goldbach was born in Königsberg, Prussia, the city noted for its famous bridge problem (which will be studied in Section 10.5). He became professor of mathematics at the Academy in St. Petersburg in 1725. In 1728 Goldbach went to Moscow to tutor the son of the Tsar. He entered the world of politics when, in 1742, he became a staff member in the Russian Ministry of Foreign Affairs. Goldbach is best known for his correspondence with eminent mathematicians, including Euler and Bernoulli, for his famous conjectures in number theory, and for several contributions to analysis.

## Greatest Common Divisors and Least Common Multiples

The largest integer that divides both of two integers is called the **greatest common divisor** of these integers.

**DEFINITION 2**   Let $a$ and $b$ be integers, not both zero. The largest integer $d$ such that $d \mid a$ and $d \mid b$ is called the *greatest common divisor* of $a$ and $b$. The greatest common divisor of $a$ and $b$ is denoted by $\gcd(a, b)$.

The greatest common divisor of two integers, not both zero, exists because the set of common divisors of these integers is nonempty and finite. One way to find the greatest common divisor of two integers is to find all the positive common divisors of both integers and then take the largest divisor. This is done in Examples 10 and 11. Later, a more efficient method of finding greatest common divisors will be given.

**EXAMPLE 10**   What is the greatest common divisor of 24 and 36?

*Solution:* The positive common divisors of 24 and 36 are 1, 2, 3, 4, 6, and 12. Hence, $\gcd(24, 36) = 12$.   ◄

**EXAMPLE 11**   What is the greatest common divisor of 17 and 22?

*Solution:* The integers 17 and 22 have no positive common divisors other than 1, so that $\gcd(17, 22) = 1$.   ◄

Because it is often important to specify that two integers have no common positive divisor other than 1, we have Definition 3.

**DEFINITION 3**   The integers $a$ and $b$ are *relatively prime* if their greatest common divisor is 1.

**EXAMPLE 12**   By Example 11 it follows that the integers 17 and 22 are relatively prime, because $\gcd(17, 22) = 1$.   ◄

Because we often need to specify that no two integers in a set of integers have a common positive divisor greater than 1, we make Definition 4.

**DEFINITION 4**   The integers $a_1, a_2, \ldots, a_n$ are *pairwise relatively prime* if $\gcd(a_i, a_j) = 1$ whenever $1 \leq i < j \leq n$.

**EXAMPLE 13**   Determine whether the integers 10, 17, and 21 are pairwise relatively prime and whether the integers 10, 19, and 24 are pairwise relatively prime.

*Solution:* Because $\gcd(10, 17) = 1$, $\gcd(10, 21) = 1$, and $\gcd(17, 21) = 1$, we conclude that 10, 17, and 21 are pairwise relatively prime.

Because $\gcd(10, 24) = 2 > 1$, we see that 10, 19, and 24 are not pairwise relatively prime.   ◄

Another way to find the greatest common divisor of two positive integers is to use the prime factorizations of these integers. Suppose that the prime factorizations of the positive integers $a$ and $b$ are

$$a = p_1^{a_1} p_2^{a_2} \cdots p_n^{a_n}, \ b = p_1^{b_1} p_2^{b_2} \cdots p_n^{b_n},$$

where each exponent is a nonnegative integer, and where all primes occurring in the prime factorization of either $a$ or $b$ are included in both factorizations, with zero exponents if necessary. Then $\gcd(a, b)$ is given by

$$\gcd(a, b) = p_1^{\min(a_1, b_1)} p_2^{\min(a_2, b_2)} \cdots p_n^{\min(a_n, b_n)},$$

where $\min(x, y)$ represents the minimum of the two numbers $x$ and $y$. To show that this formula for $\gcd(a, b)$ is valid, we must show that the integer on the right-hand side divides both $a$ and $b$, and that no larger integer also does. This integer does divide both $a$ and $b$, because the power of each prime in the factorization does not exceed the power of this prime in either the factorization of $a$ or that of $b$. Further, no larger integer can divide both $a$ and $b$, because the exponents of the primes in this factorization cannot be increased, and no other primes can be included.

**EXAMPLE 14**    Because the prime factorizations of 120 and 500 are $120 = 2^3 \cdot 3 \cdot 5$ and $500 = 2^2 \cdot 5^3$, the greatest common divisor is

$$\gcd(120, 500) = 2^{\min(3, 2)} 3^{\min(1, 0)} 5^{\min(1, 3)} = 2^2 3^0 5^1 = 20. \qquad \blacktriangleleft$$

Prime factorizations can also be used to find the **least common multiple** of two integers.

**DEFINITION 5**    The *least common multiple* of the positive integers $a$ and $b$ is the smallest positive integer that is divisible by both $a$ and $b$. The least common multiple of $a$ and $b$ is denoted by $\text{lcm}(a, b)$.

The least common multiple exists because the set of integers divisible by both $a$ and $b$ is nonempty (as $ab$ belongs to this set, for instance), and every nonempty set of positive integers has a least element (by the well-ordering property, which will be discussed in Section 5.2). Suppose that the prime factorizations of $a$ and $b$ are as before. Then the least common multiple of $a$ and $b$ is given by

$$\text{lcm}(a, b) = p_1^{\max(a_1, b_1)} p_2^{\max(a_2, b_2)} \cdots p_n^{\max(a_n, b_n)},$$

where $\max(x, y)$ denotes the maximum of the two numbers $x$ and $y$. This formula is valid because a common multiple of $a$ and $b$ has at least $\max(a_i, b_i)$ factors of $p_i$ in its prime factorization, and the least common multiple has no other prime factors besides those in $a$ and $b$.

**EXAMPLE 15**    What is the least common multiple of $2^3 3^5 7^2$ and $2^4 3^3$?

*Solution:* We have

$$\text{lcm}(2^3 3^5 7^2, 2^4 3^3) = 2^{\max(3, 4)} 3^{\max(5, 3)} 7^{\max(2, 0)} = 2^4 3^5 7^2. \qquad \blacktriangleleft$$

Theorem 5 gives the relationship between the greatest common divisor and least common multiple of two integers. It can be proved using the formulae we have derived for these quantities. The proof of this theorem is left as Exercise 31.

**THEOREM 5**   Let $a$ and $b$ be positive integers. Then

$$ab = \gcd(a, b) \cdot \text{lcm}(a, b).$$

## The Euclidean Algorithm

Links

Computing the greatest common divisor of two integers directly from the prime factorizations of these integers is inefficient. The reason is that it is time-consuming to find prime factorizations. We will give a more efficient method of finding the greatest common divisor, called the **Euclidean algorithm**. This algorithm has been known since ancient times. It is named after the ancient Greek mathematician Euclid, who included a description of this algorithm in his book *The Elements*.

Before describing the Euclidean algorithm, we will show how it is used to find $\gcd(91, 287)$. First, divide 287, the larger of the two integers, by 91, the smaller, to obtain

$$287 = 91 \cdot 3 + 14.$$

Any divisor of 91 and 287 must also be a divisor of $287 - 91 \cdot 3 = 14$. Also, any divisor of 91 and 14 must also be a divisor of $287 = 91 \cdot 3 + 14$. Hence, the greatest common divisor of 91 and 287 is the same as the greatest common divisor of 91 and 14. This means that the problem of finding $\gcd(91, 287)$ has been reduced to the problem of finding $\gcd(91, 14)$.

Next, divide 91 by 14 to obtain

$$91 = 14 \cdot 6 + 7.$$

Because any common divisor of 91 and 14 also divides $91 - 14 \cdot 6 = 7$ and any common divisor of 14 and 7 divides 91, it follows that $\gcd(91, 14) = \gcd(14, 7)$.

Continue by dividing 14 by 7, to obtain

$$14 = 7 \cdot 2.$$

Because 7 divides 14, it follows that $\gcd(14, 7) = 7$. Furthermore, because $\gcd(287, 91) = \gcd(91, 14) = \gcd(14, 7) = 7$, the original problem has been solved.

We now describe how the Euclidean algorithm works in generality. We will use successive divisions to reduce the problem of finding the greatest common divisor of two positive integers to the same problem with smaller integers, until one of the integers is zero.

The Euclidean algorithm is based on the following result about greatest common divisors and the division algorithm.

Links

EUCLID (325 B.C.E.– 265 B.C.E.)   Euclid was the author of the most successful mathematics book ever written, *The Elements*, which appeared in over 1000 different editions from ancient to modern times. Little is known about Euclid's life, other than that he taught at the famous academy at Alexandria in Egypt. Apparently, Euclid did not stress applications. When a student asked what he would get by learning geometry, Euclid explained that knowledge was worth acquiring for its own sake and told his servant to give the student a coin "because he must make a profit from what he learns."

**LEMMA 1**  Let $a = bq + r$, where $a, b, q,$ and $r$ are integers. Then $\gcd(a, b) = \gcd(b, r)$.

*Proof:* If we can show that the common divisors of $a$ and $b$ are the same as the common divisors of $b$ and $r$, we will have shown that $\gcd(a, b) = \gcd(b, r)$, because both pairs must have the same *greatest* common divisor.

So suppose that $d$ divides both $a$ and $b$. Then it follows that $d$ also divides $a - bq = r$ (from Theorem 1 of Section 4.1). Hence, any common divisor of $a$ and $b$ is also a common divisor of $b$ and $r$.

Likewise, suppose that $d$ divides both $b$ and $r$. Then $d$ also divides $bq + r = a$. Hence, any common divisor of $b$ and $r$ is also a common divisor of $a$ and $b$.

Consequently, $\gcd(a, b) = \gcd(b, r)$.  ◁

Suppose that $a$ and $b$ are positive integers with $a \geq b$. Let $r_0 = a$ and $r_1 = b$. When we successively apply the division algorithm, we obtain

$$
\begin{aligned}
r_0 &= r_1 q_1 + r_2 & 0 \leq r_2 < r_1, \\
r_1 &= r_2 q_2 + r_3 & 0 \leq r_3 < r_2, \\
&\ \ \vdots \\
r_{n-2} &= r_{n-1} q_{n-1} + r_n & 0 \leq r_n < r_{n-1}, \\
r_{n-1} &= r_n q_n.
\end{aligned}
$$

Eventually a remainder of zero occurs in this sequence of successive divisions, because the sequence of remainders $a = r_0 > r_1 > r_2 > \cdots \geq 0$ cannot contain more than $a$ terms. Furthermore, it follows from Lemma 1 that

$$
\gcd(a, b) = \gcd(r_0, r_1) = \gcd(r_1, r_2) = \cdots = \gcd(r_{n-2}, r_{n-1})
$$
$$
= \gcd(r_{n-1}, r_n) = \gcd(r_n, 0) = r_n.
$$

Hence, the greatest common divisor is the last nonzero remainder in the sequence of divisions.

**EXAMPLE 16**  Find the greatest common divisor of 414 and 662 using the Euclidean algorithm.

*Solution:* Successive uses of the division algorithm give:

$$
\begin{aligned}
662 &= 414 \cdot 1 + 248 \\
414 &= 248 \cdot 1 + 166 \\
248 &= 166 \cdot 1 + 82 \\
166 &= 82 \cdot 2 + 2 \\
82 &= 2 \cdot 41.
\end{aligned}
$$

Hence, $\gcd(414, 662) = 2$, because 2 is the last nonzero remainder.  ◀

The Euclidean algorithm is expressed in pseudocode in Algorithm 1.

---

**ALGORITHM 1** The Euclidean Algorithm.

**procedure** $gcd(a, b$: positive integers)
$x := a$
$y := b$
**while** $y \neq 0$
    $r := x \bmod y$
    $x := y$
    $y := r$
**return** $x \{gcd(a, b)$ is $x\}$

---

In Algorithm 1, the initial values of $x$ and $y$ are $a$ and $b$, respectively. At each stage of the procedure, $x$ is replaced by $y$, and $y$ is replaced by $x \bmod y$, which is the remainder when $x$ is divided by $y$. This process is repeated as long as $y \neq 0$. The algorithm terminates when $y = 0$, and the value of $x$ at that point, the last nonzero remainder in the procedure, is the greatest common divisor of $a$ and $b$.

We will study the time complexity of the Euclidean algorithm in Section 5.3, where we will show that the number of divisions required to find the greatest common divisor of $a$ and $b$, where $a \geq b$, is $O(\log b)$.

## gcds as Linear Combinations

An important result we will use throughout the remainder of this section is that the greatest common divisor of two integers $a$ and $b$ can be expressed in the form

$$sa + tb,$$

where $s$ and $t$ are integers. In other words, $gcd(a, b)$ can be expressed as a **linear combination** with integer coefficients of $a$ and $b$. For example, $gcd(6, 14) = 2$, and $2 = (-2) \cdot 6 + 1 \cdot 14$. We state this fact as Theorem 6.

**THEOREM 6**　**BÉZOUT'S THEOREM**　If $a$ and $b$ are positive integers, then there exist integers $s$ and $t$ such that $gcd(a, b) = sa + tb$.

ÉTIENNE BÉZOUT (1730–1783)　Bézout was born in Nemours, France, where his father was a magistrate. Reading the writings of the great mathematician Leonhard Euler enticed him to become a mathematician. In 1758 he was appointed to a position at the Académie des Sciences in Paris; in 1763 he was appointed examiner of the Gardes de la Marine, where he was assigned the task of writing mathematics textbooks. This assignment led to a four-volume textbook completed in 1767. Bézout is well known for his six-volume comprehensive textbook on mathematics. His textbooks were extremely popular and were studied by many generations of students hoping to enter the École Polytechnique, the famous engineering and science school. His books were translated into English and used in North America, including at Harvard.

His most important original work was published in 1779 in the book *Théorie générale des équations algébriques*, where he introduced important methods for solving simultaneous polynomial equations in many unknowns. The most well-known result in this book is now called *Bézout's theorem*, which in its general form tells us that the number of common points on two plane algebraic curves equals the product of the degrees of these curves. Bézout is also credited with inventing the determinant (which was called the Bézoutian by the great English mathematician James Joseph Sylvester). He was considered to be a kind person with a warm heart, although he had a reserved and somber personality. He was happily married and a father.

**DEFINITION 6**

If $a$ and $b$ are positive integers, then integers $s$ and $t$ such that $\gcd(a, b) = sa + tb$ are called *Bézout coefficients* of $a$ and $b$ (after Étienne Bézout, a French mathematician of the eighteenth century). Also, the equation $\gcd(a, b) = sa + tb$ is called *Bézout's identity*.

We will not give a formal proof of Theorem 6 here (see Exercise 36 in Section 5.2 and [Ro10] for proofs). We will provide an example of a general method that can be used to find a linear combination of two integers equal to their greatest common divisor. (In this section, we will assume that a linear combination has integer coefficients.) The method proceeds by working backward through the divisions of the Euclidean algorithm, so this method requires a forward pass and a backward pass through the steps of the Euclidean algorithm. (In the exercises we will describe an algorithm called the **extended Euclidean algorithm**, which can be used to express $\gcd(a, b)$ as a linear combination of $a$ and $b$ using a single pass through the steps of the Euclidean algorithm; see the preamble to Exercise 41.)

**EXAMPLE 17**

Express $\gcd(252, 198) = 18$ as a linear combination of 252 and 198.

*Solution:* To show that $\gcd(252, 198) = 18$, the Euclidean algorithm uses these divisions:

$$252 = 1 \cdot 198 + 54$$
$$198 = 3 \cdot 54 + 36$$
$$54 = 1 \cdot 36 + 18$$
$$36 = 2 \cdot 18.$$

Using the next-to-last division (the third division), we can express $\gcd(252, 198) = 18$ as a linear combination of 54 and 36. We find that

$$18 = 54 - 1 \cdot 36.$$

The second division tells us that

$$36 = 198 - 3 \cdot 54.$$

Substituting this expression for 36 into the previous equation, we can express 18 as a linear combination of 54 and 198. We have

$$18 = 54 - 1 \cdot 36 = 54 - 1 \cdot (198 - 3 \cdot 54) = 4 \cdot 54 - 1 \cdot 198.$$

The first division tells us that

$$54 = 252 - 1 \cdot 198.$$

Substituting this expression for 54 into the previous equation, we can express 18 as a linear combination of 252 and 198. We conclude that

$$18 = 4 \cdot (252 - 1 \cdot 198) - 1 \cdot 198 = 4 \cdot 252 - 5 \cdot 198,$$

completing the solution.　◀

We will use Theorem 6 to develop several useful results. One of our goals will be to prove the part of the fundamental theorem of arithmetic asserting that a positive integer has at most one prime factorization. We will show that if a positive integer has a factorization into primes, where the primes are written in nondecreasing order, then this factorization is unique.

First, we need to develop some results about divisibility.

**LEMMA 2**    If $a$, $b$, and $c$ are positive integers such that $\gcd(a, b) = 1$ and $a \mid bc$, then $a \mid c$.

*Proof:* Because $\gcd(a, b) = 1$, by Bézout's theorem there are integers $s$ and $t$ such that

$$sa + tb = 1.$$

Multiplying both sides of this equation by $c$, we obtain

$$sac + tbc = c.$$

We can now use Theorem 1 of Section 4.1 to show that $a \mid c$. By part ($ii$) of that theorem, $a \mid tbc$. Because $a \mid sac$ and $a \mid tbc$, by part ($i$) of that theorem, we conclude that $a$ divides $sac + tbc$. Because $sac + tbc = c$, we conclude that $a \mid c$, completing the proof.    ◁

We will use the following generalization of Lemma 2 in the proof of uniqueness of prime factorizations. (The proof of Lemma 3 is left as Exercise 64 in Section 5.1, because it can be most easily carried out using the method of mathematical induction, covered in that section.)

**LEMMA 3**    If $p$ is a prime and $p \mid a_1 a_2 \cdots a_n$, where each $a_i$ is an integer, then $p \mid a_i$ for some $i$.

We can now show that a factorization of an integer into primes is unique. That is, we will show that every integer can be written as the product of primes in nondecreasing order in at most one way. This is part of the fundamental theorem of arithmetic. We will prove the other part, that every integer has a factorization into primes, in Section 5.2.

*Proof (of the uniqueness of the prime factorization of a positive integer):* We will use a proof by contradiction. Suppose that the positive integer $n$ can be written as the product of primes in two different ways, say, $n = p_1 p_2 \cdots p_s$ and $n = q_1 q_2 \cdots q_t$, each $p_i$ and $q_j$ are primes such that $p_1 \le p_2 \le \cdots \le p_s$ and $q_1 \le q_2 \le \cdots \le q_t$.
When we remove all common primes from the two factorizations, we have

$$p_{i_1} p_{i_2} \cdots p_{i_u} = q_{j_1} q_{j_2} \cdots q_{j_v},$$

where no prime occurs on both sides of this equation and $u$ and $v$ are positive integers. By Lemma 3 it follows that $p_{i_1}$ divides $q_{j_k}$ for some $k$. Because no prime divides another prime, this is impossible. Consequently, there can be at most one factorization of $n$ into primes in nondecreasing order.    ◁

Lemma 2 can also be used to prove a result about dividing both sides of a congruence by the same integer. We have shown (Theorem 5 in Section 4.1) that we can multiply both sides of a congruence by the same integer. However, dividing both sides of a congruence by an integer does not always produce a valid congruence, as Example 18 shows.

**EXAMPLE 18**    The congruence $14 \equiv 8 \pmod 6$ holds, but both sides of this congruence cannot be divided by 2 to produce a valid congruence because $14/2 = 7$ and $8/2 = 4$, but $7 \not\equiv 4 \pmod 6$.    ◁

Although we cannot divide both sides of a congruence by any integer to produce a valid congruence, we can if this integer is relatively prime to the modulus. Theorem 7 establishes this important fact. We use Lemma 2 in the proof.

**THEOREM 7**    Let $m$ be a positive integer and let $a$, $b$, and $c$ be integers. If $ac \equiv bc \pmod{m}$ and $\gcd(c, m) = 1$, then $a \equiv b \pmod{m}$.

*Proof:* Because $ac \equiv bc \pmod{m}$, $m \mid ac - bc = c(a - b)$. By Lemma 2, because $\gcd(c, m) = 1$, it follows that $m \mid a - b$. We conclude that $a \equiv b \pmod{m}$.    ◁

# Exercises

1. Determine whether each of these integers is prime.
   a) 21          b) 29
   c) 71          d) 97
   e) 111         f) 143

2. Determine whether each of these integers is prime.
   a) 19          b) 27
   c) 93          d) 101
   e) 107         f) 113

3. Find the prime factorization of each of these integers.
   a) 88          b) 126          c) 729
   d) 1001        e) 1111         f) 909,090

4. Find the prime factorization of each of these integers.
   a) 39          b) 81           c) 101
   d) 143         e) 289          f) 899

5. Find the prime factorization of 10!.

*6. How many zeros are there at the end of 100!?

7. Express in pseudocode the trial division algorithm for determining whether an integer is prime.

8. Express in pseudocode the algorithm described in the text for finding the prime factorization of an integer.

9. Show that if $a^m + 1$ is composite if $a$ and $m$ are integers greater than 1 and $m$ is odd. [*Hint:* Show that $x + 1$ is a factor of the polynomial $x^m + 1$ if $m$ is odd.]

10. Show that if $2^m + 1$ is an odd prime, then $m = 2^n$ for some nonnegative integer $n$. [*Hint:* First show that the polynomial identity $x^m + 1 = (x^k + 1)(x^{k(t-1)} - x^{k(t-2)} + \cdots - x^k + 1)$ holds, where $m = kt$ and $t$ is odd.]

*11. Show that $\log_2 3$ is an irrational number. Recall that an irrational number is a real number $x$ that cannot be written as the ratio of two integers.

12. Prove that for every positive integer $n$, there are $n$ consecutive composite integers. [*Hint:* Consider the $n$ consecutive integers starting with $(n + 1)! + 2$.]

*13. Prove or disprove that there are three consecutive odd positive integers that are primes, that is, odd primes of the form $p$, $p + 2$, and $p + 4$.

14. Which positive integers less than 12 are relatively prime to 12?

15. Which positive integers less than 30 are relatively prime to 30?

16. Determine whether the integers in each of these sets are pairwise relatively prime.
    a) 21, 34, 55          b) 14, 17, 85
    c) 25, 41, 49, 64      d) 17, 18, 19, 23

17. Determine whether the integers in each of these sets are pairwise relatively prime.
    a) 11, 15, 19          b) 14, 15, 21
    c) 12, 17, 31, 37      d) 7, 8, 9, 11

18. We call a positive integer **perfect** if it equals the sum of its positive divisors other than itself.
    a) Show that 6 and 28 are perfect.
    b) Show that $2^{p-1}(2^p - 1)$ is a perfect number when $2^p - 1$ is prime.

19. Show that if $2^n - 1$ is prime, then $n$ is prime. [*Hint:* Use the identity $2^{ab} - 1 = (2^a - 1) \cdot (2^{a(b-1)} + 2^{a(b-2)} + \cdots + 2^a + 1)$.]

20. Determine whether each of these integers is prime, verifying some of Mersenne's claims.
    a) $2^7 - 1$          b) $2^9 - 1$
    c) $2^{11} - 1$        d) $2^{13} - 1$

The value of the **Euler $\phi$-function** at the positive integer $n$ is defined to be the number of positive integers less than or equal to $n$ that are relatively prime to $n$. [*Note:* $\phi$ is the Greek letter phi.]

21. Find these values of the Euler $\phi$-function.
    a) $\phi(4)$.    b) $\phi(10)$.    c) $\phi(13)$.

22. Show that $n$ is prime if and only if $\phi(n) = n - 1$.

23. What is the value of $\phi(p^k)$ when $p$ is prime and $k$ is a positive integer?

24. What are the greatest common divisors of these pairs of integers?
    a) $2^2 \cdot 3^3 \cdot 5^5, 2^5 \cdot 3^3 \cdot 5^2$
    b) $2 \cdot 3 \cdot 5 \cdot 7 \cdot 11 \cdot 13, 2^{11} \cdot 3^9 \cdot 11 \cdot 17^{14}$

**c)** $17, 17^{17}$  **d)** $2^2 \cdot 7, 5^3 \cdot 13$
**e)** $0, 5$  **f)** $2 \cdot 3 \cdot 5 \cdot 7, 2 \cdot 3 \cdot 5 \cdot 7$

**25.** What are the greatest common divisors of these pairs of integers?

**a)** $3^7 \cdot 5^3 \cdot 7^3, 2^{11} \cdot 3^5 \cdot 5^9$
**b)** $11 \cdot 13 \cdot 17, 2^9 \cdot 3^7 \cdot 5^5 \cdot 7^3$
**c)** $23^{31}, 23^{17}$
**d)** $41 \cdot 43 \cdot 53, 41 \cdot 43 \cdot 53$
**e)** $3^{13} \cdot 5^{17}, 2^{12} \cdot 7^{21}$
**f)** $1111, 0$

**26.** What is the least common multiple of each pair in Exercise 24?

**27.** What is the least common multiple of each pair in Exercise 25?

**28.** Find gcd(1000, 625) and lcm(1000, 625) and verify that gcd(1000, 625) $\cdot$ lcm(1000, 625) = 1000 $\cdot$ 625.

**29.** Find gcd(92928, 123552) and lcm(92928, 123552), and verify that gcd(92928, 123552) $\cdot$ lcm(92928, 123552) = 92928 $\cdot$ 123552. [*Hint:* First find the prime factorizations of 92928 and 123552.]

**30.** If the product of two integers is $2^7 3^8 5^2 7^{11}$ and their greatest common divisor is $2^3 3^4 5$, what is their least common multiple?

**31.** Show that if $a$ and $b$ are positive integers, then $ab =$ gcd($a, b$) $\cdot$ lcm($a, b$). [*Hint:* Use the prime factorizations of $a$ and $b$ and the formulae for gcd($a, b$) and lcm($a, b$) in terms of these factorizations.]

**32.** Use the Euclidean algorithm to find

**a)** gcd(1, 5).  **b)** gcd(100, 101).
**c)** gcd(123, 277).  **d)** gcd(1529, 14039).
**e)** gcd(1529, 14038).  **f)** gcd(11111, 111111).

**33.** Use the Euclidean algorithm to find

**a)** gcd(12, 18).  **b)** gcd(111, 201).
**c)** gcd(1001, 1331).  **d)** gcd(12345, 54321).
**e)** gcd(1000, 5040).  **f)** gcd(9888, 6060).

**34.** How many divisions are required to find gcd(21, 34) using the Euclidean algorithm?

**35.** How many divisions are required to find gcd(34, 55) using the Euclidean algorithm?

**\*36.** Show that if $a$ and $b$ are both positive integers, then $(2^a - 1) \bmod (2^b - 1) = 2^{a \bmod b} - 1$.

**\*37.** Use Exercise 36 to show that if $a$ and $b$ are positive integers, then gcd($2^a - 1, 2^b - 1$) = $2^{\gcd(a, b)} - 1$. [*Hint:* Show that the remainders obtained when the Euclidean algorithm is used to compute gcd($2^a - 1, 2^b - 1$) are of the form $2^r - 1$, where $r$ is a remainder arising when the Euclidean algorithm is used to find gcd($a, b$).]

**38.** Use Exercise 37 to show that the integers $2^{35} - 1, 2^{34} - 1, 2^{33} - 1, 2^{31} - 1, 2^{29} - 1$, and $2^{23} - 1$ are pairwise relatively prime.

**39.** Using the method followed in Example 17, express the greatest common divisor of each of these pairs of integers as a linear combination of these integers.

**a)** 10, 11  **b)** 21, 44  **c)** 36, 48
**d)** 34, 55  **e)** 117, 213  **f)** 0, 223
**g)** 123, 2347  **h)** 3454, 4666  **i)** 9999, 11111

**40.** Using the method followed in Example 17, express the greatest common divisor of each of these pairs of integers as a linear combination of these integers.

**a)** 9, 11  **b)** 33, 44  **c)** 35, 78
**d)** 21, 55  **e)** 101, 203  **f)** 124, 323
**g)** 2002, 2339  **h)** 3457, 4669  **i)** 10001, 13422

The **extended Euclidean algorithm** can be used to express gcd($a, b$) as a linear combination with integer coefficients of the integers $a$ and $b$. We set $s_0 = 1, s_1 = 0, t_0 = 0$, and $t_1 = 1$ and let $s_j = s_{j-2} - q_{j-1}s_{j-1}$ and $t_j = t_{j-2} - q_{j-1}t_{j-1}$ for $j = 2, 3, \ldots, n$, where the $q_j$ are the quotients in the divisions used when the Euclidean algorithm finds gcd($a, b$), as shown in the text. It can be shown (see [Ro10]) that gcd($a, b$) = $s_n a + t_n b$. The main advantage of the extended Euclidean algorithm is that it uses one pass through the steps of the Euclidean algorithm to find Bézout coefficients of $a$ and $b$, unlike the method in the text which uses two passes.

**41.** Use the extended Euclidean algorithm to express gcd(26, 91) as a linear combination of 26 and 91.

**42.** Use the extended Euclidean algorithm to express gcd(252, 356) as a linear combination of 252 and 356.

**43.** Use the extended Euclidean algorithm to express gcd(144, 89) as a linear combination of 144 and 89.

**44.** Use the extended Euclidean algorithm to express gcd(1001, 100001) as a linear combination of 1001 and 100001.

**45.** Describe the extended Euclidean algorithm using pseudocode.

**46.** Find the smallest positive integer with exactly $n$ different positive factors when $n$ is

**a)** 3.  **b)** 4.  **c)** 5.
**d)** 6.  **e)** 10.

**47.** Can you find a formula or rule for the $n$th term of a sequence related to the prime numbers or prime factorizations so that the initial terms of the sequence have these values?

**a)** 0, 1, 1, 0, 1, 0, 1, 0, 0, 0, 1, 0, 1, . . .
**b)** 1, 2, 3, 2, 5, 2, 7, 2, 3, 2, 11, 2, 13, 2, . . .
**c)** 1, 2, 2, 3, 2, 4, 2, 4, 3, 4, 2, 6, 2, 4, . . .
**d)** 1, 1, 1, 0, 1, 1, 1, 0, 0, 1, 1, 0, 1, 1, . . .
**e)** 1, 2, 3, 3, 5, 5, 7, 7, 7, 7, 11, 11, 13, 13, . . .
**f)** 1, 2, 6, 30, 210, 2310, 30030, 510510, 9699690, 223092870, . . .

**48.** Can you find a formula or rule for the $n$th term of a sequence related to the prime numbers or prime factorizations so that the initial terms of the sequence have these values?

**a)** 2, 2, 3, 5, 5, 7, 7, 11, 11, 11, 11, 13, 13, . . .
**b)** 0, 1, 2, 2, 3, 3, 4, 4, 4, 4, 5, 5, 6, 6, . . .
**c)** 1, 0, 0, 1, 0, 1, 0, 1, 1, 1, 0, 1, 0, 1, . . .
**d)** 1, $-1$, $-1$, 0, $-1$, 1, $-1$, 0, 0, 1, $-1$, 0, $-1$, 1, 1, . . .
**e)** 1, 1, 1, 1, 1, 0, 1, 1, 1, 0, 1, 0, 1, 0, 0, . . .
**f)** 4, 9, 25, 49, 121, 169, 289, 361, 529, 841, 961, 1369, . . .

**49.** Prove that the product of any three consecutive integers is divisible by 6.

**50.** Show that if $a$, $b$, and $m$ are integers such that $m \geq 2$ and $a \equiv b \pmod{m}$, then $\gcd(a, m) = \gcd(b, m)$.

**∗51.** Prove or disprove that $n^2 - 79n + 1601$ is prime whenever $n$ is a positive integer.

**52.** Prove or disprove that $p_1 p_2 \cdots p_n + 1$ is prime for every positive integer $n$, where $p_1, p_2, \ldots, p_n$ are the $n$ smallest prime numbers.

**53.** Show that there is a composite integer in every arithmetic progression $ak + b$, $k = 1, 2, \ldots$ where $a$ and $b$ are positive integers.

**54.** Adapt the proof in the text that there are infinitely many primes to prove that there are infinitely many primes of the form $3k + 2$, where $k$ is a nonnegative integer. [*Hint:* Suppose that there are only finitely many such primes $q_1, q_2, \ldots, q_n$, and consider the number $3q_1 q_2 \cdots q_n - 1$.]

**55.** Adapt the proof in the text that there are infinitely many primes to prove that there are infinitely many primes of the form $4k + 3$, where $k$ is a nonnegative integer. [*Hint:* Suppose that there are only finitely many such primes $q_1, q_2, \ldots, q_n$, and consider the number $4q_1 q_2 \cdots q_n - 1$.]

**∗56.** Prove that the set of positive rational numbers is countable by setting up a function that assigns to a rational number $p/q$ with $\gcd(p, q) = 1$ the base 11 number formed by the decimal representation of $p$ followed by the base 11 digit A, which corresponds to the decimal number 10, followed by the decimal representation of $q$.

**∗57.** Prove that the set of positive rational numbers is countable by showing that the function $K$ is a one-to-one correspondence between the set of positive rational numbers and the set of positive integers if $K(m/n) = p_1^{2a_1} p_2^{2a_2} \cdots p_s^{2a_s} q_1^{2b_1 - 1} q_2^{2b_2 - 1} \cdots q_t^{2b_t - 1}$, where $\gcd(m, n) = 1$ and the prime-power factorizations of $m$ and $n$ are $m = p_1^{a_1} p_2^{a_2} \cdots p_s^{a_s}$ and $n = q_1^{b_1} q_2^{b_2} \cdots q_t^{b_t}$.

# 4.4    Solving Congruences

## Introduction

Solving linear congruences, which have the form $ax \equiv b \pmod{m}$, is an essential task in the study of number theory and its applications, just as solving linear equations plays an important role in calculus and linear algebra. To solve linear congruences, we employ inverses modulo $m$. We explain how to work backwards through the steps of the Euclidean algorithm to find inverses modulo $m$. Once we have found an inverse of $a$ modulo $m$, we solve the congruence $ax \equiv b \pmod{m}$ by multiplying both sides of the congruence by this inverse.

Simultaneous systems of linear congruence have been studied since ancient times. For example, the Chinese mathematician Sun-Tsu studied them in the first century. We will show how to solve systems of linear congruences modulo pairwise relatively prime moduli. The result we will prove is called the Chinese remainder theorem, and our proof will give a method to find all solutions of such systems of congruences. We will also show how to use the Chinese remainder theorem as a basis for performing arithmetic with large integers.

We will introduce a useful result of Fermat, known as Fermat's little theorem, which states that if $p$ is prime and $p$ does not divide $a$, then $a^{p-1} \equiv 1 \pmod{p}$. We will examine the converse of this statement, which will lead us to the concept of a pseudoprime. A pseudoprime $m$ to the base $a$ is a composite integer $m$ that masquerades as a prime by satisfying the congruence $a^{m-1} \equiv 1 \pmod{m}$. We will also give an example of a Carmichael number, which is a composite integer that is a pseudoprime to all bases $a$ relatively prime to it.

We also introduce the notion of discrete logarithms, which are analogous to ordinary logarithms. To define discrete logarithms we must first define primitive roots. A primitive root of a prime $p$ is an integer $r$ such that every integer not divisible by $p$ is congruent to a power of $r$ modulo $p$. If $r$ is a primitive root of $p$ and $r^e \equiv a \pmod{p}$, then $e$ is the discrete logarithm of $a$ modulo $p$ to the base $r$. Finding discrete logarithms turns out to be an extremely difficult problem in general. The difficulty of this problem is the basis for the security of many cryptographic systems.

# 5

# Induction and Recursion

**M**any mathematical statements assert that a property is true for all positive integers. Examples of such statements are that for every positive integer $n$: $n! \leq n^n$, $n^3 - n$ is divisible by 3; a set with $n$ elements has $2^n$ subsets; and the sum of the first $n$ positive integers is $n(n + 1)/2$. A major goal of this chapter, and the book, is to give the student a thorough understanding of mathematical induction, which is used to prove results of this kind.

Proofs using mathematical induction have two parts. First, they show that the statement holds for the positive integer 1. Second, they show that if the statement holds for a positive integer then it must also hold for the next larger integer. Mathematical induction is based on the rule of inference that tells us that if $P(1)$ and $\forall k(P(k) \rightarrow P(k + 1))$ are true for the domain of positive integers, then $\forall n\, P(n)$ is true. Mathematical induction can be used to prove a tremendous variety of results. Understanding how to read and construct proofs by mathematical induction is a key goal of learning discrete mathematics.

In Chapter 2 we explicitly defined sets and functions. That is, we described sets by listing their elements or by giving some property that characterizes these elements. We gave formulae for the values of functions. There is another important way to define such objects, based on mathematical induction. To define functions, some initial terms are specified, and a rule is given for finding subsequent values from values already known. (We briefly touched on this sort of definition in Chapter 2 when we showed how sequences can be defined using recurrence relations.) Sets can be defined by listing some of their elements and giving rules for constructing elements from those already known to be in the set. Such definitions, called *recursive definitions,* are used throughout discrete mathematics and computer science. Once we have defined a set recursively, we can use a proof method called structural induction to prove results about this set.

When a procedure is specified for solving a problem, this procedure must *always* solve the problem correctly. Just testing to see that the correct result is obtained for a set of input values does not show that the procedure always works correctly. The correctness of a procedure can be guaranteed only by proving that it always yields the correct result. The final section of this chapter contains an introduction to the techniques of program verification. This is a formal technique to verify that procedures are correct. Program verification serves as the basis for attempts under way to prove in a mechanical fashion that programs are correct.

## 5.1 Mathematical Induction

### Introduction

Suppose that we have an infinite ladder, as shown in Figure 1, and we want to know whether we can reach every step on this ladder. We know two things:

1. We can reach the first rung of the ladder.
2. If we can reach a particular rung of the ladder, then we can reach the next rung.

Can we conclude that we can reach every rung? By (1), we know that we can reach the first rung of the ladder. Moreover, because we can reach the first rung, by (2), we can also reach the second rung; it is the next rung after the first rung. Applying (2) again, because we can reach the second rung, we can also reach the third rung. Continuing in this way, we can show that we

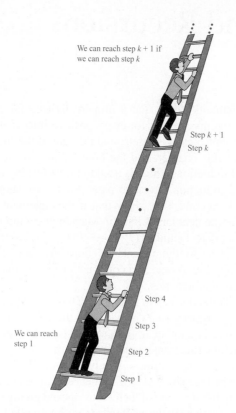

We can reach step $k + 1$ if
we can reach step $k$

Step $k + 1$

Step $k$

Step 4

Step 3

We can reach
step 1

Step 2

Step 1

**FIGURE 1    Climbing an Infinite Ladder.**

can reach the fourth rung, the fifth rung, and so on. For example, after 100 uses of (2), we know that we can reach the 101st rung. But can we conclude that we are able to reach every rung of this infinite ladder? The answer is yes, something we can verify using an important proof technique called **mathematical induction**. That is, we can show that $P(n)$ is true for every positive integer $n$, where $P(n)$ is the statement that we can reach the $n$th rung of the ladder.

Mathematical induction is an extremely important proof technique that can be used to prove assertions of this type. As we will see in this section and in subsequent sections of this chapter and later chapters, mathematical induction is used extensively to prove results about a large variety of discrete objects. For example, it is used to prove results about the complexity of algorithms, the correctness of certain types of computer programs, theorems about graphs and trees, as well as a wide range of identities and inequalities.

In this section, we will describe how mathematical induction can be used and why it is a valid proof technique. It is extremely important to note that mathematical induction can be used only to prove results obtained in some other way. It is *not* a tool for discovering formulae or theorems.

## Mathematical Induction

Assessment

In general, mathematical induction * can be used to prove statements that assert that $P(n)$ is true for all positive integers $n$, where $P(n)$ is a propositional function. A proof by mathematical

---

*Unfortunately, using the terminology "mathematical induction" clashes with the terminology used to describe different types of reasoning. In logic, **deductive reasoning** uses rules of inference to draw conclusions from premises, whereas **inductive reasoning** makes conclusions only supported, but not ensured, by evidence. Mathematical proofs, including arguments that use mathematical induction, are deductive, not inductive.

induction has two parts, a **basis step**, where we show that $P(1)$ is true, and an **inductive step**, where we show that for all positive integers $k$, if $P(k)$ is true, then $P(k+1)$ is true.

---

*PRINCIPLE OF MATHEMATICAL INDUCTION*    To prove that $P(n)$ is true for all positive integers $n$, where $P(n)$ is a propositional function, we complete two steps:

*BASIS STEP:*  We verify that $P(1)$ is true.

*INDUCTIVE STEP:*  We show that the conditional statement $P(k) \rightarrow P(k+1)$ is true for all positive integers $k$.

---

To complete the inductive step of a proof using the principle of mathematical induction, we assume that $P(k)$ is true for an arbitrary positive integer $k$ and show that under this assumption, $P(k+1)$ must also be true. The assumption that $P(k)$ is true is called the **inductive hypothesis**. Once we complete both steps in a proof by mathematical induction, we have shown that $P(n)$ is true for all positive integers, that is, we have shown that $\forall n\, P(n)$ is true where the quantification is over the set of positive integers. In the inductive step, we show that $\forall k(P(k) \rightarrow P(k+1))$ is true, where again, the domain is the set of positive integers.

Expressed as a rule of inference, this proof technique can be stated as

$$(P(1) \wedge \forall k(P(k) \rightarrow P(k+1))) \rightarrow \forall n\, P(n),$$

when the domain is the set of positive integers. Because mathematical induction is such an important technique, it is worthwhile to explain in detail the steps of a proof using this technique. The first thing we do to prove that $P(n)$ is true for all positive integers $n$ is to show that $P(1)$ is true. This amounts to showing that the particular statement obtained when $n$ is replaced by 1 in $P(n)$ is true. Then we must show that $P(k) \rightarrow P(k+1)$ is true for every positive integer $k$. To prove that this conditional statement is true for every positive integer $k$, we need to show that $P(k+1)$ cannot be false when $P(k)$ is true. This can be accomplished by assuming that $P(k)$ is true and showing that *under this hypothesis $P(k+1)$* must also be true.

***Remark:*** In a proof by mathematical induction it is *not* assumed that $P(k)$ is true for all positive integers! It is only shown that *if it is assumed* that $P(k)$ is true, then $P(k+1)$ is also true. Thus, a proof by mathematical induction is not a case of begging the question, or circular reasoning.

When we use mathematical induction to prove a theorem, we first show that $P(1)$ is true. Then we know that $P(2)$ is true, because $P(1)$ implies $P(2)$. Further, we know that $P(3)$ is true, because $P(2)$ implies $P(3)$. Continuing along these lines, we see that $P(n)$ is true for every positive integer $n$.

---

HISTORICAL NOTE    The first known use of mathematical induction is in the work of the sixteenth-century mathematician Francesco Maurolico (1494–1575). Maurolico wrote extensively on the works of classical mathematics and made many contributions to geometry and optics. In his book *Arithmeticorum Libri Duo,* Maurolico presented a variety of properties of the integers together with proofs of these properties. To prove some of these properties, he devised the method of mathematical induction. His first use of mathematical induction in this book was to prove that the sum of the first $n$ odd positive integers equals $n^2$. Augustus De Morgan is credited with the first presentation in 1838 of formal proofs using mathematical induction, as well as introducing the terminology "mathematical induction." Maurolico's proofs were informal and he never used the word "induction." See [Gu11] to learn more about the history of the method of mathematical induction.

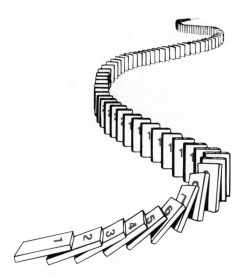

**FIGURE 2** **Illustrating How Mathematical Induction Works Using Dominoes.**

WAYS TO REMEMBER HOW MATHEMATICAL INDUCTION WORKS   Thinking of the infinite ladder and the rules for reaching steps can help you remember how mathematical induction works. Note that statements (1) and (2) for the infinite ladder are exactly the basis step and inductive step, respectively, of the proof that $P(n)$ is true for all positive integers $n$, where $P(n)$ is the statement that we can reach the $n$th rung of the ladder. Consequently, we can invoke mathematical induction to conclude that we can reach every rung.

Another way to illustrate the principle of mathematical induction is to consider an infinite row of dominoes, labeled $1, 2, 3, \ldots, n, \ldots$, where each domino is standing up. Let $P(n)$ be the proposition that domino $n$ is knocked over. If the first domino is knocked over—i.e., if $P(1)$ is true—and if, whenever the $k$th domino is knocked over, it also knocks the $(k + 1)$st domino over—i.e., if $P(k) \rightarrow P(k + 1)$ is true for all positive integers $k$—then all the dominoes are knocked over. This is illustrated in Figure 2.

## Why Mathematical Induction is Valid

Why is mathematical induction a valid proof technique? The reason comes from the well-ordering property, listed in Appendix 1, as an axiom for the set of positive integers, which states that every nonempty subset of the set of positive integers has a least element. So, suppose we know that $P(1)$ is true and that the proposition $P(k) \rightarrow P(k + 1)$ is true for all positive integers $k$. To show that $P(n)$ must be true for all positive integers $n$, assume that there is at least one positive integer for which $P(n)$ is false. Then the set $S$ of positive integers for which $P(n)$ is false is nonempty. Thus, by the well-ordering property, $S$ has a least element, which will be denoted by $m$. We know that $m$ cannot be 1, because $P(1)$ is true. Because $m$ is positive and greater than 1, $m - 1$ is a positive integer. Furthermore, because $m - 1$ is less than $m$, it is not in $S$, so $P(m - 1)$ must be true. Because the conditional statement $P(m - 1) \rightarrow P(m)$ is also true, it must be the case that $P(m)$ is true. This contradicts the choice of $m$. Hence, $P(n)$ must be true for every positive integer $n$.

## The Good and the Bad of Mathematical Induction

An important point needs to be made about mathematical induction before we commence a study of its use. The good thing about mathematical induction is that it can be used to prove

You can prove a theorem by mathematical induction even if you do not have the slightest idea why it is true!

a conjecture once it is has been made (and is true). The bad thing about it is that it cannot be used to find new theorems. Mathematicians sometimes find proofs by mathematical induction unsatisfying because they do not provide insights as to why theorems are true. Many theorems can be proved in many ways, including by mathematical induction. Proofs of these theorems by methods other than mathematical induction are often preferred because of the insights they bring.

## Examples of Proofs by Mathematical Induction

Many theorems assert that $P(n)$ is true for all positive integers $n$, where $P(n)$ is a propositional function. Mathematical induction is a technique for proving theorems of this kind. In other words, mathematical induction can be used to prove statements of the form $\forall n\, P(n)$, where the domain is the set of positive integers. Mathematical induction can be used to prove an extremely wide variety of theorems, each of which is a statement of this form. (Remember, many mathematical assertions include an implicit universal quantifier. The statement "if $n$ is a positive integer, then $n^3 - n$ is divisible by 3" is an example of this. Making the implicit universal quantifier explicit yields the statement "for every positive integer $n$, $n^3 - n$ is divisible by 3.)

We will use how theorems are proved using mathematical induction. The theorems we will prove include summation formulae, inequalities, identities for combinations of sets, divisibility results, theorems about algorithms, and some other creative results. In this section and in later sections, we will employ mathematical induction to prove many other types of results, including the correctness of computer programs and algorithms. Mathematical induction can be used to prove a wide variety of theorems, not just summation formulae, inequalities, and other types of examples we illustrate here. (For proofs by mathematical induction of many more interesting and diverse results, see the *Handbook of Mathematical Induction* by David Gunderson [Gu11]. This book is part of the extensive CRC Series in Discrete Mathematics, many of which may be of interest to readers. The author is the Series Editor of these books).

Note that there are many opportunities for errors in induction proofs. We will describe some incorrect proofs by mathematical induction at the end of this section and in the exercises. To avoid making errors in proofs by mathematical induction, try to follow the guidelines for such proofs given at the end of this section.

Look for the $\overset{\text{IH}}{=}$ symbol to see where the inductive hypothesis is used.

SEEING WHERE THE INDUCTIVE HYPOTHESIS IS USED    To help the reader understand each of the mathematical induction proofs in this section, we will note where the inductive hypothesis is used. We indicate this use in three different ways: by explicit mention in the text, by inserting the acronym IH (for inductive hypothesis) over an equals sign or a sign for an inequality, or by specifying the inductive hypothesis as the reason for a step in a multi-line display.

PROVING SUMMATION FORMULAE    We begin by using mathematical induction to prove several summation formulae. As we will see, mathematical induction is particularly well suited for proving that such formulae are valid. However, summation formulae can be proven in other ways. This is not surprising because there are often different ways to prove a theorem. The major disadvantage of using mathematical induction to prove a summation formula is that you cannot use it to derive this formula. That is, you must already have the formula before you attempt to prove it by mathematical induction.

Examples 1–4 illustrate how to use mathematical induction to prove summation formulae. The first summation formula we will prove by mathematical induction, in Example 1, is a closed formula for the sum of the smallest $n$ positive integers.

**EXAMPLE 1**   Show that if $n$ is a positive integer, then

$$1 + 2 + \cdots + n = \frac{n(n + 1)}{2}.$$

Extra
Examples

*Solution:* Let $P(n)$ be the proposition that the sum of the first $n$ positive integers, $1 + 2 + \cdots n = \frac{n(n+1)}{2}$, is $n(n + 1)/2$. We must do two things to prove that $P(n)$ is true for $n = 1, 2, 3, \ldots$. Namely, we must show that $P(1)$ is true and that the conditional statement $P(k)$ implies $P(k + 1)$ is true for $k = 1, 2, 3, \ldots$.

*BASIS STEP:* $P(1)$ is true, because $1 = \frac{1(1 + 1)}{2}$. (The left-hand side of this equation is 1 because 1 is the sum of the first positive integer. The right-hand side is found by substituting 1 for $n$ in $n(n + 1)/2$.)

*INDUCTIVE STEP:* For the inductive hypothesis we assume that $P(k)$ holds for an arbitrary positive integer $k$. That is, we assume that

If you are rusty simplifying algebraic expressions, this is the time to do some reviewing!

$$1 + 2 + \cdots + k = \frac{k(k + 1)}{2}.$$

Under this assumption, it must be shown that $P(k + 1)$ is true, namely, that

$$1 + 2 + \cdots + k + (k + 1) = \frac{(k + 1)[(k + 1) + 1]}{2} = \frac{(k + 1)(k + 2)}{2}$$

is also true. When we add $k + 1$ to both sides of the equation in $P(k)$, we obtain

$$1 + 2 + \cdots + k + (k + 1) \overset{\text{IH}}{=} \frac{k(k + 1)}{2} + (k + 1)$$

$$= \frac{k(k + 1) + 2(k + 1)}{2}$$

$$= \frac{(k + 1)(k + 2)}{2}.$$

This last equation shows that $P(k + 1)$ is true under the assumption that $P(k)$ is true. This completes the inductive step.

We have completed the basis step and the inductive step, so by mathematical induction we know that $P(n)$ is true for all positive integers $n$. That is, we have proven that $1 + 2 + \cdots + n = n(n + 1)/2$ for all positive integers $n$.   ◀

As we noted, mathematical induction is not a tool for finding theorems about all positive integers. Rather, it is a proof method for proving such results once they are conjectured. In Example 2, using mathematical induction to prove a summation formula, we will both formulate and then prove a conjecture.

**EXAMPLE 2**   Conjecture a formula for the sum of the first $n$ positive odd integers. Then prove your conjecture using mathematical induction.

*Solution:* The sums of the first $n$ positive odd integers for $n = 1, 2, 3, 4, 5$ are

$$1 = 1, \qquad\qquad 1 + 3 = 4, \qquad\qquad 1 + 3 + 5 = 9,$$
$$1 + 3 + 5 + 7 = 16, \quad 1 + 3 + 5 + 7 + 9 = 25.$$

From these values it is reasonable to conjecture that the sum of the first $n$ positive odd integers is $n^2$, that is, $1 + 3 + 5 + \cdots + (2n - 1) = n^2$. We need a method to *prove* that this *conjecture* is correct, if in fact it is.

Let $P(n)$ denote the proposition that the sum of the first $n$ odd positive integers is $n^2$. Our conjecture is that $P(n)$ is true for all positive integers. To use mathematical induction to prove this conjecture, we must first complete the basis step; that is, we must show that $P(1)$ is true. Then we must carry out the inductive step; that is, we must show that $P(k + 1)$ is true when $P(k)$ is assumed to be true. We now attempt to complete these two steps.

*BASIS STEP:*  $P(1)$ states that the sum of the first one odd positive integer is $1^2$. This is true because the sum of the first odd positive integer is 1. The basis step is complete.

*INDUCTIVE STEP:*  To complete the inductive step we must show that the proposition $P(k) \rightarrow P(k + 1)$ is true for every positive integer $k$. To do this, we first assume the inductive hypothesis. The inductive hypothesis is the statement that $P(k)$ is true for an arbitrary positive integer $k$, that is,

$$1 + 3 + 5 + \cdots + (2k - 1) = k^2.$$

(Note that the $k$th odd positive integer is $(2k - 1)$, because this integer is obtained by adding 2 a total of $k - 1$ times to 1.) To show that $\forall k (P(k) \rightarrow P(k + 1))$ is true, we must show that if $P(k)$ is true (the inductive hypothesis), then $P(k + 1)$ is true. Note that $P(k + 1)$ is the statement that

$$1 + 3 + 5 + \cdots + (2k - 1) + (2k + 1) = (k + 1)^2.$$

So, assuming that $P(k)$ is true, it follows that

$$
\begin{aligned}
1 + 3 + 5 + \cdots + (2k - 1) + (2k + 1) &= [1 + 3 + \cdots + (2k - 1)] + (2k + 1) \\
&\overset{\text{IH}}{=} k^2 + (2k + 1) \\
&= k^2 + 2k + 1 \\
&= (k + 1)^2.
\end{aligned}
$$

This shows that $P(k + 1)$ follows from $P(k)$. Note that we used the inductive hypothesis $P(k)$ in the second equality to replace the sum of the first $k$ odd positive integers by $k^2$.

We have now completed both the basis step and the inductive step. That is, we have shown that $P(1)$ is true and the conditional statement $P(k) \rightarrow P(k + 1)$ is true for all positive integers $k$. Consequently, by the principle of mathematical induction we can conclude that $P(n)$ is true for all positive integers $n$. That is, we know that $1 + 3 + 5 + \cdots + (2n - 1) = n^2$ for all positive integers $n$.  ◀

Often, we will need to show that $P(n)$ is true for $n = b, b + 1, b + 2, \ldots$, where $b$ is an integer other than 1. We can use mathematical induction to accomplish this, as long as we change the basis step by replacing $P(1)$ with $P(b)$. In other words, to use mathematical induction to show that $P(n)$ is true for $n = b, b + 1, b + 2, \ldots$, where $b$ is an integer other than 1, we show that $P(b)$ is true in the basis step. In the inductive step, we show that the conditional statement $P(k) \rightarrow P(k + 1)$ is true for $k = b, b + 1, b + 2, \ldots$. Note that $b$ can be negative, zero, or positive. Following the domino analogy we used earlier, imagine that we begin by knocking down the $b$th domino (the basis step), and as each domino falls, it knocks down the next domino (the inductive step). We leave it to the reader to show that this form of induction is valid (see Exercise 83).

We illustrate this notion in Example 3, which states that a summation formula is valid for all nonnegative integers. In this example, we need to prove that $P(n)$ is true for $n = 0, 1, 2, \ldots$. So, the basis step in Example 3 shows that $P(0)$ is true.

**EXAMPLE 3**    Use mathematical induction to show that

$$1 + 2 + 2^2 + \cdots + 2^n = 2^{n+1} - 1$$

for all nonnegative integers $n$.

*Solution:* Let $P(n)$ be the proposition that $1 + 2 + 2^2 + \cdots + 2^n = 2^{n+1} - 1$ for the integer $n$.

*BASIS STEP:* $P(0)$ is true because $2^0 = 1 = 2^1 - 1$. This completes the basis step.

*INDUCTIVE STEP:* For the inductive hypothesis, we assume that $P(k)$ is true for an arbitrary nonnegative integer $k$. That is, we assume that

$$1 + 2 + 2^2 + \cdots + 2^k = 2^{k+1} - 1.$$

To carry out the inductive step using this assumption, we must show that when we assume that $P(k)$ is true, then $P(k + 1)$ is also true. That is, we must show that

$$1 + 2 + 2^2 + \cdots + 2^k + 2^{k+1} = 2^{(k+1)+1} - 1 = 2^{k+2} - 1$$

assuming the inductive hypothesis $P(k)$. Under the assumption of $P(k)$, we see that

$$
\begin{aligned}
1 + 2 + 2^2 + \cdots + 2^k + 2^{k+1} &= (1 + 2 + 2^2 + \cdots + 2^k) + 2^{k+1} \\
&\stackrel{\text{IH}}{=} (2^{k+1} - 1) + 2^{k+1} \\
&= 2 \cdot 2^{k+1} - 1 \\
&= 2^{k+2} - 1.
\end{aligned}
$$

Note that we used the inductive hypothesis in the second equation in this string of equalities to replace $1 + 2 + 2^2 + \cdots + 2^k$ by $2^{k+1} - 1$. We have completed the inductive step.

Because we have completed the basis step and the inductive step, by mathematical induction we know that $P(n)$ is true for all nonnegative integers $n$. That is, $1 + 2 + \cdots + 2^n = 2^{n+1} - 1$ for all nonnegative integers $n$.    ◄

The formula given in Example 3 is a special case of a general result for the sum of terms of a geometric progression (Theorem 1 in Section 2.4). We will use mathematical induction to provide an alternative proof of this formula.

**EXAMPLE 4**    **Sums of Geometric Progressions**    Use mathematical induction to prove this formula for the sum of a finite number of terms of a geometric progression with initial term $a$ and common ratio $r$:

$$\sum_{j=0}^{n} ar^j = a + ar + ar^2 + \cdots + ar^n = \frac{ar^{n+1} - a}{r - 1} \qquad \text{when } r \neq 1,$$

where $n$ is a nonnegative integer.

*Solution:* To prove this formula using mathematical induction, let $P(n)$ be the statement that the sum of the first $n + 1$ terms of a geometric progression in this formula is correct.

*BASIS STEP:* $P(0)$ is true, because

$$\frac{ar^{0+1} - a}{r - 1} = \frac{ar - a}{r - 1} = \frac{a(r - 1)}{r - 1} = a.$$

*INDUCTIVE STEP:* The inductive hypothesis is the statement that $P(k)$ is true, where $k$ is an arbitrary nonnegative integer. That is, $P(k)$ is the statement that

$$a + ar + ar^2 + \cdots + ar^k = \frac{ar^{k+1} - a}{r - 1}.$$

To complete the inductive step we must show that if $P(k)$ is true, then $P(k + 1)$ is also true. To show that this is the case, we first add $ar^{k+1}$ to both sides of the equality asserted by $P(k)$. We find that

$$a + ar + ar^2 + \cdots + ar^k + ar^{k+1} \overset{\text{IH}}{=} \frac{ar^{k+1} - a}{r - 1} + ar^{k+1}.$$

Rewriting the right-hand side of this equation shows that

$$\frac{ar^{k+1} - a}{r - 1} + ar^{k+1} = \frac{ar^{k+1} - a}{r - 1} + \frac{ar^{k+2} - ar^{k+1}}{r - 1}$$

$$= \frac{ar^{k+2} - a}{r - 1}.$$

Combining these last two equations gives

$$a + ar + ar^2 + \cdots + ar^k + ar^{k+1} = \frac{ar^{k+2} - a}{r - 1}.$$

This shows that if the inductive hypothesis $P(k)$ is true, then $P(k + 1)$ must also be true. This completes the inductive argument.

We have completed the basis step and the inductive step, so by mathematical induction $P(n)$ is true for all nonnegative integers $n$. This shows that the formula for the sum of the terms of a geometric series is correct. ◀

As previously mentioned, the formula in Example 3 is the case of the formula in Example 4 with $a = 1$ and $r = 2$. The reader should verify that putting these values for $a$ and $r$ into the general formula gives the same formula as in Example 3.

**PROVING INEQUALITIES**   Mathematical induction can be used to prove a variety of inequalities that hold for all positive integers greater than a particular positive integer, as Examples 5–7 illustrate.

**EXAMPLE 5**   Use mathematical induction to prove the inequality

$$n < 2^n$$

for all positive integers $n$.

*Solution:* Let $P(n)$ be the proposition that $n < 2^n$.

*BASIS STEP:* $P(1)$ is true, because $1 < 2^1 = 2$. This completes the basis step.

*INDUCTIVE STEP:* We first assume the inductive hypothesis that $P(k)$ is true for an arbitrary positive integer $k$. That is, the inductive hypothesis $P(k)$ is the statement that $k < 2^k$. To complete the inductive step, we need to show that if $P(k)$ is true, then $P(k + 1)$, which is the statement that $k + 1 < 2^{k+1}$, is true. That is, we need to show that if $k < 2^k$, then $k + 1 < 2^{k+1}$. To show that this conditional statement is true for the positive integer $k$, we first add 1 to both sides of $k < 2^k$, and then note that $1 \le 2^k$. This tells us that

$$k + 1 \overset{\text{IH}}{<} 2^k + 1 \le 2^k + 2^k = 2 \cdot 2^k = 2^{k+1}.$$

This shows that $P(k + 1)$ is true, namely, that $k + 1 < 2^{k+1}$, based on the assumption that $P(k)$ is true. The induction step is complete.

Therefore, because we have completed both the basis step and the inductive step, by the principle of mathematical induction we have shown that $n < 2^n$ is true for all positive integers $n$. ◀

EXAMPLE 6    Use mathematical induction to prove that $2^n < n!$ for every integer $n$ with $n \ge 4$. (Note that this inequality is false for $n = 1, 2$, and 3.)

*Solution:* Let $P(n)$ be the proposition that $2^n < n!$.

*BASIS STEP:* To prove the inequality for $n \ge 4$ requires that the basis step be $P(4)$. Note that $P(4)$ is true, because $2^4 = 16 < 24 = 4!$

*INDUCTIVE STEP:* For the inductive step, we assume that $P(k)$ is true for an arbitrary integer $k$ with $k \ge 4$. That is, we assume that $2^k < k!$ for the positive integer $k$ with $k \ge 4$. We must show that under this hypothesis, $P(k + 1)$ is also true. That is, we must show that if $2^k < k!$ for an arbitrary positive integer $k$ where $k \ge 4$, then $2^{k+1} < (k + 1)!$. We have

$$
\begin{aligned}
2^{k+1} &= 2 \cdot 2^k && \text{by definition of exponent} \\
&< 2 \cdot k! && \text{by the inductive hypothesis} \\
&< (k + 1)k! && \text{because } 2 < k + 1 \\
&= (k + 1)! && \text{by definition of factorial function.}
\end{aligned}
$$

This shows that $P(k + 1)$ is true when $P(k)$ is true. This completes the inductive step of the proof.

We have completed the basis step and the inductive step. Hence, by mathematical induction $P(n)$ is true for all integers $n$ with $n \ge 4$. That is, we have proved that $2^n < n!$ is true for all integers $n$ with $n \ge 4$. ◀

An important inequality for the sum of the reciprocals of a set of positive integers will be proved in Example 7.

EXAMPLE 7    **An Inequality for Harmonic Numbers**    The **harmonic numbers** $H_j, j = 1, 2, 3, \ldots$, are defined by

$$H_j = 1 + \frac{1}{2} + \frac{1}{3} + \cdots + \frac{1}{j}.$$

For instance,

$$H_4 = 1 + \frac{1}{2} + \frac{1}{3} + \frac{1}{4} = \frac{25}{12}.$$

Use mathematical induction to show that

$$H_{2^n} \ge 1 + \frac{n}{2},$$

whenever $n$ is a nonnegative integer.

*Solution:* To carry out the proof, let $P(n)$ be the proposition that $H_{2^n} \geq 1 + \dfrac{n}{2}$.

*BASIS STEP:* $P(0)$ is true, because $H_{2^0} = H_1 = 1 \geq 1 + \dfrac{0}{2}$.

*INDUCTIVE STEP:* The inductive hypothesis is the statement that $P(k)$ is true, that is, $H_{2^k} \geq 1 + \dfrac{k}{2}$, where $k$ is an arbitrary nonnegative integer. We must show that if $P(k)$ is true, then $P(k+1)$, which states that $H_{2^{k+1}} \geq 1 + \dfrac{k+1}{2}$, is also true. So, assuming the inductive hypothesis, it follows that

$$
\begin{aligned}
H_{2^{k+1}} &= 1 + \frac{1}{2} + \frac{1}{3} + \cdots + \frac{1}{2^k} + \frac{1}{2^k+1} + \cdots + \frac{1}{2^{k+1}} && \text{by the definition of harmonic} \\
& && \text{number} \\
&= H_{2^k} + \frac{1}{2^k+1} + \cdots + \frac{1}{2^{k+1}} && \text{by the definition of } 2^k \text{th harmonic} \\
& && \text{number} \\
&\geq \left(1 + \frac{k}{2}\right) + \frac{1}{2^k+1} + \cdots + \frac{1}{2^{k+1}} && \text{by the inductive hypothesis} \\
&\geq \left(1 + \frac{k}{2}\right) + 2^k \cdot \frac{1}{2^{k+1}} && \text{because there are } 2^k \text{ terms} \\
& && \text{each} \geq 1/2^{k+1} \\
&\geq \left(1 + \frac{k}{2}\right) + \frac{1}{2} && \text{canceling a common factor of} \\
& && 2^k \text{ in second term} \\
&= 1 + \frac{k+1}{2}.
\end{aligned}
$$

This establishes the inductive step of the proof.

We have completed the basis step and the inductive step. Thus, by mathematical induction $P(n)$ is true for all nonnegative integers $n$. That is, the inequality $H_{2^n} \geq 1 + \frac{n}{2}$ for the harmonic numbers holds for all nonnegative integers $n$.    ◀

*Remark:* The inequality established here shows that the **harmonic series**

$$
1 + \frac{1}{2} + \frac{1}{3} + \cdots + \frac{1}{n} + \cdots
$$

is a divergent infinite series. This is an important example in the study of infinite series.

PROVING DIVISIBILITY RESULTS    Mathematical induction can be used to prove divisibility results about integers. Although such results are often easier to prove using basic results in number theory, it is instructive to see how to prove such results using mathematical induction, as Examples 8 and 9 illustrate.

**EXAMPLE 8**    Use mathematical induction to prove that $n^3 - n$ is divisible by 3 whenever $n$ is a positive integer. (Note that this is the statement with $p = 3$ of Fermat's little theorem, which is Theorem 3 of Section 4.4.)

Extra
Examples

*Solution:* To construct the proof, let $P(n)$ denote the proposition: "$n^3 - n$ is divisible by 3."

*BASIS STEP:* The statement $P(1)$ is true because $1^3 - 1 = 0$ is divisible by 3. This completes the basis step.

*INDUCTIVE STEP:* For the inductive hypothesis we assume that $P(k)$ is true; that is, we assume that $k^3 - k$ is divisible by 3 for an arbitrary positive integer $k$. To complete the inductive step, we must show that when we assume the inductive hypothesis, it follows that $P(k + 1)$, the statement that $(k + 1)^3 - (k + 1)$ is divisible by 3, is also true. That is, we must show that $(k + 1)^3 - (k + 1)$ is divisible by 3. Note that

$$(k + 1)^3 - (k + 1) = (k^3 + 3k^2 + 3k + 1) - (k + 1)$$
$$= (k^3 - k) + 3(k^2 + k).$$

Using the inductive hypothesis, we conclude that the first term $k^3 - k$ is divisible by 3. The second term is divisible by 3 because it is 3 times an integer. So, by part (i) of Theorem 1 in Section 4.1, we know that $(k + 1)^3 - (k + 1)$ is also divisible by 3. This completes the inductive step.

Because we have completed both the basis step and the inductive step, by the principle of mathematical induction we know that $n^3 - n$ is divisible by 3 whenever $n$ is a positive integer. ◄

The next example presents a more challenging proof by mathematical induction of a divisibility result.

**EXAMPLE 9**    Use mathematical induction to prove that $7^{n+2} + 8^{2n+1}$ is divisible by 57 for every nonnegative integer $n$.

*Solution:* To construct the proof, let $P(n)$ denote the proposition: "$7^{n+2} + 8^{2n+1}$ is divisible by 57."

*BASIS STEP:* To complete the basis step, we must show that $P(0)$ is true, because we want to prove that $P(n)$ is true for every nonnegative integer. We see that $P(0)$ is true because $7^{0+2} + 8^{2\cdot0+1} = 7^2 + 8^1 = 57$ is divisible by 57. This completes the basis step.

*INDUCTIVE STEP:* For the inductive hypothesis we assume that $P(k)$ is true for an arbitrary nonnegative integer $k$; that is, we assume that $7^{k+2} + 8^{2k+1}$ is divisible by 57. To complete the inductive step, we must show that when we assume that the inductive hypothesis $P(k)$ is true, then $P(k + 1)$, the statement that $7^{(k+1)+2} + 8^{2(k+1)+1}$ is divisible by 57, is also true.

The difficult part of the proof is to see how to use the inductive hypothesis. To take advantage of the inductive hypothesis, we use these steps:

$$7^{(k+1)+2} + 8^{2(k+1)+1} = 7^{k+3} + 8^{2k+3}$$
$$= 7 \cdot 7^{k+2} + 8^2 \cdot 8^{2k+1}$$
$$= 7 \cdot 7^{k+2} + 64 \cdot 8^{2k+1}$$
$$= 7(7^{k+2} + 8^{2k+1}) + 57 \cdot 8^{2k+1}.$$

We can now use the inductive hypothesis, which states that $7^{k+2} + 8^{2k+1}$ is divisible by 57. We will use parts (i) and (ii) of Theorem 1 in Section 4.1. By part (ii) of this theorem, and the inductive hypothesis, we conclude that the first term in this last sum, $7(7^{k+2} + 8^{2k+1})$, is divisible by 57. By part (ii) of this theorem, the second term in this sum, $57 \cdot 8^{2k+1}$, is divisible by 57. Hence, by part (i) of this theorem, we conclude that $7(7^{k+2} + 8^{2k+1}) + 57 \cdot 8^{2k+1} = 7^{k+3} + 8^{2k+3}$ is divisible by 57. This completes the inductive step.

Because we have completed both the basis step and the inductive step, by the principle of mathematical induction we know that $7^{n+2} + 8^{2n+1}$ is divisible by 57 for every nonnegative integer $n$. ◄

PROVING RESULTS ABOUT SETS    Mathematical induction can be used to prove many results about sets. In particular, in Example 10 we prove a formula for the number of subsets of a finite set and in Example 11 we establish a set identity.

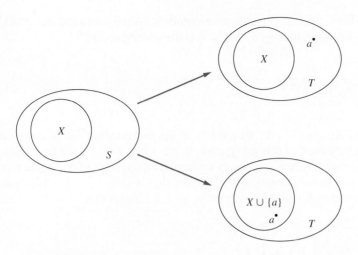

**FIGURE 3** **Generating Subsets of a Set with $k + 1$ Elements. Here $T = S \cup \{a\}$.**

EXAMPLE 10 **The Number of Subsets of a Finite Set** Use mathematical induction to show that if $S$ is a finite set with $n$ elements, where $n$ is a nonnegative integer, then $S$ has $2^n$ subsets. (We will prove this result directly in several ways in Chapter 6.)

*Solution:* Let $P(n)$ be the proposition that a set with $n$ elements has $2^n$ subsets.

*BASIS STEP:* $P(0)$ is true, because a set with zero elements, the empty set, has exactly $2^0 = 1$ subset, namely, itself.

*INDUCTIVE STEP:* For the inductive hypothesis we assume that $P(k)$ is true for an arbitrary nonnegative integer $k$, that is, we assume that every set with $k$ elements has $2^k$ subsets. It must be shown that under this assumption, $P(k + 1)$, which is the statement that every set with $k + 1$ elements has $2^{k+1}$ subsets, must also be true. To show this, let $T$ be a set with $k + 1$ elements. Then, it is possible to write $T = S \cup \{a\}$, where $a$ is one of the elements of $T$ and $S = T - \{a\}$ (and hence $|S| = k$). The subsets of $T$ can be obtained in the following way. For each subset $X$ of $S$ there are exactly two subsets of $T$, namely, $X$ and $X \cup \{a\}$. (This is illustrated in Figure 3.) These constitute all the subsets of $T$ and are all distinct. We now use the inductive hypothesis to conclude that $S$ has $2^k$ subsets, because it has $k$ elements. We also know that there are two subsets of $T$ for each subset of $S$. Therefore, there are $2 \cdot 2^k = 2^{k+1}$ subsets of $T$. This finishes the inductive argument.

Because we have completed the basis step and the inductive step, by mathematical induction it follows that $P(n)$ is true for all nonnegative integers $n$. That is, we have proved that a set with $n$ elements has $2^n$ subsets whenever $n$ is a nonnegative integer. ◀

EXAMPLE 11 Use mathematical induction to prove the following generalization of one of De Morgan's laws:

$$\overline{\bigcap_{j=1}^{n} A_j} = \bigcup_{j=1}^{n} \overline{A_j}$$

whenever $A_1, A_2, \ldots, A_n$ are subsets of a universal set $U$ and $n \geq 2$.

*Solution:* Let $P(n)$ be the identity for $n$ sets.

*BASIS STEP:* The statement $P(2)$ asserts that $\overline{A_1 \cap A_2} = \overline{A_1} \cup \overline{A_2}$. This is one of De Morgan's laws; it was proved in Example 11 of Section 2.2.

*INDUCTIVE STEP:* The inductive hypothesis is the statement that $P(k)$ is true, where $k$ is an arbitrary integer with $k \geq 2$; that is, it is the statement that

$$\overline{\bigcap_{j=1}^{k} A_j} = \bigcup_{j=1}^{k} \overline{A_j}$$

whenever $A_1, A_2, \ldots, A_k$ are subsets of the universal set $U$. To carry out the inductive step, we need to show that this assumption implies that $P(k+1)$ is true. That is, we need to show that if this equality holds for every collection of $k$ subsets of $U$, then it must also hold for every collection of $k+1$ subsets of $U$. Suppose that $A_1, A_2, \ldots, A_k, A_{k+1}$ are subsets of $U$. When the inductive hypothesis is assumed to hold, it follows that

$$\overline{\bigcap_{j=1}^{k+1} A_j} = \overline{\left( \bigcap_{j=1}^{k} A_j \right) \cap A_{k+1}} \quad \text{by the definition of intersection}$$

$$= \overline{\left( \bigcap_{j=1}^{k} A_j \right)} \cup \overline{A_{k+1}} \quad \text{by De Morgan's law (where the two sets are } \bigcap_{j=1}^{k} A_j \text{ and } A_{k+1})$$

$$= \left( \bigcup_{j=1}^{k} \overline{A_j} \right) \cup \overline{A_{k+1}} \quad \text{by the inductive hypothesis}$$

$$= \bigcup_{j=1}^{k+1} \overline{A_j} \quad \text{by the definition of union.}$$

This completes the inductive step.

Because we have completed both the basis step and the inductive step, by mathematical induction we know that $P(n)$ is true whenever $n$ is a positive integer, $n \geq 2$. That is, we know that

$$\overline{\bigcap_{j=1}^{n} A_j} = \bigcup_{j=1}^{n} \overline{A_j}$$

whenever $A_1, A_2, \ldots, A_n$ are subsets of a universal set $U$ and $n \geq 2$. ◀

PROVING RESULTS ABOUT ALGORITHMS   Next, we provide an example (somewhat more difficult than previous examples) that illustrates one of many ways mathematical induction is used in the study of algorithms. We will show how mathematical induction can be used to prove that a greedy algorithm we introduced in Section 3.1 always yields an optimal solution.

**EXAMPLE 12**   Recall the algorithm for scheduling talks discussed in Example 7 of Section 3.1. The input to this algorithm is a group of $m$ proposed talks with preset starting and ending times. The goal is to schedule as many of these lectures as possible in the main lecture hall so that no two talks overlap. Suppose that talk $t_j$ begins at time $s_j$ and ends at time $e_j$. (No two lectures can proceed in the main lecture hall at the same time, but a lecture in this hall can begin at the same time another one ends.)

Without loss of generality, we assume that the talks are listed in order of nondecreasing ending time, so that $e_1 \leq e_2 \leq \cdots \leq e_m$. The greedy algorithm proceeds by selecting at each stage a talk with the earliest ending time among all those talks that begin no sooner than when the last talk scheduled in the main lecture hall has ended. Note that a talk with the earliest end time is always selected first by the algorithm. We will show that this greedy algorithm is optimal in the sense that it always schedules the most talks possible in the main lecture hall. To prove the optimality of this algorithm we use mathematical induction on the variable $n$, the number of talks scheduled by the algorithm. We let $P(n)$ be the proposition that if the greedy algorithm schedules $n$ talks in the main lecture hall, then it is not possible to schedule more than $n$ talks in this hall.

*BASIS STEP:* Suppose that the greedy algorithm managed to schedule just one talk, $t_1$, in the main lecture hall. This means that no other talk can start at or after $e_1$, the end time of $t_1$. Otherwise, the first such talk we come to as we go through the talks in order of nondecreasing end times could be added. Hence, at time $e_1$ each of the remaining talks needs to use the main lecture hall because they all start before $e_1$ and end after $e_1$. It follows that no two talks can be scheduled because both need to use the main lecture hall at time $e_1$. This shows that $P(1)$ is true and completes the basis step.

*INDUCTIVE STEP:* The inductive hypothesis is that $P(k)$ is true, where $k$ is an arbitrary positive integer, that is, that the greedy algorithm always schedules the most possible talks when it selects $k$ talks, where $k$ is a positive integer, given any set of talks, no matter how many. We must show that $P(k + 1)$ follows from the assumption that $P(k)$ is true, that is, we must show that under the assumption of $P(k)$, the greedy algorithm always schedules the most possible talks when it selects $k + 1$ talks.

Now suppose that the greedy algorithm has selected $k + 1$ talks. Our first step in completing the inductive step is to show there is a schedule including the most talks possible that contains talk $t_1$, a talk with the earliest end time. This is easy to see because a schedule that begins with the talk $t_i$ in the list, where $i > 1$, can be changed so that talk $t_1$ replaces talk $t_i$. To see this, note that because $e_1 \le e_i$, all talks that were scheduled to follow talk $t_i$ can still be scheduled.

Once we included talk $t_1$, scheduling the talks so that as many as possible are scheduled is reduced to scheduling as many talks as possible that begin at or after time $e_1$. So, if we have scheduled as many talks as possible, the schedule of talks other than talk $t_1$ is an optimal schedule of the original talks that begin once talk $t_1$ has ended. Because the greedy algorithm schedules $k$ talks when it creates this schedule, we can apply the inductive hypothesis to conclude that it has scheduled the most possible talks. It follows that the greedy algorithm has scheduled the most possible talks, $k + 1$, when it produced a schedule with $k + 1$ talks, so $P(k + 1)$ is true. This completes the inductive step.

We have completed the basis step and the inductive step. So, by mathematical induction we know that $P(n)$ is true for all positive integers $n$. This completes the proof of optimality. That is, we have proved that when the greedy algorithm schedules $n$ talks, when $n$ is a positive integer, then it is not possible to schedule more than $n$ talks. ◀

CREATIVE USES OF MATHEMATICAL INDUCTION   Mathematical induction can often be used in unexpected ways. We will illustrate two particularly clever uses of mathematical induction here, the first relating to survivors in a pie fight and the second relating to tilings with regular triominoes of checkerboards with one square missing.

**EXAMPLE 13**

**Odd Pie Fights**   An odd number of people stand in a yard at mutually distinct distances. At the same time each person throws a pie at their nearest neighbor, hitting this person. Use mathematical induction to show that there is at least one survivor, that is, at least one person who is not hit by a pie. (This problem was introduced by Carmony [Ca79]. Note that this result is false when there are an even number of people; see Exercise 75.)

*Solution:* Let $P(n)$ be the statement that there is a survivor whenever $2n + 1$ people stand in a yard at distinct mutual distances and each person throws a pie at their nearest neighbor. To prove this result, we will show that $P(n)$ is true for all positive integers $n$. This follows because as $n$ runs through all positive integers, $2n + 1$ runs through all odd integers greater than or equal to 3. Note that one person cannot engage in a pie fight because there is no one else to throw the pie at.

*BASIS STEP:* When $n = 1$, there are $2n + 1 = 3$ people in the pie fight. Of the three people, suppose that the closest pair are $A$ and $B$, and $C$ is the third person. Because distances between pairs of people are different, the distance between $A$ and $C$ and the distance between $B$ and $C$ are both different from, and greater than, the distance between $A$ and $B$. It follows that $A$ and $B$ throw pies at each other, while $C$ throws a pie at either $A$ or $B$, whichever is closer. Hence, $C$ is not hit by a pie. This shows that at least one of the three people is not hit by a pie, completing the basis step.

*INDUCTIVE STEP:* For the inductive step, assume that $P(k)$ is true for an arbitrary odd integer $k$ with $k \geq 3$. That is, assume that there is at least one survivor whenever $2k + 1$ people stand in a yard at distinct mutual distances and each throws a pie at their nearest neighbor. We must show that if the inductive hypothesis $P(k)$ is true, then $P(k + 1)$, the statement that there is at least one survivor whenever $2(k + 1) + 1 = 2k + 3$ people stand in a yard at distinct mutual distances and each throws a pie at their nearest neighbor, is also true.

So suppose that we have $2(k + 1) + 1 = 2k + 3$ people in a yard with distinct distances between pairs of people. Let $A$ and $B$ be the closest pair of people in this group of $2k + 3$ people. When each person throws a pie at the nearest person, $A$ and $B$ throw pies at each other. We have two cases to consider, *(i)* when someone else throws a pie at either $A$ or $B$ and *(ii)* when no one else throws a pie at either $A$ or $B$.

*Case (i):* Because $A$ and $B$ throw pies at each other and someone else throws a pie at either $A$ and $B$, at least three pies are thrown at $A$ and $B$, and at most $(2k + 3) - 3 = 2k$ pies are thrown at the remaining $2k + 1$ people. This guarantees that at least one person is a survivor, for if each of these $2k + 1$ people was hit by at least one pie, a total of at least $2k + 1$ pies would have to be thrown at them. (The reasoning used in this last step is an example of the pigeonhole principle discussed further in Section 6.2.)

*Case (ii):* No one else throws a pie at either $A$ and $B$. Besides $A$ and $B$, there are $2k + 1$ people. Because the distances between pairs of these people are all different, we can use the inductive hypothesis to conclude that there is at least one survivor $S$ when these $2k + 1$ people each throws a pie at their nearest neighbor. Furthermore, $S$ is also not hit by either the pie thrown by $A$ or the pie thrown by $B$ because $A$ and $B$ throw their pies at each other, so $S$ is a survivor because $S$ is not hit by any of the pies thrown by these $2k + 3$ people.

We have completed both the basis step and the inductive step, using a proof by cases. So by mathematical induction it follows that $P(n)$ is true for all positive integers $n$. We conclude that whenever an odd number of people located in a yard at distinct mutual distances each throws a pie at their nearest neighbor, there is at least one survivor. ◀

**Links**

In Section 1.8 we discussed the tiling of checkerboards by polyominoes. Example 14 illustrates how mathematical induction can be used to prove a result about covering checkerboards with right triominoes, pieces shaped like the letter "L."

**EXAMPLE 14**   Let $n$ be a positive integer. Show that every $2^n \times 2^n$ checkerboard with one square removed can be tiled using right triominoes, where these pieces cover three squares at a time, as shown in Figure 4.

*Solution:* Let $P(n)$ be the proposition that every $2^n \times 2^n$ checkerboard with one square removed can be tiled using right triominoes. We can use mathematical induction to prove that $P(n)$ is true for all positive integers $n$.

**FIGURE 4   A Right Triomino.**

*BASIS STEP:* $P(1)$ is true, because each of the four $2 \times 2$ checkerboards with one square removed can be tiled using one right triomino, as shown in Figure 5.

**FIGURE 5    Tiling 2 × 2 Checkerboards with One Square Removed.**

*INDUCTIVE STEP:* The inductive hypothesis is the assumption that $P(k)$ is true for the positive integer $k$; that is, it is the assumption that every $2^k \times 2^k$ checkerboard with one square removed can be tiled using right triominoes. It must be shown that under the assumption of the inductive hypothesis, $P(k + 1)$ must also be true; that is, any $2^{k+1} \times 2^{k+1}$ checkerboard with one square removed can be tiled using right triominoes.

To see this, consider a $2^{k+1} \times 2^{k+1}$ checkerboard with one square removed. Split this checkerboard into four checkerboards of size $2^k \times 2^k$, by dividing it in half in both directions. This is illustrated in Figure 6. No square has been removed from three of these four checkerboards. The fourth $2^k \times 2^k$ checkerboard has one square removed, so we now use the inductive hypothesis to conclude that it can be covered by right triominoes. Now temporarily remove the square from each of the other three $2^k \times 2^k$ checkerboards that has the center of the original, larger checkerboard as one of its corners, as shown in Figure 7. By the inductive hypothesis, each of these three $2^k \times 2^k$ checkerboards with a square removed can be tiled by right triominoes. Furthermore, the three squares that were temporarily removed can be covered by one right triomino. Hence, the entire $2^{k+1} \times 2^{k+1}$ checkerboard can be tiled with right triominoes.

We have completed the basis step and the inductive step. Therefore, by mathematical induction $P(n)$ is true for all positive integers $n$. This shows that we can tile every $2^n \times 2^n$ checkerboard, where $n$ is a positive integer, with one square removed, using right triominoes. ◀

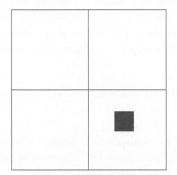

**FIGURE 6    Dividing a $2^{k+1} \times 2^{k+1}$ Checkerboard into Four $2^k \times 2^k$ Checkerboards.**

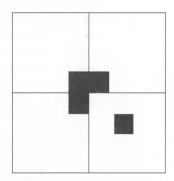

**FIGURE 7    Tiling the $2^{k+1} \times 2^{k+1}$ Checkerboard with One Square Removed.**

## Mistaken Proofs By Mathematical Induction

*Consult Common Errors in Discrete Mathematics on this book's website for more basic mistakes.*

As with every proof method, there are many opportunities for making errors when using mathematical induction. Many well-known mistaken, and often entertaining, proofs by mathematical induction of clearly false statements have been devised, as exemplified by Example 15 and Exercises 49–51. Often, it is not easy to find where the error in reasoning occurs in such mistaken proofs.

To uncover errors in proofs by mathematical induction, remember that in every such proof, both the basis step and the inductive step must be done correctly. Not completing the basis step in a supposed proof by mathematical induction can lead to mistaken proofs of clearly ridiculous statements such as "$n = n + 1$ whenever $n$ is a positive integer." (We leave it to the reader to show that it is easy to construct a correct inductive step in an attempted proof of this statement.) Locating the error in a faulty proof by mathematical induction, as Example 15 illustrates, can be quite tricky, especially when the error is hidden in the basis step.

**EXAMPLE 15**   Find the error in this "proof" of the clearly false claim that every set of lines in the plane, no two of which are parallel, meet in a common point.

*"Proof:"* Let $P(n)$ be the statement that every set of $n$ lines in the plane, no two of which are parallel, meet in a common point. We will attempt to prove that $P(n)$ is true for all positive integers $n \geq 2$.

*BASIS STEP:* The statement $P(2)$ is true because any two lines in the plane that are not parallel meet in a common point (by the definition of parallel lines).

*INDUCTIVE STEP:* The inductive hypothesis is the statement that $P(k)$ is true for the positive integer $k$, that is, it is the assumption that every set of $k$ lines in the plane, no two of which are parallel, meet in a common point. To complete the inductive step, we must show that if $P(k)$ is true, then $P(k + 1)$ must also be true. That is, we must show that if every set of $k$ lines in the plane, no two of which are parallel, meet in a common point, then every set of $k + 1$ lines in the plane, no two of which are parallel, meet in a common point. So, consider a set of $k + 1$ distinct lines in the plane. By the inductive hypothesis, the first $k$ of these lines meet in a common point $p_1$. Moreover, by the inductive hypothesis, the last $k$ of these lines meet in a common point $p_2$. We will show that $p_1$ and $p_2$ must be the same point. If $p_1$ and $p_2$ were different points, all lines containing both of them must be the same line because two points determine a line. This contradicts our assumption that all these lines are distinct. Thus, $p_1$ and $p_2$ are the same point. We conclude that the point $p_1 = p_2$ lies on all $k + 1$ lines. We have shown that $P(k + 1)$ is true assuming that $P(k)$ is true. That is, we have shown that if we assume that every $k$, $k \geq 2$, distinct lines meet in a common point, then every $k + 1$ distinct lines meet in a common point. This completes the inductive step.

We have completed the basis step and the inductive step, and supposedly we have a correct proof by mathematical induction.

*Solution:* Examining this supposed proof by mathematical induction it appears that everything is in order. However, there is an error, as there must be. The error is rather subtle. Carefully looking at the inductive step shows that this step requires that $k \geq 3$. We cannot show that $P(2)$ implies $P(3)$. When $k = 2$, our goal is to show that every three distinct lines meet in a common point. The first two lines must meet in a common point $p_1$ and the last two lines must meet in a common point $p_2$. But in this case, $p_1$ and $p_2$ do not have to be the same, because only the second line is common to both sets of lines. Here is where the inductive step fails.   ◄

## Guidelines for Proofs by Mathematical Induction

Examples 1–14 illustrate proofs by mathematical induction of a diverse collection of theorems. Each of these examples includes all the elements needed in a proof by mathematical induction. We have provided an example of an invalid proof by mathematical induction. Summarizing what we have learned from these examples, we can provide some useful guidelines for constructing correct proofs by mathematical induction. We now present these guidelines.

*Template for Proofs by Mathematical Induction*

1. Express the statement that is to be proved in the form "for all $n \geq b$, $P(n)$" for a fixed integer $b$.
2. Write out the words "Basis Step." Then show that $P(b)$ is true, taking care that the correct value of $b$ is used. This completes the first part of the proof.
3. Write out the words "Inductive Step."
4. State, and clearly identify, the inductive hypothesis, in the form "assume that $P(k)$ is true for an arbitrary fixed integer $k \geq b$."
5. State what needs to be proved under the assumption that the inductive hypothesis is true. That is, write out what $P(k + 1)$ says.
6. Prove the statement $P(k + 1)$ making use of the assumption $P(k)$. Be sure that your proof is valid for all integers $k$ with $k \geq b$, taking care that the proof works for small values of $k$, including $k = b$.
7. Clearly identify the conclusion of the inductive step, such as by saying "this completes the inductive step."
8. After completing the basis step and the inductive step, state the conclusion, namely that by mathematical induction, $P(n)$ is true for all integers $n$ with $n \geq b$.

It is worthwhile to revisit each of the mathematical induction proofs in Examples 1–14 to see how these steps are completed. It will be helpful to follow these guidelines in the solutions of the exercises that ask for proofs by mathematical induction. The guidelines that we presented can be adapted for each of the variants of mathematical induction that we introduce in the exercises and later in this chapter.

## Exercises

**1.** There are infinitely many stations on a train route. Suppose that the train stops at the first station and suppose that if the train stops at a station, then it stops at the next station. Show that the train stops at all stations.

**2.** Suppose that you know that a golfer plays the first hole of a golf course with an infinite number of holes and that if this golfer plays one hole, then the golfer goes on to play the next hole. Prove that this golfer plays every hole on the course.

Use mathematical induction in Exercises 3–17 to prove summation formulae. Be sure to identify where you use the inductive hypothesis.

**3.** Let $P(n)$ be the statement that $1^2 + 2^2 + \cdots + n^2 = n(n + 1)(2n + 1)/6$ for the positive integer $n$.
   **a)** What is the statement $P(1)$?
   **b)** Show that $P(1)$ is true, completing the basis step of the proof.
   **c)** What is the inductive hypothesis?
   **d)** What do you need to prove in the inductive step?
   **e)** Complete the inductive step, identifying where you use the inductive hypothesis.

**f)** Explain why these steps show that this formula is true whenever $n$ is a positive integer.

**4.** Let $P(n)$ be the statement that $1^3 + 2^3 + \cdots + n^3 = (n(n + 1)/2)^2$ for the positive integer $n$.
   **a)** What is the statement $P(1)$?
   **b)** Show that $P(1)$ is true, completing the basis step of the proof.
   **c)** What is the inductive hypothesis?
   **d)** What do you need to prove in the inductive step?
   **e)** Complete the inductive step, identifying where you use the inductive hypothesis.
   **f)** Explain why these steps show that this formula is true whenever $n$ is a positive integer.

**5.** Prove that $1^2 + 3^2 + 5^2 + \cdots + (2n + 1)^2 = (n + 1)(2n + 1)(2n + 3)/3$ whenever $n$ is a nonnegative integer.

**6.** Prove that $1 \cdot 1! + 2 \cdot 2! + \cdots + n \cdot n! = (n + 1)! - 1$ whenever $n$ is a positive integer.

**7.** Prove that $3 + 3 \cdot 5 + 3 \cdot 5^2 + \cdots + 3 \cdot 5^n = 3(5^{n+1} - 1)/4$ whenever $n$ is a nonnegative integer.

**8.** Prove that $2 - 2 \cdot 7 + 2 \cdot 7^2 - \cdots + 2(-7)^n = (1 - (-7)^{n+1})/4$ whenever $n$ is a nonnegative integer.

**9. a)** Find a formula for the sum of the first $n$ even positive integers.

   **b)** Prove the formula that you conjectured in part (a).

**10. a)** Find a formula for

$$\frac{1}{1 \cdot 2} + \frac{1}{2 \cdot 3} + \cdots + \frac{1}{n(n+1)}$$

   by examining the values of this expression for small values of $n$.

   **b)** Prove the formula you conjectured in part (a).

**11. a)** Find a formula for

$$\frac{1}{2} + \frac{1}{4} + \frac{1}{8} + \cdots + \frac{1}{2^n}$$

   by examining the values of this expression for small values of $n$.

   **b)** Prove the formula you conjectured in part (a).

**12.** Prove that

$$\sum_{j=0}^{n} \left(-\frac{1}{2}\right)^j = \frac{2^{n+1} + (-1)^n}{3 \cdot 2^n}$$

   whenever $n$ is a nonnegative integer.

**13.** Prove that $1^2 - 2^2 + 3^2 - \cdots + (-1)^{n-1}n^2 = (-1)^{n-1} n(n+1)/2$ whenever $n$ is a positive integer.

**14.** Prove that for every positive integer $n$, $\sum_{k=1}^{n} k2^k = (n-1)2^{n+1} + 2$.

**15.** Prove that for every positive integer $n$,

$$1 \cdot 2 + 2 \cdot 3 + \cdots + n(n+1) = n(n+1)(n+2)/3.$$

**16.** Prove that for every positive integer $n$,

$$1 \cdot 2 \cdot 3 + 2 \cdot 3 \cdot 4 + \cdots + n(n+1)(n+2)$$
$$= n(n+1)(n+2)(n+3)/4.$$

**17.** Prove that $\sum_{j=1}^{n} j^4 = n(n+1)(2n+1)(3n^2+3n-1)/30$ whenever $n$ is a positive integer.

Use mathematical induction to prove the inequalities in Exercises 18–30.

**18.** Let $P(n)$ be the statement that $n! < n^n$, where $n$ is an integer greater than 1.

   **a)** What is the statement $P(2)$?

   **b)** Show that $P(2)$ is true, completing the basis step of the proof.

   **c)** What is the inductive hypothesis?

   **d)** What do you need to prove in the inductive step?

   **e)** Complete the inductive step.

   **f)** Explain why these steps show that this inequality is true whenever $n$ is an integer greater than 1.

**19.** Let $P(n)$ be the statement that

$$1 + \frac{1}{4} + \frac{1}{9} + \cdots + \frac{1}{n^2} < 2 - \frac{1}{n},$$

   where $n$ is an integer greater than 1.

   **a)** What is the statement $P(2)$?

   **b)** Show that $P(2)$ is true, completing the basis step of the proof.

   **c)** What is the inductive hypothesis?

   **d)** What do you need to prove in the inductive step?

   **e)** Complete the inductive step.

   **f)** Explain why these steps show that this inequality is true whenever $n$ is an integer greater than 1.

**20.** Prove that $3^n < n!$ if $n$ is an integer greater than 6.

**21.** Prove that $2^n > n^2$ if $n$ is an integer greater than 4.

**22.** For which nonnegative integers $n$ is $n^2 \le n!$? Prove your answer.

**23.** For which nonnegative integers $n$ is $2n + 3 \le 2^n$? Prove your answer.

**24.** Prove that $1/(2n) \le [1 \cdot 3 \cdot 5 \cdots (2n-1)]/(2 \cdot 4 \cdots 2n)$ whenever $n$ is a positive integer.

**\*25.** Prove that if $h > -1$, then $1 + nh \le (1+h)^n$ for all nonnegative integers $n$. This is called **Bernoulli's inequality**.

**\*26.** Suppose that $a$ and $b$ are real numbers with $0 < b < a$. Prove that if $n$ is a positive integer, then $a^n - b^n \le na^{n-1}(a-b)$.

**\*27.** Prove that for every positive integer $n$,

$$1 + \frac{1}{\sqrt{2}} + \frac{1}{\sqrt{3}} + \cdots + \frac{1}{\sqrt{n}} > 2(\sqrt{n+1} - 1).$$

**28.** Prove that $n^2 - 7n + 12$ is nonnegative whenever $n$ is an integer with $n \ge 3$.

In Exercises 29 and 30, $H_n$ denotes the $n$th harmonic number.

**\*29.** Prove that $H_{2^n} \le 1 + n$ whenever $n$ is a nonnegative integer.

**\*30.** Prove that

$$H_1 + H_2 + \cdots + H_n = (n+1)H_n - n.$$

Use mathematical induction in Exercises 31–37 to prove divisibility facts.

**31.** Prove that 2 divides $n^2 + n$ whenever $n$ is a positive integer.

**32.** Prove that 3 divides $n^3 + 2n$ whenever $n$ is a positive integer.

**33.** Prove that 5 divides $n^5 - n$ whenever $n$ is a nonnegative integer.

**34.** Prove that 6 divides $n^3 - n$ whenever $n$ is a nonnegative integer.

**\*35.** Prove that $n^2 - 1$ is divisible by 8 whenever $n$ is an odd positive integer.

**\*36.** Prove that 21 divides $4^{n+1} + 5^{2n-1}$ whenever $n$ is a positive integer.

**\*37.** Prove that if $n$ is a positive integer, then 133 divides $11^{n+1} + 12^{2n-1}$.

Use mathematical induction in Exercises 38–46 to prove results about sets.

**38.** Prove that if $A_1, A_2, \ldots, A_n$ and $B_1, B_2, \ldots, B_n$ are sets such that $A_j \subseteq B_j$ for $j = 1, 2, \ldots, n$, then

$$\bigcup_{j=1}^{n} A_j \subseteq \bigcup_{j=1}^{n} B_j.$$

**39.** Prove that if $A_1, A_2, \ldots, A_n$ and $B_1, B_2, \ldots, B_n$ are sets such that $A_j \subseteq B_j$ for $j = 1, 2, \ldots, n$, then

$$\bigcap_{j=1}^{n} A_j \subseteq \bigcap_{j=1}^{n} B_j.$$

**40.** Prove that if $A_1, A_2, \ldots, A_n$ and $B$ are sets, then

$$(A_1 \cap A_2 \cap \cdots \cap A_n) \cup B$$
$$= (A_1 \cup B) \cap (A_2 \cup B) \cap \cdots \cap (A_n \cup B).$$

**41.** Prove that if $A_1, A_2, \ldots, A_n$ and $B$ are sets, then

$$(A_1 \cup A_2 \cup \cdots \cup A_n) \cap B$$
$$= (A_1 \cap B) \cup (A_2 \cap B) \cup \cdots \cup (A_n \cap B).$$

**42.** Prove that if $A_1, A_2, \ldots, A_n$ and $B$ are sets, then

$$(A_1 - B) \cap (A_2 - B) \cap \cdots \cap (A_n - B)$$
$$= (A_1 \cap A_2 \cap \cdots \cap A_n) - B.$$

**43.** Prove that if $A_1, A_2, \ldots, A_n$ are subsets of a universal set $U$, then

$$\overline{\bigcup_{k=1}^{n} A_k} = \bigcap_{k=1}^{n} \overline{A_k}.$$

**44.** Prove that if $A_1, A_2, \ldots, A_n$ and $B$ are sets, then

$$(A_1 - B) \cup (A_2 - B) \cup \cdots \cup (A_n - B)$$
$$= (A_1 \cup A_2 \cup \cdots \cup A_n) - B.$$

**45.** Prove that a set with $n$ elements has $n(n-1)/2$ subsets containing exactly two elements whenever $n$ is an integer greater than or equal to 2.

**\*46.** Prove that a set with $n$ elements has $n(n-1)(n-2)/6$ subsets containing exactly three elements whenever $n$ is an integer greater than or equal to 3.

In Exercises 47 and 48 we consider the problem of placing towers along a straight road, so that every building on the road receives cellular service. Assume that a building receives cellular service if it is within one mile of a tower.

**47.** Devise a greedy algorithm that uses the minimum number of towers possible to provide cell service to $d$ buildings located at positions $x_1, x_2, \ldots, x_d$ from the start of the road. [*Hint:* At each step, go as far as possible along the road before adding a tower so as not to leave any buildings without coverage.]

**\*48.** Use mathematical induction to prove that the algorithm you devised in Exercise 47 produces an optimal solution, that is, that it uses the fewest towers possible to provide cellular service to all buildings.

Exercises 49–51 present incorrect proofs using mathematical induction. You will need to identify an error in reasoning in each exercise.

**49.** What is wrong with this "proof" that all horses are the same color?
Let $P(n)$ be the proposition that all the horses in a set of $n$ horses are the same color.

*Basis Step:* Clearly, $P(1)$ is true.

*Inductive Step:* Assume that $P(k)$ is true, so that all the horses in any set of $k$ horses are the same color. Consider any $k + 1$ horses; number these as horses $1, 2, 3, \ldots, k, k+1$. Now the first $k$ of these horses all must have the same color, and the last $k$ of these must also have the same color. Because the set of the first $k$ horses and the set of the last $k$ horses overlap, all $k + 1$ must be the same color. This shows that $P(k + 1)$ is true and finishes the proof by induction.

**50.** What is wrong with this "proof"?
*"Theorem"* For every positive integer $n$, $\sum_{i=1}^{n} i = (n + \frac{1}{2})^2/2$.

*Basis Step:* The formula is true for $n = 1$.

*Inductive Step:* Suppose that $\sum_{i=1}^{n} i = (n + \frac{1}{2})^2/2$. Then $\sum_{i=1}^{n+1} i = (\sum_{i=1}^{n} i) + (n + 1)$. By the inductive hypothesis, $\sum_{i=1}^{n+1} i = (n + \frac{1}{2})^2/2 + n + 1 = (n^2 + n + \frac{1}{4})/2 + n + 1 = (n^2 + 3n + \frac{9}{4})/2 = (n + \frac{3}{2})^2/2 = [(n + 1) + \frac{1}{2}]^2/2$, completing the inductive step.

**51.** What is wrong with this "proof"?
*"Theorem"* For every positive integer $n$, if $x$ and $y$ are positive integers with $\max(x, y) = n$, then $x = y$.

*Basis Step:* Suppose that $n = 1$. If $\max(x, y) = 1$ and $x$ and $y$ are positive integers, we have $x = 1$ and $y = 1$.

*Inductive Step:* Let $k$ be a positive integer. Assume that whenever $\max(x, y) = k$ and $x$ and $y$ are positive integers, then $x = y$. Now let $\max(x, y) = k + 1$, where $x$ and $y$ are positive integers. Then $\max(x - 1, y - 1) = k$, so by the inductive hypothesis, $x - 1 = y - 1$. It follows that $x = y$, completing the inductive step.

**52.** Suppose that $m$ and $n$ are positive integers with $m > n$ and $f$ is a function from $\{1, 2, \ldots, m\}$ to $\{1, 2, \ldots, n\}$. Use mathematical induction on the variable $n$ to show that $f$ is not one-to-one.

**\*53.** Use mathematical induction to show that $n$ people can divide a cake (where each person gets one or more separate pieces of the cake) so that the cake is divided fairly, that is, in the sense that each person thinks he or she got at least $(1/n)$th of the cake. [*Hint:* For the inductive step, take a fair division of the cake among the first $k$ people, have each person divide their share into what this person thinks are $k + 1$ equal portions, and then have the $(k + 1)$st person select a portion from each of the $k$ people. When showing this produces a fair division for $k + 1$ people, suppose that person $k + 1$ thinks that person $i$ got $p_i$ of the cake where $\sum_{i=1}^{k} p_i = 1$.]

**54.** Use mathematical induction to show that given a set of $n + 1$ positive integers, none exceeding $2n$, there is at least one integer in this set that divides another integer in the set.

**\*55.** A knight on a chessboard can move one space horizontally (in either direction) and two spaces vertically (in either direction) or two spaces horizontally (in either direction) and one space vertically (in either direction). Suppose that we have an infinite chessboard, made up of all squares $(m, n)$ where $m$ and $n$ are nonnegative integers that denote the row number and the column number of the square, respectively. Use mathematical induction to show that a knight starting at $(0, 0)$ can visit every square using a finite sequence of moves. [*Hint:* Use induction on the variable $s = m + n$.]

**56.** Suppose that
$$\mathbf{A} = \begin{bmatrix} a & 0 \\ 0 & b \end{bmatrix},$$
where $a$ and $b$ are real numbers. Show that
$$\mathbf{A}^n = \begin{bmatrix} a^n & 0 \\ 0 & b^n \end{bmatrix}$$
for every positive integer $n$.

**57.** (*Requires calculus*) Use mathematical induction to prove that the derivative of $f(x) = x^n$ equals $nx^{n-1}$ whenever $n$ is a positive integer. (For the inductive step, use the product rule for derivatives.)

**58.** Suppose that $\mathbf{A}$ and $\mathbf{B}$ are square matrices with the property $\mathbf{AB} = \mathbf{BA}$. Show that $\mathbf{AB}^n = \mathbf{B}^n\mathbf{A}$ for every positive integer $n$.

**59.** Suppose that $m$ is a positive integer. Use mathematical induction to prove that if $a$ and $b$ are integers with $a \equiv b \pmod{m}$, then $a^k \equiv b^k \pmod{m}$ whenever $k$ is a nonnegative integer.

**60.** Use mathematical induction to show that $\neg(p_1 \vee p_2 \vee \cdots \vee p_n)$ is equivalent to $\neg p_1 \wedge \neg p_2 \wedge \cdots \wedge \neg p_n$ whenever $p_1, p_2, \ldots, p_n$ are propositions.

**\*61.** Show that
$$[(p_1 \rightarrow p_2) \wedge (p_2 \rightarrow p_3) \wedge \cdots \wedge (p_{n-1} \rightarrow p_n)]$$
$$\rightarrow [(p_1 \wedge p_2 \wedge \cdots \wedge p_{n-1}) \rightarrow p_n]$$
is a tautology whenever $p_1, p_2, \ldots, p_n$ are propositions, where $n \geq 2$.

**\*62.** Show that $n$ lines separate the plane into $(n^2 + n + 2)/2$ regions if no two of these lines are parallel and no three pass through a common point.

**\*\*63.** Let $a_1, a_2, \ldots, a_n$ be positive real numbers. The **arithmetic mean** of these numbers is defined by
$$A = (a_1 + a_2 + \cdots + a_n)/n,$$
and the **geometric mean** of these numbers is defined by
$$G = (a_1 a_2 \cdots a_n)^{1/n}.$$
Use mathematical induction to prove that $A \geq G$.

**64.** Use mathematical induction to prove Lemma 3 of Section 4.3, which states that if $p$ is a prime and $p \mid a_1 a_2 \cdots a_n$, where $a_i$ is an integer for $i = 1, 2, 3, \ldots, n$, then $p \mid a_i$ for some integer $i$.

**65.** Show that if $n$ is a positive integer, then
$$\sum_{\{a_1,\ldots,a_k\} \subseteq \{1,2,\ldots,n\}} \frac{1}{a_1 a_2 \cdots a_k} = n.$$
(Here the sum is over all nonempty subsets of the set of the $n$ smallest positive integers.)

**\*66.** Use the well-ordering property to show that the following form of mathematical induction is a valid method to prove that $P(n)$ is true for all positive integers $n$.

*Basis Step:* $P(1)$ and $P(2)$ are true.

*Inductive Step:* For each positive integer $k$, if $P(k)$ and $P(k + 1)$ are both true, then $P(k + 2)$ is true.

**67.** Show that if $A_1, A_2, \ldots, A_n$ are sets where $n \geq 2$, and for all pairs of integers $i$ and $j$ with $1 \leq i < j \leq n$ either $A_i$ is a subset of $A_j$ or $A_j$ is a subset of $A_i$, then there is an integer $i$, $1 \leq i \leq n$ such that $A_i$ is a subset of $A_j$ for all integers $j$ with $1 \leq j \leq n$.

**\*68.** A guest at a party is a **celebrity** if this person is known by every other guest, but knows none of them. There is at most one celebrity at a party, for if there were two, they would know each other. A particular party may have no celebrity. Your assignment is to find the celebrity, if one exists, at a party, by asking only one type of question—asking a guest whether they know a second guest. Everyone must answer your questions truthfully. That is, if Alice and Bob are two people at the party, you can ask Alice whether she knows Bob; she must answer correctly. Use mathematical induction to show that if there are $n$ people at the party, then you can find the celebrity, if there is one, with $3(n - 1)$ questions. [*Hint:* First ask a question to eliminate one person as a celebrity. Then use the inductive hypothesis to identify a potential celebrity. Finally, ask two more questions to determine whether that person is actually a celebrity.]

Suppose there are $n$ people in a group, each aware of a scandal no one else in the group knows about. These people communicate by telephone; when two people in the group talk, they share information about all scandals each knows about. For example, on the first call, two people share information, so by the end of the call, each of these people knows about two scandals. The **gossip problem** asks for $G(n)$, the minimum number of telephone calls that are needed for all $n$ people to learn about all the scandals. Exercises 69–71 deal with the gossip problem.

**69.** Find $G(1)$, $G(2)$, $G(3)$, and $G(4)$.

**70.** Use mathematical induction to prove that $G(n) \leq 2n - 4$ for $n \geq 4$. [*Hint:* In the inductive step, have a new person call a particular person at the start and at the end.]

**\*\*71.** Prove that $G(n) = 2n - 4$ for $n \geq 4$.

**\*72.** Show that it is possible to arrange the numbers $1, 2, \ldots, n$ in a row so that the average of any two of these numbers never appears between them. [*Hint:* Show that it suffices to prove this fact when $n$ is a power of 2. Then use mathematical induction to prove the result when $n$ is a power of 2.]

**\*73.** Show that if $I_1, I_2, \ldots, I_n$ is a collection of open intervals on the real number line, $n \geq 2$, and every pair of these intervals has a nonempty intersection, that is, $I_i \cap I_j \neq \emptyset$ whenever $1 \leq i \leq n$ and $1 \leq j \leq n$, then the intersection of all these sets is nonempty, that is, $I_1 \cap I_2 \cap \cdots \cap I_n \neq \emptyset$. (Recall that an **open interval** is the set of real numbers $x$ with $a < x < b$, where $a$ and $b$ are real numbers with $a < b$.)

Sometimes we cannot use mathematical induction to prove a result we believe to be true, but we can use mathematical induction to prove a stronger result. Because the inductive hypothesis of the stronger result provides more to work with, this process is called **inductive loading**. We use inductive loading in Exercise 74.

**74.** Suppose that we want to prove that

$$\frac{1}{2} \cdot \frac{3}{4} \cdots \frac{2n-1}{2n} < \frac{1}{\sqrt{3n}}$$

for all positive integers $n$.

**a)** Show that if we try to prove this inequality using mathematical induction, the basis step works, but the inductive step fails.

**b)** Show that mathematical induction can be used to prove the stronger inequality

$$\frac{1}{2} \cdot \frac{3}{4} \cdots \frac{2n-1}{2n} < \frac{1}{\sqrt{3n+1}}$$

for all integers greater than 1, which, together with a verification for the case where $n = 1$, establishes the weaker inequality we originally tried to prove using mathematical induction.

**75.** Let $n$ be an even positive integer. Show that when $n$ people stand in a yard at mutually distinct distances and each

person throws a pie at their nearest neighbor, it is possible that everyone is hit by a pie.

**76.** Construct a tiling using right triominoes of the $4 \times 4$ checkerboard with the square in the upper left corner removed.

**77.** Construct a tiling using right triominoes of the $8 \times 8$ checkerboard with the square in the upper left corner removed.

**78.** Prove or disprove that all checkerboards of these shapes can be completely covered using right triominoes whenever $n$ is a positive integer.

**a)** $3 \times 2^n$            **b)** $6 \times 2^n$
**c)** $3^n \times 3^n$          **d)** $6^n \times 6^n$

**\*79.** Show that a three-dimensional $2^n \times 2^n \times 2^n$ checkerboard with one $1 \times 1 \times 1$ cube missing can be completely covered by $2 \times 2 \times 2$ cubes with one $1 \times 1 \times 1$ cube removed.

**\*80.** Show that an $n \times n$ checkerboard with one square removed can be completely covered using right triominoes if $n > 5$, $n$ is odd, and $3 \nmid n$.

**81.** Show that a $5 \times 5$ checkerboard with a corner square removed can be tiled using right triominoes.

**\*82.** Find a $5 \times 5$ checkerboard with a square removed that cannot be tiled using right triominoes. Prove that such a tiling does not exist for this board.

**83.** Use the principle of mathematical induction to show that $P(n)$ is true for $n = b, b + 1, b + 2, \ldots$, where $b$ is an integer, if $P(b)$ is true and the conditional statement $P(k) \rightarrow P(k + 1)$ is true for all integers $k$ with $k \geq b$.

# 5.2    Strong Induction and Well-Ordering

## Introduction

In Section 5.1 we introduced mathematical induction and we showed how to use it to prove a variety of theorems. In this section we will introduce another form of mathematical induction, called **strong induction**, which can often be used when we cannot easily prove a result using mathematical induction. The basis step of a proof by strong induction is the same as a proof of the same result using mathematical induction. That is, in a strong induction proof that $P(n)$ is true for all positive integers $n$, the basis step shows that $P(1)$ is true. However, the inductive steps in these two proof methods are different. In a proof by mathematical induction, the inductive step shows that if the inductive hypothesis $P(k)$ is true, then $P(k + 1)$ is also true. In a proof by strong induction, the inductive step shows that if $P(j)$ is true for all positive integers not exceeding $k$, then $P(k + 1)$ is true. That is, for the inductive hypothesis we assume that $P(j)$ is true for $j = 1, 2, \ldots, k$.

The validity of both mathematical induction and strong induction follow from the well-ordering property in Appendix 1. In fact, mathematical induction, strong induction, and well-ordering are all equivalent principles (as shown in Exercises 41, 42, and 43). That is, the validity of each can be proved from either of the other two. This means that a proof using one of these two principles can be rewritten as a proof using either of the other two principles. Just as it is sometimes the case that it is much easier to see how to prove a result using strong induction rather than mathematical induction, it is sometimes easier to use well-ordering than one of the two forms of mathematical induction. In this section we will give some examples of how the well-ordering property can be used to prove theorems.

# Strong Induction

Before we illustrate how to use strong induction, we state this principle again.

*STRONG INDUCTION*   To prove that $P(n)$ is true for all positive integers $n$, where $P(n)$ is a propositional function, we complete two steps:

*BASIS STEP:*   We verify that the proposition $P(1)$ is true.

*INDUCTIVE STEP:*   We show that the conditional statement $[P(1) \land P(2) \land \cdots \land P(k)] \to P(k + 1)$ is true for all positive integers $k$.

Note that when we use strong induction to prove that $P(n)$ is true for all positive integers $n$, our inductive hypothesis is the assumption that $P(j)$ is true for $j = 1, 2, \ldots, k$. That is, the inductive hypothesis includes all $k$ statements $P(1), P(2), \ldots, P(k)$. Because we can use all $k$ statements $P(1), P(2), \ldots, P(k)$ to prove $P(k + 1)$, rather than just the statement $P(k)$ as in a proof by mathematical induction, strong induction is a more flexible proof technique. Because of this, some mathematicians prefer to always use strong induction instead of mathematical induction, even when a proof by mathematical induction is easy to find.

You may be surprised that mathematical induction and strong induction are equivalent. That is, each can be shown to be a valid proof technique assuming that the other is valid. In particular, any proof using mathematical induction can also be considered to be a proof by strong induction because the inductive hypothesis of a proof by mathematical induction is part of the inductive hypothesis in a proof by strong induction. That is, if we can complete the inductive step of a proof using mathematical induction by showing that $P(k + 1)$ follows from $P(k)$ for every positive integer $k$, then it also follows that $P(k + 1)$ follows from all the statements $P(1)$, $P(2), \ldots, P(k)$, because we are assuming that not only $P(k)$ is true, but also more, namely, that the $k - 1$ statements $P(1), P(2), \ldots, P(k - 1)$ are true. However, it is much more awkward to convert a proof by strong induction into a proof using the principle of mathematical induction. (See Exercise 42.)

Strong induction is sometimes called the **second principle of mathematical induction** or **complete induction**. When the terminology "complete induction" is used, the principle of mathematical induction is called **incomplete induction**, a technical term that is a somewhat unfortunate choice because there is nothing incomplete about the principle of mathematical induction; after all, it is a valid proof technique.

STRONG INDUCTION AND THE INFINITE LADDER   To better understand strong induction, consider the infinite ladder in Section 5.1. Strong induction tells us that we can reach all rungs if

1.  we can reach the first rung, and
2.  for every integer $k$, if we can reach all the first $k$ rungs, then we can reach the $(k + 1)$st rung.

That is, if $P(n)$ is the statement that we can reach the $n$th rung of the ladder, by strong induction we know that $P(n)$ is true for all positive integers $n$, because (1) tells us $P(1)$ is true, completing the basis step and (2) tells us that $P(1) \land P(2) \land \cdots \land P(k)$ implies $P(k + 1)$, completing the inductive step.

Example 1 illustrates how strong induction can help us prove a result that cannot easily be proved using the principle of mathematical induction.

**EXAMPLE 1**     Suppose we can reach the first and second rungs of an infinite ladder, and we know that if we can reach a rung, then we can reach two rungs higher. Can we prove that we can reach every rung using the principle of mathematical induction? Can we prove that we can reach every rung using strong induction?

*Solution:* We first try to prove this result using the principle of mathematical induction.

*BASIS STEP:*   The basis step of such a proof holds; here it simply verifies that we can reach the first rung.

*ATTEMPTED INDUCTIVE STEP:*   The inductive hypothesis is the statement that we can reach the $k$th rung of the ladder. To complete the inductive step, we need to show that if we assume the inductive hypothesis for the positive integer $k$, namely, if we assume that we can reach the $k$th rung of the ladder, then we can show that we can reach the $(k + 1)$st rung of the ladder. However, there is no obvious way to complete this inductive step because we do not know from the given information that we can reach the $(k + 1)$st rung from the $k$th rung. After all, we only know that if we can reach a rung we can reach the rung two higher.

Now consider a proof using strong induction.

*BASIS STEP:*   The basis step is the same as before; it simply verifies that we can reach the first rung.

*INDUCTIVE STEP:*   The inductive hypothesis states that we can reach each of the first $k$ rungs. To complete the inductive step, we need to show that if we assume that the inductive hypothesis is true, that is, if we can reach each of the first $k$ rungs, then we can reach the $(k + 1)$st rung. We already know that we can reach the second rung. We can complete the inductive step by noting that as long as $k \geq 2$, we can reach the $(k + 1)$st rung from the $(k - 1)$st rung because we know we can climb two rungs from a rung we can already reach, and because $k - 1 \leq k$, by the inductive hypothesis we can reach the $(k - 1)$st rung. This completes the inductive step and finishes the proof by strong induction.

We have proved that if we can reach the first two rungs of an infinite ladder and for every positive integer $k$ if we can reach all the first $k$ rungs then we can reach the $(k + 1)$st rung, then we can reach all rungs of the ladder.   ◀

## Examples of Proofs Using Strong Induction

Now that we have both mathematical induction and strong induction, how do we decide which method to apply in a particular situation? Although there is no cut-and-dried answer, we can supply some useful pointers. In practice, you should use mathematical induction when it is straightforward to prove that $P(k) \rightarrow P(k + 1)$ is true for all positive integers $k$. This is the case for all the proofs in the examples in Section 5.1. In general, you should restrict your use of the principle of mathematical induction to such scenarios. Unless you can clearly see that the inductive step of a proof by mathematical induction goes through, you should attempt a proof by strong induction. That is, use strong induction and not mathematical induction when you see how to prove that $P(k + 1)$ is true from the assumption that $P(j)$ is true for all positive integers $j$ not exceeding $k$, but you cannot see how to prove that $P(k + 1)$ follows from just $P(k)$. Keep this in mind as you examine the proofs in this section. For each of these proofs, consider why strong induction works better than mathematical induction.

We will illustrate how strong induction is employed in Examples 2–4. In these examples, we will prove a diverse collection of results. Pay particular attention to the inductive step in each of these examples, where we show that a result $P(k + 1)$ follows under the assumption that $P(j)$ holds for all positive integers $j$ not exceeding $k$, where $P(n)$ is a propositional function.

We begin with one of the most prominent uses of strong induction, the part of the fundamental theorem of arithmetic that tells us that every positive integer can be written as the product of primes.

**EXAMPLE 2**

Show that if $n$ is an integer greater than 1, then $n$ can be written as the product of primes.

*Solution:* Let $P(n)$ be the proposition that $n$ can be written as the product of primes.

*BASIS STEP:* $P(2)$ is true, because 2 can be written as the product of one prime, itself. (Note that $P(2)$ is the first case we need to establish.)

*INDUCTIVE STEP:* The inductive hypothesis is the assumption that $P(j)$ is true for all integers $j$ with $2 \leq j \leq k$, that is, the assumption that $j$ can be written as the product of primes whenever $j$ is a positive integer at least 2 and not exceeding $k$. To complete the inductive step, it must be shown that $P(k + 1)$ is true under this assumption, that is, that $k + 1$ is the product of primes.

There are two cases to consider, namely, when $k + 1$ is prime and when $k + 1$ is composite. If $k + 1$ is prime, we immediately see that $P(k + 1)$ is true. Otherwise, $k + 1$ is composite and can be written as the product of two positive integers $a$ and $b$ with $2 \leq a \leq b < k + 1$. Because both $a$ and $b$ are integers at least 2 and not exceeding $k$, we can use the inductive hypothesis to write both $a$ and $b$ as the product of primes. Thus, if $k + 1$ is composite, it can be written as the product of primes, namely, those primes in the factorization of $a$ and those in the factorization of $b$. ◀

*Remark:* Because 1 can be thought of as the *empty* product of no primes, we could have started the proof in Example 2 with $P(1)$ as the basis step. We chose not to do so because many people find this confusing.

Example 2 completes the proof of the fundamental theorem of arithmetic, which asserts that every nonnegative integer can be written uniquely as the product of primes in nondecreasing order. We showed in Section 4.3 that an integer has at most one such factorization into primes. Example 2 shows there is at least one such factorization.

Next, we show how strong induction can be used to prove that a player has a winning strategy in a game.

**EXAMPLE 3**

Consider a game in which two players take turns removing any positive number of matches they want from one of two piles of matches. The player who removes the last match wins the game. Show that if the two piles contain the same number of matches initially, the second player can always guarantee a win.

*Solution:* Let $n$ be the number of matches in each pile. We will use strong induction to prove $P(n)$, the statement that the second player can win when there are initially $n$ matches in each pile.

*BASIS STEP:* When $n = 1$, the first player has only one choice, removing one match from one of the piles, leaving a single pile with a single match, which the second player can remove to win the game.

*INDUCTIVE STEP:* The inductive hypothesis is the statement that $P(j)$ is true for all $j$ with $1 \leq j \leq k$, that is, the assumption that the second player can always win whenever there are $j$ matches, where $1 \leq j \leq k$ in each of the two piles at the start of the game. We need to show that $P(k + 1)$ is true, that is, that the second player can win when there are initially $k + 1$ matches in each pile, under the assumption that $P(j)$ is true for $j = 1, 2, \ldots, k$. So suppose that there are $k + 1$ matches in each of the two piles at the start of the game and suppose that the first player removes $r$ matches $(1 \leq r \leq k)$ from one of the piles, leaving $k + 1 - r$ matches in this pile. By removing the same number of matches from the other pile, the second player creates the situation where there are two piles each with $k + 1 - r$ matches. Because $1 \leq k + 1 - r \leq k$, we can now use the inductive hypothesis to conclude that the second player can always win. We complete the proof by noting that if the first player removes all $k + 1$ matches from one of the piles, the second player can win by removing all the remaining matches. ◄

Using the principle of mathematical induction, instead of strong induction, to prove the results in Examples 2 and 3 is difficult. However, as Example 4 shows, some results can be readily proved using either the principle of mathematical induction or strong induction.

Before we present Example 4, note that we can slightly modify strong induction to handle a wider variety of situations. In particular, we can adapt strong induction to handle cases where the inductive step is valid only for integers greater than a particular integer. Let $b$ be a fixed integer and $j$ a fixed positive integer. The form of strong induction we need tells us that $P(n)$ is true for all integers $n$ with $n \geq b$ if we can complete these two steps:

*BASIS STEP:* We verify that the propositions $P(b)$, $P(b + 1)$, ..., $P(b + j)$ are true.

*INDUCTIVE STEP:* We show that $[P(b) \wedge P(b + 1) \wedge \cdots \wedge P(k)] \rightarrow P(k + 1)$ is true for every integer $k \geq b + j$.

We will use this alternative form in the strong induction proof in Example 4. That this alternative form is equivalent to strong induction is left as Exercise 28.

**EXAMPLE 4**  Prove that every amount of postage of 12 cents or more can be formed using just 4-cent and 5-cent stamps.

*Solution:* We will prove this result using the principle of mathematical induction. Then we will present a proof using strong induction. Let $P(n)$ be the statement that postage of $n$ cents can be formed using 4-cent and 5-cent stamps.

We begin by using the principle of mathematical induction.

*BASIS STEP:* Postage of 12 cents can be formed using three 4-cent stamps.

*INDUCTIVE STEP:* The inductive hypothesis is the statement that $P(k)$ is true. That is, under this hypothesis, postage of $k$ cents can be formed using 4-cent and 5-cent stamps. To complete the inductive step, we need to show that when we assume $P(k)$ is true, then $P(k + 1)$ is also true where $k \geq 12$. That is, we need to show that if we can form postage of $k$ cents, then we can form postage of $k + 1$ cents. So, assume the inductive hypothesis is true; that is, assume that we can form postage of $k$ cents using 4-cent and 5-cent stamps. We consider two cases, when at least one 4-cent stamp has been used and when no 4-cent stamps have been used. First, suppose that at least one 4-cent stamp was used to form postage of $k$ cents. Then we can replace this stamp with a 5-cent stamp to form postage of $k + 1$ cents. But if no 4-cent stamps were used, we can form postage of $k$ cents using only 5-cent stamps. Moreover, because $k \geq 12$, we needed at least three 5-cent stamps to form postage of $k$ cents. So, we can replace three 5-cent stamps with four 4-cent stamps to form postage of $k + 1$ cents. This completes the inductive step.

Because we have completed the basis step and the inductive step, we know that $P(n)$ is true for all $n \geq 12$. That is, we can form postage of $n$ cents, where $n \geq 12$ using just 4-cent and 5-cent stamps. This completes the proof by mathematical induction.

Next, we will use strong induction to prove the same result. In this proof, in the basis step we show that $P(12)$, $P(13)$, $P(14)$, and $P(15)$ are true, that is, that postage of 12, 13, 14, or 15 cents can be formed using just 4-cent and 5-cent stamps. In the inductive step we show how to get postage of $k + 1$ cents for $k \geq 15$ from postage of $k - 3$ cents.

*BASIS STEP:* We can form postage of 12, 13, 14, and 15 cents using three 4-cent stamps, two 4-cent stamps and one 5-cent stamp, one 4-cent stamp and two 5-cent stamps, and three 5-cent stamps, respectively. This shows that $P(12)$, $P(13)$, $P(14)$, and $P(15)$ are true. This completes the basis step.

*INDUCTIVE STEP:* The inductive hypothesis is the statement that $P(j)$ is true for $12 \leq j \leq k$, where $k$ is an integer with $k \geq 15$. To complete the inductive step, we assume that we can form postage of $j$ cents, where $12 \leq j \leq k$. We need to show that under the assumption that $P(k+1)$ is true, we can also form postage of $k+1$ cents. Using the inductive hypothesis, we can assume that $P(k-3)$ is true because $k-3 \geq 12$, that is, we can form postage of $k-3$ cents using just 4-cent and 5-cent stamps. To form postage of $k+1$ cents, we need only add another 4-cent stamp to the stamps we used to form postage of $k-3$ cents. That is, we have shown that if the inductive hypothesis is true, then $P(k+1)$ is also true. This completes the inductive step.

Because we have completed the basis step and the inductive step of a strong induction proof, we know by strong induction that $P(n)$ is true for all integers $n$ with $n \geq 12$. That is, we know that every postage of $n$ cents, where $n$ is at least 12, can be formed using 4-cent and 5-cent stamps. This finishes the proof by strong induction.

(There are other ways to approach this problem besides those described here. Can you find a solution that does not use mathematical induction?) ◄

## Using Strong Induction in Computational Geometry

Our next example of strong induction will come from **computational geometry**, the part of discrete mathematics that studies computational problems involving geometric objects. Computational geometry is used extensively in computer graphics, computer games, robotics, scientific calculations, and a vast array of other areas. Before we can present this result, we introduce some terminology, possibly familiar from earlier studies in geometry.

A **polygon** is a closed geometric figure consisting of a sequence of line segments $s_1, s_2, \ldots, s_n$, called **sides**. Each pair of consecutive sides, $s_i$ and $s_{i+1}$, $i = 1, 2, \ldots, n-1$, as well as the last side $s_n$ and the first side $s_1$, of the polygon meet at a common endpoint, called a **vertex**. A polygon is called **simple** if no two nonconsecutive sides intersect. Every simple polygon divides the plane into two regions: its **interior**, consisting of the points inside the curve, and its **exterior**, consisting of the points outside the curve. This last fact is surprisingly complicated to prove. It is a special case of the famous Jordan curve theorem, which tells us that every simple curve divides the plane into two regions; see [Or00], for example.

A polygon is called **convex** if every line segment connecting two points in the interior of the polygon lies entirely inside the polygon. (A polygon that is not convex is said to be **nonconvex**.) Figure 1 displays some polygons; polygons (a) and (b) are convex, but polygons (c) and (d) are not. A **diagonal** of a simple polygon is a line segment connecting two nonconsecutive vertices of the polygon, and a diagonal is called an **interior diagonal** if it lies entirely inside the polygon, except for its endpoints. For example, in polygon (d), the line segment connecting $a$ and $f$ is an interior diagonal, but the line segment connecting $a$ and $d$ is a diagonal that is not an interior diagonal.

One of the most basic operations of computational geometry involves dividing a simple polygon into triangles by adding nonintersecting diagonals. This process is called **triangulation**. Note that a simple polygon can have many different triangulations, as shown in Figure 2. Perhaps the most basic fact in computational geometry is that it is possible to triangulate every simple

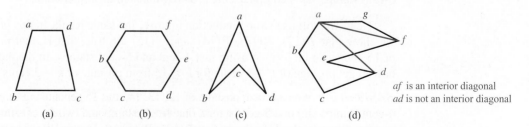

*af* is an interior diagonal
*ad* is not an interior diagonal

**FIGURE 1** **Convex and Nonconvex Polygons.**

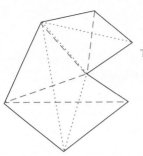

Two different triangulations of a simple polygon with seven sides into five triangles, shown with dotted lines and with dashed lines, respectively

**FIGURE 2   Triangulations of a Polygon.**

polygon, as we state in Theorem 1. Furthermore, this theorem tells us that every triangulation of a simple polygon with $n$ sides includes $n - 2$ triangles.

**THEOREM 1**  A simple polygon with $n$ sides, where $n$ is an integer with $n \geq 3$, can be triangulated into $n - 2$ triangles.

It seems obvious that we should be able to triangulate a simple polygon by successively adding interior diagonals. Consequently, a proof by strong induction seems promising. However, such a proof requires this crucial lemma.

**LEMMA 1**  Every simple polygon with at least four sides has an interior diagonal.

Although Lemma 1 seems particularly simple, it is surprisingly tricky to prove. In fact, as recently as 30 years ago, a variety of incorrect proofs thought to be correct were commonly seen in books and articles. We defer the proof of Lemma 1 until after we prove Theorem 1. It is not uncommon to prove a theorem pending the later proof of an important lemma.

*Proof (of Theorem 1):*  We will prove this result using strong induction. Let $T(n)$ be the statement that every simple polygon with $n$ sides can be triangulated into $n - 2$ triangles.

*BASIS STEP:* $T(3)$ is true because a simple polygon with three sides is a triangle. We do not need to add any diagonals to triangulate a triangle; it is already triangulated into one triangle, itself. Consequently, every simple polygon with $n = 3$ has can be triangulated into $n - 2 = 3 - 2 = 1$ triangle.

*INDUCTIVE STEP:*  For the inductive hypothesis, we assume that $T(j)$ is true for all integers $j$ with $3 \leq j \leq k$. That is, we assume that we can triangulate a simple polygon with $j$ sides into $j - 2$ triangles whenever $3 \leq j \leq k$. To complete the inductive step, we must show that when we assume the inductive hypothesis, $P(k + 1)$ is true, that is, that every simple polygon with $k + 1$ sides can be triangulated into $(k + 1) - 2 = k - 1$ triangles.

So, suppose that we have a simple polygon $P$ with $k + 1$ sides. Because $k + 1 \geq 4$, Lemma 1 tells us that $P$ has an interior diagonal $ab$. Now, $ab$ splits $P$ into two simple polygons $Q$, with $s$ sides, and $R$, with $t$ sides. The sides of $Q$ and $R$ are the sides of $P$, together with the side $ab$, which is a side of both $Q$ and $R$. Note that $3 \leq s \leq k$ and $3 \leq t \leq k$ because both $Q$ and $R$ have at least one fewer side than $P$ does (after all, each of these is formed from $P$ by deleting at least two sides and replacing these sides by the diagonal $ab$). Furthermore, the number of sides of $P$ is two less than the sum of the numbers of sides of $Q$ and the number of

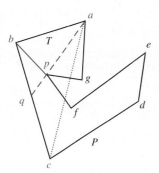

T is the triangle $abc$

$p$ is the vertex of P inside T such that the $\angle bap$ is smallest

$bp$ must be an interior diagonal of P

**FIGURE 3** **Constructing an Interior Diagonal of a Simple Polygon.**

sides of $R$, because each side of $P$ is a side of either $Q$ or of $R$, but not both, and the diagonal $ab$ is a side of both $Q$ and $R$, but not $P$. That is, $k + 1 = s + t - 2$.

We now use the inductive hypothesis. Because both $3 \le s \le k$ and $3 \le t \le k$, by the inductive hypothesis we can triangulate $Q$ and $R$ into $s - 2$ and $t - 2$ triangles, respectively. Next, note that these triangulations together produce a triangulation of $P$. (Each diagonal added to triangulate one of these smaller polygons is also a diagonal of $P$.) Consequently, we can triangulate $P$ into a total of $(s - 2) + (t - 2) = s + t - 4 = (k + 1) - 2$ triangles. This completes the proof by strong induction. That is, we have shown that every simple polygon with $n$ sides, where $n \ge 3$, can be triangulated into $n - 2$ triangles. ◁

We now return to our proof of Lemma 1. We present a proof published by Chung-Wu Ho [Ho75]. Note that although this proof may be omitted without loss of continuity, it does provide a correct proof of a result proved incorrectly by many mathematicians.

*Proof:* Suppose that $P$ is a simple polygon drawn in the plane. Furthermore, suppose that $b$ is the point of $P$ or in the interior of $P$ with the least $y$-coordinate among the vertices with the smallest $x$-coordinate. Then $b$ must be a vertex of $P$, for if it is an interior point, there would have to be a vertex of $P$ with a smaller $x$-coordinate. Two other vertices each share an edge with $b$, say $a$ and $c$. It follows that the angle in the interior of $P$ formed by $ab$ and $bc$ must be less than 180 degrees (otherwise, there would be points of $P$ with smaller $x$-coordinates than $b$).

Now let $T$ be the triangle $\triangle abc$. If there are no vertices of $P$ on or inside $T$, we can connect $a$ and $c$ to obtain an interior diagonal. On the other hand, if there are vertices of $P$ inside $T$, we will find a vertex $p$ of $P$ on or inside $T$ such that $bp$ is an interior diagonal. (This is the tricky part. Ho noted that in many published proofs of this lemma a vertex $p$ was found such that $bp$ was not necessarily an interior diagonal of $P$. See Exercise 21.) The key is to select a vertex $p$ such that the angle $\angle bap$ is smallest. To see this, note that the ray starting at $a$ and passing through $p$ hits the line segment $bc$ at a point, say $q$. It then follows that the triangle $\triangle baq$ cannot contain any vertices of $P$ in its interior. Hence, we can connect $b$ and $p$ to produce an interior diagonal of $P$. Locating this vertex $p$ is illustrated in Figure 3. ◁

## Proofs Using the Well-Ordering Property

The validity of both the principle of mathematical induction and strong induction follows from a fundamental axiom of the set of integers, the **well-ordering property** (see Appendix 1). The well-ordering property states that every nonempty set of nonnegative integers has a least element. We will show how the well-ordering property can be used directly in proofs. Furthermore, it can be shown (see Exercises 41, 42, and 43) that the well-ordering property, the principle of mathematical induction, and strong induction are all equivalent. That is, the validity of each of these three proof techniques implies the validity of the other two techniques. In Section 5.1 we showed that the principle of mathematical induction follows from the well-ordering property. The other parts of this equivalence are left as Exercises 31, 42, and 43.

THE WELL-ORDERING PROPERTY   Every nonempty set of nonnegative integers has a least element.

The well-ordering property can often be used directly in proofs.

**EXAMPLE 5**   Use the well-ordering property to prove the division algorithm. Recall that the division algorithm states that if $a$ is an integer and $d$ is a positive integer, then there are unique integers $q$ and $r$ with $0 \leq r < d$ and $a = dq + r$.

Extra
Examples

*Solution:* Let $S$ be the set of nonnegative integers of the form $a - dq$, where $q$ is an integer. This set is nonempty because $-dq$ can be made as large as desired (taking $q$ to be a negative integer with large absolute value). By the well-ordering property, $S$ has a least element $r = a - dq_0$.

The integer $r$ is nonnegative. It is also the case that $r < d$. If it were not, then there would be a smaller nonnegative element in $S$, namely, $a - d(q_0 + 1)$. To see this, suppose that $r \geq d$. Because $a = dq_0 + r$, it follows that $a - d(q_0 + 1) = (a - dq_0) - d = r - d \geq 0$. Consequently, there are integers $q$ and $r$ with $0 \leq r < d$. The proof that $q$ and $r$ are unique is left as Exercise 37.   ◀

**EXAMPLE 6**   In a round-robin tournament every player plays every other player exactly once and each match has a winner and a loser. We say that the players $p_1, p_2, \ldots, p_m$ form a *cycle* if $p_1$ beats $p_2$, $p_2$ beats $p_3, \ldots, p_{m-1}$ beats $p_m$, and $p_m$ beats $p_1$. Use the well-ordering principle to show that if there is a cycle of length $m$ $(m \geq 3)$ among the players in a round-robin tournament, there must be a cycle of three of these players.

*Solution:* We assume that there is no cycle of three players. Because there is at least one cycle in the round-robin tournament, the set of all positive integers $n$ for which there is a cycle of length $n$ is nonempty. By the well-ordering property, this set of positive integers has a least element $k$, which by assumption must be greater than three. Consequently, there exists a cycle of players $p_1, p_2, p_3, \ldots, p_k$ and no shorter cycle exists.

Because there is no cycle of three players, we know that $k > 3$. Consider the first three elements of this cycle, $p_1$, $p_2$, and $p_3$. There are two possible outcomes of the match between $p_1$ and $p_3$. If $p_3$ beats $p_1$, it follows that $p_1$, $p_2$, $p_3$ is a cycle of length three, contradicting our assumption that there is no cycle of three players. Consequently, it must be the case that $p_1$ beats $p_3$. This means that we can omit $p_2$ from the cycle $p_1, p_2, p_3, \ldots, p_k$ to obtain the cycle $p_1, p_3, p_4, \ldots, p_k$ of length $k - 1$, contradicting the assumption that the smallest cycle has length $k$. We conclude that there must be a cycle of length three.   ◀

# Exercises

**1.** Use strong induction to show that if you can run one mile or two miles, and if you can always run two more miles once you have run a specified number of miles, then you can run any number of miles.

**2.** Use strong induction to show that all dominoes fall in an infinite arrangement of dominoes if you know that the first three dominoes fall, and that when a domino falls, the domino three farther down in the arrangement also falls.

**3.** Let $P(n)$ be the statement that a postage of $n$ cents can be formed using just 3-cent stamps and 5-cent stamps. The

parts of this exercise outline a strong induction proof that $P(n)$ is true for $n \geq 8$.

**a)** Show that the statements $P(8)$, $P(9)$, and $P(10)$ are true, completing the basis step of the proof.

**b)** What is the inductive hypothesis of the proof?

**c)** What do you need to prove in the inductive step?

**d)** Complete the inductive step for $k \geq 10$.

**e)** Explain why these steps show that this statement is true whenever $n \geq 8$.

**4.** Let $P(n)$ be the statement that a postage of $n$ cents can be formed using just 4-cent stamps and 7-cent stamps. The parts of this exercise outline a strong induction proof that $P(n)$ is true for $n \geq 18$.

a) Show statements $P(18)$, $P(19)$, $P(20)$, and $P(21)$ are true, completing the basis step of the proof.

b) What is the inductive hypothesis of the proof?

c) What do you need to prove in the inductive step?

d) Complete the inductive step for $k \geq 21$.

e) Explain why these steps show that this statement is true whenever $n \geq 18$.

**5. a)** Determine which amounts of postage can be formed using just 4-cent and 11-cent stamps.

b) Prove your answer to (a) using the principle of mathematical induction. Be sure to state explicitly your inductive hypothesis in the inductive step.

c) Prove your answer to (a) using strong induction. How does the inductive hypothesis in this proof differ from that in the inductive hypothesis for a proof using mathematical induction?

**6. a)** Determine which amounts of postage can be formed using just 3-cent and 10-cent stamps.

b) Prove your answer to (a) using the principle of mathematical induction. Be sure to state explicitly your inductive hypothesis in the inductive step.

c) Prove your answer to (a) using strong induction. How does the inductive hypothesis in this proof differ from that in the inductive hypothesis for a proof using mathematical induction?

**7.** Which amounts of money can be formed using just two-dollar bills and five-dollar bills? Prove your answer using strong induction.

**8.** Suppose that a store offers gift certificates in denominations of 25 dollars and 40 dollars. Determine the possible total amounts you can form using these gift certificates. Prove your answer using strong induction.

**∗9.** Use strong induction to prove that $\sqrt{2}$ is irrational. [*Hint:* Let $P(n)$ be the statement that $\sqrt{2} \neq n/b$ for any positive integer $b$.]

**10.** Assume that a chocolate bar consists of $n$ squares arranged in a rectangular pattern. The entire bar, or any smaller rectangular piece of the bar, can be broken along a vertical or a horizontal line separating the squares. Assuming that only one piece can be broken at a time, determine how many breaks you must successively make to break the bar into $n$ separate squares. Use strong induction to prove your answer.

**11.** Consider this variation of the game of Nim. The game begins with $n$ matches. Two players take turns removing matches, one, two, or three at a time. The player removing the last match loses. Use strong induction to show that if each player plays the best strategy possible, the first player wins if $n = 4j$, $4j + 2$, or $4j + 3$ for some nonnegative integer $j$ and the second player wins in the remaining case when $n = 4j + 1$ for some nonnegative integer $j$.

**12.** Use strong induction to show that every positive integer $n$ can be written as a sum of distinct powers of two, that is, as a sum of a subset of the integers $2^0 = 1, 2^1 = 2, 2^2 = 4$, and so on. [*Hint:* For the inductive step, separately consider the case where $k + 1$ is even and where it is odd. When it is even, note that $(k + 1)/2$ is an integer.]

**∗13.** A jigsaw puzzle is put together by successively joining pieces that fit together into blocks. A move is made each time a piece is added to a block, or when two blocks are joined. Use strong induction to prove that no matter how the moves are carried out, exactly $n - 1$ moves are required to assemble a puzzle with $n$ pieces.

**14.** Suppose you begin with a pile of $n$ stones and split this pile into $n$ piles of one stone each by successively splitting a pile of stones into two smaller piles. Each time you split a pile you multiply the number of stones in each of the two smaller piles you form, so that if these piles have $r$ and $s$ stones in them, respectively, you compute $rs$. Show that no matter how you split the piles, the sum of the products computed at each step equals $n(n - 1)/2$.

**15.** Prove that the first player has a winning strategy for the game of Chomp, introduced in Example 12 in Section 1.8, if the initial board is square. [*Hint:* Use strong induction to show that this strategy works. For the first move, the first player chomps all cookies except those in the left and top edges. On subsequent moves, after the second player has chomped cookies on either the top or left edge, the first player chomps cookies in the same relative positions in the left or top edge, respectively.]

**∗16.** Prove that the first player has a winning strategy for the game of Chomp, introduced in Example 12 in Section 1.8, if the initial board is two squares wide, that is, a $2 \times n$ board. [*Hint:* Use strong induction. The first move of the first player should be to chomp the cookie in the bottom row at the far right.]

**17.** Use strong induction to show that if a simple polygon with at least four sides is triangulated, then at least two of the triangles in the triangulation have two sides that border the exterior of the polygon.

**∗18.** Use strong induction to show that when a simple polygon $P$ with consecutive vertices $v_1, v_2, \ldots, v_n$ is triangulated into $n - 2$ triangles, the $n - 2$ triangles can be numbered $1, 2, \ldots, n - 2$ so that $v_i$ is a vertex of triangle $i$ for $i = 1, 2, \ldots, n - 2$.

**∗19. Pick's theorem** says that the area of a simple polygon $P$ in the plane with vertices that are all lattice points (that is, points with integer coordinates) equals $I(P) + B(P)/2 - 1$, where $I(P)$ and $B(P)$ are the number of lattice points in the interior of $P$ and on the boundary of $P$, respectively. Use strong induction on the number of vertices of $P$ to prove Pick's theorem. [*Hint:* For the basis step, first prove the theorem for rectangles, then for right triangles, and finally for all triangles by noting that the area of a triangle is the area of a larger rectangle containing it with the areas of at most three triangles subtracted. For the inductive step, take advantage of Lemma 1.]

**\*\*20.** Suppose that $P$ is a simple polygon with vertices $v_1, v_2, \ldots, v_n$ listed so that consecutive vertices are connected by an edge, and $v_1$ and $v_n$ are connected by an edge. A vertex $v_i$ is called an **ear** if the line segment connecting the two vertices adjacent to $v_i$ is an interior diagonal of the simple polygon. Two ears $v_i$ and $v_j$ are called **nonoverlapping** if the interiors of the triangles with vertices $v_i$ and its two adjacent vertices and $v_j$ and its two adjacent vertices do not intersect. Prove that every simple polygon with at least four vertices has at least two nonoverlapping ears.

**21.** In the proof of Lemma 1 we mentioned that many incorrect methods for finding a vertex $p$ such that the line segment $bp$ is an interior diagonal of $P$ have been published. This exercise presents some of the incorrect ways $p$ has been chosen in these proofs. Show, by considering one of the polygons drawn here, that for each of these choices of $p$, the line segment $bp$ is not necessarily an interior diagonal of $P$.

   **a)** $p$ is the vertex of $P$ such that the angle $\angle abp$ is smallest.

   **b)** $p$ is the vertex of $P$ with the least $x$-coordinate (other than $b$).

   **c)** $p$ is the vertex of $P$ that is closest to $b$.

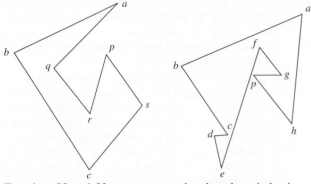

Exercises 22 and 23 present examples that show inductive loading can be used to prove results in computational geometry.

**\*22.** Let $P(n)$ be the statement that when nonintersecting diagonals are drawn inside a convex polygon with $n$ sides, at least two vertices of the polygon are not endpoints of any of these diagonals.

   **a)** Show that when we attempt to prove $P(n)$ for all integers $n$ with $n \geq 3$ using strong induction, the inductive step does not go through.

   **b)** Show that we can prove that $P(n)$ is true for all integers $n$ with $n \geq 3$ by proving by strong induction the stronger assertion $Q(n)$, for $n \geq 4$, where $Q(n)$ states that whenever nonintersecting diagonals are drawn inside a convex polygon with $n$ sides, at least two *nonadjacent* vertices are not endpoints of any of these diagonals.

**23.** Let $E(n)$ be the statement that in a triangulation of a simple polygon with $n$ sides, at least one of the triangles in the triangulation has two sides bordering the exterior of the polygon.

   **a)** Explain where a proof using strong induction that $E(n)$ is true for all integers $n \geq 4$ runs into difficulties.

   **b)** Show that we can prove that $E(n)$ is true for all integers $n \geq 4$ by proving by strong induction the stronger statement $T(n)$ for all integers $n \geq 4$, which states that in every triangulation of a simple polygon, at least two of the triangles in the triangulation have two sides bordering the exterior of the polygon.

**\*24.** A stable assignment, defined in the preamble to Exercise 60 in Section 3.1, is called **optimal for suitors** if no stable assignment exists in which a suitor is paired with a suitee whom this suitor prefers to the person to whom this suitor is paired in this stable assignment. Use strong induction to show that the deferred acceptance algorithm produces a stable assignment that is optimal for suitors.

**25.** Suppose that $P(n)$ is a propositional function. Determine for which positive integers $n$ the statement $P(n)$ must be true, and justify your answer, if

   **a)** $P(1)$ is true; for all positive integers $n$, if $P(n)$ is true, then $P(n + 2)$ is true.

   **b)** $P(1)$ and $P(2)$ are true; for all positive integers $n$, if $P(n)$ and $P(n + 1)$ are true, then $P(n + 2)$ is true.

   **c)** $P(1)$ is true; for all positive integers $n$, if $P(n)$ is true, then $P(2n)$ is true.

   **d)** $P(1)$ is true; for all positive integers $n$, if $P(n)$ is true, then $P(n + 1)$ is true.

**26.** Suppose that $P(n)$ is a propositional function. Determine for which nonnegative integers $n$ the statement $P(n)$ must be true if

   **a)** $P(0)$ is true; for all nonnegative integers $n$, if $P(n)$ is true, then $P(n + 2)$ is true.

   **b)** $P(0)$ is true; for all nonnegative integers $n$, if $P(n)$ is true, then $P(n + 3)$ is true.

   **c)** $P(0)$ and $P(1)$ are true; for all nonnegative integers $n$, if $P(n)$ and $P(n + 1)$ are true, then $P(n + 2)$ is true.

   **d)** $P(0)$ is true; for all nonnegative integers $n$, if $P(n)$ is true, then $P(n + 2)$ and $P(n + 3)$ are true.

**27.** Show that if the statement $P(n)$ is true for infinitely many positive integers $n$ and $P(n + 1) \to P(n)$ is true for all positive integers $n$, then $P(n)$ is true for all positive integers $n$.

**28.** Let $b$ be a fixed integer and $j$ a fixed positive integer. Show that if $P(b), P(b + 1), \ldots, P(b + j)$ are true and $[P(b) \wedge P(b + 1) \wedge \cdots \wedge P(k)] \to P(k + 1)$ is true for every integer $k \geq b + j$, then $P(n)$ is true for all integers $n$ with $n \geq b$.

**29.** What is wrong with this "proof" by strong induction?

*"Theorem"* For every nonnegative integer $n$, $5n = 0$.

*Basis Step:* $5 \cdot 0 = 0$.

*Inductive Step:* Suppose that $5j = 0$ for all nonnegative integers $j$ with $0 \leq j \leq k$. Write $k + 1 = i + j$, where $i$ and $j$ are natural numbers less than $k + 1$. By the inductive hypothesis, $5(k + 1) = 5(i + j) = 5i + 5j = 0 + 0 = 0$.

**\*30.** Find the flaw with the following "proof" that $a^n = 1$ for all nonnegative integers $n$, whenever $a$ is a nonzero real number.

*Basis Step:* $a^0 = 1$ is true by the definition of $a^0$.

*Inductive Step:* Assume that $a^j = 1$ for all nonnegative integers $j$ with $j \le k$. Then note that

$$a^{k+1} = \frac{a^k \cdot a^k}{a^{k-1}} = \frac{1 \cdot 1}{1} = 1.$$

**\*31.** Show that strong induction is a valid method of proof by showing that it follows from the well-ordering property.

**32.** Find the flaw with the following "proof" that every postage of three cents or more can be formed using just three-cent and four-cent stamps.

*Basis Step:* We can form postage of three cents with a single three-cent stamp and we can form postage of four cents using a single four-cent stamp.

*Inductive Step:* Assume that we can form postage of $j$ cents for all nonnegative integers $j$ with $j \le k$ using just three-cent and four-cent stamps. We can then form postage of $k + 1$ cents by replacing one three-cent stamp with a four-cent stamp or by replacing two four-cent stamps by three three-cent stamps.

**33.** Show that we can prove that $P(n, k)$ is true for all pairs of positive integers $n$ and $k$ if we show

a) $P(1, 1)$ is true and $P(n, k) \to [P(n+1, k) \wedge P(n, k+1)]$ is true for all positive integers $n$ and $k$.

b) $P(1, k)$ is true for all positive integers $k$, and $P(n, k) \to P(n+1, k)$ is true for all positive integers $n$ and $k$.

c) $P(n, 1)$ is true for all positive integers $n$, and $P(n, k) \to P(n, k+1)$ is true for all positive integers $n$ and $k$.

**34.** Prove that $\sum_{j=1}^{n} j(j+1)(j+2) \cdots (j+k-1) = n(n+1)(n+2) \cdots (n+k)/(k+1)$ for all positive integers $k$ and $n$. [*Hint:* Use a technique from Exercise 33.]

**\*35.** Show that if $a_1, a_2, \ldots, a_n$ are $n$ distinct real numbers, exactly $n - 1$ multiplications are used to compute the product of these $n$ numbers no matter how parentheses are inserted into their product. [*Hint:* Use strong induction and consider the last multiplication.]

**\*36.** The well-ordering property can be used to show that there is a unique greatest common divisor of two positive integers. Let $a$ and $b$ be positive integers, and let $S$ be

the set of positive integers of the form $as + bt$, where $s$ and $t$ are integers.

a) Show that $S$ is nonempty.

b) Use the well-ordering property to show that $S$ has a smallest element $c$.

c) Show that if $d$ is a common divisor of $a$ and $b$, then $d$ is a divisor of $c$.

d) Show that $c \mid a$ and $c \mid b$. [*Hint:* First, assume that $c \nmid a$. Then $a = qc + r$, where $0 < r < c$. Show that $r \in S$, contradicting the choice of $c$.]

e) Conclude from (c) and (d) that the greatest common divisor of $a$ and $b$ exists. Finish the proof by showing that this greatest common divisor is unique.

**37.** Let $a$ be an integer and $d$ be a positive integer. Show that the integers $q$ and $r$ with $a = dq + r$ and $0 \le r < d$, which were shown to exist in Example 5, are unique.

**38.** Use mathematical induction to show that a rectangular checkerboard with an even number of cells and two squares missing, one white and one black, can be covered by dominoes.

**\*\*39.** Can you use the well-ordering property to prove the statement: "Every positive integer can be described using no more than fifteen English words"? Assume the words come from a particular dictionary of English. [*Hint:* Suppose that there are positive integers that cannot be described using no more than fifteen English words. By well ordering, *the smallest positive integer that cannot be described using no more than fifteen English words* would then exist.]

**40.** Use the well-ordering principle to show that if $x$ and $y$ are real numbers with $x < y$, then there is a rational number $r$ with $x < r < y$. [*Hint:* Use the Archimedean property, given in Appendix 1, to find a positive integer $A$ with $A > 1/(y - x)$. Then show that there is a rational number $r$ with denominator $A$ between $x$ and $y$ by looking at the numbers $\lfloor x \rfloor + j/A$, where $j$ is a positive integer.]

**\*41.** Show that the well-ordering property can be proved when the principle of mathematical induction is taken as an axiom.

**\*42.** Show that the principle of mathematical induction and strong induction are equivalent; that is, each can be shown to be valid from the other.

**\*43.** Show that we can prove the well-ordering property when we take strong induction as an axiom instead of taking the well-ordering property as an axiom.

# 5.3 Recursive Definitions and Structural Induction

## Introduction

Sometimes it is difficult to define an object explicitly. However, it may be easy to define this object in terms of itself. This process is called **recursion**. For instance, the picture shown in Figure 1 is produced recursively. First, an original picture is given. Then a process of successively superimposing centered smaller pictures on top of the previous pictures is carried out.

# 6

# Counting

Combinatorics, the study of arrangements of objects, is an important part of discrete mathematics. This subject was studied as long ago as the seventeenth century, when combinatorial questions arose in the study of gambling games. Enumeration, the counting of objects with certain properties, is an important part of combinatorics. We must count objects to solve many different types of problems. For instance, counting is used to determine the complexity of algorithms. Counting is also required to determine whether there are enough telephone numbers or Internet protocol addresses to meet demand. Recently, it has played a key role in mathematical biology, especially in sequencing DNA. Furthermore, counting techniques are used extensively when probabilities of events are computed.

The basic rules of counting, which we will study in Section 6.1, can solve a tremendous variety of problems. For instance, we can use these rules to enumerate the different telephone numbers possible in the United States, the allowable passwords on a computer system, and the different orders in which the runners in a race can finish. Another important combinatorial tool is the pigeonhole principle, which we will study in Section 6.2. This states that when objects are placed in boxes and there are more objects than boxes, then there is a box containing at least two objects. For instance, we can use this principle to show that among a set of 15 or more students, at least 3 were born on the same day of the week.

We can phrase many counting problems in terms of ordered or unordered arrangements of the objects of a set with or without repetitions. These arrangements, called permutations and combinations, are used in many counting problems. For instance, suppose the 100 top finishers on a competitive exam taken by 2000 students are invited to a banquet. We can count the possible sets of 100 students that will be invited, as well as the ways in which the top 10 prizes can be awarded.

Another problem in combinatorics involves generating all the arrangements of a specified kind. This is often important in computer simulations. We will devise algorithms to generate arrangements of various types.

## 6.1 The Basics of Counting

### Introduction

Suppose that a password on a computer system consists of six, seven, or eight characters. Each of these characters must be a digit or a letter of the alphabet. Each password must contain at least one digit. How many such passwords are there? The techniques needed to answer this question and a wide variety of other counting problems will be introduced in this section.

Counting problems arise throughout mathematics and computer science. For example, we must count the successful outcomes of experiments and all the possible outcomes of these experiments to determine probabilities of discrete events. We need to count the number of operations used by an algorithm to study its time complexity.

We will introduce the basic techniques of counting in this section. These methods serve as the foundation for almost all counting techniques.

# Basic Counting Principles

Assessment

We first present two basic counting principles, the **product rule** and the **sum rule**. Then we will show how they can be used to solve many different counting problems.

The product rule applies when a procedure is made up of separate tasks.

> THE PRODUCT RULE Suppose that a procedure can be broken down into a sequence of two tasks. If there are $n_1$ ways to do the first task and for each of these ways of doing the first task, there are $n_2$ ways to do the second task, then there are $n_1 n_2$ ways to do the procedure.

Extra Examples

Examples 1–10 show how the product rule is used.

**EXAMPLE 1**    A new company with just two employees, Sanchez and Patel, rents a floor of a building with 12 offices. How many ways are there to assign different offices to these two employees?

*Solution:* The procedure of assigning offices to these two employees consists of assigning an office to Sanchez, which can be done in 12 ways, then assigning an office to Patel different from the office assigned to Sanchez, which can be done in 11 ways. By the product rule, there are $12 \cdot 11 = 132$ ways to assign offices to these two employees.    ◀

**EXAMPLE 2**    The chairs of an auditorium are to be labeled with an uppercase English letter followed by a positive integer not exceeding 100. What is the largest number of chairs that can be labeled differently?

*Solution:* The procedure of labeling a chair consists of two tasks, namely, assigning to the seat one of the 26 uppercase English letters, and then assigning to it one of the 100 possible integers. The product rule shows that there are $26 \cdot 100 = 2600$ different ways that a chair can be labeled. Therefore, the largest number of chairs that can be labeled differently is 2600.    ◀

**EXAMPLE 3**    There are 32 microcomputers in a computer center. Each microcomputer has 24 ports. How many different ports to a microcomputer in the center are there?

*Solution:* The procedure of choosing a port consists of two tasks, first picking a microcomputer and then picking a port on this microcomputer. Because there are 32 ways to choose the micro-computer and 24 ways to choose the port no matter which microcomputer has been selected, the product rule shows that there are $32 \cdot 24 = 768$ ports.    ◀

An extended version of the product rule is often useful. Suppose that a procedure is carried out by performing the tasks $T_1, T_2, \ldots, T_m$ in sequence. If each task $T_i$, $i = 1, 2, \ldots, n$, can be done in $n_i$ ways, regardless of how the previous tasks were done, then there are $n_1 \cdot n_2 \cdots \cdot n_m$ ways to carry out the procedure. This version of the product rule can be proved by mathematical induction from the product rule for two tasks (see Exercise 72).

**EXAMPLE 4**    How many different bit strings of length seven are there?

*Solution:* Each of the seven bits can be chosen in two ways, because each bit is either 0 or 1. Therefore, the product rule shows there are a total of $2^7 = 128$ different bit strings of length seven.    ◀

**EXAMPLE 5**    How many different license plates can be made if each plate contains a sequence of three uppercase English letters followed by three digits (and no sequences of letters are prohibited, even if they are obscene)?

$$\underbrace{-\ -\ -}_{\substack{\text{26 choices}\\\text{for each}\\\text{letter}}}\quad\underbrace{-\ -\ -}_{\substack{\text{10 choices}\\\text{for each}\\\text{digit}}}$$

*Solution:* There are 26 choices for each of the three uppercase English letters and ten choices for each of the three digits. Hence, by the product rule there are a total of $26 \cdot 26 \cdot 26 \cdot 10 \cdot 10 \cdot 10 = 17{,}576{,}000$ possible license plates.  ◀

**EXAMPLE 6**    **Counting Functions**    How many functions are there from a set with $m$ elements to a set with $n$ elements?

*Solution:* A function corresponds to a choice of one of the $n$ elements in the codomain for each of the $m$ elements in the domain. Hence, by the product rule there are $n \cdot n \cdot \cdots \cdot n = n^m$ functions from a set with $m$ elements to one with $n$ elements. For example, there are $5^3 = 125$ different functions from a set with three elements to a set with five elements.  ◀

**EXAMPLE 7**    **Counting One-to-One Functions**    How many one-to-one functions are there from a set with $m$ elements to one with $n$ elements?

*Solution:* First note that when $m > n$ there are no one-to-one functions from a set with $m$ elements to a set with $n$ elements.

Counting the number of onto functions is harder. We'll do this in Chapter 8.

Now let $m \le n$. Suppose the elements in the domain are $a_1, a_2, \ldots, a_m$. There are $n$ ways to choose the value of the function at $a_1$. Because the function is one-to-one, the value of the function at $a_2$ can be picked in $n - 1$ ways (because the value used for $a_1$ cannot be used again). In general, the value of the function at $a_k$ can be chosen in $n - k + 1$ ways. By the product rule, there are $n(n - 1)(n - 2) \cdots (n - m + 1)$ one-to-one functions from a set with $m$ elements to one with $n$ elements.

For example, there are $5 \cdot 4 \cdot 3 = 60$ one-to-one functions from a set with three elements to a set with five elements.  ◀

**EXAMPLE 8**    **The Telephone Numbering Plan**    The *North American numbering plan (NANP)* specifies the format of telephone numbers in the U.S., Canada, and many other parts of North America. A telephone number in this plan consists of 10 digits, which are split into a three-digit area code, a three-digit office code, and a four-digit station code. Because of signaling considerations, there are certain restrictions on some of these digits. To specify the allowable format, let $X$ denote a digit that can take any of the values 0 through 9, let $N$ denote a digit that can take any of the values 2 through 9, and let $Y$ denote a digit that must be a 0 or a 1. Two numbering plans, which will be called the old plan, and the new plan, will be discussed. (The old plan, in use in the 1960s, has been replaced by the new plan, but the recent rapid growth in demand for new numbers for mobile phones and devices will eventually make even this new plan obsolete. In this example, the letters used to represent digits follow the conventions of the *North American Numbering Plan*.) As will be shown, the new plan allows the use of more numbers.

In the old plan, the formats of the area code, office code, and station code are *NYX*, *NNX*, and *XXXX*, respectively, so that telephone numbers had the form *NYX-NNX-XXXX*. In the new plan, the formats of these codes are *NXX*, *NXX*, and *XXXX*, respectively, so that telephone numbers have the form *NXX-NXX-XXXX*. How many different North American telephone numbers are possible under the old plan and under the new plan?

Current projections are that by 2038, it will be necessary to add one or more digits to North American telephone numbers.

*Solution:* By the product rule, there are $8 \cdot 2 \cdot 10 = 160$ area codes with format *NYX* and $8 \cdot 10 \cdot 10 = 800$ area codes with format *NXX*. Similarly, by the product rule, there are $8 \cdot 8 \cdot 10 = 640$ office codes with format *NNX*. The product rule also shows that there are $10 \cdot 10 \cdot 10 \cdot 10 = 10{,}000$ station codes with format *XXXX*.

Note that we have ignored restrictions that rule out N11 station codes for most area codes.

Consequently, applying the product rule again, it follows that under the old plan there are

$$160 \cdot 640 \cdot 10,000 = 1,024,000,000$$

different numbers available in North America. Under the new plan, there are

$$800 \cdot 800 \cdot 10,000 = 6,400,000,000$$

different numbers available. ◀

**EXAMPLE 9** What is the value of $k$ after the following code, where $n_1, n_2, \ldots, n_m$ are positive integers, has been executed?

```
k := 0
for i₁ := 1 to n₁
    for i₂ := 1 to n₂
            .
            .
            .
        for iₘ := 1 to nₘ
            k := k + 1
```

*Solution:* The initial value of $k$ is zero. Each time the nested loop is traversed, 1 is added to $k$. Let $T_i$ be the task of traversing the $i$th loop. Then the number of times the loop is traversed is the number of ways to do the tasks $T_1, T_2, \ldots, T_m$. The number of ways to carry out the task $T_j$, $j = 1, 2, \ldots, m$, is $n_j$, because the $j$th loop is traversed once for each integer $i_j$ with $1 \le i_j \le n_j$. By the product rule, it follows that the nested loop is traversed $n_1 n_2 \cdots n_m$ times. Hence, the final value of $k$ is $n_1 n_2 \cdots n_m$. ◀

**EXAMPLE 10** **Counting Subsets of a Finite Set** Use the product rule to show that the number of different subsets of a finite set $S$ is $2^{|S|}$.

*Solution:* Let $S$ be a finite set. List the elements of $S$ in arbitrary order. Recall from Section 2.2 that there is a one-to-one correspondence between subsets of $S$ and bit strings of length $|S|$. Namely, a subset of $S$ is associated with the bit string with a 1 in the $i$th position if the $i$th element in the list is in the subset, and a 0 in this position otherwise. By the product rule, there are $2^{|S|}$ bit strings of length $|S|$. Hence, $|P(S)| = 2^{|S|}$. (Recall that we used mathematical induction to prove this fact in Example 10 of Section 5.1.) ◀

The product rule is often phrased in terms of sets in this way: If $A_1, A_2, \ldots, A_m$ are finite sets, then the number of elements in the Cartesian product of these sets is the product of the number of elements in each set. To relate this to the product rule, note that the task of choosing an element in the Cartesian product $A_1 \times A_2 \times \cdots \times A_m$ is done by choosing an element in $A_1$, an element in $A_2, \ldots$, and an element in $A_m$. By the product rule it follows that

$$|A_1 \times A_2 \times \cdots \times A_m| = |A_1| \cdot |A_2| \cdot \cdots \cdot |A_m|.$$

**EXAMPLE 11** **DNA and Genomes** The hereditary information of a living organism is encoded using de-oxyribonucleic acid (DNA), or in certain viruses, ribonucleic acid (RNA). DNA and RNA are extremely complex molecules, with different molecules interacting in a vast variety of ways to enable living process. For our purposes, we give only the briefest description of how DNA and RNA encode genetic information.

DNA molecules consist of two strands consisting of blocks known as nucleotides. Each nucleotide contains subcomponents called **bases**, each of which is adenine (A), cytosine (C), guanine (G), or thymine (T). The two strands of DNA are held together by hydrogen bonds connecting different bases, with A bonding only with T, and C bonding only with G. Unlike DNA, RNA is single stranded, with uracil (U) replacing thymine as a base. So, in DNA the possible base pairs are A-T and C-G, while in RNA they are A-U, and C-G. The DNA of a living creature consists of multiple pieces of DNA forming separate chromosomes. A **gene** is a segment of a DNA molecule that encodes a particular protein. The entirety of genetic information of an organism is called its **genome**.

Sequences of bases in DNA and RNA encode long chains of proteins called amino acids. There are 22 essential amino acids for human beings. We can quickly see that a sequence of at least three bases are needed to encode these 22 different amino acid. First note, that because there are four possibilities for each base in DNA, A, C, G, and T, by the product rule there are $4^2 = 16 < 22$ different sequences of two bases. However, there are $4^3 = 64$ different sequences of three bases, which provide enough different sequences to encode the 22 different amino acids (even after taking into account that several different sequences of three bases encode the same amino acid).

The DNA of simple living creatures such as algae and bacteria have between $10^5$ and $10^7$ links, where each link is one of the four possible bases. More complex organisms, such as insects, birds, and mammals have between $10^8$ and $10^{10}$ links in their DNA. So, by the product rule, there are at least $4^{10^5}$ different sequences of bases in the DNA of simple organisms and at least $4^{10^8}$ different sequences of bases in the DNA of more complex organisms. These are both incredibly huge numbers, which helps explain why there is such tremendous variability among living organisms. In the past several decades techniques have been developed for determining the genome of different organisms. The first step is to locate each gene in the DNA of an organism. The next task, called **gene sequencing**, is the determination of the sequence of links on each gene. (Of course, the specific sequence of kinks on these genes depends on the particular individual representative of a species whose DNA is analyzed.) For example, the human genome includes approximately 23,000 genes, each with 1,000 or more links. Gene sequencing techniques take advantage of many recently developed algorithms and are based on numerous new ideas in combinatorics. Many mathematicians and computer scientists work on problems involving genomes, taking part in the fast moving fields of bioinformatics and computational biology. ◄

Soon it won't be that costly to have your own genetic code found.

We now introduce the sum rule.

> **THE SUM RULE** If a task can be done either in one of $n_1$ ways or in one of $n_2$ ways, where none of the set of $n_1$ ways is the same as any of the set of $n_2$ ways, then there are $n_1 + n_2$ ways to do the task.

Example 12 illustrates how the sum rule is used.

**EXAMPLE 12**    Suppose that either a member of the mathematics faculty or a student who is a mathematics major is chosen as a representative to a university committee. How many different choices are there for this representative if there are 37 members of the mathematics faculty and 83 mathematics majors and no one is both a faculty member and a student?

*Solution:* There are 37 ways to choose a member of the mathematics faculty and there are 83 ways to choose a student who is a mathematics major. Choosing a member of the mathematics faculty is never the same as choosing a student who is a mathematics major because no one is both a faculty member and a student. By the sum rule it follows that there are $37 + 83 = 120$ possible ways to pick this representative.    ◄

We can extend the sum rule to more than two tasks. Suppose that a task can be done in one of $n_1$ ways, in one of $n_2$ ways, ... , or in one of $n_m$ ways, where none of the set of $n_i$ ways of doing the task is the same as any of the set of $n_j$ ways, for all pairs $i$ and $j$ with $1 \leq i < j \leq m$. Then the number of ways to do the task is $n_1 + n_2 + \cdots + n_m$. This extended version of the sum rule is often useful in counting problems, as Examples 13 and 14 show. This version of the sum rule can be proved using mathematical induction from the sum rule for two sets. (This is Exercise 71.)

**EXAMPLE 13**    A student can choose a computer project from one of three lists. The three lists contain 23, 15, and 19 possible projects, respectively. No project is on more than one list. How many possible projects are there to choose from?

*Solution:* The student can choose a project by selecting a project from the first list, the second list, or the third list. Because no project is on more than one list, by the sum rule there are $23 + 15 + 19 = 57$ ways to choose a project.    ◄

**EXAMPLE 14**    What is the value of $k$ after the following code, where $n_1, n_2, \ldots, n_m$ are positive integers, has been executed?

```
k := 0
for i₁ := 1 to n₁
    k := k + 1
for i₂ := 1 to n₂
    k := k + 1
        .
        .
        .
for iₘ := 1 to nₘ
    k := k + 1
```

*Solution:* The initial value of $k$ is zero. This block of code is made up of $m$ different loops. Each time a loop is traversed, 1 is added to $k$. To determine the value of $k$ after this code has been executed, we need to determine how many times we traverse a loop. Note that there are $n_i$ ways to traverse the $i$th loop. Because we only traverse one loop at a time, the sum rule shows that the final value of $k$, which is the number of ways to traverse one of the $m$ loops is $n_1 + n_2 + \cdots + n_m$.    ◄

The sum rule can be phrased in terms of sets as: If $A_1, A_2, \ldots, A_m$ are pairwise disjoint finite sets, then the number of elements in the union of these sets is the sum of the numbers of elements in the sets. To relate this to our statement of the sum rule, note there are $|A_i|$ ways to choose an element from $A_i$ for $i = 1, 2, \ldots, m$. Because the sets are pairwise disjoint, when we select an element from one of the sets $A_i$, we do not also select an element from a different set $A_j$. Consequently, by the sum rule, because we cannot select an element from two of these sets at the same time, the number of ways to choose an element from one of the sets, which is the number of elements in the union, is

$$|A_1 \cup A_2 \cup \cdots \cup A_m| = |A_1| + |A_2| + \cdots + |A_m| \text{ when } A_i \cap A_j = \emptyset \text{ for all } i, j.$$

This equality applies only when the sets in question are pairwise disjoint. The situation is much more complicated when these sets have elements in common. That situation will be briefly discussed later in this section and discussed in more depth in Chapter 8.

## More Complex Counting Problems

Many counting problems cannot be solved using just the sum rule or just the product rule. However, many complicated counting problems can be solved using both of these rules in combination. We begin by counting the number of variable names in the programming language BASIC. (In the exercises, we consider the number of variable names in JAVA.) Then we will count the number of valid passwords subject to a particular set of restrictions.

**EXAMPLE 15**

Extra
Examples

In a version of the computer language BASIC, the name of a variable is a string of one or two alphanumeric characters, where uppercase and lowercase letters are not distinguished. (An *alphanumeric* character is either one of the 26 English letters or one of the 10 digits.) Moreover, a variable name must begin with a letter and must be different from the five strings of two characters that are reserved for programming use. How many different variable names are there in this version of BASIC?

*Solution:* Let $V$ equal the number of different variable names in this version of BASIC. Let $V_1$ be the number of these that are one character long and $V_2$ be the number of these that are two characters long. Then by the sum rule, $V = V_1 + V_2$. Note that $V_1 = 26$, because a one-character variable name must be a letter. Furthermore, by the product rule there are $26 \cdot 36$ strings of length two that begin with a letter and end with an alphanumeric character. However, five of these are excluded, so $V_2 = 26 \cdot 36 - 5 = 931$. Hence, there are $V = V_1 + V_2 = 26 + 931 = 957$ different names for variables in this version of BASIC. ◀

**EXAMPLE 16**

Each user on a computer system has a password, which is six to eight characters long, where each character is an uppercase letter or a digit. Each password must contain at least one digit. How many possible passwords are there?

*Solution:* Let $P$ be the total number of possible passwords, and let $P_6$, $P_7$, and $P_8$ denote the number of possible passwords of length 6, 7, and 8, respectively. By the sum rule, $P = P_6 + P_7 + P_8$. We will now find $P_6$, $P_7$, and $P_8$. Finding $P_6$ directly is difficult. To find $P_6$ it is easier to find the number of strings of uppercase letters and digits that are six characters long, including those with no digits, and subtract from this the number of strings with no digits. By the product rule, the number of strings of six characters is $36^6$, and the number of strings with no digits is $26^6$. Hence,

$$P_6 = 36^6 - 26^6 = 2{,}176{,}782{,}336 - 308{,}915{,}776 = 1{,}867{,}866{,}560.$$

Similarly, we have

$$P_7 = 36^7 - 26^7 = 78{,}364{,}164{,}096 - 8{,}031{,}810{,}176 = 70{,}332{,}353{,}920$$

and

$$P_8 = 36^8 - 26^8 = 2{,}821{,}109{,}907{,}456 - 208{,}827{,}064{,}576$$
$$= 2{,}612{,}282{,}842{,}880.$$

Consequently,

$$P = P_6 + P_7 + P_8 = 2{,}684{,}483{,}063{,}360.$$ ◀

**EXAMPLE 17**

Links

**Counting Internet Addresses** In the Internet, which is made up of interconnected physical networks of computers, each computer (or more precisely, each network connection of a computer) is assigned an *Internet address*. In Version 4 of the Internet Protocol (IPv4), now in use,

| Bit Number | 0 | 1 | 2 | 3 | 4 | | 8 | 16 | 24 | 31 |
|---|---|---|---|---|---|---|---|---|---|---|
| Class A | 0 | | netid | | | | | hostid | | |
| Class B | 1 | 0 | | netid | | | | | hostid | |
| Class C | 1 | 1 | 0 | | netid | | | | | hostid |
| Class D | 1 | 1 | 1 | 0 | | | Multicast Address | | | |
| Class E | 1 | 1 | 1 | 1 | 0 | | Address | | | |

**FIGURE 1    Internet Addresses (IPv4).**

an address is a string of 32 bits. It begins with a *network number* (*netid*). The netid is followed by a *host number* (*hostid*), which identifies a computer as a member of a particular network.

Three forms of addresses are used, with different numbers of bits used for netids and hostids. **Class A addresses**, used for the largest networks, consist of 0, followed by a 7-bit netid and a 24-bit hostid. **Class B addresses**, used for medium-sized networks, consist of 10, followed by a 14-bit netid and a 16-bit hostid. **Class C addresses**, used for the smallest networks, consist of 110, followed by a 21-bit netid and an 8-bit hostid. There are several restrictions on addresses because of special uses: 1111111 is not available as the netid of a Class A network, and the hostids consisting of all 0s and all 1s are not available for use in any network. A computer on the Internet has either a Class A, a Class B, or a Class C address. (Besides Class A, B, and C addresses, there are also Class D addresses, reserved for use in multicasting when multiple computers are addressed at a single time, consisting of 1110 followed by 28 bits, and Class E addresses, reserved for future use, consisting of 11110 followed by 27 bits. Neither Class D nor Class E addresses are assigned as the IPv4 address of a computer on the Internet.) Figure 1 illustrates IPv4 addressing. (Limitations on the number of Class A and Class B netids have made IPv4 addressing inadequate; IPv6, a new version of IP, uses 128-bit addresses to solve this problem.)

*The lack of available IPv4 address has become a crisis!*

How many different IPv4 addresses are available for computers on the Internet?

*Solution:* Let $x$ be the number of available addresses for computers on the Internet, and let $x_A$, $x_B$, and $x_C$ denote the number of Class A, Class B, and Class C addresses available, respectively. By the sum rule, $x = x_A + x_B + x_C$.

To find $x_A$, note that there are $2^7 - 1 = 127$ Class A netids, recalling that the netid 1111111 is unavailable. For each netid, there are $2^{24} - 2 = 16,777,214$ hostids, recalling that the hostids consisting of all 0s and all 1s are unavailable. Consequently, $x_A = 127 \cdot 16,777,214 = 2,130,706,178$.

To find $x_B$ and $x_C$, note that there are $2^{14} = 16,384$ Class B netids and $2^{21} = 2,097,152$ Class C netids. For each Class B netid, there are $2^{16} - 2 = 65,534$ hostids, and for each Class C netid, there are $2^8 - 2 = 254$ hostids, recalling that in each network the hostids consisting of all 0s and all 1s are unavailable. Consequently, $x_B = 1,073,709,056$ and $x_C = 532,676,608$.

We conclude that the total number of IPv4 addresses available is $x = x_A + x_B + x_C = 2,130,706,178 + 1,073,709,056 + 532,676,608 = 3,737,091,842$. ◀

## The Subtraction Rule (Inclusion–Exclusion for Two Sets)

*Overcounting is perhaps the most common enumeration error.*

Suppose that a task can be done in one of two ways, but some of the ways to do it are common to both ways. In this situation, we cannot use the sum rule to count the number of ways to do the task. If we add the number of ways to do the tasks in these two ways, we get an overcount of the total number of ways to do it, because the ways to do the task that are common to the two ways are counted twice. To correctly count the number of ways to do the two tasks, we must subtract the number of ways that are counted twice. This leads us to an important counting rule.

THE SUBTRACTION RULE If a task can be done in either $n_1$ ways or $n_2$ ways, then the number of ways to do the task is $n_1 + n_2$ minus the number of ways to do the task that are common to the two different ways.

The subtraction rule is also known as the **principle of inclusion–exclusion**, especially when it is used to count the number of elements in the union of two sets. Suppose that $A_1$ and $A_2$ are sets. Then, there are $|A_1|$ ways to select an element from $A_1$ and $|A_2|$ ways to select an element from $A_2$. The number of ways to select an element from $A_1$ or from $A_2$, that is, the number of ways to select an element from their union, is the sum of the number of ways to select an element from $A_1$ and the number of ways to select an element from $A_2$, minus the number of ways to select an element that is in both $A_1$ and $A_2$. Because there are $|A_1 \cup A_2|$ ways to select an element in either $A_1$ or in $A_2$, and $|A_1 \cap A_2|$ ways to select an element common to both sets, we have

$$|A_1 \cup A_2| = |A_1| + |A_2| - |A_1 \cap A_2|.$$

This is the formula given in Section 2.2 for the number of elements in the union of two sets.

Example 18 illustrates how we can solve counting problems using the subtraction principle.

**EXAMPLE 18**  How many bit strings of length eight either start with a 1 bit or end with the two bits 00?

*Solution:* We can construct a bit string of length eight that either starts with a 1 bit or ends with the two bits 00, by constructing a bit string of length eight beginning with a 1 bit or by constructing a bit string of length eight that ends with the two bits 00. We can construct a bit string of length eight that begins with a 1 in $2^7 = 128$ ways. This follows by the product rule, because the first bit can be chosen in only one way and each of the other seven bits can be chosen in two ways. Similarly, we can construct a bit string of length eight ending with the two bits 00, in $2^6 = 64$ ways. This follows by the product rule, because each of the first six bits can be chosen in two ways and the last two bits can be chosen in only one way.

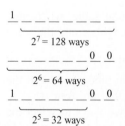

Some of the ways to construct a bit string of length eight starting with a 1 are the same as the ways to construct a bit string of length eight that ends with the two bits 00. There are $2^5 = 32$ ways to construct such a string. This follows by the product rule, because the first bit can be chosen in only one way, each of the second through the sixth bits can be chosen in two ways, and the last two bits can be chosen in one way. Consequently, the number of bit strings of length eight that begin with a 1 or end with a 00, which equals the number of ways to construct a bit string of length eight that begins with a 1 or that ends with 00, equals $128 + 64 - 32 = 160$. ◀

We present an example that illustrates how the formulation of the principle of inclusion–exclusion can be used to solve counting problems.

**EXAMPLE 19**  A computer company receives 350 applications from computer graduates for a job planning a line of new Web servers. Suppose that 220 of these applicants majored in computer science, 147 majored in business, and 51 majored both in computer science and in business. How many of these applicants majored neither in computer science nor in business?

*Solution:* To find the number of these applicants who majored neither in computer science nor in business, we can subtract the number of students who majored either in computer science or in business (or both) from the total number of applicants. Let $A_1$ be the set of students who majored in computer science and $A_2$ the set of students who majored in business. Then $A_1 \cup A_2$ is the set of students who majored in computer science or business (or both), and $A_1 \cap A_2$ is the set of students who majored both in computer science and in business. By the subtraction rule the number of students who majored either in computer science or in business (or both) equals

$$|A_1 \cup A_2| = |A_1| + |A_2| - |A_1 \cap A_2| = 220 + 147 - 51 = 316.$$

We conclude that $350 - 316 = 34$ of the applicants majored neither in computer science nor in business.  ◀

The subtraction rule, or the principle of inclusion–exclusion, can be generalized to find the number of ways to do one of $n$ different tasks or, equivalently, to find the number of elements in the union of $n$ sets, whenever $n$ is a positive integer. We will study the inclusion–exclusion principle and some of its many applications in Chapter 8.

## The Division Rule

We have introduced the product, sum, and subtraction rules for counting. You may wonder whether there is also a division rule for counting. In fact, there is such a rule, which can be useful when solving certain types of enumeration problems.

THE DIVISION RULE  There are $n/d$ ways to do a task if it can be done using a procedure that can be carried out in $n$ ways, and for every way $w$, exactly $d$ of the $n$ ways correspond to way $w$.

We can restate the division rule in terms of sets: "If the finite set $A$ is the union of $n$ pairwise disjoint subsets each with $d$ elements, then $n = |A|/d$."

We can also formulate the division rule in terms of functions: "If $f$ is a function from $A$ to $B$ where $A$ and $B$ are finite sets, and that for every value $y \in B$ there are exactly $d$ values $x \in A$ such that $f(x) = y$ (in which case, we say that $f$ is $d$-to-one), then $|B| = |A|/d$."

We illustrate the use of the division rule for counting with an example.

EXAMPLE 20   How many different ways are there to seat four people around a circular table, where two seatings are considered the same when each person has the same left neighbor and the same right neighbor?

*Solution:* We arbitrarily select a seat at the table and label it seat 1. We number the rest of the seats in numerical order, proceeding clockwise around the table. Note that are four ways to select the person for seat 1, three ways to select the person for seat 2, two ways to select the person for seat 3, and one way to select the person for seat 4. Thus, there are $4! = 24$ ways to order the given four people for these seats. However, each of the four choices for seat 1 leads to the same arrangement, as we distinguish two arrangements only when one of the people has a different immediate left or immediate right neighbor. Because there are four ways to choose the person for seat 1, by the division rule there are $24/4 = 6$ different seating arrangements of four people around the circular table.  ◀

FIGURE 2   Bit Strings of Length Four without Consecutive 1s.

## Tree Diagrams

Counting problems can be solved using **tree diagrams**. A tree consists of a root, a number of branches leaving the root, and possible additional branches leaving the endpoints of other branches. (We will study trees in detail in Chapter 11.) To use trees in counting, we use a branch to represent each possible choice. We represent the possible outcomes by the leaves, which are the endpoints of branches not having other branches starting at them.

Note that when a tree diagram is used to solve a counting problem, the number of choices of which branch to follow to reach a leaf can vary (see Example 21, for example).

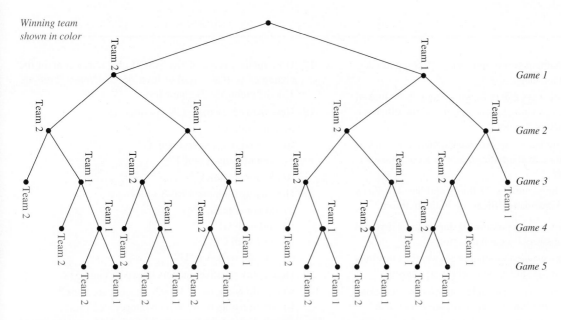

**FIGURE 3  Best Three Games Out of Five Playoffs.**

**EXAMPLE 21**   How many bit strings of length four do not have two consecutive 1s?

*Solution:* The tree diagram in Figure 2 displays all bit strings of length four without two consecutive 1s. We see that there are eight bit strings of length four without two consecutive 1s. ◀

**EXAMPLE 22**   A playoff between two teams consists of at most five games. The first team that wins three games wins the playoff. In how many different ways can the playoff occur?

*Solution:* The tree diagram in Figure 3 displays all the ways the playoff can proceed, with the winner of each game shown. We see that there are 20 different ways for the playoff to occur. ◀

**EXAMPLE 23**   Suppose that "I Love New Jersey" T-shirts come in five different sizes: S, M, L, XL, and XXL. Further suppose that each size comes in four colors, white, red, green, and black, except for XL, which comes only in red, green, and black, and XXL, which comes only in green and black. How many different shirts does a souvenir shop have to stock to have at least one of each available size and color of the T-shirt?

*Solution:* The tree diagram in Figure 4 displays all possible size and color pairs. It follows that the souvenir shop owner needs to stock 17 different T-shirts. ◀

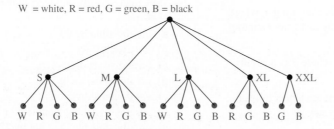

**FIGURE 4   Counting Varieties of T-Shirts.**

# Exercises

1. There are 18 mathematics majors and 325 computer science majors at a college.
   a) In how many ways can two representatives be picked so that one is a mathematics major and the other is a computer science major?
   b) In how many ways can one representative be picked who is either a mathematics major or a computer science major?

2. An office building contains 27 floors and has 37 offices on each floor. How many offices are in the building?

3. A multiple-choice test contains 10 questions. There are four possible answers for each question.
   a) In how many ways can a student answer the questions on the test if the student answers every question?
   b) In how many ways can a student answer the questions on the test if the student can leave answers blank?

4. A particular brand of shirt comes in 12 colors, has a male version and a female version, and comes in three sizes for each sex. How many different types of this shirt are made?

5. Six different airlines fly from New York to Denver and seven fly from Denver to San Francisco. How many different pairs of airlines can you choose on which to book a trip from New York to San Francisco via Denver, when you pick an airline for the flight to Denver and an airline for the continuation flight to San Francisco?

6. There are four major auto routes from Boston to Detroit and six from Detroit to Los Angeles. How many major auto routes are there from Boston to Los Angeles via Detroit?

7. How many different three-letter initials can people have?

8. How many different three-letter initials with none of the letters repeated can people have?

9. How many different three-letter initials are there that begin with an $A$?

10. How many bit strings are there of length eight?

11. How many bit strings of length ten both begin and end with a 1?

12. How many bit strings are there of length six or less, not counting the empty string?

13. How many bit strings with length not exceeding $n$, where $n$ is a positive integer, consist entirely of 1s, not counting the empty string?

14. How many bit strings of length $n$, where $n$ is a positive integer, start and end with 1s?

15. How many strings are there of lowercase letters of length four or less, not counting the empty string?

16. How many strings are there of four lowercase letters that have the letter $x$ in them?

17. How many strings of five ASCII characters contain the character @ ("at" sign) at least once? [*Note:* There are 128 different ASCII characters.]

18. How many 5-element DNA sequences
    a) end with A?
    b) start with T and end with G?
    c) contain only A and T?
    d) do not contain C?

19. How many 6-element RNA sequences
    a) do not contain U?
    b) end with GU?
    c) start with C?
    d) contain only A or U?

20. How many positive integers between 5 and 31
    a) are divisible by 3? Which integers are these?
    b) are divisible by 4? Which integers are these?
    c) are divisible by 3 and by 4? Which integers are these?

21. How many positive integers between 50 and 100
    a) are divisible by 7? Which integers are these?
    b) are divisible by 11? Which integers are these?
    c) are divisible by both 7 and 11? Which integers are these?

22. How many positive integers less than 1000
    a) are divisible by 7?
    b) are divisible by 7 but not by 11?
    c) are divisible by both 7 and 11?
    d) are divisible by either 7 or 11?
    e) are divisible by exactly one of 7 and 11?
    f) are divisible by neither 7 nor 11?
    g) have distinct digits?
    h) have distinct digits and are even?

23. How many positive integers between 100 and 999 inclusive
    a) are divisible by 7?
    b) are odd?
    c) have the same three decimal digits?
    d) are not divisible by 4?
    e) are divisible by 3 or 4?
    f) are not divisible by either 3 or 4?
    g) are divisible by 3 but not by 4?
    h) are divisible by 3 and 4?

24. How many positive integers between 1000 and 9999 inclusive
    a) are divisible by 9?
    b) are even?
    c) have distinct digits?
    d) are not divisible by 3?
    e) are divisible by 5 or 7?
    f) are not divisible by either 5 or 7?
    g) are divisible by 5 but not by 7?
    h) are divisible by 5 and 7?

**25.** How many strings of three decimal digits

 **a)** do not contain the same digit three times?

 **b)** begin with an odd digit?

 **c)** have exactly two digits that are 4s?

**26.** How many strings of four decimal digits

 **a)** do not contain the same digit twice?

 **b)** end with an even digit?

 **c)** have exactly three digits that are 9s?

**27.** A committee is formed consisting of one representative from each of the 50 states in the United States, where the representative from a state is either the governor or one of the two senators from that state. How many ways are there to form this committee?

**28.** How many license plates can be made using either three digits followed by three uppercase English letters or three uppercase English letters followed by three digits?

**29.** How many license plates can be made using either two uppercase English letters followed by four digits or two digits followed by four uppercase English letters?

**30.** How many license plates can be made using either three uppercase English letters followed by three digits or four uppercase English letters followed by two digits?

**31.** How many license plates can be made using either two or three uppercase English letters followed by either two or three digits?

**32.** How many strings of eight uppercase English letters are there

 **a)** if letters can be repeated?

 **b)** if no letter can be repeated?

 **c)** that start with X, if letters can be repeated?

 **d)** that start with X, if no letter can be repeated?

 **e)** that start and end with X, if letters can be repeated?

 **f)** that start with the letters BO (in that order), if letters can be repeated?

 **g)** that start and end with the letters BO (in that order), if letters can be repeated?

 **h)** that start or end with the letters BO (in that order), if letters can be repeated?

**33.** How many strings of eight English letters are there

 **a)** that contain no vowels, if letters can be repeated?

 **b)** that contain no vowels, if letters cannot be repeated?

 **c)** that start with a vowel, if letters can be repeated?

 **d)** that start with a vowel, if letters cannot be repeated?

 **e)** that contain at least one vowel, if letters can be repeated?

 **f)** that contain exactly one vowel, if letters can be repeated?

 **g)** that start with X and contain at least one vowel, if letters can be repeated?

 **h)** that start and end with X and contain at least one vowel, if letters can be repeated?

**34.** How many different functions are there from a set with 10 elements to sets with the following numbers of elements?

 **a)** 2      **b)** 3      **c)** 4      **d)** 5

**35.** How many one-to-one functions are there from a set with five elements to sets with the following number of elements?

 **a)** 4      **b)** 5      **c)** 6      **d)** 7

**36.** How many functions are there from the set $\{1, 2, \ldots, n\}$, where $n$ is a positive integer, to the set $\{0, 1\}$?

**37.** How many functions are there from the set $\{1, 2, \ldots, n\}$, where $n$ is a positive integer, to the set $\{0, 1\}$

 **a)** that are one-to-one?

 **b)** that assign 0 to both 1 and $n$?

 **c)** that assign 1 to exactly one of the positive integers less than $n$?

**38.** How many partial functions (see Section 2.3) are there from a set with five elements to sets with each of these number of elements?

 **a)** 1      **b)** 2      **c)** 5      **d)** 9

**39.** How many partial functions (see Definition 13 of Section 2.3) are there from a set with $m$ elements to a set with $n$ elements, where $m$ and $n$ are positive integers?

**40.** How many subsets of a set with 100 elements have more than one element?

**41.** A **palindrome** is a string whose reversal is identical to the string. How many bit strings of length $n$ are palindromes?

**42.** How many 4-element DNA sequences

 **a)** do not contain the base T?

 **b)** contain the sequence ACG?

 **c)** contain all four bases A, T, C, and G?

 **d)** contain exactly three of the four bases A, T, C, and G?

**43.** How many 4-element RNA sequences

 **a)** contain the base U?

 **b)** do not contain the sequence CUG?

 **c)** do not contain all four bases A, U, C, and G?

 **d)** contain exactly two of the four bases A, U, C, and G?

**44.** How many ways are there to seat four of a group of ten people around a circular table where two seatings are considered the same when everyone has the same immediate left and immediate right neighbor?

**45.** How many ways are there to seat six people around a circular table where two seatings are considered the same when everyone has the same two neighbors without regard to whether they are right or left neighbors?

**46.** In how many ways can a photographer at a wedding arrange 6 people in a row from a group of 10 people, where the bride and the groom are among these 10 people, if

 **a)** the bride must be in the picture?

 **b)** both the bride and groom must be in the picture?

 **c)** exactly one of the bride and the groom is in the picture?

**47.** In how many ways can a photographer at a wedding arrange six people in a row, including the bride and groom, if

 **a)** the bride must be next to the groom?

 **b)** the bride is not next to the groom?

 **c)** the bride is positioned somewhere to the left of the groom?

**48.** How many bit strings of length seven either begin with two 0s or end with three 1s?

**49.** How many bit strings of length 10 either begin with three 0s or end with two 0s?

**\*50.** How many bit strings of length 10 contain either five consecutive 0s or five consecutive 1s?

**\*\*51.** How many bit strings of length eight contain either three consecutive 0s or four consecutive 1s?

**52.** Every student in a discrete mathematics class is either a computer science or a mathematics major or is a joint major in these two subjects. How many students are in the class if there are 38 computer science majors (including joint majors), 23 mathematics majors (including joint majors), and 7 joint majors?

**53.** How many positive integers not exceeding 100 are divisible either by 4 or by 6?

**54.** How many different initials can someone have if a person has at least two, but no more than five, different initials? Assume that each initial is one of the 26 uppercase letters of the English language.

**55.** Suppose that a password for a computer system must have at least 8, but no more than 12, characters, where each character in the password is a lowercase English letter, an uppercase English letter, a digit, or one of the six special characters $*$, $>$, $<$, $!$, $+$, and $=$.

    **a)** How many different passwords are available for this computer system?

    **b)** How many of these passwords contain at least one occurrence of at least one of the six special characters?

    **c)** Using your answer to part (a), determine how long it takes a hacker to try every possible password, assuming that it takes one nanosecond for a hacker to check each possible password.

**56.** The name of a variable in the C programming language is a string that can contain uppercase letters, lowercase letters, digits, or underscores. Further, the first character in the string must be a letter, either uppercase or lowercase, or an underscore. If the name of a variable is determined by its first eight characters, how many different variables can be named in C? (Note that the name of a variable may contain fewer than eight characters.)

**57.** The name of a variable in the JAVA programming language is a string of between 1 and 65,535 characters, inclusive, where each character can be an uppercase or a lowercase letter, a dollar sign, an underscore, or a digit, except that the first character must not be a digit. Determine the number of different variable names in JAVA.

**58.** The International Telecommunications Union (ITU) specifies that a telephone number must consist of a country code with between 1 and 3 digits, except that the code 0 is not available for use as a country code, followed by a number with at most 15 digits. How many available possible telephone numbers are there that satisfy these restrictions?

**59.** Suppose that at some future time every telephone in the world is assigned a number that contains a country code 1 to 3 digits long, that is, of the form $X$, $XX$, or $XXX$, followed by a 10-digit telephone number of the form $NXX$-$NXX$-$XXXX$ (as described in Example 8). How many different telephone numbers would be available worldwide under this numbering plan?

**60.** A key in the Vigenère cryptosystem is a string of English letters, where the case of the letters does not matter. How many different keys for this cryptosystem are there with three, four, five, or six letters?

**61.** A wired equivalent privacy (WEP) key for a wireless fidelity (WiFi) network is a string of either 10, 26, or 58 hexadecimal digits. How many different WEP keys are there?

**62.** Suppose that $p$ and $q$ are prime numbers and that $n = pq$. Use the principle of inclusion–exclusion to find the number of positive integers not exceeding $n$ that are relatively prime to $n$.

**63.** Use the principle of inclusion–exclusion to find the number of positive integers less than 1,000,000 that are not divisible by either 4 or by 6.

**64.** Use a tree diagram to find the number of bit strings of length four with no three consecutive 0s.

**65.** How many ways are there to arrange the letters $a$, $b$, $c$, and $d$ such that $a$ is not followed immediately by $b$?

**66.** Use a tree diagram to find the number of ways that the World Series can occur, where the first team that wins four games out of seven wins the series.

**67.** Use a tree diagram to determine the number of subsets of $\{3, 7, 9, 11, 24\}$ with the property that the sum of the elements in the subset is less than 28.

**68. a)** Suppose that a store sells six varieties of soft drinks: cola, ginger ale, orange, root beer, lemonade, and cream soda. Use a tree diagram to determine the number of different types of bottles the store must stock to have all varieties available in all size bottles if all varieties are available in 12-ounce bottles, all but lemonade are available in 20-ounce bottles, only cola and ginger ale are available in 32-ounce bottles, and all but lemonade and cream soda are available in 64-ounce bottles?

    **b)** Answer the question in part (a) using counting rules.

**69. a)** Suppose that a popular style of running shoe is available for both men and women. The woman's shoe comes in sizes 6, 7, 8, and 9, and the man's shoe comes in sizes 8, 9, 10, 11, and 12. The man's shoe comes in white and black, while the woman's shoe comes in white, red, and black. Use a tree diagram to determine the number of different shoes that a store has to stock to have at least one pair of this type of running shoe for all available sizes and colors for both men and women.

    **b)** Answer the question in part (a) using counting rules.

**\*70.** Use the product rule to show that there are $2^{2^n}$ different truth tables for propositions in $n$ variables.

**71.** Use mathematical induction to prove the sum rule for $m$ tasks from the sum rule for two tasks.

**72.** Use mathematical induction to prove the product rule for $m$ tasks from the product rule for two tasks.

**73.** How many diagonals does a convex polygon with $n$ sides have? (Recall that a polygon is convex if every line segment connecting two points in the interior or boundary of the polygon lies entirely within this set and that a diagonal of a polygon is a line segment connecting two vertices that are not adjacent.)

**74.** Data are transmitted over the Internet in **datagrams**, which are structured blocks of bits. Each datagram contains header information organized into a maximum of 14 different fields (specifying many things, including the source and destination addresses) and a data area that contains the actual data that are transmitted. One of the 14 header fields is the **header length field** (denoted by HLEN), which is specified by the protocol to be 4 bits long and that specifies the header length in terms of 32-bit blocks of bits. For example, if HLEN = 0110, the header

is made up of six 32-bit blocks. Another of the 14 header fields is the 16-bit-long **total length field** (denoted by TOTAL LENGTH), which specifies the length in bits of the entire datagram, including both the header fields and the data area. The length of the data area is the total length of the datagram minus the length of the header.

**a)** The largest possible value of TOTAL LENGTH (which is 16 bits long) determines the maximum total length in octets (blocks of 8 bits) of an Internet datagram. What is this value?

**b)** The largest possible value of HLEN (which is 4 bits long) determines the maximum total header length in 32-bit blocks. What is this value? What is the maximum total header length in octets?

**c)** The minimum (and most common) header length is 20 octets. What is the maximum total length in octets of the data area of an Internet datagram?

**d)** How many different strings of octets in the data area can be transmitted if the header length is 20 octets and the total length is as long as possible?

# 6.2    The Pigeonhole Principle

## Introduction

Links

Suppose that a flock of 20 pigeons flies into a set of 19 pigeonholes to roost. Because there are 20 pigeons but only 19 pigeonholes, a least one of these 19 pigeonholes must have at least two pigeons in it. To see why this is true, note that if each pigeonhole had at most one pigeon in it, at most 19 pigeons, one per hole, could be accommodated. This illustrates a general principle called the **pigeonhole principle**, which states that if there are more pigeons than pigeonholes, then there must be at least one pigeonhole with at least two pigeons in it (see Figure 1). Of course, this principle applies to other objects besides pigeons and pigeonholes.

**THEOREM 1**    **THE PIGEONHOLE PRINCIPLE**    If $k$ is a positive integer and $k + 1$ or more objects are placed into $k$ boxes, then there is at least one box containing two or more of the objects.

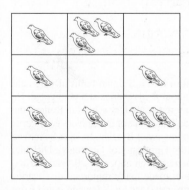
(a)

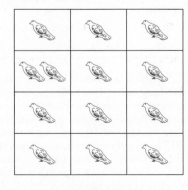
(b)

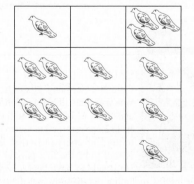
(c)

**FIGURE 1    There Are More Pigeons Than Pigeonholes.**

*Proof:* We prove the pigeonhole principle using a proof by contraposition. Suppose that none of the $k$ boxes contains more than one object. Then the total number of objects would be at most $k$. This is a contradiction, because there are at least $k + 1$ objects.    ◁

The pigeonhole principle is also called the **Dirichlet drawer principle**, after the nineteenth-century German mathematician G. Lejeune Dirichlet, who often used this principle in his work. (Dirichlet was not the first person to use this principle; a demonstration that there were at least two Parisians with the same number of hairs on their heads dates back to the 17th century—see Exercise 33.) It is an important additional proof technique supplementing those we have developed in earlier chapters. We introduce it in this chapter because of its many important applications to combinatorics.

We will illustrate the usefulness of the pigeonhole principle. We first show that it can be used to prove a useful corollary about functions.

**COROLLARY 1**    A function $f$ from a set with $k + 1$ or more elements to a set with $k$ elements is not one-to-one.

*Proof:* Suppose that for each element $y$ in the codomain of $f$ we have a box that contains all elements $x$ of the domain of $f$ such that $f(x) = y$. Because the domain contains $k + 1$ or more elements and the codomain contains only $k$ elements, the pigeonhole principle tells us that one of these boxes contains two or more elements $x$ of the domain. This means that $f$ cannot be one-to-one.    ◁

Examples 1–3 show how the pigeonhole principle is used.

**EXAMPLE 1**    Among any group of 367 people, there must be at least two with the same birthday, because there are only 366 possible birthdays.    ◀

**EXAMPLE 2**    In any group of 27 English words, there must be at least two that begin with the same letter, because there are 26 letters in the English alphabet.    ◀

**EXAMPLE 3**    How many students must be in a class to guarantee that at least two students receive the same score on the final exam, if the exam is graded on a scale from 0 to 100 points?

*Solution:* There are 101 possible scores on the final. The pigeonhole principle shows that among any 102 students there must be at least 2 students with the same score.    ◀

**Links** 🖱

G. LEJEUNE DIRICHLET (1805–1859)    G. Lejeune Dirichlet was born into a Belgian family living near Cologne, Germany. His father was a postmaster. He became passionate about mathematics at a young age. He was spending all his spare money on mathematics books by the time he entered secondary school in Bonn at the age of 12. At 14 he entered the Jesuit College in Cologne, and at 16 he began his studies at the University of Paris. In 1825 he returned to Germany and was appointed to a position at the University of Breslau. In 1828 he moved to the University of Berlin. In 1855 he was chosen to succeed Gauss at the University of Göttingen. Dirichlet is said to be the first person to master Gauss's *Disquisitiones Arithmeticae*, which appeared 20 years earlier. He is said to have kept a copy at his side even when he traveled. Dirichlet made many important discoveries in number theory, including the theorem that there are infinitely many primes in arithmetical progressions $an + b$ when $a$ and $b$ are relatively prime. He proved the $n = 5$ case of Fermat's last theorem, that there are no nontrivial solutions in integers to $x^5 + y^5 = z^5$. Dirichlet also made many contributions to analysis. Dirichlet was considered to be an excellent teacher who could explain ideas with great clarity. He was married to Rebecca Mendelssohn, one of the sisters of the composer Frederick Mendelssohn.

The pigeonhole principle is a useful tool in many proofs, including proofs of surprising results, such as that given in Example 4.

**EXAMPLE 4**

Show that for every integer $n$ there is a multiple of $n$ that has only 0s and 1s in its decimal expansion.

*Solution:* Let $n$ be a positive integer. Consider the $n + 1$ integers $1, 11, 111, \ldots, 11 \ldots 1$ (where the last integer in this list is the integer with $n + 1$ 1s in its decimal expansion). Note that there are $n$ possible remainders when an integer is divided by $n$. Because there are $n + 1$ integers in this list, by the pigeonhole principle there must be two with the same remainder when divided by $n$. The larger of these integers less the smaller one is a multiple of $n$, which has a decimal expansion consisting entirely of 0s and 1s. ◀

## The Generalized Pigeonhole Principle

The pigeonhole principle states that there must be at least two objects in the same box when there are more objects than boxes. However, even more can be said when the number of objects exceeds a multiple of the number of boxes. For instance, among any set of 21 decimal digits there must be 3 that are the same. This follows because when 21 objects are distributed into 10 boxes, one box must have more than 2 objects.

**THEOREM 2**    **THE GENERALIZED PIGEONHOLE PRINCIPLE**    If $N$ objects are placed into $k$ boxes, then there is at least one box containing at least $\lceil N/k \rceil$ objects.

*Proof:* We will use a proof by contraposition. Suppose that none of the boxes contains more than $\lceil N/k \rceil - 1$ objects. Then, the total number of objects is at most

$$k \left( \left\lceil \frac{N}{k} \right\rceil - 1 \right) < k \left( \left( \frac{N}{k} + 1 \right) - 1 \right) = N,$$

where the inequality $\lceil N/k \rceil < (N/k) + 1$ has been used. This is a contradiction because there are a total of $N$ objects. ◁

A common type of problem asks for the minimum number of objects such that at least $r$ of these objects must be in one of $k$ boxes when these objects are distributed among the boxes. When we have $N$ objects, the generalized pigeonhole principle tells us there must be at least $r$ objects in one of the boxes as long as $\lceil N/k \rceil \geq r$. The smallest integer $N$ with $N/k > r - 1$, namely, $N = k(r - 1) + 1$, is the smallest integer satisfying the inequality $\lceil N/k \rceil \geq r$. Could a smaller value of $N$ suffice? The answer is no, because if we had $k(r - 1)$ objects, we could put $r - 1$ of them in each of the $k$ boxes and no box would have at least $r$ objects.

When thinking about problems of this type, it is useful to consider how you can avoid having at least $r$ objects in one of the boxes as you add successive objects. To avoid adding a $r$th object to any box, you eventually end up with $r - 1$ objects in each box. There is no way to add the next object without putting an $r$th object in that box.

Examples 5–8 illustrate how the generalized pigeonhole principle is applied.

**EXAMPLE 5**    Among 100 people there are at least $\lceil 100/12 \rceil = 9$ who were born in the same month. ◀

**EXAMPLE 6**

What is the minimum number of students required in a discrete mathematics class to be sure that at least six will receive the same grade, if there are five possible grades, A, B, C, D, and F?

*Solution:* The minimum number of students needed to ensure that at least six students receive the same grade is the smallest integer $N$ such that $\lceil N/5 \rceil = 6$. The smallest such integer is $N = 5 \cdot 5 + 1 = 26$. If you have only 25 students, it is possible for there to be five who have received each grade so that no six students have received the same grade. Thus, 26 is the minimum number of students needed to ensure that at least six students will receive the same grade. ◀

**EXAMPLE 7**

**a)** How many cards must be selected from a standard deck of 52 cards to guarantee that at least three cards of the same suit are chosen?
**b)** How many must be selected to guarantee that at least three hearts are selected?

A standard deck of 52 cards has 13 kinds of cards, with four cards of each of kind, one in each of the four suits, hearts, diamonds, spades, and clubs.

*Solution:* **a)** Suppose there are four boxes, one for each suit, and as cards are selected they are placed in the box reserved for cards of that suit. Using the generalized pigeonhole principle, we see that if $N$ cards are selected, there is at least one box containing at least $\lceil N/4 \rceil$ cards. Consequently, we know that at least three cards of one suit are selected if $\lceil N/4 \rceil \geq 3$. The smallest integer $N$ such that $\lceil N/4 \rceil \geq 3$ is $N = 2 \cdot 4 + 1 = 9$, so nine cards suffice. Note that if eight cards are selected, it is possible to have two cards of each suit, so more than eight cards are needed. Consequently, nine cards must be selected to guarantee that at least three cards of one suit are chosen. One good way to think about this is to note that after the eighth card is chosen, there is no way to avoid having a third card of some suit.

**b)** We do not use the generalized pigeonhole principle to answer this question, because we want to make sure that there are three hearts, not just three cards of one suit. Note that in the worst case, we can select all the clubs, diamonds, and spades, 39 cards in all, before we select a single heart. The next three cards will be all hearts, so we may need to select 42 cards to get three hearts. ◀

**EXAMPLE 8**

What is the least number of area codes needed to guarantee that the 25 million phones in a state can be assigned distinct 10-digit telephone numbers? (Assume that telephone numbers are of the form *NXX-NXX-XXXX*, where the first three digits form the area code, $N$ represents a digit from 2 to 9 inclusive, and $X$ represents any digit.)

*Solution:* There are eight million different phone numbers of the form *NXX-XXXX* (as shown in Example 8 of Section 6.1). Hence, by the generalized pigeonhole principle, among 25 million telephones, at least $\lceil 25,000,000/8,000,000 \rceil = 4$ of them must have identical phone numbers. Hence, at least four area codes are required to ensure that all 10-digit numbers are different. ◀

Example 9, although not an application of the generalized pigeonhole principle, makes use of similar principles.

**EXAMPLE 9**

Suppose that a computer science laboratory has 15 workstations and 10 servers. A cable can be used to directly connect a workstation to a server. For each server, only one direct connection to that server can be active at any time. We want to guarantee that at any time any set of 10 or fewer workstations can simultaneously access different servers via direct connections. Although we could do this by connecting every workstation directly to every server (using 150 connections), what is the minimum number of direct connections needed to achieve this goal?

*Solution:* Suppose that we label the workstations $W_1, W_2, \ldots, W_{15}$ and the servers $S_1, S_2, \ldots, S_{10}$. Furthermore, suppose that we connect $W_k$ to $S_k$ for $k = 1, 2, \ldots, 10$ and each of $W_{11}, W_{12}, W_{13}, W_{14},$ and $W_{15}$ to all 10 servers. We have a total of 60 direct connections. Clearly any set of 10 or fewer workstations can simultaneously access different servers. We see this by noting that if workstation $W_j$ is included with $1 \leq j \leq 10$, it can access server $S_j$, and for each workstation $W_k$ with $k \geq 11$ included, there must be a corresponding workstation $W_j$

with $1 \leq j \leq 10$ not included, so $W_k$ can access server $S_j$. (This follows because there are at least as many available servers $S_j$ as there are workstations $W_j$ with $1 \leq j \leq 10$ not included.)

Now suppose there are fewer than 60 direct connections between workstations and servers. Then some server would be connected to at most $\lfloor 59/10 \rfloor = 5$ workstations. (If all servers were connected to at least six workstations, there would be at least $6 \cdot 10 = 60$ direct connections.) This means that the remaining nine servers are not enough to allow the other 10 workstations to simultaneously access different servers. Consequently, at least 60 direct connections are needed. It follows that 60 is the answer.    ◀

## Some Elegant Applications of the Pigeonhole Principle

In many interesting applications of the pigeonhole principle, the objects to be placed in boxes must be chosen in a clever way. A few such applications will be described here.

**EXAMPLE 10**    During a month with 30 days, a baseball team plays at least one game a day, but no more than 45 games. Show that there must be a period of some number of consecutive days during which the team must play exactly 14 games.

*Solution:* Let $a_j$ be the number of games played on or before the $j$th day of the month. Then $a_1, a_2, \ldots, a_{30}$ is an increasing sequence of distinct positive integers, with $1 \leq a_j \leq 45$. Moreover, $a_1 + 14, a_2 + 14, \ldots, a_{30} + 14$ is also an increasing sequence of distinct positive integers, with $15 \leq a_j + 14 \leq 59$.

The 60 positive integers $a_1, a_2, \ldots, a_{30}, a_1 + 14, a_2 + 14, \ldots, a_{30} + 14$ are all less than or equal to 59. Hence, by the pigeonhole principle two of these integers are equal. Because the integers $a_j$, $j = 1, 2, \ldots, 30$ are all distinct and the integers $a_j + 14$, $j = 1, 2, \ldots, 30$ are all distinct, there must be indices $i$ and $j$ with $a_i = a_j + 14$. This means that exactly 14 games were played from day $j + 1$ to day $i$.    ◀

**EXAMPLE 11**    Show that among any $n + 1$ positive integers not exceeding $2n$ there must be an integer that divides one of the other integers.

*Solution:* Write each of the $n + 1$ integers $a_1, a_2, \ldots, a_{n+1}$ as a power of 2 times an odd integer. In other words, let $a_j = 2^{k_j} q_j$ for $j = 1, 2, \ldots, n + 1$, where $k_j$ is a nonnegative integer and $q_j$ is odd. The integers $q_1, q_2, \ldots, q_{n+1}$ are all odd positive integers less than $2n$. Because there are only $n$ odd positive integers less than $2n$, it follows from the pigeonhole principle that two of the integers $q_1, q_2, \ldots, q_{n+1}$ must be equal. Therefore, there are distinct integers $i$ and $j$ such that $q_i = q_j$. Let $q$ be the common value of $q_i$ and $q_j$. Then, $a_i = 2^{k_i} q$ and $a_j = 2^{k_j} q$. It follows that if $k_i < k_j$, then $a_i$ divides $a_j$; while if $k_i > k_j$, then $a_j$ divides $a_i$.    ◀

A clever application of the pigeonhole principle shows the existence of an increasing or a decreasing subsequence of a certain length in a sequence of distinct integers. We review some definitions before this application is presented. Suppose that $a_1, a_2, \ldots, a_N$ is a sequence of real numbers. A **subsequence** of this sequence is a sequence of the form $a_{i_1}, a_{i_2}, \ldots, a_{i_m}$, where $1 \leq i_1 < i_2 < \cdots < i_m \leq N$. Hence, a subsequence is a sequence obtained from the original sequence by including some of the terms of the original sequence in their original order, and perhaps not including other terms. A sequence is called **strictly increasing** if each term is larger than the one that precedes it, and it is called **strictly decreasing** if each term is smaller than the one that precedes it.

**THEOREM 3**    Every sequence of $n^2 + 1$ distinct real numbers contains a subsequence of length $n + 1$ that is either strictly increasing or strictly decreasing.

We give an example before presenting the proof of Theorem 3.

**EXAMPLE 12**   The sequence 8, 11, 9, 1, 4, 6, 12, 10, 5, 7 contains 10 terms. Note that $10 = 3^2 + 1$. There are four strictly increasing subsequences of length four, namely, 1, 4, 6, 12; 1, 4, 6, 7; 1, 4, 6, 10; and 1, 4, 5, 7. There is also a strictly decreasing subsequence of length four, namely, 11, 9, 6, 5. ◄

The proof of the theorem will now be given.

*Proof:* Let $a_1, a_2, \ldots, a_{n^2+1}$ be a sequence of $n^2 + 1$ distinct real numbers. Associate an ordered pair with each term of the sequence, namely, associate $(i_k, d_k)$ to the term $a_k$, where $i_k$ is the length of the longest increasing subsequence starting at $a_k$, and $d_k$ is the length of the longest decreasing subsequence starting at $a_k$.

Suppose that there are no increasing or decreasing subsequences of length $n + 1$. Then $i_k$ and $d_k$ are both positive integers less than or equal to $n$, for $k = 1, 2, \ldots, n^2 + 1$. Hence, by the product rule there are $n^2$ possible ordered pairs for $(i_k, d_k)$. By the pigeonhole principle, two of these $n^2 + 1$ ordered pairs are equal. In other words, there exist terms $a_s$ and $a_t$, with $s < t$ such that $i_s = i_t$ and $d_s = d_t$. We will show that this is impossible. Because the terms of the sequence are distinct, either $a_s < a_t$ or $a_s > a_t$. If $a_s < a_t$, then, because $i_s = i_t$, an increasing subsequence of length $i_t + 1$ can be built starting at $a_s$, by taking $a_s$ followed by an increasing subsequence of length $i_t$ beginning at $a_t$. This is a contradiction. Similarly, if $a_s > a_t$, the same reasoning shows that $d_s$ must be greater than $d_t$, which is a contradiction. ◁

The final example shows how the generalized pigeonhole principle can be applied to an important part of combinatorics called **Ramsey theory**, after the English mathematician F. P. Ramsey. In general, Ramsey theory deals with the distribution of subsets of elements of sets.

**EXAMPLE 13**   Assume that in a group of six people, each pair of individuals consists of two friends or two enemies. Show that there are either three mutual friends or three mutual enemies in the group.

*Solution:* Let $A$ be one of the six people. Of the five other people in the group, there are either three or more who are friends of $A$, or three or more who are enemies of $A$. This follows from the generalized pigeonhole principle, because when five objects are divided into two sets, one of the sets has at least $\lceil 5/2 \rceil = 3$ elements. In the former case, suppose that $B$, $C$, and $D$ are friends of $A$. If any two of these three individuals are friends, then these two and $A$ form a group of three mutual friends. Otherwise, $B$, $C$, and $D$ form a set of three mutual enemies. The proof in the latter case, when there are three or more enemies of $A$, proceeds in a similar manner. ◄

The **Ramsey number** $R(m, n)$, where $m$ and $n$ are positive integers greater than or equal to 2, denotes the minimum number of people at a party such that there are either $m$ mutual friends or $n$ mutual enemies, assuming that every pair of people at the party are friends or enemies. Example 13 shows that $R(3, 3) \leq 6$. We conclude that $R(3, 3) = 6$ because in a group of five

people where every two people are friends or enemies, there may not be three mutual friends or three mutual enemies (see Exercise 26).

It is possible to prove some useful properties about Ramsey numbers, but for the most part it is difficult to find their exact values. Note that by symmetry it can be shown that $R(m, n) = R(n, m)$ (see Exercise 30). We also have $R(2, n) = n$ for every positive integer $n \geq 2$ (see Exercise 29). The exact values of only nine Ramsey numbers $R(m, n)$ with $3 \leq m \leq n$ are known, including $R(4, 4) = 18$. Only bounds are known for many other Ramsey numbers, including $R(5, 5)$, which is known to satisfy $43 \leq R(5, 5) \leq 49$. The reader interested in learning more about Ramsey numbers should consult [MiRo91] or [GrRoSp90].

# Exercises

1. Show that in any set of six classes, each meeting regularly once a week on a particular day of the week, there must be two that meet on the same day, assuming that no classes are held on weekends.

2. Show that if there are 30 students in a class, then at least two have last names that begin with the same letter.

3. A drawer contains a dozen brown socks and a dozen black socks, all unmatched. A man takes socks out at random in the dark.
   a) How many socks must he take out to be sure that he has at least two socks of the same color?
   b) How many socks must he take out to be sure that he has at least two black socks?

4. A bowl contains 10 red balls and 10 blue balls. A woman selects balls at random without looking at them.
   a) How many balls must she select to be sure of having at least three balls of the same color?
   b) How many balls must she select to be sure of having at least three blue balls?

5. Show that among any group of five (not necessarily consecutive) integers, there are two with the same remainder when divided by 4.

6. Let $d$ be a positive integer. Show that among any group of $d + 1$ (not necessarily consecutive) integers there are two with exactly the same remainder when they are divided by $d$.

7. Let $n$ be a positive integer. Show that in any set of $n$ consecutive integers there is exactly one divisible by $n$.

8. Show that if $f$ is a function from $S$ to $T$, where $S$ and $T$ are finite sets with $|S| > |T|$, then there are elements $s_1$ and $s_2$ in $S$ such that $f(s_1) = f(s_2)$, or in other words, $f$ is not one-to-one.

9. What is the minimum number of students, each of whom comes from one of the 50 states, who must be enrolled in a university to guarantee that there are at least 100 who come from the same state?

*10. Let $(x_i, y_i), i = 1, 2, 3, 4, 5$, be a set of five distinct points with integer coordinates in the $xy$ plane. Show that the midpoint of the line joining at least one pair of these points has integer coordinates.

*11. Let $(x_i, y_i, z_i), i = 1, 2, 3, 4, 5, 6, 7, 8, 9$, be a set of nine distinct points with integer coordinates in $xyz$ space. Show that the midpoint of at least one pair of these points has integer coordinates.

12. How many ordered pairs of integers $(a, b)$ are needed to guarantee that there are two ordered pairs $(a_1, b_1)$ and $(a_2, b_2)$ such that $a_1 \bmod 5 = a_2 \bmod 5$ and $b_1 \bmod 5 = b_2 \bmod 5$?

13. a) Show that if five integers are selected from the first eight positive integers, there must be a pair of these integers with a sum equal to 9.
    b) Is the conclusion in part (a) true if four integers are selected rather than five?

14. a) Show that if seven integers are selected from the first 10 positive integers, there must be at least two pairs of these integers with the sum 11.
    b) Is the conclusion in part (a) true if six integers are selected rather than seven?

15. How many numbers must be selected from the set $\{1, 2, 3, 4, 5, 6\}$ to guarantee that at least one pair of these numbers add up to 7?

16. How many numbers must be selected from the set $\{1, 3, 5, 7, 9, 11, 13, 15\}$ to guarantee that at least one pair of these numbers add up to 16?

17. A company stores products in a warehouse. Storage bins in this warehouse are specified by their aisle, location in the aisle, and shelf. There are 50 aisles, 85 horizontal locations in each aisle, and 5 shelves throughout the warehouse. What is the least number of products the company can have so that at least two products must be stored in the same bin?

18. Suppose that there are nine students in a discrete mathematics class at a small college.
    a) Show that the class must have at least five male students or at least five female students.
    b) Show that the class must have at least three male students or at least seven female students.

19. Suppose that every student in a discrete mathematics class of 25 students is a freshman, a sophomore, or a junior.
    a) Show that there are at least nine freshmen, at least nine sophomores, or at least nine juniors in the class.

**b)** Show that there are either at least three freshmen, at least 19 sophomores, or at least five juniors in the class.

**20.** Find an increasing subsequence of maximal length and a decreasing subsequence of maximal length in the sequence 22, 5, 7, 2, 23, 10, 15, 21, 3, 17.

**21.** Construct a sequence of 16 positive integers that has no increasing or decreasing subsequence of five terms.

**22.** Show that if there are 101 people of different heights standing in a line, it is possible to find 11 people in the order they are standing in the line with heights that are either increasing or decreasing.

**\*23.** Show that whenever 25 girls and 25 boys are seated around a circular table there is always a person both of whose neighbors are boys.

**\*\*24.** Suppose that 21 girls and 21 boys enter a mathematics competition. Furthermore, suppose that each entrant solves at most six questions, and for every boy-girl pair, there is at least one question that they both solved. Show that there is a question that was solved by at least three girls and at least three boys.

**\*25.** Describe an algorithm in pseudocode for producing the largest increasing or decreasing subsequence of a sequence of distinct integers.

**26.** Show that in a group of five people (where any two people are either friends or enemies), there are not necessarily three mutual friends or three mutual enemies.

**27.** Show that in a group of 10 people (where any two people are either friends or enemies), there are either three mutual friends or four mutual enemies, and there are either three mutual enemies or four mutual friends.

**28.** Use Exercise 27 to show that among any group of 20 people (where any two people are either friends or enemies), there are either four mutual friends or four mutual enemies.

**29.** Show that if $n$ is an integer with $n \geq 2$, then the Ramsey number $R(2, n)$ equals $n$. (Recall that Ramsey numbers were discussed after Example 13 in Section 6.2.)

**30.** Show that if $m$ and $n$ are integers with $m \geq 2$ and $n \geq 2$, then the Ramsey numbers $R(m, n)$ and $R(n, m)$ are equal. (Recall that Ramsey numbers were discussed after Example 13 in Section 6.2.)

**31.** Show that there are at least six people in California (population: 37 million) with the same three initials who were born on the same day of the year (but not necessarily in the same year). Assume that everyone has three initials.

**32.** Show that if there are 100,000,000 wage earners in the United States who earn less than 1,000,000 dollars (but at least a penny), then there are two who earned exactly the same amount of money, to the penny, last year.

**33.** In the 17th century, there were more than 800,000 inhabitants of Paris. At the time, it was believed that no one had more than 200,000 hairs on their head. Assuming these numbers are correct and that everyone has at least one hair on their head (that is, no one is completely bald), use the pigeonhole principle to show, as the French writer Pierre

Nicole did, that there had to be two Parisians with the same number of hairs on their heads. Then use the generalized pigeonhole principle to show that there had to be at least five Parisians at that time with the same number of hairs on their heads.

**34.** Assuming that no one has more than 1,000,000 hairs on the head of any person and that the population of New York City was 8,008,278 in 2010, show there had to be at least nine people in New York City in 2010 with the same number of hairs on their heads.

**35.** There are 38 different time periods during which classes at a university can be scheduled. If there are 677 different classes, how many different rooms will be needed?

**36.** A computer network consists of six computers. Each computer is directly connected to at least one of the other computers. Show that there are at least two computers in the network that are directly connected to the same number of other computers.

**37.** A computer network consists of six computers. Each computer is directly connected to zero or more of the other computers. Show that there are at least two computers in the network that are directly connected to the same number of other computers. [*Hint:* It is impossible to have a computer linked to none of the others and a computer linked to all the others.]

**38.** Find the least number of cables required to connect eight computers to four printers to guarantee that for every choice of four of the eight computers, these four computers can directly access four different printers. Justify your answer.

**39.** Find the least number of cables required to connect 100 computers to 20 printers to guarantee that 2every subset of 20 computers can directly access 20 different printers. (Here, the assumptions about cables and computers are the same as in Example 9.) Justify your answer.

**\*40.** Prove that at a party where there are at least two people, there are two people who know the same number of other people there.

**41.** An arm wrestler is the champion for a period of 75 hours. (Here, by an hour, we mean a period starting from an exact hour, such as 1 P.M., until the next hour.) The arm wrestler had at least one match an hour, but no more than 125 total matches. Show that there is a period of consecutive hours during which the arm wrestler had exactly 24 matches.

**\*42.** Is the statement in Exercise 41 true if 24 is replaced by
**a)** 2?  **b)** 23?  **c)** 25?  **d)** 30?

**43.** Show that if $f$ is a function from $S$ to $T$, where $S$ and $T$ are nonempty finite sets and $m = \lceil |S| / |T| \rceil$, then there are at least $m$ elements of $S$ mapped to the same value of $T$. That is, show that there are distinct elements $s_1, s_2, \ldots, s_m$ of $S$ such that $f(s_1) = f(s_2) = \cdots = f(s_m)$.

**44.** There are 51 houses on a street. Each house has an address between 1000 and 1099, inclusive. Show that at least two houses have addresses that are consecutive integers.

**\*45.** Let $x$ be an irrational number. Show that for some positive integer $j$ not exceeding the positive integer $n$, the absolute value of the difference between $jx$ and the nearest integer to $jx$ is less than $1/n$.

**46.** Let $n_1, n_2, \ldots, n_t$ be positive integers. Show that if $n_1 + n_2 + \cdots + n_t - t + 1$ objects are placed into $t$ boxes, then for some $i$, $i = 1, 2, \ldots, t$, the $i$th box contains at least $n_i$ objects.

**\*47.** An alternative proof of Theorem 3 based on the generalized pigeonhole principle is outlined in this exercise. The notation used is the same as that used in the proof in the text.

**a)** Assume that $i_k \leq n$ for $k = 1, 2, \ldots, n^2 + 1$. Use the generalized pigeonhole principle to show that there are $n + 1$ terms $a_{k_1}, a_{k_2}, \ldots, a_{k_{n+1}}$ with $i_{k_1} = i_{k_2} = \cdots = i_{k_{n+1}}$, where $1 \leq k_1 < k_2 < \cdots < k_{n+1}$.

**b)** Show that $a_{k_j} > a_{k_{j+1}}$ for $j = 1, 2, \ldots, n$. [*Hint:* Assume that $a_{k_j} < a_{k_{j+1}}$, and show that this implies that $i_{k_j} > i_{k_{j+1}}$, which is a contradiction.]

**c)** Use parts (a) and (b) to show that if there is no increasing subsequence of length $n + 1$, then there must be a decreasing subsequence of this length.

**6.3**    # Permutations and Combinations

## Introduction

Many counting problems can be solved by finding the number of ways to arrange a specified number of distinct elements of a set of a particular size, where the order of these elements matters. Many other counting problems can be solved by finding the number of ways to select a particular number of elements from a set of a particular size, where the order of the elements selected does not matter. For example, in how many ways can we select three students from a group of five students to stand in line for a picture? How many different committees of three students can be formed from a group of four students? In this section we will develop methods to answer questions such as these.

## Permutations

We begin by solving the first question posed in the introduction to this section, as well as related questions.

**EXAMPLE 1**    In how many ways can we select three students from a group of five students to stand in line for a picture? In how many ways can we arrange all five of these students in a line for a picture?

*Solution:* First, note that the order in which we select the students matters. There are five ways to select the first student to stand at the start of the line. Once this student has been selected, there are four ways to select the second student in the line. After the first and second students have been selected, there are three ways to select the third student in the line. By the product rule, there are $5 \cdot 4 \cdot 3 = 60$ ways to select three students from a group of five students to stand in line for a picture.

To arrange all five students in a line for a picture, we select the first student in five ways, the second in four ways, the third in three ways, the fourth in two ways, and the fifth in one way. Consequently, there are $5 \cdot 4 \cdot 3 \cdot 2 \cdot 1 = 120$ ways to arrange all five students in a line for a picture.    ◄

Example 1 illustrates how ordered arrangements of distinct objects can be counted. This leads to some terminology.

A **permutation** of a set of distinct objects is an ordered arrangement of these objects. We also are interested in ordered arrangements of some of the elements of a set. An ordered arrangement of $r$ elements of a set is called an ***r*-permutation**.

**EXAMPLE 2**  Let $S = \{1, 2, 3\}$. The ordered arrangement $3, 1, 2$ is a permutation of $S$. The ordered arrangement $3, 2$ is a 2-permutation of $S$. ◀

The number of $r$-permutations of a set with $n$ elements is denoted by $P(n, r)$. We can find $P(n, r)$ using the product rule.

**EXAMPLE 3**  Let $S = \{a, b, c\}$. The 2-permutations of $S$ are the ordered arrangements $a, b; a, c; b, a; b, c; c, a;$ and $c, b$. Consequently, there are six 2-permutations of this set with three elements. There are always six 2-permutations of a set with three elements. There are three ways to choose the first element of the arrangement. There are two ways to choose the second element of the arrangement, because it must be different from the first element. Hence, by the product rule, we see that $P(3, 2) = 3 \cdot 2 = 6$. the first element. By the product rule, it follows that $P(3, 2) = 3 \cdot 2 = 6$. ◀

We now use the product rule to find a formula for $P(n, r)$ whenever $n$ and $r$ are positive integers with $1 \leq r \leq n$.

**THEOREM 1**  If $n$ is a positive integer and $r$ is an integer with $1 \leq r \leq n$, then there are

$$P(n, r) = n(n - 1)(n - 2) \cdots (n - r + 1)$$

$r$-permutations of a set with $n$ distinct elements.

*Proof:* We will use the product rule to prove that this formula is correct. The first element of the permutation can be chosen in $n$ ways because there are $n$ elements in the set. There are $n - 1$ ways to choose the second element of the permutation, because there are $n - 1$ elements left in the set after using the element picked for the first position. Similarly, there are $n - 2$ ways to choose the third element, and so on, until there are exactly $n - (r - 1) = n - r + 1$ ways to choose the $r$th element. Consequently, by the product rule, there are

$$n(n - 1)(n - 2) \cdots (n - r + 1)$$

$r$-permutations of the set. ◁

Note that $P(n, 0) = 1$ whenever $n$ is a nonnegative integer because there is exactly one way to order zero elements. That is, there is exactly one list with no elements in it, namely the empty list.

We now state a useful corollary of Theorem 1.

**COROLLARY 1**  If $n$ and $r$ are integers with $0 \leq r \leq n$, then $P(n, r) = \dfrac{n!}{(n - r)!}$.

*Proof:* When $n$ and $r$ are integers with $1 \leq r \leq n$, by Theorem 1 we have

$$P(n, r) = n(n - 1)(n - 2) \cdots (n - r + 1) = \frac{n!}{(n - r)!}$$

Because $\dfrac{n!}{(n - 0)!} = \dfrac{n!}{n!} = 1$ whenever $n$ is a nonnegative integer, we see that the formula $P(n, r) = \dfrac{n!}{(n - r)!}$ also holds when $r = 0$. ◁

By Theorem 1 we know that if $n$ is a positive integer, then $P(n, n) = n!$. We will illustrate this result with some examples.

**EXAMPLE 4** How many ways are there to select a first-prize winner, a second-prize winner, and a third-prize winner from 100 different people who have entered a contest?

*Solution:* Because it matters which person wins which prize, the number of ways to pick the three prize winners is the number of ordered selections of three elements from a set of 100 elements, that is, the number of 3-permutations of a set of 100 elements. Consequently, the answer is

$$P(100, 3) = 100 \cdot 99 \cdot 98 = 970,200.$$ ◀

**EXAMPLE 5** Suppose that there are eight runners in a race. The winner receives a gold medal, the second-place finisher receives a silver medal, and the third-place finisher receives a bronze medal. How many different ways are there to award these medals, if all possible outcomes of the race can occur and there are no ties?

*Solution:* The number of different ways to award the medals is the number of 3-permutations of a set with eight elements. Hence, there are $P(8, 3) = 8 \cdot 7 \cdot 6 = 336$ possible ways to award the medals. ◀

**EXAMPLE 6** Suppose that a saleswoman has to visit eight different cities. She must begin her trip in a specified city, but she can visit the other seven cities in any order she wishes. How many possible orders can the saleswoman use when visiting these cities?

*Solution:* The number of possible paths between the cities is the number of permutations of seven elements, because the first city is determined, but the remaining seven can be ordered arbitrarily. Consequently, there are $7! = 7 \cdot 6 \cdot 5 \cdot 4 \cdot 3 \cdot 2 \cdot 1 = 5040$ ways for the saleswoman to choose her tour. If, for instance, the saleswoman wishes to find the path between the cities with minimum distance, and she computes the total distance for each possible path, she must consider a total of 5040 paths! ◀

**EXAMPLE 7** How many permutations of the letters $ABCDEFGH$ contain the string $ABC$?

*Solution:* Because the letters $ABC$ must occur as a block, we can find the answer by finding the number of permutations of six objects, namely, the block $ABC$ and the individual letters $D$, $E$, $F$, $G$, and $H$. Because these six objects can occur in any order, there are $6! = 720$ permutations of the letters $ABCDEFGH$ in which $ABC$ occurs as a block. ◀

## Combinations

We now turn our attention to counting unordered selections of objects. We begin by solving a question posed in the introduction to this section of the chapter.

**EXAMPLE 8** How many different committees of three students can be formed from a group of four students?

*Solution:* To answer this question, we need only find the number of subsets with three elements from the set containing the four students. We see that there are four such subsets, one for each of the four students, because choosing three students is the same as choosing one of the four students to leave out of the group. This means that there are four ways to choose the three students for the committee, where the order in which these students are chosen does not matter. ◀

Links

Example 8 illustrates that many counting problems can be solved by finding the number of subsets of a particular size of a set with $n$ elements, where $n$ is a positive integer.

An **$r$-combination** of elements of a set is an unordered selection of $r$ elements from the set. Thus, an $r$-combination is simply a subset of the set with $r$ elements.

**EXAMPLE 9**    Let $S$ be the set $\{1, 2, 3, 4\}$. Then $\{1, 3, 4\}$ is a 3-combination from $S$. (Note that $\{4, 1, 3\}$ is the same 3-combination as $\{1, 3, 4\}$, because the order in which the elements of a set are listed does not matter.) ◀

The number of $r$-combinations of a set with $n$ distinct elements is denoted by $C(n, r)$. Note that $C(n, r)$ is also denoted by $\binom{n}{r}$ and is called a **binomial coefficient**. We will learn where this terminology comes from in Section 6.4.

**EXAMPLE 10**    We see that $C(4, 2) = 6$, because the 2-combinations of $\{a, b, c, d\}$ are the six subsets $\{a, b\}$, $\{a, c\}$, $\{a, d\}$, $\{b, c\}$, $\{b, d\}$, and $\{c, d\}$. ◀

We can determine the number of $r$-combinations of a set with $n$ elements using the formula for the number of $r$-permutations of a set. To do this, note that the $r$-permutations of a set can be obtained by first forming $r$-combinations and then ordering the elements in these combinations. The proof of Theorem 2, which gives the value of $C(n, r)$, is based on this observation.

**THEOREM 2**    The number of $r$-combinations of a set with $n$ elements, where $n$ is a nonnegative integer and $r$ is an integer with $0 \leq r \leq n$, equals

$$C(n, r) = \frac{n!}{r! \, (n - r)!}.$$

*Proof:* The $P(n, r)$ $r$-permutations of the set can be obtained by forming the $C(n, r)$ $r$-combinations of the set, and then ordering the elements in each $r$-combination, which can be done in $P(r, r)$ ways. Consequently, by the product rule,

$$P(n, r) = C(n, r) \cdot P(r, r).$$

This implies that

$$C(n, r) = \frac{P(n, r)}{P(r, r)} = \frac{n!/(n - r)!}{r!/(r - r)!} = \frac{n!}{r! \, (n - r)!}.$$

We can also use the division rule for counting to construct a proof of this theorem. Because the order of elements in a combination does not matter and there are $P(r, r)$ ways to order $r$ elements in an $r$-combination of $n$ elements, each of the $C(n, r)$ $r$-combinations of a set with $n$ elements corresponds to exactly $P(r, r)$ $r$-permutations. Hence, by the division rule, $C(n, r) = \frac{P(n,r)}{P(r,r)}$, which implies as before that $C(n, r) = \frac{n!}{r! \, (n-r)!}$. ◁

The formula in Theorem 2, although explicit, is not helpful when $C(n, r)$ is computed for large values of $n$ and $r$. The reasons are that it is practical to compute exact values of factorials exactly only for small integer values, and when floating point arithmetic is used, the formula in Theorem 2 may produce a value that is not an integer. When computing $C(n, r)$, first note that when we cancel out $(n - r)!$ from the numerator and denominator of the expression for $C(n, r)$ in Theorem 2, we obtain

$$C(n, r) = \frac{n!}{r! \, (n - r)!} = \frac{n(n - 1) \cdots (n - r + 1)}{r!}.$$

Consequently, to compute $C(n, r)$ you can cancel out all the terms in the larger factorial in the denominator from the numerator and denominator, then multiply all the terms that do not cancel in the numerator and finally divide by the smaller factorial in the denominator. [When doing this calculation by hand, instead of by machine, it is also worthwhile to factor out common factors in the numerator $n(n-1)\cdots(n-r+1)$ and in the denominator $r!$.] Note that many calculators have a built-in function for $C(n, r)$ that can be used for relatively small values of $n$ and $r$ and many computational programs can be used to find $C(n, r)$. [Such functions may be called *choose(n, k)* or *binom(n, k)*].

Example 11 illustrates how $C(n, k)$ is computed when $k$ is relatively small compared to $n$ and when $k$ is close to $n$. It also illustrates a key identity enjoyed by the numbers $C(n, k)$.

**EXAMPLE 11**    How many poker hands of five cards can be dealt from a standard deck of 52 cards? Also, how many ways are there to select 47 cards from a standard deck of 52 cards?

*Solution:* Because the order in which the five cards are dealt from a deck of 52 cards does not matter, there are

$$C(52, 5) = \frac{52!}{5!47!}$$

different hands of five cards that can be dealt. To compute the value of $C(52, 5)$, first divide the numerator and denominator by 47! to obtain

$$C(52, 5) = \frac{52 \cdot 51 \cdot 50 \cdot 49 \cdot 48}{5 \cdot 4 \cdot 3 \cdot 2 \cdot 1}.$$

This expression can be simplified by first dividing the factor 5 in the denominator into the factor 50 in the numerator to obtain a factor 10 in the numerator, then dividing the factor 4 in the denominator into the factor 48 in the numerator to obtain a factor of 12 in the numerator, then dividing the factor 3 in the denominator into the factor 51 in the numerator to obtain a factor of 17 in the numerator, and finally, dividing the factor 2 in the denominator into the factor 52 in the numerator to obtain a factor of 26 in the numerator. We find that

$$C(52, 5) = 26 \cdot 17 \cdot 10 \cdot 49 \cdot 12 = 2{,}598{,}960.$$

Consequently, there are 2,598,960 different poker hands of five cards that can be dealt from a standard deck of 52 cards.

Note that there are

$$C(52, 47) = \frac{52!}{47!5!}$$

different ways to select 47 cards from a standard deck of 52 cards. We do not need to compute this value because $C(52, 47) = C(52, 5)$. (Only the order of the factors 5! and 47! is different in the denominators in the formulae for these quantities.) It follows that there are also 2,598,960 different ways to select 47 cards from a standard deck of 52 cards. ◄

In Example 11 we observed that $C(52, 5) = C(52, 47)$. This is a special case of the useful identity for the number of $r$-combinations of a set given in Corollary 2.

**COROLLARY 2**    Let $n$ and $r$ be nonnegative integers with $r \le n$. Then $C(n, r) = C(n, n-r)$.

*Proof:* From Theorem 2 it follows that

$$C(n, r) = \frac{n!}{r!(n-r)!}$$

and

$$C(n, n - r) = \frac{n!}{(n - r)! \, [n - (n - r)]!} = \frac{n!}{(n - r)! \, r!}.$$

Hence, $C(n, r) = C(n, n - r)$.    ◁

We can also prove Corollary 2 without relying on algebraic manipulation. Instead, we can use a combinatorial proof. We describe this important type of proof in Definition 1.

**DEFINITION 1**

A *combinatorial proof* of an identity is a proof that uses counting arguments to prove that both sides of the identity count the same objects but in different ways or a proof that is based on showing that there is a bijection between the sets of objects counted by the two sides of the identity. These two types of proofs are called *double counting proofs* and *bijective proofs*, respectively.

Many identities involving binomial coefficients can be proved using combinatorial proofs. We now show how to prove Corollary 2 using a combinatorial proof. We will provide both a double counting proof and a bijective proof, both based on the same basic idea.

Combinatorial proofs are almost always much shorter and provide more insights than proofs based on algebraic manipulation.

*Proof:* We will use a bijective proof to show that $C(n, r) = C(n, n - r)$ for all integers $n$ and $r$ with $0 \leq r \leq n$. Suppose that $S$ is a set with $n$ elements. The function that maps a subset $A$ of $S$ to $\overline{A}$ is a bijection between subsets of $S$ with $r$ elements and subsets with $n - r$ elements (as the reader should verify). The identity $C(n, r) = C(n, n - r)$ follows because when there is a bijection between two finite sets, the two sets must have the same number of elements.

Alternatively, we can reformulate this argument as a double counting proof. By definition, the number of subsets of $S$ with $r$ elements equals $C(n, r)$. But each subset $A$ of $S$ is also determined by specifying which elements are not in $A$, and so are in $\overline{A}$. Because the complement of a subset of $S$ with $r$ elements has $n - r$ elements, there are also $C(n, n - r)$ subsets of $S$ with $r$ elements. It follows that $C(n, r) = C(n, n - r)$.    ◁

**EXAMPLE 12**

How many ways are there to select five players from a 10-member tennis team to make a trip to a match at another school?

*Solution:* The answer is given by the number of 5-combinations of a set with 10 elements. By Theorem 2, the number of such combinations is

$$C(10, 5) = \frac{10!}{5! \, 5!} = 252.$$    ◀

**EXAMPLE 13**

A group of 30 people have been trained as astronauts to go on the first mission to Mars. How many ways are there to select a crew of six people to go on this mission (assuming that all crew members have the same job)?

*Solution:* The number of ways to select a crew of six from the pool of 30 people is the number of 6-combinations of a set with 30 elements, because the order in which these people are chosen does not matter. By Theorem 2, the number of such combinations is

$$C(30, 6) = \frac{30!}{6! \, 24!} = \frac{30 \cdot 29 \cdot 28 \cdot 27 \cdot 26 \cdot 25}{6 \cdot 5 \cdot 4 \cdot 3 \cdot 2 \cdot 1} = 593,775.$$    ◀

**EXAMPLE 14**  How many bit strings of length $n$ contain exactly $r$ 1s?

*Solution:* The positions of $r$ 1s in a bit string of length $n$ form an $r$-combination of the set $\{1, 2, 3, \ldots, n\}$. Hence, there are $C(n, r)$ bit strings of length $n$ that contain exactly $r$ 1s.  ◄

**EXAMPLE 15**  Suppose that there are 9 faculty members in the mathematics department and 11 in the computer science department. How many ways are there to select a committee to develop a discrete mathematics course at a school if the committee is to consist of three faculty members from the mathematics department and four from the computer science department?

*Solution:* By the product rule, the answer is the product of the number of 3-combinations of a set with nine elements and the number of 4-combinations of a set with 11 elements. By Theorem 2, the number of ways to select the committee is

$$C(9, 3) \cdot C(11, 4) = \frac{9!}{3!6!} \cdot \frac{11!}{4!7!} = 84 \cdot 330 = 27{,}720.$$

◄

# Exercises

**1.** List all the permutations of $\{a, b, c\}$.

**2.** How many different permutations are there of the set $\{a, b, c, d, e, f, g\}$?

**3.** How many permutations of $\{a, b, c, d, e, f, g\}$ end with $a$?

**4.** Let $S = \{1, 2, 3, 4, 5\}$.
   **a)** List all the 3-permutations of $S$.
   **b)** List all the 3-combinations of $S$.

**5.** Find the value of each of these quantities.
   **a)** $P(6, 3)$      **b)** $P(6, 5)$
   **c)** $P(8, 1)$      **d)** $P(8, 5)$
   **e)** $P(8, 8)$      **f)** $P(10, 9)$

**6.** Find the value of each of these quantities.
   **a)** $C(5, 1)$      **b)** $C(5, 3)$
   **c)** $C(8, 4)$      **d)** $C(8, 8)$
   **e)** $C(8, 0)$      **f)** $C(12, 6)$

**7.** Find the number of 5-permutations of a set with nine elements.

**8.** In how many different orders can five runners finish a race if no ties are allowed?

**9.** How many possibilities are there for the win, place, and show (first, second, and third) positions in a horse race with 12 horses if all orders of finish are possible?

**10.** There are six different candidates for governor of a state. In how many different orders can the names of the candidates be printed on a ballot?

**11.** How many bit strings of length 10 contain
   **a)** exactly four 1s?
   **b)** at most four 1s?
   **c)** at least four 1s?
   **d)** an equal number of 0s and 1s?

**12.** How many bit strings of length 12 contain
   **a)** exactly three 1s?
   **b)** at most three 1s?
   **c)** at least three 1s?
   **d)** an equal number of 0s and 1s?

**13.** A group contains $n$ men and $n$ women. How many ways are there to arrange these people in a row if the men and women alternate?

**14.** In how many ways can a set of two positive integers less than 100 be chosen?

**15.** In how many ways can a set of five letters be selected from the English alphabet?

**16.** How many subsets with an odd number of elements does a set with 10 elements have?

**17.** How many subsets with more than two elements does a set with 100 elements have?

**18.** A coin is flipped eight times where each flip comes up either heads or tails. How many possible outcomes
   **a)** are there in total?
   **b)** contain exactly three heads?
   **c)** contain at least three heads?
   **d)** contain the same number of heads and tails?

**19.** A coin is flipped 10 times where each flip comes up either heads or tails. How many possible outcomes
   **a)** are there in total?
   **b)** contain exactly two heads?
   **c)** contain at most three tails?
   **d)** contain the same number of heads and tails?

**20.** How many bit strings of length 10 have
   **a)** exactly three 0s?
   **b)** more 0s than 1s?
   **c)** at least seven 1s?
   **d)** at least three 1s?

**21.** How many permutations of the letters *ABCDEFG* contain

   **a)** the string *BCD*?

   **b)** the string *CFGA*?

   **c)** the strings *BA* and *GF*?

   **d)** the strings *ABC* and *DE*?

   **e)** the strings *ABC* and *CDE*?

   **f)** the strings *CBA* and *BED*?

**22.** How many permutations of the letters *ABCDEFGH* contain

   **a)** the string *ED*?

   **b)** the string *CDE*?

   **c)** the strings *BA* and *FGH*?

   **d)** the strings *AB*, *DE*, and *GH*?

   **e)** the strings *CAB* and *BED*?

   **f)** the strings *BCA* and *ABF*?

**23.** How many ways are there for eight men and five women to stand in a line so that no two women stand next to each other? [*Hint:* First position the men and then consider possible positions for the women.]

**24.** How many ways are there for 10 women and six men to stand in a line so that no two men stand next to each other? [*Hint:* First position the women and then consider possible positions for the men.]

**25.** One hundred tickets, numbered 1, 2, 3, . . . , 100, are sold to 100 different people for a drawing. Four different prizes are awarded, including a grand prize (a trip to Tahiti). How many ways are there to award the prizes if

   **a)** there are no restrictions?

   **b)** the person holding ticket 47 wins the grand prize?

   **c)** the person holding ticket 47 wins one of the prizes?

   **d)** the person holding ticket 47 does not win a prize?

   **e)** the people holding tickets 19 and 47 both win prizes?

   **f)** the people holding tickets 19, 47, and 73 all win prizes?

   **g)** the people holding tickets 19, 47, 73, and 97 all win prizes?

   **h)** none of the people holding tickets 19, 47, 73, and 97 wins a prize?

   **i)** the grand prize winner is a person holding ticket 19, 47, 73, or 97?

   **j)** the people holding tickets 19 and 47 win prizes, but the people holding tickets 73 and 97 do not win prizes?

**26.** Thirteen people on a softball team show up for a game.

   **a)** How many ways are there to choose 10 players to take the field?

   **b)** How many ways are there to assign the 10 positions by selecting players from the 13 people who show up?

   **c)** Of the 13 people who show up, three are women. How many ways are there to choose 10 players to take the field if at least one of these players must be a woman?

**27.** A club has 25 members.

   **a)** How many ways are there to choose four members of the club to serve on an executive committee?

   **b)** How many ways are there to choose a president, vice president, secretary, and treasurer of the club, where no person can hold more than one office?

**28.** A professor writes 40 discrete mathematics true/false questions. Of the statements in these questions, 17 are true. If the questions can be positioned in any order, how many different answer keys are possible?

**∗29.** How many 4-permutations of the positive integers not exceeding 100 contain three consecutive integers $k, k + 1, k + 2$, in the correct order

   **a)** where these consecutive integers can perhaps be separated by other integers in the permutation?

   **b)** where they are in consecutive positions in the permutation?

**30.** Seven women and nine men are on the faculty in the mathematics department at a school.

   **a)** How many ways are there to select a committee of five members of the department if at least one woman must be on the committee?

   **b)** How many ways are there to select a committee of five members of the department if at least one woman and at least one man must be on the committee?

**31.** The English alphabet contains 21 consonants and five vowels. How many strings of six lowercase letters of the English alphabet contain

   **a)** exactly one vowel?

   **b)** exactly two vowels?

   **c)** at least one vowel?

   **d)** at least two vowels?

**32.** How many strings of six lowercase letters from the English alphabet contain

   **a)** the letter *a*?

   **b)** the letters *a* and *b*?

   **c)** the letters *a* and *b* in consecutive positions with *a* preceding *b*, with all the letters distinct?

   **d)** the letters *a* and *b*, where *a* is somewhere to the left of *b* in the string, with all the letters distinct?

**33.** Suppose that a department contains 10 men and 15 women. How many ways are there to form a committee with six members if it must have the same number of men and women?

**34.** Suppose that a department contains 10 men and 15 women. How many ways are there to form a committee with six members if it must have more women than men?

**35.** How many bit strings contain exactly eight 0s and 10 1s if every 0 must be immediately followed by a 1?

**36.** How many bit strings contain exactly five 0s and 14 1s if every 0 must be immediately followed by two 1s?

**37.** How many bit strings of length 10 contain at least three 1s and at least three 0s?

**38.** How many ways are there to select 12 countries in the United Nations to serve on a council if 3 are selected from a block of 45, 4 are selected from a block of 57, and the others are selected from the remaining 69 countries?

**39.** How many license plates consisting of three letters followed by three digits contain no letter or digit twice?

A **circular $r$-permutation of $n$** people is a seating of $r$ of these $n$ people around a circular table, where seatings are considered to be the same if they can be obtained from each other by rotating the table.

**40.** Find the number of circular 3-permutations of 5 people.

**41.** Find a formula for the number of circular $r$-permutations of $n$ people.

**42.** Find a formula for the number of ways to seat $r$ of $n$ people around a circular table, where seatings are considered the same if every person has the same two neighbors without regard to which side these neighbors are sitting on.

**43.** How many ways are there for a horse race with three horses to finish if ties are possible? [*Note:* Two or three horses may tie.]

**\*44.** How many ways are there for a horse race with four horses to finish if ties are possible? [*Note:* Any number of the four horses may tie.)

**\*45.** There are six runners in the 100-yard dash. How many ways are there for three medals to be awarded if ties are possible? (The runner or runners who finish with the fastest time receive gold medals, the runner or runners who finish with exactly one runner ahead receive silver medals, and the runner or runners who finish with exactly two runners ahead receive bronze medals.)

**\*46.** This procedure is used to break ties in games in the championship round of the World Cup soccer tournament. Each team selects five players in a prescribed order. Each of these players takes a penalty kick, with a player from the first team followed by a player from the second team and so on, following the order of players specified. If the score is still tied at the end of the 10 penalty kicks, this procedure is repeated. If the score is still tied after 20 penalty kicks, a sudden-death shootout occurs, with the first team scoring an unanswered goal victorious.

a) How many different scoring scenarios are possible if the game is settled in the first round of 10 penalty kicks, where the round ends once it is impossible for a team to equal the number of goals scored by the other team?

b) How many different scoring scenarios for the first and second groups of penalty kicks are possible if the game is settled in the second round of 10 penalty kicks?

c) How many scoring scenarios are possible for the full set of penalty kicks if the game is settled with no more than 10 total additional kicks after the two rounds of five kicks for each team?

# 6.4   Binomial Coefficients and Identities

As we remarked in Section 6.3, the number of $r$-combinations from a set with $n$ elements is often denoted by $\binom{n}{r}$. This number is also called a **binomial coefficient** because these numbers occur as coefficients in the expansion of powers of binomial expressions such as $(a + b)^n$. We will discuss the **binomial theorem**, which gives a power of a binomial expression as a sum of terms involving binomial coefficients. We will prove this theorem using a combinatorial proof. We will also show how combinatorial proofs can be used to establish some of the many different identities that express relationships among binomial coefficients.

## The Binomial Theorem

Links

The binomial theorem gives the coefficients of the expansion of powers of binomial expressions. A **binomial** expression is simply the sum of two terms, such as $x + y$. (The terms can be products of constants and variables, but that does not concern us here.)

Example 1 illustrates how the coefficients in a typical expansion can be found and prepares us for the statement of the binomial theorem.

**EXAMPLE 1** The expansion of $(x + y)^3$ can be found using combinatorial reasoning instead of multiplying the three terms out. When $(x + y)^3 = (x + y)(x + y)(x + y)$ is expanded, all products of a term in the first sum, a term in the second sum, and a term in the third sum are added. Terms of the form $x^3$, $x^2y$, $xy^2$, and $y^3$ arise. To obtain a term of the form $x^3$, an $x$ must be chosen in each of the sums, and this can be done in only one way. Thus, the $x^3$ term in the product has a coefficient of 1. To obtain a term of the form $x^2y$, an $x$ must be chosen in two of the three sums (and consequently a $y$ in the other sum). Hence, the number of such terms is the number of 2-combinations of three objects, namely, $\binom{3}{2}$. Similarly, the number of terms of the form $xy^2$ is the number of ways to pick one of the three sums to obtain an $x$ (and consequently take a $y$

from each of the other two sums). This can be done in $\binom{3}{1}$ ways. Finally, the only way to obtain a $y^3$ term is to choose the $y$ for each of the three sums in the product, and this can be done in exactly one way. Consequently, it follows that

$$(x + y)^3 = (x + y)(x + y)(x + y) = (xx + xy + yx + yy)(x + y)$$
$$= xxx + xxy + xyx + xyy + yxx + yxy + yyx + yyy$$
$$= x^3 + 3x^2 y + 3xy^2 + y^3.$$

◀

We now state the binomial theorem.

**THEOREM 1**    **THE BINOMIAL THEOREM**    Let $x$ and $y$ be variables, and let $n$ be a nonnegative integer. Then

$$(x + y)^n = \sum_{j=0}^{n} \binom{n}{j} x^{n-j} y^j = \binom{n}{0} x^n + \binom{n}{1} x^{n-1} y + \cdots + \binom{n}{n-1} xy^{n-1} + \binom{n}{n} y^n.$$

*Proof:* We use a combinatorial proof. The terms in the product when it is expanded are of the form $x^{n-j} y^j$ for $j = 0, 1, 2, \ldots, n$. To count the number of terms of the form $x^{n-j} y^j$, note that to obtain such a term it is necessary to choose $n - j$ $x$s from the $n$ sums (so that the other $j$ terms in the product are $y$s). Therefore, the coefficient of $x^{n-j} y^j$ is $\binom{n}{n-j}$, which is equal to $\binom{n}{j}$. This proves the theorem.    ◁

Some computational uses of the binomial theorem are illustrated in Examples 2–4.

**EXAMPLE 2**    What is the expansion of $(x + y)^4$?

*Solution:* From the binomial theorem it follows that

$$(x + y)^4 = \sum_{j=0}^{4} \binom{4}{j} x^{4-j} y^j$$

$$= \binom{4}{0} x^4 + \binom{4}{1} x^3 y + \binom{4}{2} x^2 y^2 + \binom{4}{3} xy^3 + \binom{4}{4} y^4$$

$$= x^4 + 4x^3 y + 6x^2 y^2 + 4xy^3 + y^4.$$

◀

**EXAMPLE 3**    What is the coefficient of $x^{12} y^{13}$ in the expansion of $(x + y)^{25}$?

*Solution:* From the binomial theorem it follows that this coefficient is

$$\binom{25}{13} = \frac{25!}{13!\, 12!} = 5,200,300.$$

◀

**EXAMPLE 4**    What is the coefficient of $x^{12} y^{13}$ in the expansion of $(2x - 3y)^{25}$?

*Solution:* First, note that this expression equals $(2x + (-3y))^{25}$. By the binomial theorem, we have

$$(2x + (-3y))^{25} = \sum_{j=0}^{25} \binom{25}{j} (2x)^{25-j} (-3y)^j.$$

Consequently, the coefficient of $x^{12}y^{13}$ in the expansion is obtained when $j = 13$, namely,

$$\binom{25}{13}2^{12}(-3)^{13} = -\frac{25!}{13!\,12!}2^{12}3^{13}.$$

◀

We can prove some useful identities using the binomial theorem, as Corollaries 1, 2, and 3 demonstrate.

**COROLLARY 1**     Let $n$ be a nonnegative integer. Then

$$\sum_{k=0}^{n}\binom{n}{k} = 2^n.$$

*Proof:* Using the binomial theorem with $x = 1$ and $y = 1$, we see that

$$2^n = (1+1)^n = \sum_{k=0}^{n}\binom{n}{k}1^k 1^{n-k} = \sum_{k=0}^{n}\binom{n}{k}.$$

This is the desired result.

◁

There is also a nice combinatorial proof of Corollary 1, which we now present.

*Proof:* A set with $n$ elements has a total of $2^n$ different subsets. Each subset has zero elements, one element, two elements, ..., or $n$ elements in it. There are $\binom{n}{0}$ subsets with zero elements, $\binom{n}{1}$ subsets with one element, $\binom{n}{2}$ subsets with two elements, ..., and $\binom{n}{n}$ subsets with $n$ elements. Therefore,

$$\sum_{k=0}^{n}\binom{n}{k}$$

counts the total number of subsets of a set with $n$ elements. By equating the two formulas we have for the number of subsets of a set with $n$ elements, we see that

$$\sum_{k=0}^{n}\binom{n}{k} = 2^n.$$

◁

**COROLLARY 2**     Let $n$ be a positive integer. Then

$$\sum_{k=0}^{n}(-1)^k\binom{n}{k} = 0.$$

*Proof:* When we use the binomial theorem with $x = -1$ and $y = 1$, we see that

$$0 = 0^n = ((-1)+1)^n = \sum_{k=0}^{n}\binom{n}{k}(-1)^k 1^{n-k} = \sum_{k=0}^{n}\binom{n}{k}(-1)^k.$$

This proves the corollary.

◁

*Remark:* Corollary 2 implies that

$$\binom{n}{0} + \binom{n}{2} + \binom{n}{4} + \cdots = \binom{n}{1} + \binom{n}{3} + \binom{n}{5} + \cdots .$$

**COROLLARY 3**    Let $n$ be a nonnegative integer. Then

$$\sum_{k=0}^{n} 2^k \binom{n}{k} = 3^n.$$

*Proof:* We recognize that the left-hand side of this formula is the expansion of $(1+2)^n$ provided by the binomial theorem. Therefore, by the binomial theorem, we see that

$$(1+2)^n = \sum_{k=0}^{n} \binom{n}{k} 1^{n-k} 2^k = \sum_{k=0}^{n} \binom{n}{k} 2^k.$$

Hence

$$\sum_{k=0}^{n} 2^k \binom{n}{k} = 3^n.$$

◁

## Pascal's Identity and Triangle

The binomial coefficients satisfy many different identities. We introduce one of the most important of these now.

**THEOREM 2**    **PASCAL'S IDENTITY**    Let $n$ and $k$ be positive integers with $n \geq k$. Then

$$\binom{n+1}{k} = \binom{n}{k-1} + \binom{n}{k}.$$

*Proof:* We will use a combinatorial proof. Suppose that $T$ is a set containing $n+1$ elements. Let $a$ be an element in $T$, and let $S = T - \{a\}$. Note that there are $\binom{n+1}{k}$ subsets of $T$ containing $k$ elements. However, a subset of $T$ with $k$ elements either contains $a$ together with $k-1$ elements of $S$, or contains $k$ elements of $S$ and does not contain $a$. Because there are $\binom{n}{k-1}$ subsets of $k-1$ elements of $S$, there are $\binom{n}{k-1}$ subsets of $k$ elements of $T$ that contain $a$. And there are $\binom{n}{k}$ subsets of $k$ elements of $T$ that do not contain $a$, because there are $\binom{n}{k}$ subsets of $k$ elements of $S$. Consequently,

$$\binom{n+1}{k} = \binom{n}{k-1} + \binom{n}{k}.$$

◁

*Remark:* It is also possible to prove this identity by algebraic manipulation from the formula for $\binom{n}{r}$ (see Exercise 19).

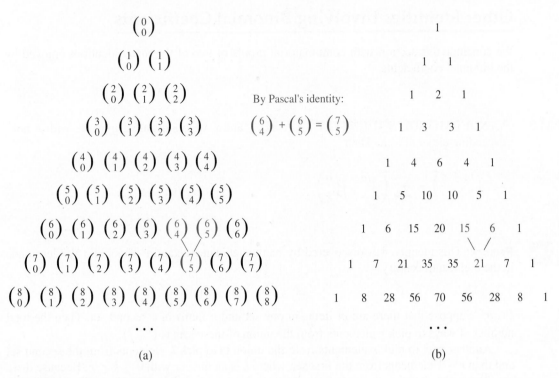

**FIGURE 1** **Pascal's Triangle.**

***Remark:*** Pascal's identity, together with the initial conditions $\binom{n}{0} = \binom{n}{n} = 1$ for all integers $n$, can be used to recursively define binomial coefficients. This recursive definition is useful in the computation of binomial coefficients because only addition, and not multiplication, of integers is needed to use this recursive definition.

Pascal's identity is the basis for a geometric arrangement of the binomial coefficients in a triangle, as shown in Figure 1.

The $n$th row in the triangle consists of the binomial coefficients

$$\binom{n}{k}, \ k = 0, 1, \ldots, n.$$

This triangle is known as **Pascal's triangle**. Pascal's identity shows that when two adjacent binomial coefficients in this triangle are added, the binomial coefficient in the next row between these two coefficients is produced.

BLAISE PASCAL (1623–1662) Blaise Pascal exhibited his talents at an early age, although his father, who had made discoveries in analytic geometry, kept mathematics books away from him to encourage other interests. At 16 Pascal discovered an important result concerning conic sections. At 18 he designed a calculating machine, which he built and sold. Pascal, along with Fermat, laid the foundations for the modern theory of probability. In this work, he made new discoveries concerning what is now called Pascal's triangle. In 1654, Pascal abandoned his mathematical pursuits to devote himself to theology. After this, he returned to mathematics only once. One night, distracted by a severe toothache, he sought comfort by studying the mathematical properties of the cycloid. Miraculously, his pain subsided, which he took as a sign of divine approval of the study of mathematics.

## Other Identities Involving Binomial Coefficients

We conclude this section with combinatorial proofs of two of the many identities enjoyed by the binomial coefficients.

**THEOREM 3**  **VANDERMONDE'S IDENTITY**  Let $m$, $n$, and $r$ be nonnegative integers with $r$ not exceeding either $m$ or $n$. Then

$$\binom{m+n}{r} = \sum_{k=0}^{r} \binom{m}{r-k}\binom{n}{k}.$$

Links

**Remark:** This identity was discovered by mathematician Alexandre-Théophile Vandermonde in the eighteenth century.

*Proof:* Suppose that there are $m$ items in one set and $n$ items in a second set. Then the total number of ways to pick $r$ elements from the union of these sets is $\binom{m+n}{r}$.

Another way to pick $r$ elements from the union is to pick $k$ elements from the second set and then $r - k$ elements from the first set, where $k$ is an integer with $0 \leq k \leq r$. Because there are $\binom{n}{k}$ ways to choose $k$ elements from the second set and $\binom{m}{r-k}$ ways to choose $r - k$ elements from the first set, the product rule tells us that this can be done in $\binom{m}{r-k}\binom{n}{k}$ ways. Hence, the total number of ways to pick $r$ elements from the union also equals $\sum_{k=0}^{r} \binom{m}{r-k}\binom{n}{k}$.

We have found two expressions for the number of ways to pick $r$ elements from the union of a set with $m$ items and a set with $n$ items. Equating them gives us Vandermonde's identity.  ◁

Corollary 4 follows from Vandermonde's identity.

**COROLLARY 4**  If $n$ is a nonnegative integer, then

$$\binom{2n}{n} = \sum_{k=0}^{n} \binom{n}{k}^2.$$

*Proof:* We use Vandermonde's identity with $m = r = n$ to obtain

$$\binom{2n}{n} = \sum_{k=0}^{n} \binom{n}{n-k}\binom{n}{k} = \sum_{k=0}^{n} \binom{n}{k}^2.$$

The last equality was obtained using the identity $\binom{n}{k} = \binom{n}{n-k}$.  ◁

Links

ALEXANDRE-THÉOPHILE VANDERMONDE (1735–1796)  Because Alexandre-Théophile Vandermonde was a sickly child, his physician father directed him to a career in music. However, he later developed an interest in mathematics. His complete mathematical work consists of four papers published in 1771–1772. These papers include fundamental contributions on the roots of equations, on the theory of determinants, and on the knight's tour problem (introduced in the exercises in Section 10.5). Vandermonde's interest in mathematics lasted for only 2 years. Afterward, he published papers on harmony, experiments with cold, and the manufacture of steel. He also became interested in politics, joining the cause of the French revolution and holding several different positions in government.

We can prove combinatorial identities by counting bit strings with different properties, as the proof of Theorem 4 will demonstrate.

**THEOREM 4**      Let $n$ and $r$ be nonnegative integers with $r \leq n$. Then

$$\binom{n+1}{r+1} = \sum_{j=r}^{n} \binom{j}{r}.$$

*Proof:* We use a combinatorial proof. By Example 14 in Section 6.3, the left-hand side, $\binom{n+1}{r+1}$, counts the bit strings of length $n + 1$ containing $r + 1$ ones.

We show that the right-hand side counts the same objects by considering the cases corresponding to the possible locations of the final 1 in a string with $r + 1$ ones. This final one must occur at position $r + 1, r + 2, \ldots,$ or $n + 1$. Furthermore, if the last one is the $k$th bit there must be $r$ ones among the first $k - 1$ positions. Consequently, by Example 14 in Section 6.3, there are $\binom{k-1}{r}$ such bit strings. Summing over $k$ with $r + 1 \leq k \leq n + 1$, we find that there are

$$\sum_{k=r+1}^{n+1} \binom{k-1}{r} = \sum_{j=r}^{n} \binom{j}{r}$$

bit strings of length $n$ containing exactly $r + 1$ ones. (Note that the last step follows from the change of variables $j = k - 1$.) Because the left-hand side and the right-hand side count the same objects, they are equal. This completes the proof.    ◁

# Exercises

**1.** Find the expansion of $(x + y)^4$

   **a)** using combinatorial reasoning, as in Example 1.
   **b)** using the binomial theorem.

**2.** Find the expansion of $(x + y)^5$

   **a)** using combinatorial reasoning, as in Example 1.
   **b)** using the binomial theorem.

**3.** Find the expansion of $(x + y)^6$.

**4.** Find the coefficient of $x^5 y^8$ in $(x + y)^{13}$.

**5.** How many terms are there in the expansion of $(x + y)^{100}$ after like terms are collected?

**6.** What is the coefficient of $x^7$ in $(1 + x)^{11}$?

**7.** What is the coefficient of $x^9$ in $(2 - x)^{19}$?

**8.** What is the coefficient of $x^8 y^9$ in the expansion of $(3x + 2y)^{17}$?

**9.** What is the coefficient of $x^{101} y^{99}$ in the expansion of $(2x - 3y)^{200}$?

**\*10.** Give a formula for the coefficient of $x^k$ in the expansion of $(x + 1/x)^{100}$, where $k$ is an integer.

**\*11.** Give a formula for the coefficient of $x^k$ in the expansion of $(x^2 - 1/x)^{100}$, where $k$ is an integer.

**12.** The row of Pascal's triangle containing the binomial coefficients $\binom{10}{k}, 0 \leq k \leq 10$, is:

   1   10   45   120   210   252   210   120   45   10   1

Use Pascal's identity to produce the row immediately following this row in Pascal's triangle.

**13.** What is the row of Pascal's triangle containing the binomial coefficients $\binom{9}{k}, 0 \leq k \leq 9$?

**14.** Show that if $n$ is a positive integer, then $1 = \binom{n}{0} < \binom{n}{1} < \cdots < \binom{n}{\lfloor n/2 \rfloor} = \binom{n}{\lceil n/2 \rceil} > \cdots > \binom{n}{n-1} > \binom{n}{n} = 1$.

**15.** Show that $\binom{n}{k} \leq 2^n$ for all positive integers $n$ and all integers $k$ with $0 \leq k \leq n$.

**16. a)** Use Exercise 14 and Corollary 1 to show that if $n$ is an integer greater than 1, then $\binom{n}{\lfloor n/2 \rfloor} \geq 2^n/n$.

   **b)** Conclude from part (a) that if $n$ is a positive integer, then $\binom{2n}{n} \geq 4^n/2n$.

**☞ 17.** Show that if $n$ and $k$ are integers with $1 \leq k \leq n$, then $\binom{n}{k} \leq n^k/2^{k-1}$.

**18.** Suppose that $b$ is an integer with $b \geq 7$. Use the binomial theorem and the appropriate row of Pascal's triangle to find the base-$b$ expansion of $(11)_b^4$ [that is, the fourth power of the number $(11)_b$ in base-$b$ notation].

**19.** Prove Pascal's identity, using the formula for $\binom{n}{r}$.

**20.** Suppose that $k$ and $n$ are integers with $1 \leq k < n$. Prove the **hexagon identity**

$$\binom{n-1}{k-1}\binom{n}{k+1}\binom{n+1}{k} = \binom{n-1}{k}\binom{n}{k-1}\binom{n+1}{k+1},$$

which relates terms in Pascal's triangle that form a hexagon.

**21.** Prove that if $n$ and $k$ are integers with $1 \le k \le n$, then $k\binom{n}{k} = n\binom{n-1}{k-1}$,

   **a)** using a combinatorial proof. [*Hint:* Show that the two sides of the identity count the number of ways to select a subset with $k$ elements from a set with $n$ elements and then an element of this subset.]

   **b)** using an algebraic proof based on the formula for $\binom{n}{r}$ given in Theorem 2 in Section 6.3.

**22.** Prove the identity $\binom{n}{r}\binom{r}{k} = \binom{n}{k}\binom{n-k}{r-k}$, whenever $n$, $r$, and $k$ are nonnegative integers with $r \le n$ and $k \le r$,

   **a)** using a combinatorial argument.

   **b)** using an argument based on the formula for the number of $r$-combinations of a set with $n$ elements.

**23.** Show that if $n$ and $k$ are positive integers, then

$$\binom{n+1}{k} = (n+1)\binom{n}{k-1} / k.$$

Use this identity to construct an inductive definition of the binomial coefficients.

**24.** Show that if $p$ is a prime and $k$ is an integer such that $1 \le k \le p - 1$, then $p$ divides $\binom{p}{k}$.

**25.** Let $n$ be a positive integer. Show that

$$\binom{2n}{n+1} + \binom{2n}{n} = \binom{2n+2}{n+1}/2.$$

**\*26.** Let $n$ and $k$ be integers with $1 \le k \le n$. Show that

$$\sum_{k=1}^{n} \binom{n}{k}\binom{n}{k-1} = \binom{2n+2}{n+1}/2 - \binom{2n}{n}.$$

**\*27.** Prove the **hockeystick identity**

$$\sum_{k=0}^{r} \binom{n+k}{k} = \binom{n+r+1}{r}$$

whenever $n$ and $r$ are positive integers,

   **a)** using a combinatorial argument.

   **b)** using Pascal's identity.

**28.** Show that if $n$ is a positive integer, then $\binom{2n}{2} = 2\binom{n}{2} + n^2$

   **a)** using a combinatorial argument.

   **b)** by algebraic manipulation.

**\*29.** Give a combinatorial proof that $\sum_{k=1}^{n} k\binom{n}{k} = n2^{n-1}$. [*Hint:* Count in two ways the number of ways to select a committee and to then select a leader of the committee.]

**\*30.** Give a combinatorial proof that $\sum_{k=1}^{n} k\binom{n}{k}^2 = n\binom{2n-1}{n-1}$. [*Hint:* Count in two ways the number of ways to select a committee, with $n$ members from a group of $n$ mathematics professors and $n$ computer science professors, such that the chairperson of the committee is a mathematics professor.]

**31.** Show that a nonempty set has the same number of subsets with an odd number of elements as it does subsets with an even number of elements.

**\*32.** Prove the binomial theorem using mathematical induction.

**33.** In this exercise we will count the number of paths in the $xy$ plane between the origin $(0, 0)$ and point $(m, n)$, where $m$ and $n$ are nonnegative integers, such that each path is made up of a series of steps, where each step is a move one unit to the right or a move one unit upward. (No moves to the left or downward are allowed.) Two such paths from $(0, 0)$ to $(5, 3)$ are illustrated here.

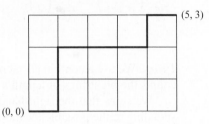

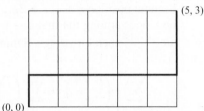

   **a)** Show that each path of the type described can be represented by a bit string consisting of $m$ 0s and $n$ 1s, where a 0 represents a move one unit to the right and a 1 represents a move one unit upward.

   **b)** Conclude from part (a) that there are $\binom{m+n}{n}$ paths of the desired type.

**34.** Use Exercise 33 to give an alternative proof of Corollary 2 in Section 6.3, which states that $\binom{n}{k} = \binom{n}{n-k}$ whenever $k$ is an integer with $0 \le k \le n$. [*Hint:* Consider the number of paths of the type described in Exercise 33 from $(0, 0)$ to $(n - k, k)$ and from $(0, 0)$ to $(k, n - k)$.]

**35.** Use Exercise 33 to prove Theorem 4. [*Hint:* Count the number of paths with $n$ steps of the type described in Exercise 33. Every such path must end at one of the points $(n - k, k)$ for $k = 0, 1, 2, \ldots, n$.]

**36.** Use Exercise 33 to prove Pascal's identity. [*Hint:* Show that a path of the type described in Exercise 33 from $(0, 0)$ to $(n + 1 - k, k)$ passes through either $(n + 1 - k, k - 1)$ or $(n - k, k)$, but not through both.]

**37.** Use Exercise 33 to prove the hockeystick identity from Exercise 27. [*Hint:* First, note that the number of paths from $(0, 0)$ to $(n + 1, r)$ equals $\binom{n+1+r}{r}$. Second, count the number of paths by summing the number of these paths that start by going $k$ units upward for $k = 0, 1, 2, \ldots, r$.]

**38.** Give a combinatorial proof that if $n$ is a positive integer then $\sum_{k=0}^{n} k^2\binom{n}{k} = n(n + 1)2^{n-2}$. [*Hint:* Show that both sides count the ways to select a subset of a set of $n$ elements together with two not necessarily distinct elements from this subset. Furthermore, express the right-hand side as $n(n - 1)2^{n-2} + n2^{n-1}$.]

**\*39.** Determine a formula involving binomial coefficients for the $n$th term of a sequence if its initial terms are those listed. [*Hint:* Looking at Pascal's triangle will be helpful.

Although infinitely many sequences start with a specified set of terms, each of the following lists is the start of a sequence of the type desired.]

**a)** 1, 3, 6, 10, 15, 21, 28, 36, 45, 55, 66, ...

**b)** 1, 4, 10, 20, 35, 56, 84, 120, 165, 220, ...

**c)** 1, 2, 6, 20, 70, 252, 924, 3432, 12870, 48620, ...

**d)** 1, 1, 2, 3, 6, 10, 20, 35, 70, 126, ...

**e)** 1, 1, 1, 3, 1, 5, 15, 35, 1, 9, ...

**f)** 1, 3, 15, 84, 495, 3003, 18564, 116280, 735471, 4686825, ...

# 6.5   Generalized Permutations and Combinations

## Introduction

Links

In many counting problems, elements may be used repeatedly. For instance, a letter or digit may be used more than once on a license plate. When a dozen donuts are selected, each variety can be chosen repeatedly. This contrasts with the counting problems discussed earlier in the chapter where we considered only permutations and combinations in which each item could be used at most once. In this section we will show how to solve counting problems where elements may be used more than once.

Also, some counting problems involve indistinguishable elements. For instance, to count the number of ways the letters of the word *SUCCESS* can be rearranged, the placement of identical letters must be considered. This contrasts with the counting problems discussed earlier where all elements were considered distinguishable. In this section we will describe how to solve counting problems in which some elements are indistinguishable.

Moreover, in this section we will explain how to solve another important class of counting problems, problems involving counting the ways distinguishable elements can be placed in boxes. An example of this type of problem is the number of different ways poker hands can be dealt to four players.

Taken together, the methods described earlier in this chapter and the methods introduced in this section form a useful toolbox for solving a wide range of counting problems. When the additional methods discussed in Chapter 8 are added to this arsenal, you will be able to solve a large percentage of the counting problems that arise in a wide range of areas of study.

## Permutations with Repetition

Counting permutations when repetition of elements is allowed can easily be done using the product rule, as Example 1 shows.

EXAMPLE 1    How many strings of length $r$ can be formed from the uppercase letters of the English alphabet?

*Solution:* By the product rule, because there are 26 uppercase English letters, and because each letter can be used repeatedly, we see that there are $26^r$ strings of uppercase English letters of length $r$.  ◀

The number of $r$-permutations of a set with $n$ elements when repetition is allowed is given in Theorem 1.

THEOREM 1    The number of $r$-permutations of a set of $n$ objects with repetition allowed is $n^r$.

*Proof:* There are $n$ ways to select an element of the set for each of the $r$ positions in the $r$-permutation when repetition is allowed, because for each choice all $n$ objects are available. Hence, by the product rule there are $n^r$ $r$-permutations when repetition is allowed.  ◀

## Combinations with Repetition

Consider these examples of combinations with repetition of elements allowed.

**EXAMPLE 2**   How many ways are there to select four pieces of fruit from a bowl containing apples, oranges, and pears if the order in which the pieces are selected does not matter, only the type of fruit and not the individual piece matters, and there are at least four pieces of each type of fruit in the bowl?

*Solution:* To solve this problem we list all the ways possible to select the fruit. There are 15 ways:

| | | |
|---|---|---|
| 4 apples | 4 oranges | 4 pears |
| 3 apples, 1 orange | 3 apples, 1 pear | 3 oranges, 1 apple |
| 3 oranges, 1 pear | 3 pears, 1 apple | 3 pears, 1 orange |
| 2 apples, 2 oranges | 2 apples, 2 pears | 2 oranges, 2 pears |
| 2 apples, 1 orange, 1 pear | 2 oranges, 1 apple, 1 pear | 2 pears, 1 apple, 1 orange |

The solution is the number of 4-combinations with repetition allowed from a three-element set, {*apple, orange, pear*}.   ◄

To solve more complex counting problems of this type, we need a general method for counting the $r$-combinations of an $n$-element set. In Example 3 we will illustrate such a method.

**EXAMPLE 3**   How many ways are there to select five bills from a cash box containing $1 bills, $2 bills, $5 bills, $10 bills, $20 bills, $50 bills, and $100 bills? Assume that the order in which the bills are chosen does not matter, that the bills of each denomination are indistinguishable, and that there are at least five bills of each type.

*Solution:* Because the order in which the bills are selected does not matter and seven different types of bills can be selected as many as five times, this problem involves counting 5-combinations with repetition allowed from a set with seven elements. Listing all possibilities would be tedious, because there are a large number of solutions. Instead, we will illustrate the use of a technique for counting combinations with repetition allowed.

Suppose that a cash box has seven compartments, one to hold each type of bill, as illustrated in Figure 1. These compartments are separated by six dividers, as shown in the picture. The choice of five bills corresponds to placing five markers in the compartments holding different types of bills. Figure 2 illustrates this correspondence for three different ways to select five bills, where the six dividers are represented by bars and the five bills by stars.

The number of ways to select five bills corresponds to the number of ways to arrange six bars and five stars in a row with a total of 11 positions. Consequently, the number of ways to select the five bills is the number of ways to select the positions of the five stars from the 11 positions. This corresponds to the number of unordered selections of 5 objects from a set of 11

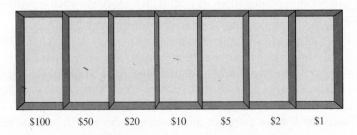

$100    $50    $20    $10    $5    $2    $1

**FIGURE 1   Cash Box with Seven Types of Bills.**

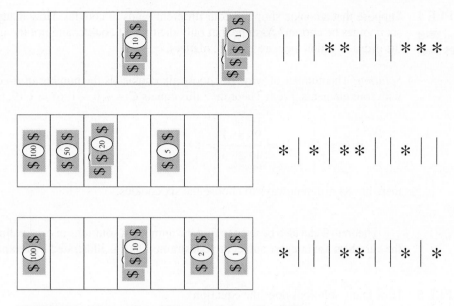

**FIGURE 2** **Examples of Ways to Select Five Bills.**

objects, which can be done in $C(11, 5)$ ways. Consequently, there are

$$C(11, 5) = \frac{11!}{5!\,6!} = 462$$

ways to choose five bills from the cash box with seven types of bills. ◀

Theorem 2 generalizes this discussion.

**THEOREM 2**
There are $C(n + r - 1, r) = C(n + r - 1, n - 1)$ $r$-combinations from a set with $n$ elements when repetition of elements is allowed.

*Proof:* Each $r$-combination of a set with $n$ elements when repetition is allowed can be represented by a list of $n - 1$ bars and $r$ stars. The $n - 1$ bars are used to mark off $n$ different cells, with the $i$th cell containing a star for each time the $i$th element of the set occurs in the combination. For instance, a 6-combination of a set with four elements is represented with three bars and six stars. Here

$$** \mid * \mid \mid ***$$

represents the combination containing exactly two of the first element, one of the second element, none of the third element, and three of the fourth element of the set.

As we have seen, each different list containing $n - 1$ bars and $r$ stars corresponds to an $r$-combination of the set with $n$ elements, when repetition is allowed. The number of such lists is $C(n - 1 + r, r)$, because each list corresponds to a choice of the $r$ positions to place the $r$ stars from the $n - 1 + r$ positions that contain $r$ stars and $n - 1$ bars. The number of such lists is also equal to $C(n - 1 + r, n - 1)$, because each list corresponds to a choice of the $n - 1$ positions to place the $n - 1$ bars. ◁

Examples 4–6 show how Theorem 2 is applied.

**EXAMPLE 4**

Suppose that a cookie shop has four different kinds of cookies. How many different ways can six cookies be chosen? Assume that only the type of cookie, and not the individual cookies or the order in which they are chosen, matters.

*Solution:* The number of ways to choose six cookies is the number of 6-combinations of a set with four elements. From Theorem 2 this equals $C(4 + 6 - 1, 6) = C(9, 6)$. Because

$$C(9, 6) = C(9, 3) = \frac{9 \cdot 8 \cdot 7}{1 \cdot 2 \cdot 3} = 84,$$

there are 84 different ways to choose the six cookies.    ◀

Theorem 2 can also be used to find the number of solutions of certain linear equations where the variables are integers subject to constraints. This is illustrated by Example 5.

**EXAMPLE 5**    How many solutions does the equation

$$x_1 + x_2 + x_3 = 11$$

have, where $x_1$, $x_2$, and $x_3$ are nonnegative integers?

*Solution:* To count the number of solutions, we note that a solution corresponds to a way of selecting 11 items from a set with three elements so that $x_1$ items of type one, $x_2$ items of type two, and $x_3$ items of type three are chosen. Hence, the number of solutions is equal to the number of 11-combinations with repetition allowed from a set with three elements. From Theorem 2 it follows that there are

$$C(3 + 11 - 1, 11) = C(13, 11) = C(13, 2) = \frac{13 \cdot 12}{1 \cdot 2} = 78$$

solutions.

The number of solutions of this equation can also be found when the variables are subject to constraints. For instance, we can find the number of solutions where the variables are integers with $x_1 \geq 1$, $x_2 \geq 2$, and $x_3 \geq 3$. A solution to the equation subject to these constraints corresponds to a selection of 11 items with $x_1$ items of type one, $x_2$ items of type two, and $x_3$ items of type three, where, in addition, there is at least one item of type one, two items of type two, and three items of type three. So, a solution corresponds to a choice of one item of type one, two of type two, and three of type three, together with a choice of five additional items of any type. By Theorem 2 this can be done in

$$C(3 + 5 - 1, 5) = C(7, 5) = C(7, 2) = \frac{7 \cdot 6}{1 \cdot 2} = 21$$

ways. Thus, there are 21 solutions of the equation subject to the given constraints.    ◀

Example 6 shows how counting the number of combinations with repetition allowed arises in determining the value of a variable that is incremented each time a certain type of nested loop is traversed.

| TABLE 1 Combinations and Permutations With and Without Repetition. | | |
|---|---|---|
| *Type* | *Repetition Allowed?* | *Formula* |
| $r$-permutations | No | $\dfrac{n!}{(n-r)!}$ |
| $r$-combinations | No | $\dfrac{n!}{r!\,(n-r)!}$ |
| $r$-permutations | Yes | $n^r$ |
| $r$-combinations | Yes | $\dfrac{(n+r-1)!}{r!\,(n-1)!}$ |

**EXAMPLE 6**   What is the value of $k$ after the following pseudocode has been executed?

```
k := 0
for i₁ := 1 to n
    for i₂ := 1 to i₁
        .
        .
        .
        for iₘ := 1 to iₘ₋₁
            k := k + 1
```

*Solution:* Note that the initial value of $k$ is 0 and that 1 is added to $k$ each time the nested loop is traversed with a sequence of integers $i_1, i_2, \ldots, i_m$ such that

$$1 \le i_m \le i_{m-1} \le \cdots \le i_1 \le n.$$

The number of such sequences of integers is the number of ways to choose $m$ integers from $\{1, 2, \ldots, n\}$, with repetition allowed. (To see this, note that once such a sequence has been selected, if we order the integers in the sequence in nondecreasing order, this uniquely defines an assignment of $i_m, i_{m-1}, \ldots, i_1$. Conversely, every such assignment corresponds to a unique unordered set.) Hence, from Theorem 2, it follows that $k = C(n + m - 1, m)$ after this code has been executed.   ◀

The formulae for the numbers of ordered and unordered selections of $r$ elements, chosen with and without repetition allowed from a set with $n$ elements, are shown in Table 1.

## Permutations with Indistinguishable Objects

Some elements may be indistinguishable in counting problems. When this is the case, care must be taken to avoid counting things more than once. Consider Example 7.

**EXAMPLE 7**   How many different strings can be made by reordering the letters of the word *SUCCESS*?

*Solution:* Because some of the letters of *SUCCESS* are the same, the answer is *not* given by the number of permutations of seven letters. This word contains three *S*s, two *C*s, one *U*, and one *E*. To determine the number of different strings that can be made by reordering the letters, first note that the three *S*s can be placed among the seven positions in $C(7, 3)$ different ways, leaving four positions free. Then the two $C$s can be placed in $C(4, 2)$ ways, leaving two free positions. The $U$ can be placed in $C(2, 1)$ ways, leaving just one position free. Hence $E$ can be placed in $C(1, 1)$ way. Consequently, from the product rule, the number of different strings that can be made is

$$C(7, 3)C(4, 2)C(2, 1)C(1, 1) = \frac{7!}{3!\,4!} \cdot \frac{4!}{2!\,2!} \cdot \frac{2!}{1!\,1!} \cdot \frac{1!}{1!\,0!}$$

$$= \frac{7!}{3!\,2!\,1!\,1!}$$

$$= 420 . \qquad \blacktriangleleft$$

We can prove Theorem 3 using the same sort of reasoning as in Example 7.

**THEOREM 3**    The number of different permutations of $n$ objects, where there are $n_1$ indistinguishable objects of type 1, $n_2$ indistinguishable objects of type 2, ..., and $n_k$ indistinguishable objects of type $k$, is

$$\frac{n!}{n_1!\,n_2!\cdots n_k!}.$$

*Proof:* To determine the number of permutations, first note that the $n_1$ objects of type one can be placed among the $n$ positions in $C(n, n_1)$ ways, leaving $n - n_1$ positions free. Then the objects of type two can be placed in $C(n - n_1, n_2)$ ways, leaving $n - n_1 - n_2$ positions free. Continue placing the objects of type three, ..., type $k - 1$, until at the last stage, $n_k$ objects of type $k$ can be placed in $C(n - n_1 - n_2 - \cdots - n_{k-1}, n_k)$ ways. Hence, by the product rule, the total number of different permutations is

$$C(n, n_1)C(n - n_1, n_2) \cdots C(n - n_1 - \cdots - n_{k-1}, n_k)$$

$$= \frac{n!}{n_1!\,(n - n_1)!} \frac{(n - n_1)!}{n_2!\,(n - n_1 - n_2)!} \cdots \frac{(n - n_1 - \cdots - n_{k-1})!}{n_k!\,0!}$$

$$= \frac{n!}{n_1!\,n_2!\cdots n_k!}. \qquad \triangleleft$$

## Distributing Objects into Boxes

**Links**

Many counting problems can be solved by enumerating the ways objects can be placed into boxes (where the order these objects are placed into the boxes does not matter). The objects can be either *distinguishable*, that is, different from each other, or *indistinguishable*, that is, considered identical. Distinguishable objects are sometimes said to be *labeled*, whereas indistinguishable objects are said to be *unlabeled*. Similarly, boxes can be *distinguishable*, that is, different, or *indinguishable*, that is, identical. Distinguishable boxes are often said to be *labeled*, while indistinguishable boxes are said to be *unlabeled*. When you solve a counting problem using the model of distributing objects into boxes, you need to determine whether the objects are distinguishable and whether the boxes are distinguishable. Although the context of the counting problem makes these two decisions clear, counting problems are sometimes ambiguous and it may be unclear which model applies. In such a case it is best to state whatever assumptions you are making and explain why the particular model you choose conforms to your assumptions.

Extra
Examples
We will see that there are closed formulae for counting the ways to distribute objects, distinguishable or indistinguishable, into distinguishable boxes. We are not so lucky when we count the ways to distribute objects, distinguishable or indistinguishable, into indistinguishable boxes; there are no closed formulae to use in these cases.

DISTINGUISHABLE OBJECTS AND DISTINGUISHABLE BOXES   We first consider the case when distinguishable objects are placed into distinguishable boxes. Consider Example 8 in which the objects are cards and the boxes are hands of players.

**EXAMPLE 8**   How many ways are there to distribute hands of 5 cards to each of four players from the standard deck of 52 cards?

*Solution:* We will use the product rule to solve this problem. To begin, note that the first player can be dealt 5 cards in $C(52, 5)$ ways. The second player can be dealt 5 cards in $C(47, 5)$ ways, because only 47 cards are left. The third player can be dealt 5 cards in $C(42, 5)$ ways. Finally, the fourth player can be dealt 5 cards in $C(37, 5)$ ways. Hence, the total number of ways to deal four players 5 cards each is

$$C(52, 5)C(47, 5)C(42, 5)C(37, 5) = \frac{52!}{47!\,5!} \cdot \frac{47!}{42!\,5!} \cdot \frac{42!}{37!\,5!} \cdot \frac{37!}{32!\,5!}$$

$$= \frac{52!}{5!\,5!\,5!\,5!\,32!}.$$   ◄

**Remark:** The solution to Example 8 equals the number of permutations of 52 objects, with 5 indistinguishable objects of each of four different types, and 32 objects of a fifth type. This equality can be seen by defining a one-to-one correspondence between permutations of this type and distributions of cards to the players. To define this correspondence, first order the cards from 1 to 52. Then cards dealt to the first player correspond to the cards in the positions assigned to objects of the first type in the permutation. Similarly, cards dealt to the second, third, and fourth players, respectively, correspond to cards in the positions assigned to objects of the second, third, and fourth type, respectively. The cards not dealt to any player correspond to cards in the positions assigned to objects of the fifth type. The reader should verify that this is a one-to-one correspondence.

Example 8 is a typical problem that involves distributing distinguishable objects into distinguishable boxes. The distinguishable objects are the 52 cards, and the five distinguishable boxes are the hands of the four players and the rest of the deck. Counting problems that involve distributing distinguishable objects into boxes can be solved using Theorem 4.

**THEOREM 4**   The number of ways to distribute $n$ distinguishable objects into $k$ distinguishable boxes so that $n_i$ objects are placed into box $i$, $i = 1, 2, \ldots, k$, equals

$$\frac{n!}{n_1!\,n_2! \cdots n_k!}.$$

Theorem 4 can be proved using the product rule. We leave the details as Exercise 47. It can also be proved (see Exercise 48) by setting up a one-to-one correspondence between the permutations counted by Theorem 3 and the ways to distribute objects counted by Theorem 4.

INDISTINGUISHABLE OBJECTS AND DISTINGUISHABLE BOXES   Counting the number of ways of placing $n$ indistinguishable objects into $k$ distinguishable boxes turns out to be the same as counting the number of $n$-combinations for a set with $k$ elements when repetitions are allowed. The reason behind this is that there is a one-to-one correspondence between *n*-combinations from a set with *k* elements when repetition is allowed and the ways to place *n* indistinguishable balls into *k* distinguishable boxes. To set up this correspondence, we put a ball in the *i*th bin each time the *i*th element of the set is included in the *n*-combination.

**EXAMPLE 9**  How many ways are there to place 10 indistinguishable balls into eight distinguishable bins?

*Solution:* The number of ways to place 10 indistinguishable balls into eight bins equals the number of 10-combinations from a set with eight elements when repetition is allowed. Consequently, there are

$$C(8 + 10 - 1, 10) = C(17, 10) = \frac{17!}{10!7!} = 19,448.$$

◀

This means that there are $C(n + r - 1, n - 1)$ ways to place *r* indistinguishable objects into *n* distinguishable boxes.

**DISTINGUISHABLE OBJECTS AND INDISTINGUISHABLE BOXES**   Counting the ways to place *n* distinguishable objects into *k* indistinguishable boxes is more difficult than counting the ways to place objects, distinguishable or indistinguishable objects, into distinguishable boxes. We illustrate this with an example.

**EXAMPLE 10**  How many ways are there to put four different employees into three indistinguishable offices, when each office can contain any number of employees?

*Solution:* We will solve this problem by enumerating all the ways these employees can be placed into the offices. We represent the four employees by *A*, *B*, *C*, and *D*. First, we note that we can distribute employees so that all four are put into one office, three are put into one office and a fourth is put into a second office, two employees are put into one office and two put into a second office, and finally, two are put into one office, and one each put into the other two offices. Each way to distribute these employees to these offices can be represented by a way to partition the elements *A*, *B*, *C*, and *D* into disjoint subsets.

We can put all four employees into one office in exactly one way, represented by $\{\{A, B, C, D\}\}$. We can put three employees into one office and the fourth employee into a different office in exactly four ways, represented by $\{\{A, B, C\}, \{D\}\}$, $\{\{A, B, D\}, \{C\}\}$, $\{\{A, C, D\}, \{B\}\}$, and $\{\{B, C, D\}, \{A\}\}$. We can put two employees into one office and two into a second office in exactly three ways, represented by $\{\{A, B\}, \{C, D\}\}$, $\{\{A, C\}, \{B, D\}\}$, and $\{\{A, D\}, \{B, C\}\}$. Finally, we can put two employees into one office, and one each into each of the remaining two offices in six ways, represented by $\{\{A, B\}, \{C\}, \{D\}\}$, $\{\{A, C\}, \{B\}, \{D\}\}$, $\{\{A, D\}, \{B\}, \{C\}\}$, $\{\{B, C\}, \{A\}, \{D\}\}$, $\{\{B, D\}, \{A\}, \{C\}\}$, and $\{\{C, D\}, \{A\}, \{B\}\}$.

Counting all the possibilities, we find that there are 14 ways to put four different employees into three indistinguishable offices. Another way to look at this problem is to look at the number of offices into which we put employees. Note that there are six ways to put four different employees into three indistinguishable offices so that no office is empty, seven ways to put four different employees into two indistinguishable offices so that no office is empty, and one way to put four employees into one office so that it is not empty.  ◀

There is no simple closed formula for the number of ways to distribute *n* distinguishable objects into *j* indistinguishable boxes. However, there is a formula involving a summation, which we will now describe. Let $S(n, j)$ denote the number of ways to distribute *n* distinguishable objects into *j* indistinguishable boxes so that no box is empty. The numbers $S(n, j)$ are called **Stirling numbers of the second kind**. For instance, Example 10 shows that $S(4, 3) = 6$, $S(4, 2) = 7$, and $S(4, 1) = 1$. We see that the number of ways to distribute *n* distinguishable objects into *k* indistinguishable boxes (where the number of boxes that are nonempty equals *k*, $k - 1, \ldots, 2$, or 1) equals $\sum_{j=1}^{k} S(n, j)$. For instance, following the reasoning in Example 10, the number of ways to distribute four distinguishable objects into three indistinguishable boxes equals $S(4, 1) + S(4, 2) + S(4, 3) = 1 + 7 + 6 = 14$. Using the inclusion–exclusion principle (see Section 8.6) it can be shown that

$$S(n, j) = \frac{1}{j!} \sum_{i=0}^{j-1} (-1)^i \binom{j}{i} (j - i)^n.$$

Consequently, the number of ways to distribute $n$ distinguishable objects into $k$ indistinguishable boxes equals

$$\sum_{j=1}^{k} S(n, j) = \sum_{j=1}^{k} \frac{1}{j!} \sum_{i=0}^{j-1} (-1)^i \binom{j}{i} (j - i)^n.$$

***Remark:*** The reader may be curious about the Stirling numbers of the first kind. A combinatorial definition of the **signless Stirling numbers of the first kind**, the absolute values of the Stirling numbers of the first kind, can be found in the preamble to Exercise 47 in the Supplementary Exercises. For the definition of Stirling numbers of the first kind, for more information about Stirling numbers of the second kind, and to learn more about Stirling numbers of the first kind and the relationship between Stirling numbers of the first and second kind, see combinatorics textbooks such as [Bó07], [Br99], and [RoTe05], and Chapter 6 in [MiRo91].

INDISTINGUISHABLE OBJECTS AND INDISTINGUISHABLE BOXES   Some counting problems can be solved by determining the number of ways to distribute indistinguishable objects into indistinguishable boxes. We illustrate this principle with an example.

**EXAMPLE 11**   How many ways are there to pack six copies of the same book into four identical boxes, where a box can contain as many as six books?

*Solution:* We will enumerate all ways to pack the books. For each way to pack the books, we will list the number of books in the box with the largest number of books, followed by the numbers of books in each box containing at least one book, in order of decreasing number of books in a box. The ways we can pack the books are

> 6
> 5, 1
> 4, 2
> 4, 1, 1
> 3, 3
> 3, 2, 1
> 3, 1, 1, 1
> 2, 2, 2
> 2, 2, 1, 1.

For example, 4, 1, 1 indicates that one box contains four books, a second box contains a single book, and a third box contains a single book (and the fourth box is empty). We conclude that there are nine allowable ways to pack the books, because we have listed them all.   ◄

Observe that distributing $n$ indistinguishable objects into $k$ indistinguishable boxes is the same as writing $n$ as the sum of at most $k$ positive integers in nonincreasing order. If $a_1 + a_2 + \cdots + a_j = n$, where $a_1, a_2, \ldots, a_j$ are positive integers with $a_1 \geq a_2 \geq \cdots \geq a_j$, we say that $a_1, a_2, \ldots, a_j$ is a **partition** of the positive integer $n$ into $j$ positive integers. We see that if $p_k(n)$ is the number of partitions of $n$ into at most $k$ positive integers, then there are $p_k(n)$ ways to distribute $n$ indistinguishable objects into $k$ indistinguishable boxes. No simple closed formula exists for this number. For more information about partitions of positive integers, see [Ro11].

## Exercises

1. In how many different ways can five elements be selected in order from a set with three elements when repetition is allowed?

2. In how many different ways can five elements be selected in order from a set with five elements when repetition is allowed?

3. How many strings of six letters are there?

4. Every day a student randomly chooses a sandwich for lunch from a pile of wrapped sandwiches. If there are six kinds of sandwiches, how many different ways are there for the student to choose sandwiches for the seven days of a week if the order in which the sandwiches are chosen matters?

5. How many ways are there to assign three jobs to five employees if each employee can be given more than one job?

6. How many ways are there to select five unordered elements from a set with three elements when repetition is allowed?

7. How many ways are there to select three unordered elements from a set with five elements when repetition is allowed?

8. How many different ways are there to choose a dozen donuts from the 21 varieties at a donut shop?

9. A bagel shop has onion bagels, poppy seed bagels, egg bagels, salty bagels, pumpernickel bagels, sesame seed bagels, raisin bagels, and plain bagels. How many ways are there to choose

   a) six bagels?
   b) a dozen bagels?
   c) two dozen bagels?
   d) a dozen bagels with at least one of each kind?
   e) a dozen bagels with at least three egg bagels and no more than two salty bagels?

10. A croissant shop has plain croissants, cherry croissants, chocolate croissants, almond croissants, apple croissants, and broccoli croissants. How many ways are there to choose

    a) a dozen croissants?
    b) three dozen croissants?
    c) two dozen croissants with at least two of each kind?
    d) two dozen croissants with no more than two broccoli croissants?
    e) two dozen croissants with at least five chocolate croissants and at least three almond croissants?
    f) two dozen croissants with at least one plain croissant, at least two cherry croissants, at least three chocolate croissants, at least one almond croissant, at least two apple croissants, and no more than three broccoli croissants?

11. How many ways are there to choose eight coins from a piggy bank containing 100 identical pennies and 80 identical nickels?

12. How many different combinations of pennies, nickels, dimes, quarters, and half dollars can a piggy bank contain if it has 20 coins in it?

13. A book publisher has 3000 copies of a discrete mathematics book. How many ways are there to store these books in their three warehouses if the copies of the book are indistinguishable?

14. How many solutions are there to the equation

$$x_1 + x_2 + x_3 + x_4 = 17,$$

where $x_1, x_2, x_3$, and $x_4$ are nonnegative integers?

15. How many solutions are there to the equation

$$x_1 + x_2 + x_3 + x_4 + x_5 = 21,$$

where $x_i, i = 1, 2, 3, 4, 5$, is a nonnegative integer such that

   a) $x_1 \geq 1$?
   b) $x_i \geq 2$ for $i = 1, 2, 3, 4, 5$?
   c) $0 \leq x_1 \leq 10$?
   d) $0 \leq x_1 \leq 3, 1 \leq x_2 < 4$, and $x_3 \geq 15$?

16. How many solutions are there to the equation

$$x_1 + x_2 + x_3 + x_4 + x_5 + x_6 = 29,$$

where $x_i, i = 1, 2, 3, 4, 5, 6$, is a nonnegative integer such that

   a) $x_i > 1$ for $i = 1, 2, 3, 4, 5, 6$?
   b) $x_1 \geq 1, x_2 \geq 2, x_3 \geq 3, x_4 \geq 4, x_5 > 5$, and $x_6 \geq 6$?
   c) $x_1 \leq 5$?
   d) $x_1 < 8$ and $x_2 > 8$?

17. How many strings of 10 ternary digits (0, 1, or 2) are there that contain exactly two 0s, three 1s, and five 2s?

18. How many strings of 20-decimal digits are there that contain two 0s, four 1s, three 2s, one 3, two 4s, three 5s, two 7s, and three 9s?

19. Suppose that a large family has 14 children, including two sets of identical triplets, three sets of identical twins, and two individual children. How many ways are there to seat these children in a row of chairs if the identical triplets or twins cannot be distinguished from one another?

20. How many solutions are there to the inequality

$$x_1 + x_2 + x_3 \leq 11,$$

where $x_1, x_2$, and $x_3$ are nonnegative integers? [*Hint:* Introduce an auxiliary variable $x_4$ such that $x_1 + x_2 + x_3 + x_4 = 11$.]

21. How many ways are there to distribute six indistinguishable balls into nine distinguishable bins?

22. How many ways are there to distribute 12 indistinguishable balls into six distinguishable bins?

23. How many ways are there to distribute 12 distinguishable objects into six distinguishable boxes so that two objects are placed in each box?

24. How many ways are there to distribute 15 distinguishable objects into five distinguishable boxes so that the boxes have one, two, three, four, and five objects in them, respectively.

**25.** How many positive integers less than 1,000,000 have the sum of their digits equal to 19?

**26.** How many positive integers less than 1,000,000 have exactly one digit equal to 9 and have a sum of digits equal to 13?

**27.** There are 10 questions on a discrete mathematics final exam. How many ways are there to assign scores to the problems if the sum of the scores is 100 and each question is worth at least 5 points?

**28.** Show that there are $C(n + r - q_1 - q_2 - \cdots - q_r - 1, n - q_1 - q_2 - \cdots - q_r)$ different unordered selections of $n$ objects of $r$ different types that include at least $q_1$ objects of type one, $q_2$ objects of type two, ..., and $q_r$ objects of type $r$.

**29.** How many different bit strings can be transmitted if the string must begin with a 1 bit, must include three additional 1 bits (so that a total of four 1 bits is sent), must include a total of 12 0 bits, and must have at least two 0 bits following each 1 bit?

**30.** How many different strings can be made from the letters in *MISSISSIPPI*, using all the letters?

**31.** How many different strings can be made from the letters in *ABRACADABRA*, using all the letters?

**32.** How many different strings can be made from the letters in *AARDVARK*, using all the letters, if all three *A*s must be consecutive?

**33.** How many different strings can be made from the letters in *ORONO*, using some or all of the letters?

**34.** How many strings with five or more characters can be formed from the letters in *SEERESS*?

**35.** How many strings with seven or more characters can be formed from the letters in *EVERGREEN*?

**36.** How many different bit strings can be formed using six 1s and eight 0s?

**37.** A student has three mangos, two papayas, and two kiwi fruits. If the student eats one piece of fruit each day, and only the type of fruit matters, in how many different ways can these fruits be consumed?

**38.** A professor packs her collection of 40 issues of a mathematics journal in four boxes with 10 issues per box. How many ways can she distribute the journals if

   **a)** each box is numbered, so that they are distinguishable?

   **b)** the boxes are identical, so that they cannot be distinguished?

**39.** How many ways are there to travel in $xyz$ space from the origin $(0, 0, 0)$ to the point $(4, 3, 5)$ by taking steps one unit in the positive $x$ direction, one unit in the positive $y$ direction, or one unit in the positive $z$ direction? (Moving in the negative $x$, $y$, or $z$ direction is prohibited, so that no backtracking is allowed.)

**40.** How many ways are there to travel in $xyzw$ space from the origin $(0, 0, 0, 0)$ to the point $(4, 3, 5, 4)$ by taking steps one unit in the positive $x$, positive $y$, positive $z$, or positive $w$ direction?

**41.** How many ways are there to deal hands of seven cards to each of five players from a standard deck of 52 cards?

**42.** In bridge, the 52 cards of a standard deck are dealt to four players. How many different ways are there to deal bridge hands to four players?

**43.** How many ways are there to deal hands of five cards to each of six players from a deck containing 48 different cards?

**44.** In how many ways can a dozen books be placed on four distinguishable shelves

   **a)** if the books are indistinguishable copies of the same title?

   **b)** if no two books are the same, and the positions of the books on the shelves matter? [*Hint:* Break this into 12 tasks, placing each book separately. Start with the sequence 1, 2, 3, 4 to represent the shelves. Represent the books by $b_i$, $i = 1, 2, \ldots, 12$. Place $b_1$ to the right of one of the terms in 1, 2, 3, 4. Then successively place $b_2, b_3, \ldots,$ and $b_{12}$.]

**45.** How many ways can $n$ books be placed on $k$ distinguishable shelves

   **a)** if the books are indistinguishable copies of the same title?

   **b)** if no two books are the same, and the positions of the books on the shelves matter?

**46.** A shelf holds 12 books in a row. How many ways are there to choose five books so that no two adjacent books are chosen? [*Hint:* Represent the books that are chosen by bars and the books not chosen by stars. Count the number of sequences of five bars and seven stars so that no two bars are adjacent.]

**∗47.** Use the product rule to prove Theorem 4, by first placing objects in the first box, then placing objects in the second box, and so on.

**∗48.** Prove Theorem 4 by first setting up a one-to-one correspondence between permutations of $n$ objects with $n_i$ indistinguishable objects of type $i$, $i = 1, 2, 3, \ldots, k$, and the distributions of $n$ objects in $k$ boxes such that $n_i$ objects are placed in box $i$, $i = 1, 2, 3, \ldots, k$ and then applying Theorem 3.

**∗49.** In this exercise we will prove Theorem 2 by setting up a one-to-one correspondence between the set of $r$-combinations with repetition allowed of $S = \{1, 2, 3, \ldots, n\}$ and the set of $r$-combinations of the set $T = \{1, 2, 3, \ldots, n + r - 1\}$.

   **a)** Arrange the elements in an $r$-combination, with repetition allowed, of $S$ into an increasing sequence $x_1 \leq x_2 \leq \cdots \leq x_r$. Show that the sequence formed by adding $k - 1$ to the $k$th term is strictly increasing. Conclude that this sequence is made up of $r$ distinct elements from $T$.

   **b)** Show that the procedure described in (a) defines a one-to-one correspondence between the set of $r$-combinations, with repetition allowed, of $S$ and the $r$-combinations of $T$. [*Hint:* Show the correspondence can be reversed by associating to the $r$-combination $\{x_1, x_2, \ldots, x_r\}$ of $T$, with $1 \leq x_1 < x_2 < \cdots < x_r \leq n + r - 1$, the $r$-combination with repetition allowed from $S$, formed by subtracting $k - 1$ from the $k$th element.]

c) Conclude that there are $C(n + r - 1, r)$ $r$-combinations with repetition allowed from a set with $n$ elements.

50. How many ways are there to distribute five distinguishable objects into three indistinguishable boxes?

51. How many ways are there to distribute six distinguishable objects into four indistinguishable boxes so that each of the boxes contains at least one object?

52. How many ways are there to put five temporary employees into four identical offices?

53. How many ways are there to put six temporary employees into four identical offices so that there is at least one temporary employee in each of these four offices?

54. How many ways are there to distribute five indistinguishable objects into three indistinguishable boxes?

55. How many ways are there to distribute six indistinguishable objects into four indistinguishable boxes so that each of the boxes contains at least one object?

56. How many ways are there to pack eight identical DVDs into five indistinguishable boxes so that each box contains at least one DVD?

57. How many ways are there to pack nine identical DVDs into three indistinguishable boxes so that each box contains at least two DVDs?

58. How many ways are there to distribute five balls into seven boxes if each box must have at most one ball in it if

a) both the balls and boxes are labeled?

b) the balls are labeled, but the boxes are unlabeled?

c) the balls are unlabeled, but the boxes are labeled?

d) both the balls and boxes are unlabeled?

59. How many ways are there to distribute five balls into three boxes if each box must have at least one ball in it if

a) both the balls and boxes are labeled?

b) the balls are labeled, but the boxes are unlabeled?

c) the balls are unlabeled, but the boxes are labeled?

d) both the balls and boxes are unlabeled?

60. Suppose that a basketball league has 32 teams, split into two conferences of 16 teams each. Each conference is split into three divisions. Suppose that the North Central Division has five teams. Each of the teams in the North Central Division plays four games against each of the other teams in this division, three games against each of the 11 remaining teams in the conference, and two games against each of the 16 teams in the other conference. In how many different orders can the games of one of the teams in the North Central Division be scheduled?

*61. Suppose that a weapons inspector must inspect each of five different sites twice, visiting one site per day. The inspector is free to select the order in which to visit these sites, but cannot visit site X, the most suspicious site, on two consecutive days. In how many different orders can the inspector visit these sites?

62. How many different terms are there in the expansion of $(x_1 + x_2 + \cdots + x_m)^n$ after all terms with identical sets of exponents are added?

*63. Prove the **Multinomial Theorem**: If $n$ is a positive integer, then

$$(x_1 + x_2 + \cdots + x_m)^n$$

$$= \sum_{n_1 + n_2 + \cdots + n_m = n} C(n; n_1, n_2, \ldots, n_m) x_1^{n_1} x_2^{n_2} \cdots x_m^{n_m},$$

where

$$C(n; n_1, n_2, \ldots, n_m) = \frac{n!}{n_1! \, n_2! \cdots n_m!}$$

is a **multinomial coefficient**.

64. Find the expansion of $(x + y + z)^4$.

65. Find the coefficient of $x^3 y^2 z^5$ in $(x + y + z)^{10}$.

66. How many terms are there in the expansion of

$$(x + y + z)^{100}?$$

# 6.6    Generating Permutations and Combinations

## Introduction

Methods for counting various types of permutations and combinations were described in the previous sections of this chapter, but sometimes permutations or combinations need to be generated, not just counted. Consider the following three problems. First, suppose that a salesperson must visit six different cities. In which order should these cities be visited to minimize total travel time? One way to determine the best order is to determine the travel time for each of the $6! = 720$ different orders in which the cities can be visited and choose the one with the smallest travel time. Second, suppose we are given a set of six positive integers and wish to find a subset of them that has 100 as their sum, if such a subset exists. One way to find these numbers is to generate all $2^6 = 64$ subsets and check the sum of their elements. Third, suppose a laboratory has 95 employees. A group of 12 of these employees with a particular set of 25 skills is needed for a project. (Each employee can have one or more of these skills.) One way to find such a

# CHAPTER

# 7

# Discrete Probability

Combinatorics and probability theory share common origins. The theory of probability was first developed more than 300 years ago, when certain gambling games were analyzed. Although probability theory was originally invented to study gambling, it now plays an essential role in a wide variety of disciplines. For example, probability theory is extensively applied in the study of genetics, where it can be used to help understand the inheritance of traits. Of course, probability still remains an extremely popular part of mathematics because of its applicability to gambling, which continues to be an extremely popular human endeavor.

In computer science, probability theory plays an important role in the study of the complexity of algorithms. In particular, ideas and techniques from probability theory are used to determine the average-case complexity of algorithms. Probabilistic algorithms can be used to solve many problems that cannot be easily or practically solved by deterministic algorithms. In a probabilistic algorithm, instead of always following the same steps when given the same input, as a deterministic algorithm does, the algorithm makes one or more random choices, which may lead to different output. In combinatorics, probability theory can even be used to show that objects with certain properties exist. The probabilistic method, a technique in combinatorics introduced by Paul Erdős and Alfréd Rényi, shows that an object with a specified property exists by showing that there is a positive probability that a randomly constructed object has this property. Probability theory can help us answer questions that involve uncertainty, such as determining whether we should reject an incoming mail message as spam based on the words that appear in the message.

## 7.1 An Introduction to Discrete Probability

### Introduction

Probability theory dates back to 1526 when the Italian mathematician, physician, and gambler Girolamo Cardano wrote the first known systematic treatment of the subject in his book *Liber de Ludo Aleae* (*Book on Games of Chance*). (This book was not published until 1663, which may have held back the development of probability theory.) In the seventeenth century the French mathematician Blaise Pascal determined the odds of winning some popular bets based on the outcome when a pair of dice is repeatedly rolled. In the eighteenth century, the French mathematician Laplace, who also studied gambling, defined the probability of an event as the number of successful outcomes divided by the number of possible outcomes. For instance, the probability that a die comes up an odd number when it is rolled is the number of successful outcomes—namely, the number of ways it can come up odd—divided by the number of possible outcomes—namely, the number of different ways the die can come up. There are a total of six possible outcomes—namely, 1, 2, 3, 4, 5, and 6—and exactly three of these are successful outcomes—namely, 1, 3, and 5. Hence, the probability that the die comes up an odd number is $3/6 = 1/2$. (Note that it has been assumed that all possible outcomes are equally likely, or, in other words, that the die is fair.)

In this section we will restrict ourselves to experiments that have finitely many, equally likely, outcomes. This permits us to use Laplace's definition of the probability of an event. We will continue our study of probability in Section 7.2, where we will study experiments with finitely many outcomes that are not necessarily equally likely. In Section 7.2 we will also introduce some key concepts in probability theory, including conditional probability, independence of events, and random variables. In Section 7.4 we will introduce the concepts of the expectation and variance of a random variable.

## Finite Probability

An **experiment** is a procedure that yields one of a given set of possible outcomes. The **sample space** of the experiment is the set of possible outcomes. An **event** is a subset of the sample space. Laplace's definition of the probability of an event with finitely many possible outcomes will now be stated.

**DEFINITION 1**

> If $S$ is a finite nonempty sample space of equally likely outcomes, and $E$ is an event, that is, a subset of $S$, then the *probability* of $E$ is $p(E) = \dfrac{|E|}{|S|}$.

*The probability of an event can never be negative or more than one!*

According to Laplace's definition, the probability of an event is between 0 and 1. To see this, note that if $E$ is an event from a finite sample space $S$, then $0 \le |E| \le |S|$, because $E \subseteq S$. Thus, $0 \le p(E) = |E|/|S| \le 1$.

Examples 1–7 illustrate how the probability of an event is found.

**EXAMPLE 1**   An urn contains four blue balls and five red balls. What is the probability that a ball chosen at random from the urn is blue?

*Solution:* To calculate the probability, note that there are nine possible outcomes, and four of these possible outcomes produce a blue ball. Hence, the probability that a blue ball is chosen is 4/9.   ◀

**EXAMPLE 2**   What is the probability that when two dice are rolled, the sum of the numbers on the two dice is 7?

*Solution:* There are a total of 36 equally likely possible outcomes when two dice are rolled. (The product rule can be used to see this; because each die has six possible outcomes, the total

GIROLAMO CARDANO (1501–1576)   Cardano, born in Pavia, Italy, was the illegitimate child of Fazio Cardano, a lawyer, mathematician, and friend of Leonardo da Vinci, and Chiara Micheria, a young widow. In spite of illness and poverty, Cardano was able to study at the universities of Pavia and Padua, from where he received his medical degree. Cardano was not accepted into Milan's College of Physicians because of his illegitimate birth, as well as his eccentricity and confrontational style. Nevertheless, his medical skills were highly regarded. One of his main accomplishments as a physician is the first description of typhoid fever.

Cardano published more than 100 books on a diverse range of subjects, including medicine, the natural sciences, mathematics, gambling, physical inventions and experiments, and astrology. He also wrote a fascinating autobiography. In mathematics, Cardano's book *Ars Magna*, published in 1545, established the foundations of abstract algebra. This was the most comprehensive book on abstract algebra for more than a century; it presents many novel ideas of Cardano and of others, including methods for solving cubic and quartic equations from their coefficients. Cardano also made several important contributions to cryptography. Cardano was an advocate of education for the deaf, believing, unlike his contemporaries, that deaf people could learn to read and write before learning to speak, and could use their minds just as well as hearing people.

Cardano was often short of money. However, he kept himself solvent through gambling and winning money by beating others at chess. His book about games of chance, *Liber de Ludo Aleae*, written in 1526 (but published in 1663), offers the first systematic treatment of probability; it also describes effective ways to cheat. Cardano was considered to be a man of dubious moral character; he was often described as a liar, gambler, lecher, and heretic.

number of outcomes when two dice are rolled is $6^2 = 36$.) There are six successful outcomes, namely, $(1, 6)$, $(2, 5)$, $(3, 4)$, $(4, 3)$, $(5, 2)$, and $(6, 1)$, where the values of the first and second dice are represented by an ordered pair. Hence, the probability that a seven comes up when two fair dice are rolled is $6/36 = 1/6$. ◀

**Links**

Lotteries are extremely popular throughout the world. We can easily compute the odds of winning different types of lotteries, as illustrated in Examples 3 and 4. (The odd of winning the popular Mega Millions and Powerball lotteries are studied in the supplementary exercises.)

**EXAMPLE 3**     In a lottery, players win a large prize when they pick four digits that match, in the correct order, four digits selected by a random mechanical process. A smaller prize is won if only three digits are matched. What is the probability that a player wins the large prize? What is the probability that a player wins the small prize?

*Solution:* There is only one way to choose all four digits correctly. By the product rule, there are $10^4 = 10,000$ ways to choose four digits. Hence, the probability that a player wins the large prize is $1/10,000 = 0.0001$.

Players win the smaller prize when they correctly choose exactly three of the four digits. Exactly one digit must be wrong to get three digits correct, but not all four correct. By the sum rule, to find the number of ways to choose exactly three digits correctly, we add the number of ways to choose four digits matching the digits picked in all but the $i$th position, for $i = 1, 2, 3, 4$.

To count the number of successes with the first digit incorrect, note that there are nine possible choices for the first digit (all but the one correct digit), and one choice for each of the other digits, namely, the correct digits for these slots. Hence, there are nine ways to choose four digits where the first digit is incorrect, but the last three are correct. Similarly, there are nine ways to choose four digits where the second digit is incorrect, nine with the third digit incorrect, and nine with the fourth digit incorrect. Hence, there is a total of 36 ways to choose four digits with exactly three of the four digits correct. Thus, the probability that a player wins the smaller prize is $36/10,000 = 9/2500 = 0.0036$. ◀

**EXAMPLE 4**     There are many lotteries now that award enormous prizes to people who correctly choose a set of six numbers out of the first $n$ positive integers, where $n$ is usually between 30 and 60. What is the probability that a person picks the correct six numbers out of 40?

*Solution:* There is only one winning combination. The total number of ways to choose six numbers out of 40 is

$$C(40, 6) = \frac{40!}{34! \, 6!} = 3,838,380.$$

Consequently, the probability of picking a winning combination is $1/3,838,380 \approx 0.00000026$. (Here the symbol $\approx$ means approximately equal to.) ◀

**Links**

PIERRE-SIMON LAPLACE (1749–1827)     Pierre-Simon Laplace came from humble origins in Normandy. In his childhood he was educated in a school run by the Benedictines. At 16 he entered the University of Caen intending to study theology. However, he soon realized his true interests were in mathematics. After completing his studies, he was named a provisional professor at Caen, and in 1769 he became professor of mathematics at the Paris Military School.

Laplace is best known for his contributions to celestial mechanics, the study of the motions of heavenly bodies. His *Traité de Mécanique Céleste* is considered one of the greatest scientific works of the early nineteenth century. Laplace was one of the founders of probability theory and made many contributions to mathematical statistics. His work in this area is documented in his book *Théorie Analytique des Probabilités*, in which he defined the probability of an event as the ratio of the number of favorable outcomes to the total number of outcomes of an experiment.

Laplace was famous for his political flexibility. He was loyal, in succession, to the French Republic, Napoleon, and King Louis XVIII. This flexibility permitted him to be productive before, during, and after the French Revolution.

Links

Poker, and other card games, are growing in popularity. To win at these games it helps to know the probability of different hands. We can find the probability of specific hands that arise in card games using the techniques developed so far. A deck of cards contains 52 cards. There are 13 different kinds of cards, with four cards of each kind. (Among the terms commonly used instead of "kind" are "rank," "face value," "denomination," and "value.") These kinds are twos, threes, fours, fives, sixes, sevens, eights, nines, tens, jacks, queens, kings, and aces. There are also four suits: spades, clubs, hearts, and diamonds, each containing 13 cards, with one card of each kind in a suit. In many poker games, a hand consists of five cards.

**EXAMPLE 5**     Find the probability that a hand of five cards in poker contains four cards of one kind.

*Solution:* By the product rule, the number of hands of five cards with four cards of one kind is the product of the number of ways to pick one kind, the number of ways to pick the four of this kind out of the four in the deck of this kind, and the number of ways to pick the fifth card. This is

$$C(13, 1)C(4, 4)C(48, 1).$$

By Example 11 in Section 6.3 there are $C(52, 5)$ different hands of five cards. Hence, the probability that a hand contains four cards of one kind is

$$\frac{C(13, 1)C(4, 4)C(48, 1)}{C(52, 5)} = \frac{13 \cdot 1 \cdot 48}{2,598,960} \approx 0.00024. \qquad \blacktriangleleft$$

**EXAMPLE 6**     What is the probability that a poker hand contains a full house, that is, three of one kind and two of another kind?

*Solution:* By the product rule, the number of hands containing a full house is the product of the number of ways to pick two kinds in order, the number of ways to pick three out of four for the first kind, and the number of ways to pick two out of four for the second kind. (Note that the order of the two kinds matters, because, for instance, three queens and two aces is different from three aces and two queens.) We see that the number of hands containing a full house is

$$P(13, 2)C(4, 3)C(4, 2) = 13 \cdot 12 \cdot 4 \cdot 6 = 3744.$$

Because there are $C(52, 5) = 2,598,960$ poker hands, the probability of a full house is

$$\frac{3744}{2,598,960} \approx 0.0014. \qquad \blacktriangleleft$$

**EXAMPLE 7**     What is the probability that the numbers 11, 4, 17, 39, and 23 are drawn in that order from a bin containing 50 balls labeled with the numbers 1, 2, ..., 50 if (a) the ball selected is not returned to the bin before the next ball is selected and (b) the ball selected is returned to the bin before the next ball is selected?

*Solution:* (a) By the product rule, there are $50 \cdot 49 \cdot 48 \cdot 47 \cdot 46 = 254,251,200$ ways to select the balls because each time a ball is drawn there is one fewer ball to choose from. Consequently, the probability that 11, 4, 17, 39, and 23 are drawn in that order is $1/254,251,200$. This is an example of **sampling without replacement**.

(b) By the product rule, there are $50^5 = 312,500,000$ ways to select the balls because there are 50 possible balls to choose from each time a ball is drawn. Consequently, the probability that 11, 4, 17, 39, and 23 are drawn in that order is $1/312,500,000$. This is an example of **sampling with replacement**. $\qquad \blacktriangleleft$

## Probabilities of Complements and Unions of Events

We can use counting techniques to find the probability of events derived from other events.

**THEOREM 1**   Let $E$ be an event in a sample space $S$. The probability of the event $\overline{E} = S - E$, the complementary event of $E$, is given by

$$p(\overline{E}) = 1 - p(E).$$

*Proof:* To find the probability of the event $\overline{E} = S - E$, note that $|\overline{E}| = |S| - |E|$. Hence,

$$p(\overline{E}) = \frac{|S| - |E|}{|S|} = 1 - \frac{|E|}{|S|} = 1 - p(E).$$

◁

There is an alternative strategy for finding the probability of an event when a direct approach does not work well. Instead of determining the probability of the event, the probability of its complement can be found. This is often easier to do, as Example 8 shows.

**EXAMPLE 8**   A sequence of 10 bits is randomly generated. What is the probability that at least one of these bits is 0?

*Solution:* Let $E$ be the event that at least one of the 10 bits is 0. Then $\overline{E}$ is the event that all the bits are 1s. Because the sample space $S$ is the set of all bit strings of length 10, it follows that

$$p(E) = 1 - p(\overline{E}) = 1 - \frac{|\overline{E}|}{|S|} = 1 - \frac{1}{2^{10}}$$

$$= 1 - \frac{1}{1024} = \frac{1023}{1024}.$$

Hence, the probability that the bit string will contain at least one 0 bit is $1023/1024$. It is quite difficult to find this probability directly without using Theorem 1.   ◀

We can also find the probability of the union of two events.

**THEOREM 2**   Let $E_1$ and $E_2$ be events in the sample space $S$. Then

$$p(E_1 \cup E_2) = p(E_1) + p(E_2) - p(E_1 \cap E_2).$$

*Proof:* Using the formula given in Section 2.2 for the number of elements in the union of two sets, it follows that

$$|E_1 \cup E_2| = |E_1| + |E_2| - |E_1 \cap E_2|.$$

Hence,

$$p(E_1 \cup E_2) = \frac{|E_1 \cup E_2|}{|S|}$$

$$= \frac{|E_1| + |E_2| - |E_1 \cap E_2|}{|S|}$$

$$= \frac{|E_1|}{|S|} + \frac{|E_2|}{|S|} - \frac{|E_1 \cap E_2|}{|S|}$$

$$= p(E_1) + p(E_2) - p(E_1 \cap E_2).$$    ◁

**EXAMPLE 9**    What is the probability that a positive integer selected at random from the set of positive integers not exceeding 100 is divisible by either 2 or 5?

*Solution:* Let $E_1$ be the event that the integer selected at random is divisible by 2, and let $E_2$ be the event that it is divisible by 5. Then $E_1 \cup E_2$ is the event that it is divisible by either 2 or 5. Also, $E_1 \cap E_2$ is the event that it is divisible by both 2 and 5, or equivalently, that it is divisible by 10. Because $|E_1| = 50$, $|E_2| = 20$, and $|E_1 \cap E_2| = 10$, it follows that

$$p(E_1 \cup E_2) = p(E_1) + p(E_2) - p(E_1 \cap E_2)$$

$$= \frac{50}{100} + \frac{20}{100} - \frac{10}{100} = \frac{3}{5}.$$    ◀

## Probabilistic Reasoning

A common problem is determining which of two events is more likely. Analyzing the probabilities of such events can be tricky. Example 10 describes a problem of this type. It discusses a famous problem originating with the television game show *Let's Make a Deal* and named after the host of the show, Monty Hall.

**EXAMPLE 10**    **The Monty Hall Three-Door Puzzle**   Suppose you are a game show contestant. You have a chance to win a large prize. You are asked to select one of three doors to open; the large prize is behind one of the three doors and the other two doors are losers. Once you select a door, the game show host, who knows what is behind each door, does the following. First, whether or not you selected the winning door, he opens one of the other two doors that he knows is a losing door (selecting at random if both are losing doors). Then he asks you whether you would like to switch doors. Which strategy should you use? Should you change doors or keep your original selection, or does it not matter?

*Solution:* The probability you select the correct door (before the host opens a door and asks you whether you want to change) is 1/3, because the three doors are equally likely to be the correct door. The probability this is the correct door does not change once the game show host opens one of the other doors, because he will always open a door that the prize is not behind.

The probability that you selected incorrectly is the probability the prize is behind one of the two doors you did not select. Consequently, the probability that you selected incorrectly is 2/3. If you selected incorrectly, when the game show host opens a door to show you that the prize is not behind it, the prize is behind the other door. You will always win if your initial choice was incorrect and you change doors. So, by changing doors, the probability you win is 2/3. In other words, you should always change doors when given the chance to do so by the game show host. This doubles the probability that you will win. (A more rigorous treatment of this puzzle can be found in Exercise 15 of Section 7.3. For much more on this famous puzzle and its variations, see [Ro09].)    ◀

# Exercises

1. What is the probability that a card selected at random from a standard deck of 52 cards is an ace?

2. What is the probability that a fair die comes up six when it is rolled?

3. What is the probability that a randomly selected integer chosen from the first 100 positive integers is odd?

4. What is the probability that a randomly selected day of a leap year (with 366 possible days) is in April?

5. What is the probability that the sum of the numbers on two dice is even when they are rolled?

6. What is the probability that a card selected at random from a standard deck of 52 cards is an ace or a heart?

7. What is the probability that when a coin is flipped six times in a row, it lands heads up every time?

8. What is the probability that a five-card poker hand contains the ace of hearts?

9. What is the probability that a five-card poker hand does not contain the queen of hearts?

10. What is the probability that a five-card poker hand contains the two of diamonds and the three of spades?

11. What is the probability that a five-card poker hand contains the two of diamonds, the three of spades, the six of hearts, the ten of clubs, and the king of hearts?

12. What is the probability that a five-card poker hand contains exactly one ace?

13. What is the probability that a five-card poker hand contains at least one ace?

14. What is the probability that a five-card poker hand contains cards of five different kinds?

15. What is the probability that a five-card poker hand contains two pairs (that is, two of each of two different kinds and a fifth card of a third kind)?

16. What is the probability that a five-card poker hand contains a flush, that is, five cards of the same suit?

17. What is the probability that a five-card poker hand contains a straight, that is, five cards that have consecutive kinds? (Note that an ace can be considered either the lowest card of an A-2-3-4-5 straight or the highest card of a 10-J-Q-K-A straight.)

18. What is the probability that a five-card poker hand contains a straight flush, that is, five cards of the same suit of consecutive kinds?

\*19. What is the probability that a five-card poker hand contains cards of five different kinds and does not contain a flush or a straight?

20. What is the probability that a five-card poker hand contains a royal flush, that is, the 10, jack, queen, king, and ace of one suit?

21. What is the probability that a fair die never comes up an even number when it is rolled six times?

22. What is the probability that a positive integer not exceeding 100 selected at random is divisible by 3?

23. What is the probability that a positive integer not exceeding 100 selected at random is divisible by 5 or 7?

24. Find the probability of winning a lottery by selecting the correct six integers, where the order in which these integers are selected does not matter, from the positive integers not exceeding

   a) 30.   b) 36.   c) 42.   d) 48.

25. Find the probability of winning a lottery by selecting the correct six integers, where the order in which these integers are selected does not matter, from the positive integers not exceeding

   a) 50.   b) 52.   c) 56.   d) 60.

26. Find the probability of selecting none of the correct six integers in a lottery, where the order in which these integers are selected does not matter, from the positive integers not exceeding

   a) 40.   b) 48.   c) 56.   d) 64.

27. Find the probability of selecting exactly one of the correct six integers in a lottery, where the order in which these integers are selected does not matter, from the positive integers not exceeding

   a) 40.   b) 48.   c) 56.   d) 64.

28. In a superlottery, a player selects 7 numbers out of the first 80 positive integers. What is the probability that a person wins the grand prize by picking 7 numbers that are among the 11 numbers selected at random by a computer.

29. In a superlottery, players win a fortune if they choose the eight numbers selected by a computer from the positive integers not exceeding 100. What is the probability that a player wins this superlottery?

30. What is the probability that a player of a lottery wins the prize offered for correctly choosing five (but not six) numbers out of six integers chosen at random from the integers between 1 and 40, inclusive?

31. Suppose that 100 people enter a contest and that different winners are selected at random for first, second, and third prizes. What is the probability that Michelle wins one of these prizes if she is one of the contestants?

32. Suppose that 100 people enter a contest and that different winners are selected at random for first, second, and third prizes. What is the probability that Kumar, Janice, and Pedro each win a prize if each has entered the contest?

33. What is the probability that Abby, Barry, and Sylvia win the first, second, and third prizes, respectively, in a drawing if 200 people enter a contest and

   a) no one can win more than one prize.
   b) winning more than one prize is allowed.

34. What is the probability that Bo, Colleen, Jeff, and Rohini win the first, second, third, and fourth prizes, respectively, in a drawing if 50 people enter a contest and

   a) no one can win more than one prize.
   b) winning more than one prize is allowed.

**35.** In roulette, a wheel with 38 numbers is spun. Of these, 18 are red, and 18 are black. The other two numbers, which are neither black nor red, are 0 and 00. The probability that when the wheel is spun it lands on any particular number is 1/38.

**a)** What is the probability that the wheel lands on a red number?

**b)** What is the probability that the wheel lands on a black number twice in a row?

**c)** What is the probability that the wheel lands on 0 or 00?

**d)** What is the probability that in five spins the wheel never lands on either 0 or 00?

**e)** What is the probability that the wheel lands on one of the first six integers on one spin, but does not land on any of them on the next spin?

**36.** Which is more likely: rolling a total of 8 when two dice are rolled or rolling a total of 8 when three dice are rolled?

**37.** Which is more likely: rolling a total of 9 when two dice are rolled or rolling a total of 9 when three dice are rolled?

**38.** Two events $E_1$ and $E_2$ are called **independent** if $p(E_1 \cap E_2) = p(E_1)p(E_2)$. For each of the following pairs of events, which are subsets of the set of all possible outcomes when a coin is tossed three times, determine whether or not they are independent.

**a)** $E_1$: tails comes up with the coin is tossed the first time; $E_2$: heads comes up when the coin is tossed the second time.

**b)** $E_1$: the first coin comes up tails; $E_2$: two, and not three, heads come up in a row.

**c)** $E_1$: the second coin comes up tails; $E_2$: two, and not three, heads come up in a row.

(We will study independence of events in more depth in Section 7.2.)

**39.** Explain what is wrong with the statement that in the Monty Hall Three-Door Puzzle the probability that the prize is behind the first door you select and the probability that the prize is behind the other of the two doors that Monty does not open are both 1/2, because there are two doors left.

**40.** Suppose that instead of three doors, there are four doors in the Monty Hall puzzle. What is the probability that you win by not changing once the host, who knows what is behind each door, opens a losing door and gives you the chance to change doors? What is the probability that you win by changing the door you select to one of the two remaining doors among the three that you did not select?

**41.** This problem was posed by the Chevalier de Méré and was solved by Blaise Pascal and Pierre de Fermat.

**a)** Find the probability of rolling at least one six when a fair die is rolled four times.

**b)** Find the probability that a double six comes up at least once when a pair of dice is rolled 24 times. Answer the query the Chevalier de Méré made to Pascal asking whether this probability was greater than 1/2.

**c)** Is it more likely that a six comes up at least once when a fair die is rolled four times or that a double six comes up at least once when a pair of dice is rolled 24 times?

# 7.2 Probability Theory

## Introduction

Links

In Section 7.1 we introduced the notion of the probability of an event. (Recall that an event is a subset of the possible outcomes of an experiment.) We defined the probability of an event $E$ as Laplace did, that is,

$$p(E) = \frac{|E|}{|S|},$$

the number of outcomes in $E$ divided by the total number of outcomes. This definition assumes that all outcomes are equally likely. However, many experiments have outcomes that are not equally likely. For instance, a coin may be biased so that it comes up heads twice as often as tails. Similarly, the likelihood that the input of a linear search is a particular element in a list, or is not in the list, depends on how the input is generated. How can we model the likelihood of events in such situations? In this section we will show how to define probabilities of outcomes to study probabilities of experiments where outcomes may not be equally likely.

Suppose that a fair coin is flipped four times, and the first time it comes up heads. Given this information, what is the probability that heads comes up three times? To answer this and similar questions, we will introduce the concept of *conditional probability*. Does knowing that the first flip comes up heads change the probability that heads comes up three times? If not, these two events are called *independent*, a concept studied later in this section.

Many questions address a particular numerical value associated with the outcome of an experiment. For instance, when we flip a coin 100 times, what is the probability that exactly 40 heads appear? How many heads should we expect to appear? In this section we will introduce *random variables*, which are functions that associate numerical values to the outcomes of experiments.

## Assigning Probabilities

Let $S$ be the sample space of an experiment with a finite or countable number of outcomes. We assign a probability $p(s)$ to each outcome $s$. We require that two conditions be met:

$(i)$   $0 \le p(s) \le 1$ for each $s \in S$

and

$(ii)$   $\displaystyle\sum_{s \in S} p(s) = 1.$

Condition $(i)$ states that the probability of each outcome is a nonnegative real number no greater than 1. Condition $(ii)$ states that the sum of the probabilities of all possible outcomes should be 1; that is, when we do the experiment, it is a certainty that one of these outcomes occurs. (Note that when the sample space is infinite, $\sum_{s \in S} p(s)$ is a convergent infinite series.) This is a generalization of Laplace's definition in which each of $n$ outcomes is assigned a probability of $1/n$. Indeed, conditions $(i)$ and $(ii)$ are met when Laplace's definition of probabilities of equally likely outcomes is used and $S$ is finite. (See Exercise 4.)

Note that when there are $n$ possible outcomes, $x_1, x_2, \ldots, x_n$, the two conditions to be met are

$(i)$   $0 \le p(x_i) \le 1$ for $i = 1, 2, \ldots, n$

and

$(ii)$   $\displaystyle\sum_{i=1}^{n} p(x_i) = 1.$

The function $p$ from the set of all outcomes of the sample space $S$ is called a **probability distribution**.

To model an experiment, the probability $p(s)$ assigned to an outcome $s$ should equal the limit of the number of times $s$ occurs divided by the number of times the experiment is performed, as this number grows without bound. (We will assume that all experiments discussed have outcomes that are predictable on the average, so that this limit exists. We also assume that the outcomes of successive trials of an experiment do not depend on past results.)

---

HISTORICAL NOTE   The Chevalier de Méré was a French nobleman, a famous gambler, and a bon vivant. He was successful at making bets with odds slightly greater than 1/2 (such as having at least one six come up in four tosses of a fair die). His correspondence with Pascal asking about the probability of having at least one double six come up when a pair of dice is rolled 24 times led to the development of probability theory. According to one account, Pascal wrote to Fermat about the Chevalier saying something like "He's a good guy but, alas, he's no mathematician."

*Remark:* We will not discuss probabilities of events when the set of outcomes is not finite or countable, such as when the outcome of an experiment can be any real number. In such cases, integral calculus is usually required for the study of the probabilities of events.

We can model experiments in which outcomes are either equally likely or not equally likely by choosing the appropriate function $p(s)$, as Example 1 illustrates.

EXAMPLE 1    What probabilities should we assign to the outcomes $H$ (heads) and $T$ (tails) when a fair coin is flipped? What probabilities should be assigned to these outcomes when the coin is biased so that heads comes up twice as often as tails?

*Solution:* For a fair coin, the probability that heads comes up when the coin is flipped equals the probability that tails comes up, so the outcomes are equally likely. Consequently, we assign the probability $1/2$ to each of the two possible outcomes, that is, $p(H) = p(T) = 1/2$.
For the biased coin we have

$$p(H) = 2p(T).$$

Because

$$p(H) + p(T) = 1,$$

it follows that

$$2p(T) + p(T) = 3p(T) = 1.$$

We conclude that $p(T) = 1/3$ and $p(H) = 2/3$.    ◀

DEFINITION 1    Suppose that $S$ is a set with $n$ elements. The *uniform distribution* assigns the probability $1/n$ to each element of $S$.

We now define the probability of an event as the sum of the probabilities of the outcomes in this event.

DEFINITION 2    The *probability* of the event $E$ is the sum of the probabilities of the outcomes in $E$. That is,

$$p(E) = \sum_{s \in E} p(s).$$

(Note that when $E$ is an infinite set, $\sum_{s \in E} p(s)$ is a convergent infinite series.)

Note that when there are $n$ outcomes in the event $E$, that is, if $E = \{a_1, a_2, \ldots, a_n\}$, then $p(E) = \sum_{i=1}^{n} p(a_i)$. Note also that the uniform distribution assigns the same probability to an event that Laplace's original definition of probability assigns to this event. The experiment of selecting an element from a sample space with a uniform distribution is called selecting an element of $S$ **at random**.

EXAMPLE 2    Suppose that a die is biased (or loaded) so that 3 appears twice as often as each other number but that the other five outcomes are equally likely. What is the probability that an odd number appears when we roll this die?

*Solution:* We want to find the probability of the event $E = \{1, 3, 5\}$. By Exercise 2, we have

$$p(1) = p(2) = p(4) = p(5) = p(6) = 1/7; \; p(3) = 2/7.$$

It follows that

$$p(E) = p(1) + p(3) + p(5) = 1/7 + 2/7 + 1/7 = 4/7.$$   ◀

When possible outcomes are equally likely and there are a finite number of possible outcomes, the definition of the probability of an event given in this section (Definition 2) agrees with Laplace's definition (Definition 1 of Section 7.1). To see this, suppose that there are $n$ equally likely outcomes; each possible outcome has probability $1/n$, because the sum of their probabilities is 1. Suppose the event $E$ contains $m$ outcomes. According to Definition 2,

$$p(E) = \sum_{i=1}^{m} \frac{1}{n} = \frac{m}{n}.$$

Because $|E| = m$ and $|S| = n$, it follows that

$$p(E) = \frac{m}{n} = \frac{|E|}{|S|}.$$

This is Laplace's definition of the probability of the event $E$.

## Probabilities of Complements and Unions of Events

The formulae for probabilities of combinations of events in Section 7.1 continue to hold when we use Definition 2 to define the probability of an event. For example, Theorem 1 of Section 7.1 asserts that

$$p(\overline{E}) = 1 - p(E),$$

where $\overline{E}$ is the complementary event of the event $E$. This equality also holds when Definition 2 is used. To see this, note that because the sum of the probabilities of the $n$ possible outcomes is 1, and each outcome is either in $E$ or in $\overline{E}$, but not in both, we have

$$\sum_{s \in S} p(s) = 1 = p(E) + p(\overline{E}).$$

Hence, $p(\overline{E}) = 1 - p(E)$.

Under Laplace's definition, by Theorem 2 in Section 7.1, we have

$$p(E_1 \cup E_2) = p(E_1) + p(E_2) - p(E_1 \cap E_2)$$

whenever $E_1$ and $E_2$ are events in a sample space $S$. This also holds when we define the probability of an event as we do in this section. To see this, note that $p(E_1 \cup E_2)$ is the sum of the probabilities of the outcomes in $E_1 \cup E_2$. When an outcome $x$ is in one, but not both, of $E_1$ and $E_2$, $p(x)$ occurs in exactly one of the sums for $p(E_1)$ and $p(E_2)$. When an outcome $x$ is in both $E_1$ and $E_2$, $p(x)$ occurs in the sum for $p(E_1)$, in the sum for $p(E_2)$, and in the sum for $p(E_1 \cap E_2)$, so it occurs $1 + 1 - 1 = 1$ time on the right-hand side. Consequently, the left-hand side and right-hand side are equal.

Also, note that if the events $E_1$ and $E_2$ are disjoint, then $p(E_1 \cap E_2) = 0$, which implies that

$$p(E_1 \cup E_2) = p(E_1) + p(E_2) - p(E_1 \cap E_2) = p(E_1) + p(E_2).$$

Theorem 1 generalizes this last formula by providing a formula for the probability of the union of pairwise disjoint events.

**THEOREM 1**    If $E_1, E_2, \ldots$ is a sequence of pairwise disjoint events in a sample space $S$, then

$$p\left(\bigcup_i E_i\right) = \sum_i p(E_i).$$

(Note that this theorem applies when the sequence $E_1, E_2, \ldots$ consists of a finite number or a countably infinite number of pairwise disjoint events.)

We leave the proof of Theorem 1 to the reader (see Exercises 36 and 37).

## Conditional Probability

**Links**

Suppose that we flip a coin three times, and all eight possibilities are equally likely. Moreover, suppose we know that the event $F$, that the first flip comes up tails, occurs. Given this information, what is the probability of the event $E$, that an odd number of tails appears? Because the first flip comes up tails, there are only four possible outcomes: *TTT*, *TTH*, *THT*, and *THH*, where $H$ and $T$ represent heads and tails, respectively. An odd number of tails appears only for the outcomes *TTT* and *THH*. Because the eight outcomes have equal probability, each of the four possible outcomes, given that $F$ occurs, should also have an equal probability of $1/4$. This suggests that we should assign the probability of $2/4 = 1/2$ to $E$, given that $F$ occurs. This probability is called the **conditional probability** of $E$ given $F$.

In general, to find the conditional probability of $E$ given $F$, we use $F$ as the sample space. For an outcome from $E$ to occur, this outcome must also belong to $E \cap F$. With this motivation, we make Definition 3.

**DEFINITION 3**    Let $E$ and $F$ be events with $p(F) > 0$. The *conditional probability* of $E$ given $F$, denoted by $p(E \mid F)$, is defined as

$$p(E \mid F) = \frac{p(E \cap F)}{p(F)}.$$

**EXAMPLE 3**

**Extra Examples**

A bit string of length four is generated at random so that each of the 16 bit strings of length four is equally likely. What is the probability that it contains at least two consecutive 0s, given that its first bit is a 0? (We assume that 0 bits and 1 bits are equally likely.)

*Solution:* Let $E$ be the event that a bit string of length four contains at least two consecutive 0s, and let $F$ be the event that the first bit of a bit string of length four is a 0. The probability that a bit string of length four has at least two consecutive 0s, given that its first bit is a 0, equals

$$p(E \mid F) = \frac{p(E \cap F)}{p(F)}.$$

Because $E \cap F = \{0000, 0001, 0010, 0011, 0100\}$, we see that $p(E \cap F) = 5/16$. Because there are eight bit strings of length four that start with a 0, we have $p(F) = 8/16 = 1/2$. Consequently,

$$p(E \mid F) = \frac{5/16}{1/2} = \frac{5}{8}.$$ ◀

**EXAMPLE 4**    What is the conditional probability that a family with two children has two boys, given they have at least one boy? Assume that each of the possibilities $BB$, $BG$, $GB$, and $GG$ is equally likely, where $B$ represents a boy and $G$ represents a girl. (Note that $BG$ represents a family with an older boy and a younger girl while $GB$ represents a family with an older girl and a younger boy.)

*Solution:* Let $E$ be the event that a family with two children has two boys, and let $F$ be the event that a family with two children has at least one boy. It follows that $E = \{BB\}$, $F = \{BB,\ BG,\ GB\}$, and $E \cap F = \{BB\}$. Because the four possibilities are equally likely, it follows that $p(F) = 3/4$ and $p(E \cap F) = 1/4$. We conclude that

$$p(E \mid F) = \frac{p(E \cap F)}{p(F)} = \frac{1/4}{3/4} = \frac{1}{3}.$$ ◀

## Independence

**Links**

Suppose a coin is flipped three times, as described in the introduction to our discussion of conditional probability. Does knowing that the first flip comes up tails (event $F$) alter the probability that tails comes up an odd number of times (event $E$)? In other words, is it the case that $p(E \mid F) = p(E)$? This equality is valid for the events $E$ and $F$, because $p(E \mid F) = 1/2$ and $p(E) = 1/2$. Because this equality holds, we say that $E$ and $F$ are **independent events**. When two events are independent, the occurrence of one of the events gives no information about the probability that the other event occurs.

Because $p(E \mid F) = p(E \cap F)/p(F)$, asking whether $p(E \mid F) = p(E)$ is the same as asking whether $p(E \cap F) = p(E)p(F)$. This leads to Definition 4.

**DEFINITION 4**    The events $E$ and $F$ are *independent* if and only if $p(E \cap F) = p(E)p(F)$.

**EXAMPLE 5**    Suppose $E$ is the event that a randomly generated bit string of length four begins with a 1 and $F$ is the event that this bit string contains an even number of 1s. Are $E$ and $F$ independent, if the 16 bit strings of length four are equally likely?

**Extra Examples**

*Solution:* There are eight bit strings of length four that begin with a one: 1000, 1001, 1010, 1011, 1100, 1101, 1110, and 1111. There are also eight bit strings of length four that contain an even number of ones: 0000, 0011, 0101, 0110, 1001, 1010, 1100, 1111. Because there are 16 bit strings of length four, it follows that

$$p(E) = p(F) = 8/16 = 1/2.$$

Because $E \cap F = \{1111, 1100, 1010, 1001\}$, we see that

$$p(E \cap F) = 4/16 = 1/4.$$

Because

$$p(E \cap F) = 1/4 = (1/2)(1/2) = p(E)p(F),$$

we conclude that $E$ and $F$ are independent. ◀

Probability has many applications to genetics, as Examples 6 and 7 illustrate.

**EXAMPLE 6** Assume, as in Example 4, that each of the four ways a family can have two children is equally likely. Are the events $E$, that a family with two children has two boys, and $F$, that a family with two children has at least one boy, independent?

*Solution:* Because $E = \{BB\}$, we have $p(E) = 1/4$. In Example 4 we showed that $p(F) = 3/4$ and that $p(E \cap F) = 1/4$. But $p(E)p(F) = \frac{1}{4} \cdot \frac{3}{4} = \frac{3}{16}$. Therefore $p(E \cap F) \neq p(E)p(F)$, so the events $E$ and $F$ are not independent. ◀

**EXAMPLE 7** Are the events $E$, that a family with three children has children of both sexes, and $F$, that this family has at most one boy, independent? Assume that the eight ways a family can have three children are equally likely.

*Solution:* By assumption, each of the eight ways a family can have three children, *BBB, BBG, BGB, BGG, GBB, GBG, GGB,* and *GGG,* has a probability of 1/8. Because $E = \{BBG,\ BGB,\ BGG,\ GBB,\ GBG,\ GGB\}$, $F = \{BGG,\ GBG,\ GGB,\ GGG\}$, and $E \cap F = \{BGG,\ GBG,\ GGB\}$, it follows that $p(E) = 6/8 = 3/4$, $p(F) = 4/8 = 1/2$, and $p(E \cap F) = 3/8$. Because

$$p(E)p(F) = \frac{3}{4} \cdot \frac{1}{2} = \frac{3}{8},$$

it follows that $p(E \cap F) = p(E)p(F)$, so $E$ and $F$ are independent. (This conclusion may seem surprising. Indeed, if we change the number of children, the conclusion may no longer hold. See Exercise 27.) ◀

PAIRWISE AND MUTUAL INDEPENDENCE  We can also define the independence of more than two events. However, there are two different types of independence, given in Definition 5.

**DEFINITION 5** The events $E_1, E_2, \ldots, E_n$ are *pairwise independent* if and only if $p(E_i \cap E_j) = p(E_i)p(E_j)$ for all pairs of integers $i$ and $j$ with $1 \leq i < j \leq n$. These events are *mutually independent* if $p(E_{i_1} \cap E_{i_2} \cap \cdots \cap E_{i_m}) = p(E_{i_1})p(E_{i_2}) \cdots p(E_{i_m})$ whenever $i_j, j = 1, 2, \ldots, m$, are integers with $1 \leq i_1 < i_2 < \cdots < i_m \leq n$ and $m \geq 2$.

From Definition 5, we see that every set of $n$ mutually independent events is also pairwise independent. However, $n$ pairwise independent events are not necessarily mutually independent, as we see in Exercise 25 in the Supplementary Exercises. Many theorems about $n$ events include the hypothesis that these events are mutually independent, and not just pairwise independent. We will introduce several such theorems later in this chapter.

## Bernoulli Trials and the Binomial Distribution

Suppose that an experiment can have only two possible outcomes. For instance, when a bit is generated at random, the possible outcomes are 0 and 1. When a coin is flipped, the possible outcomes are heads and tails. Each performance of an experiment with two possible outcomes is called a **Bernoulli trial**, after James Bernoulli, who made important contributions to probability theory. In general, a possible outcome of a Bernoulli trial is called a **success** or a **failure**. If $p$ is the probability of a success and $q$ is the probability of a failure, it follows that $p + q = 1$.

Links

Many problems can be solved by determining the probability of $k$ successes when an experiment consists of $n$ mutually independent Bernoulli trials. (Bernoulli trials are **mutually independent** if the conditional probability of success on any given trial is $p$, given any information whatsoever about the outcomes of the other trials.) Consider Example 8.

**EXAMPLE 8**  A coin is biased so that the probability of heads is 2/3. What is the probability that exactly four heads come up when the coin is flipped seven times, assuming that the flips are independent?

*Solution:* There are $2^7 = 128$ possible outcomes when a coin is flipped seven times. The number of ways four of the seven flips can be heads is $C(7, 4)$. Because the seven flips are independent, the probability of each of these outcomes (four heads and three tails) is $(2/3)^4(1/3)^3$. Consequently, the probability that exactly four heads appear is

$$C(7, 4)(2/3)^4(1/3)^3 = \frac{35 \cdot 16}{3^7} = \frac{560}{2187}.$$   ◀

Following the same reasoning as was used in Example 8, we can find the probability of $k$ successes in $n$ independent Bernoulli trials.

**THEOREM 2**

The probability of exactly $k$ successes in $n$ independent Bernoulli trials, with probability of success $p$ and probability of failure $q = 1 - p$, is

$$C(n, k)p^k q^{n-k}.$$

*Proof:* When $n$ Bernoulli trials are carried out, the outcome is an $n$-tuple $(t_1, t_2, \ldots, t_n)$, where $t_i = S$ (for success) or $t_i = F$ (for failure) for $i = 1, 2, \ldots, n$. Because the $n$ trials are independent, the probability of each outcome of $n$ trials consisting of $k$ successes and $n - k$ failures (in any order) is $p^k q^{n-k}$. Because there are $C(n, k)$ $n$-tuples of $S$'s and $F$'s that contain exactly $k$ $S$'s, the probability of exactly $k$ successes is

$$C(n, k)p^k q^{n-k}.$$   ◁

We denote by $b(k; n, p)$ the probability of $k$ successes in $n$ independent Bernoulli trials with probability of success $p$ and probability of failure $q = 1 - p$. Considered as a function of $k$, we call this function the **binomial distribution**. Theorem 2 tells us that $b(k; n, p) = C(n, k)p^k q^{n-k}$.

**EXAMPLE 9**

Extra Examples

Suppose that the probability that a 0 bit is generated is 0.9, that the probability that a 1 bit is generated is 0.1, and that bits are generated independently. What is the probability that exactly eight 0 bits are generated when 10 bits are generated?

*Solution:* By Theorem 2, the probability that exactly eight 0 bits are generated is

$$b(8; 10, 0.9) = C(10, 8)(0.9)^8(0.1)^2 = 0.1937102445.$$   ◀

Links

JAMES BERNOULLI (1654–1705)   James Bernoulli (also known as Jacob I), was born in Basel, Switzerland. He is one of the eight prominent mathematicians in the Bernoulli family (see Section 10.1 for the Bernoulli family tree of mathematicians). Following his father's wish, James studied theology and entered the ministry. But contrary to the desires of his parents, he also studied mathematics and astronomy. He traveled throughout Europe from 1676 to 1682, learning about the latest discoveries in mathematics and the sciences. Upon returning to Basel in 1682, he founded a school for mathematics and the sciences. He was appointed professor of mathematics at the University of Basel in 1687, remaining in this position for the rest of his life.

James Bernoulli is best known for the work *Ars Conjectandi*, published eight years after his death. In this work, he described the known results in probability theory and in enumeration, often providing alternative proofs of known results. This work also includes the application of probability theory to games of chance and his introduction of the theorem known as the **law of large numbers**. This law states that if $\epsilon > 0$, as $n$ becomes arbitrarily large the probability approaches 1 that the fraction of times an event $E$ occurs during $n$ trials is within $\epsilon$ of $p(E)$.

Note that the sum of the probabilities that there are $k$ successes when $n$ independent Bernoulli trials are carried out, for $k = 0, 1, 2, \ldots, n$, equals

$$\sum_{k=0}^{n} C(n, k) p^k q^{n-k} = (p + q)^n = 1,$$

as should be the case. The first equality in this string of equalities is a consequence of the binomial theorem (see Section 6.4). The second equality follows because $q = 1 - p$.

## Random Variables

Many problems are concerned with a numerical value associated with the outcome of an experiment. For instance, we may be interested in the total number of one bits in a randomly generated string of 10 bits; or in the number of times tails come up when a coin is flipped 20 times. To study problems of this type we introduce the concept of a random variable.

**DEFINITION 6**

A *random variable* is a function from the sample space of an experiment to the set of real numbers. That is, a random variable assigns a real number to each possible outcome.

***Remark:*** Note that a random variable is a function. It is not a variable, and it is not random! The name *random variable* (the translation of *variabile casuale*) was introduced by the Italian mathematician F. P. Cantelli in 1916. In the late 1940s, the mathematicians, W. Feller and J. L. Doob flipped a coin to see whether both would use "random variable" or the more fitting term "chance variable." Feller won; unfortunately "random varible" was used in both books and ever since.

**EXAMPLE 10**

Suppose that a coin is flipped three times. Let $X(t)$ be the random variable that equals the number of heads that appear when $t$ is the outcome. Then $X(t)$ takes on the following values:

$$X(HHH) = 3,$$
$$X(HHT) = X(HTH) = X(THH) = 2,$$
$$X(TTH) = X(THT) = X(HTT) = 1,$$
$$X(TTT) = 0.$$

◀

**DEFINITION 7**

The *distribution* of a random variable $X$ on a sample space $S$ is the set of pairs $(r, p(X = r))$ for all $r \in X(S)$, where $p(X = r)$ is the probability that $X$ takes the value $r$. (The set of pairs in this distribution is determined by the probabilities $p(X = r)$ for $r \in X(S)$.)

**EXAMPLE 11**

Each of the eight possible outcomes when a fair coin is flipped three times has probability $1/8$. So, the distribution of the random variable $X(t)$ in Example 10 is determined by the probabilities $P(X = 3) = 1/8$, $P(X = 2) = 3/8$, $P(X = 1) = 3/8$, and $P(X = 0) = 1/8$. Consequently, the distribution of $X(t)$ in Example 10 is the set of pairs $(3, 1/8)$, $(2, 3/8)$, $(1, 3/8)$, and $(0, 1/8)$. ◀

**EXAMPLE 12**

Let $X$ be the sum of the numbers that appear when a pair of dice is rolled. What are the values of this random variable for the 36 possible outcomes $(i, j)$, where $i$ and $j$ are the numbers that appear on the first die and the second die, respectively, when these two dice are rolled?

*Solution:* The random variable $X$ takes on the following values:

$$X((1, 1)) = 2,$$
$$X((1, 2)) = X((2, 1)) = 3,$$
$$X((1, 3)) = X((2, 2)) = X((3, 1)) = 4,$$
$$X((1, 4)) = X((2, 3)) = X((3, 2)) = X((4, 1)) = 5,$$
$$X((1, 5)) = X((2, 4)) = X((3, 3)) = X((4, 2)) = X((5, 1)) = 6,$$
$$X((1, 6)) = X((2, 5)) = X((3, 4)) = X((4, 3)) = X((5, 2)) = X((6, 1)) = 7,$$
$$X((2, 6)) = X((3, 5)) = X((4, 4)) = X((5, 3)) = X((6, 2)) = 8,$$
$$X((3, 6)) = X((4, 5)) = X((5, 4)) = X((6, 3)) = 9,$$
$$X((4, 6)) = X((5, 5)) = X((6, 4)) = 10,$$
$$X((5, 6)) = X((6, 5)) = 11,$$
$$X((6, 6)) = 12.$$

◀

We will continue our study of random variables in Section 7.4, where we will show how they can be used in a variety of applications.

## The Birthday Problem

A famous puzzle asks for the smallest number of people needed in a room so that it is more likely than not that at least two of them have the same day of the year as their birthday. Most people find the answer, which we determine in Example 13, to be surprisingly small. After we solve this famous problem, we will show how similar reasoning can be adapted to solve a question about hashing functions.

**EXAMPLE 13**

Links

**The Birthday Problem**    What is the minimum number of people who need to be in a room so that the probability that at least two of them have the same birthday is greater than $1/2$?

*Solution:* First, we state some assumptions. We assume that the birthdays of the people in the room are independent. Furthermore, we assume that each birthday is equally likely and that there are 366 days in the year. (In reality, more people are born on some days of the year than others, such as days nine months after some holidays including New Year's Eve, and only leap years have 366 days.)

To find the probability that at least two of $n$ people in a room have the same birthday, we first calculate the probability $p_n$ that these people all have different birthdays. Then, the probability that at least two people have the same birthday is $1- p_n$. To compute $p_n$, we consider the birthdays of the $n$ people in some fixed order. Imagine them entering the room one at a time; we will compute the probability that each successive person entering the room has a birthday different from those of the people already in the room.

The birthday of the first person certainly does not match the birthday of someone already in the room. The probability that the birthday of the second person is different from that of the first person is $365/366$ because the second person has a different birthday when he or she was born on one of the 365 days of the year other than the day the first person was born. (The assumption that it is equally likely for someone to be born on any of the 366 days of the year enters into this and subsequent steps.)

The probability that the third person has a birthday different from both the birthdays of the first and second people given that these two people have different birthdays is $364/366$. In general, the probability that the $j$th person, with $2 \leq j \leq 366$, has a birthday different from the birthdays of the $j - 1$ people already in the room given that these $j - 1$ people have different birthdays is

$$\frac{366 - (j - 1)}{366} = \frac{367 - j}{366}.$$

Because we have assumed that the birthdays of the people in the room are independent, we can conclude that the probability that the $n$ people in the room have different birthdays is

$$p_n = \frac{365}{366} \frac{364}{366} \frac{363}{366} \cdots \frac{367 - n}{366}.$$

It follows that the probability that among $n$ people there are at least two people with the same birthday is

$$1 - p_n = 1 - \frac{365}{366} \frac{364}{366} \frac{363}{366} \cdots \frac{367 - n}{366}.$$

To determine the minimum number of people in the room so that the probability that at least two of them have the same birthday is greater than $1/2$, we use the formula we have found for $1 - p_n$ to compute it for increasing values of $n$ until it becomes greater than $1/2$. (There are more sophisticated approaches using calculus that can eliminate this computation, but we will not use them here.) After considerable computation we find that for $n = 22$, $1 - p_n \approx 0.475$, while for $n = 23$, $1 - p_n \approx 0.506$. Consequently, the minimum number of people needed so that the probability that at least two people have the same birthday is greater than $1/2$ is 23.    ◀

The solution to the birthday problem leads to the solution of the question in Example 14 about hashing functions.

**EXAMPLE 14**    **Probability of a Collision in Hashing Functions**    Recall from Section 4.5 that a hashing function $h(k)$ is a mapping of the keys (of the records that are to be stored in a database) to storage locations. Hashing functions map a large universe of keys (such as the approximately 300 million Social Security numbers in the United States) to a much smaller set of storage locations. A good hashing function yields few **collisions**, which are mappings of two different keys to the same memory location, when relatively few of the records are in play in a given application. What is the probability that no two keys are mapped to the same location by a hashing function, or, in other words, that there are no collisions?

*Solution:* To calculate this probability, we assume that the probability that a randomly selected key is mapped to a location is $1/m$, where $m$ is the number of available locations, that is, the hashing function distributes keys uniformly. (In practice, hashing functions may not satisfy this assumption. However, for a good hashing function, this assumption should be close to correct.) Furthermore, we assume that the keys of the records selected have an equal probability to be any of the elements of the key universe and that these keys are independently selected.

Suppose that the keys are $k_1, k_2, \ldots, k_n$. When we add the second record, the probability that it is mapped to a location different from the location of the first record, that $h(k_2) \neq h(k_1)$, is $(m - 1)/m$ because there are $m - 1$ free locations after the first record has been placed. The probability that the third record is mapped to a free location after the first and second records have been placed without a collision is $(m - 2)/m$. In general, the probability that the $j$th record is mapped to a free location after the first $j - 1$ records have been mapped to locations $h(k_1)$, $h(k_2), \ldots, h(k_{j-1})$ without collisions is $(m - (j - 1))/m$ because $j - 1$ of the $m$ locations are taken.

Because the keys are independent, the probability that all $n$ keys are mapped to different locations is

$$p_n = \frac{m - 1}{m} \cdot \frac{m - 2}{m} \cdot \cdots \cdot \frac{m - n + 1}{m}.$$

It follows that the probability that there is at least one collision, that is, at least two keys are mapped to the same location, is

$$1 - p_n = 1 - \frac{m-1}{m} \cdot \frac{m-2}{m} \cdot \ldots \cdot \frac{m-n+1}{m}.$$

Techniques from calculus can be used to find the smallest value of $n$ given a value of $m$ such that the probability of a collision is greater than a particular threshold. It can be shown that the smallest integer $n$ such that the probability of a collision is greater than $1/2$ is approximately $n = 1.177\sqrt{m}$. For example, when $m = 1,000,000$, the smallest integer $n$ such that the probability of a collision is greater than $1/2$ is 1178. ◀

## Monte Carlo Algorithms

The algorithms discussed so far in this book are all deterministic. That is, each algorithm always proceeds in the same way whenever given the same input. However, there are many situations where we would like an algorithm to make a random choice at one or more steps. Such a situation arises when a deterministic algorithm would have to go through a huge number, or even an unknown number, of possible cases. Algorithms that make random choices at one or more steps are called **probabilistic algorithms**. We will discuss a particular class of probabilistic algorithms in this section, namely, **Monte Carlo algorithms**, for decision problems. Monte Carlo algorithms always produce answers to problems, but a small probability remains that these answers may be incorrect. However, the probability that the answer is incorrect decreases rapidly when the algorithm carries out sufficient computation. Decision problems have either "true" or "false" as their answer. The designation "Monte Carlo" is a reference to the famous casino in Monaco; the use of randomness and the repetitive processes in these algorithms make them similar to some gambling games. This name was introduced by the inventors of Monte Carlo methods, including Stan Ulam, Enrico Fermi, and John von Neumann.

> Monte Carlo methods were invented to help develop the first nuclear weapons.

A Monte Carlo algorithm for a decision problem uses a sequence of tests. The probability that the algorithm answers the decision problem correctly increases as more tests are carried out. At each step of the algorithm, possible responses are "true," which means that the answer is "true" and no additional iterations are needed, or "unknown," which means that the answer could be either "true" or "false." After running all the iterations in such an algorithm, the final answer produced is "true" if at least one iteration yields the answer "true," and the answer is "false" if every iteration yields the answer "unknown." If the correct answer is "false," then the algorithm answers "false," because every iteration will yield "unknown." However, if the correct answer is "true," then the algorithm could answer either "true" or "false," because it may be possible that each iteration produced the response "unknown" even though the correct response was "true." We will show that this possibility becomes extremely unlikely as the number of tests increases.

Suppose that $p$ is the probability that the response of a test is "true," given that the answer is "true." It follows that $1 - p$ is the probability that the response is "unknown," given that the answer is "true." Because the algorithm answers "false" when all $n$ iterations yield the answer "unknown" and the iterations perform independent tests, the probability of error is $(1 - p)^n$. When $p \neq 0$, this probability approaches 0 as the number of tests increases. Consequently, the probability that the algorithm answers "true" when the answer is "true" approaches 1.

**EXAMPLE 15**   **Quality Control**   (This example is adapted from [AhUl95].) Suppose that a manufacturer orders processor chips in batches of size $n$, where $n$ is a positive integer. The chip maker has tested only some of these batches to make sure that all the chips in the batch are good (replacing any bad chips found during testing with good ones). In previously untested batches, the probability that a particular chip is bad has been observed to be 0.1 when random testing is done. The PC manufacturer wants to decide whether all the chips in a batch are good. To do this, the PC manufacturer can test each chip in a batch to see whether it is good. However, this requires $n$ tests. Assuming that each test can be carried out in constant time, these tests require $O(n)$ seconds. Can the PC manufacturer determine whether a batch of chips has been tested by the chip maker using less time?

*Solution:* We can use a Monte Carlo algorithm to determine whether a batch of chips has been tested by the chip maker as long as we are willing to accept some probability of error. The algorithm is set up to answer the question: "Has this batch of chips not been tested by the chip maker?" It proceeds by successively selecting chips at random from the batch and testing them one by one. When a bad chip is encountered, the algorithm answers "true" and stops. If a tested chip is good, the algorithm answers "unknown" and goes on to the next chip. After the algorithm has tested a specified number of chips, say $k$ chips, without getting an answer of "true," the algorithm terminates with the answer "false"; that is, the algorithm concludes that the batch is good, that is, that the chip maker has tested all the chips in the batch.

The only way for this algorithm to answer incorrectly is for it to conclude that an untested batch of chips has been tested by the chip maker. The probability that a chip is good, but that it came from an untested batch, is $1 - 0.1 = 0.9$. Because the events of testing different chips from a batch are independent, the probability that all $k$ steps of the algorithm produce the answer "unknown," given that the batch of chips is untested, is $0.9^k$.

By taking $k$ large enough, we can make this probability as small as we like. For example, by testing 66 chips, the probability that the algorithm decides a batch has been tested by the chip maker is $0.9^{66}$, which is less than 0.001. That is, the probability is less than 1 in 1000 that the algorithm has answered incorrectly. Note that this probability is independent of $n$, the number of chips in a batch. That is, the Monte Carlo algorithm uses a constant number, or $O(1)$, tests and requires $O(1)$ seconds, no matter how many chips are in a batch. As long as the PC manufacturer can live with an error rate of less than 1 in 1000, the Monte Carlo algorithm will save the PC manufacturer a lot of testing. If a smaller error rate is needed, the PC manufacturer can test more chips in each batch; the reader can verify that 132 tests lower the error rate to less than 1 in 1,000,000. ◀

**EXAMPLE 16**   **Probabilistic Primality Testing**   In Chapter 4 we remarked that a composite integer, that is, an integer greater than one that is not prime, passes Miller's test (see the preamble to Exercise 44 in Section 4.4) for fewer than $n/4$ bases $b$ with $1 < b < n$. This observation is the basis for a Monte Carlo algorithm to determine whether an integer greater than one is prime. Because large primes play an essential role in public-key cryptography (see Section 4.6), being able to generate large primes quickly has become extremely important.

The goal of the algorithm is to decide the question "Is $n$ composite?" Given an integer $n$ greater than one, we select an integer $b$ at random with $1 < b < n$ and determine whether $n$ passes Miller's test to the base $b$. If $n$ fails the test, the answer is "true" because $n$ must be composite, and the algorithm ends. Otherwise, we perform the test $k$ times, where $k$ is a positive integer. Each time we select a random integer $b$ and determine whether $n$ passes Miller's test to the base $b$. If the answer is "unknown" at each step, the algorithm answers "false," that is, it says that $n$ is not composite, so that it is prime. The only possibility for the algorithm to return an incorrect answer occurs when $n$ is composite, and the answer "unknown" is the output at each of the $k$ iterations. The probability that a composite integer $n$ passes Miller's test for a randomly selected base $b$ is less than $1/4$. Because the integer $b$ with $1 < b < n$ is selected at random at each iteration and these iterations are independent, the probability that $n$ is composite but the algorithm responds that $n$ is prime is less than $(1/4)^k$. By taking $k$ to be sufficiently large, we can make this probability extremely small. For example, with 10 iterations, the probability that the algorithm decides that $n$ is prime when it really is composite is less than 1 in 1,000,000. With 30 iterations, this probability drops to less than 1 in $10^{18}$, an extremely unlikely event.

To generate large primes, say with 200 digits, we randomly choose an integer $n$ with 200 digits and run this algorithm, with 30 iterations. If the algorithm decides that $n$ is prime, we

A number that passes many iterations of a probabilistic primality test is called an *industrial strength prime*, even though it may be composite.

can use it as one of the two primes used in an encryption key for the RSA cryptosystem. If $n$ is actually composite and is used as part of the key, the procedures used to decrypt messages will not produce the original encrypted message. The key is then discarded and two new possible primes are used. ◀

## The Probabilistic Method

We discussed existence proofs in Chapter 1 and illustrated the difference between constructive existence proofs and nonconstructive existence proofs. The probabilistic method, introduced by Paul Erdős and Alfréd Rényi, is a powerful technique that can be used to create nonconstructive existence proofs. To use the probabilistic method to prove results about a set $S$, such as the existence of an element in $S$ with a specified property, we assign probabilities to the elements of $S$. We then use methods from probability theory to prove results about the elements of $S$. In particular, we can show that an element with a specified property exists by showing that the probability an element $x \in S$ has this property is positive. The probabilistic method is based on the equivalent statement in Theorem 3.

**THEOREM 3**    **THE PROBABILISTIC METHOD**   If the probability that an element chosen at random from a $S$ does not have a particular property is less than 1, there exists an element in $S$ with this property.

An existence proof based on the probabilistic method is nonconstructive because it does not find a particular element with the desired property.

   We illustrate the power of the probabilistic method by finding a lower bound for the Ramsey number $R(k, k)$. Recall from Section 6.2 that $R(k, k)$ equals the minimum number of people at a party needed to ensure that there are at least $k$ mutual friends or $k$ mutual enemies (assuming that any two people are friends or enemies).

**THEOREM 4**    If $k$ is an integer with $k \geq 2$, then $R(k, k) \geq 2^{k/2}$.

*Proof:* We note that the theorem holds for $k = 2$ and $k = 3$ because $R(2, 2) = 2$ and $R(3, 3) = 6$, as was shown in Section 6.2. Now suppose that $k \geq 4$. We will use the probabilistic method to show that if there are fewer than $2^{k/2}$ people at a party, it is possible that no $k$ of them are mutual friends or mutual enemies. This will show that $R(k, k)$ is at least $2^{k/2}$.

   To use the probabilistic method, we assume that it is equally likely for two people to be friends or enemies. (Note that this assumption does not have to be realistic.) Suppose there are $n$ people at the party. It follows that there are $\binom{n}{k}$ different sets of $k$ people at this party, which we list as $S_1, S_2, \ldots, S_{\binom{n}{k}}$. Let $E_i$ be the event that all $k$ people in $S_i$ are either mutual friends or mutual enemies. The probability that there are either $k$ mutual friends or $k$ mutual enemies among the $n$ people equals $p(\bigcup_{i=1}^{\binom{n}{k}} E_i)$.

   According to our assumption it is equally likely for two people to be friends or enemies. The probability that two people are friends equals the probability that they are enemies; both probabilities equal $1/2$. Furthermore, there are $\binom{k}{2} = k(k-1)/2$ pairs of people in $S_i$ because there are $k$ people in $S_i$. Hence, the probability that all $k$ people in $S_i$ are mutual friends and the probability that all $k$ people in $S_i$ are mutual enemies both equal $(1/2)^{k(k-1)/2}$. It follows that $p(E_i) = 2(1/2)^{k(k-1)/2}$.

The probability that there are either $k$ mutual friends or $k$ mutual enemies in the group of $n$ people equals $p(\bigcup_{i=1}^{\binom{n}{k}} E_i)$. Using Boole's inequality (Exercise 15), it follows that

$$p\left(\bigcup_{i=1}^{\binom{n}{k}} E_i\right) \leq \sum_{i=1}^{\binom{n}{k}} p(E_i) = \binom{n}{k} \cdot 2\left(\frac{1}{2}\right)^{k(k-1)/2}.$$

By Exercise 17 in Section 6.4, we have $\binom{n}{k} \leq n^k/2^{k-1}$. Hence,

$$\binom{n}{k} 2\left(\frac{1}{2}\right)^{k(k-1)/2} \leq \frac{n^k}{2^{k-1}} 2\left(\frac{1}{2}\right)^{k(k-1)/2}.$$

Now if $n < 2^{k/2}$, we have

$$\frac{n^k}{2^{k-1}} 2\left(\frac{1}{2}\right)^{k(k-1)/2} < \frac{2^{k(k/2)}}{2^{k-1}} 2\left(\frac{1}{2}\right)^{k(k-1)/2} = 2^{2-(k/2)} \leq 1,$$

where the last step follows because $k \geq 4$.

We can now conclude that $p(\bigcup_{i=1}^{\binom{n}{k}} E_i) < 1$ when $k \geq 4$. Hence, the probability of the complementary event, that there is no set of either $k$ mutual friends or mutual enemies at the party, is greater than 0. It follows that if $n < 2^{k/2}$, there is at least one set such that no subset of $k$ people are mutual friends or mutual enemies. ◁

## Exercises

1. What probability should be assigned to the outcome of heads when a biased coin is tossed, if heads is three times as likely to come up as tails? What probability should be assigned to the outcome of tails?

2. Find the probability of each outcome when a loaded die is rolled, if a 3 is twice as likely to appear as each of the other five numbers on the die.

3. Find the probability of each outcome when a biased die is rolled, if rolling a 2 or rolling a 4 is three times as likely as rolling each of the other four numbers on the die and it is equally likely to roll a 2 or a 4.

4. Show that conditions (*i*) and (*ii*) are met under Laplace's definition of probability, when outcomes are equally likely.

5. A pair of dice is loaded. The probability that a 4 appears on the first die is 2/7, and the probability that a 3 appears on the second die is 2/7. Other outcomes for each die appear with probability 1/7. What is the probability of 7 appearing as the sum of the numbers when the two dice are rolled?

6. What is the probability of these events when we randomly select a permutation of $\{1, 2, 3\}$?
   a) 1 precedes 3.
   b) 3 precedes 1.
   c) 3 precedes 1 and 3 precedes 2.

7. What is the probability of these events when we randomly select a permutation of $\{1, 2, 3, 4\}$?
   a) 1 precedes 4.
   b) 4 precedes 1.
   c) 4 precedes 1 and 4 precedes 2.
   d) 4 precedes 1, 4 precedes 2, and 4 precedes 3.
   e) 4 precedes 3 and 2 precedes 1.

8. What is the probability of these events when we randomly select a permutation of $\{1, 2, \ldots, n\}$ where $n \geq 4$?
   a) 1 precedes 2.
   b) 2 precedes 1.
   c) 1 immediately precedes 2.
   d) $n$ precedes 1 and $n-1$ precedes 2.
   e) $n$ precedes 1 and $n$ precedes 2.

9. What is the probability of these events when we randomly select a permutation of the 26 lowercase letters of the English alphabet?
   a) The permutation consists of the letters in reverse alphabetic order.
   b) $z$ is the first letter of the permutation.
   c) $z$ precedes $a$ in the permutation.
   d) $a$ immediately precedes $z$ in the permutation.
   e) $a$ immediately precedes $m$, which immediately precedes $z$ in the permutation.
   f) $m$, $n$, and $o$ are in their original places in the permutation.

**10.** What is the probability of these events when we randomly select a permutation of the 26 lowercase letters of the English alphabet?

   **a)** The first 13 letters of the permutation are in alphabetical order.

   **b)** $a$ is the first letter of the permutation and $z$ is the last letter.

   **c)** $a$ and $z$ are next to each other in the permutation.

   **d)** $a$ and $b$ are not next to each other in the permutation.

   **e)** $a$ and $z$ are separated by at least 23 letters in the permutation.

   **f)** $z$ precedes both $a$ and $b$ in the permutation.

**11.** Suppose that $E$ and $F$ are events such that $p(E) = 0.7$ and $p(F) = 0.5$. Show that $p(E \cup F) \geq 0.7$ and $p(E \cap F) \geq 0.2$.

**12.** Suppose that $E$ and $F$ are events such that $p(E) = 0.8$ and $p(F) = 0.6$. Show that $p(E \cup F) \geq 0.8$ and $p(E \cap F) \geq 0.4$.

**13.** Show that if $E$ and $F$ are events, then $p(E \cap F) \geq p(E) + p(F) - 1$. This is known as **Bonferroni's inequality**.

**14.** Use mathematical induction to prove the following generalization of Bonferroni's inequality:

$$p(E_1 \cap E_2 \cap \cdots \cap E_n)$$
$$\geq p(E_1) + p(E_2) + \cdots + p(E_n) - (n - 1),$$

where $E_1, E_2, \ldots, E_n$ are $n$ events.

**15.** Show that if $E_1, E_2, \ldots, E_n$ are events from a finite sample space, then

$$p(E_1 \cup E_2 \cup \cdots \cup E_n)$$
$$\leq p(E_1) + p(E_2) + \cdots + p(E_n).$$

This is known as **Boole's inequality**.

**16.** Show that if $E$ and $F$ are independent events, then $\overline{E}$ and $\overline{F}$ are also independent events.

**17.** If $E$ and $F$ are independent events, prove or disprove that $\overline{E}$ and $F$ are necessarily independent events.

In Exercises 18, 20, and 21 assume that the year has 366 days and all birthdays are equally likely. In Exercise 19 assume it is equally likely that a person is born in any given month of the year.

**18. a)** What is the probability that two people chosen at random were born on the same day of the week?

   **b)** What is the probability that in a group of $n$ people chosen at random, there are at least two born on the same day of the week?

   **c)** How many people chosen at random are needed to make the probability greater than $1/2$ that there are at least two people born on the same day of the week?

**19. a)** What is the probability that two people chosen at random were born during the same month of the year?

   **b)** What is the probability that in a group of $n$ people chosen at random, there are at least two born in the same month of the year?

   **c)** How many people chosen at random are needed to make the probability greater than $1/2$ that there are at least two people born in the same month of the year?

**20.** Find the smallest number of people you need to choose at random so that the probability that at least one of them has a birthday today exceeds $1/2$.

**21.** Find the smallest number of people you need to choose at random so that the probability that at least two of them were both born on April 1 exceeds $1/2$.

**\*22.** February 29 occurs only in leap years. Years divisible by 4, but not by 100, are always leap years. Years divisible by 100, but not by 400, are not leap years, but years divisible by 400 are leap years.

   **a)** What probability distribution for birthdays should be used to reflect how often February 29 occurs?

   **b)** Using the probability distribution from part (a), what is the probability that in a group of $n$ people at least two have the same birthday?

**23.** What is the conditional probability that exactly four heads appear when a fair coin is flipped five times, given that the first flip came up heads?

**24.** What is the conditional probability that exactly four heads appear when a fair coin is flipped five times, given that the first flip came up tails?

**25.** What is the conditional probability that a randomly generated bit string of length four contains at least two consecutive 0s, given that the first bit is a 1? (Assume the probabilities of a 0 and a 1 are the same.)

**26.** Let $E$ be the event that a randomly generated bit string of length three contains an odd number of 1s, and let $F$ be the event that the string starts with 1. Are $E$ and $F$ independent?

**27.** Let $E$ and $F$ be the events that a family of $n$ children has children of both sexes and has at most one boy, respectively. Are $E$ and $F$ independent if

   **a)** $n = 2$?    **b)** $n = 4$?    **c)** $n = 5$?

**28.** Assume that the probability a child is a boy is 0.51 and that the sexes of children born into a family are independent. What is the probability that a family of five children has

   **a)** exactly three boys?

   **b)** at least one boy?

   **c)** at least one girl?

   **d)** all children of the same sex?

**29.** A group of six people play the game of "odd person out" to determine who will buy refreshments. Each person flips a fair coin. If there is a person whose outcome is not the same as that of any other member of the group, this person has to buy the refreshments. What is the probability that there is an odd person out after the coins are flipped once?

**30.** Find the probability that a randomly generated bit string of length 10 does not contain a 0 if bits are independent and if

   **a)** a 0 bit and a 1 bit are equally likely.

   **b)** the probability that a bit is a 1 is 0.6.

   **c)** the probability that the $i$th bit is a 1 is $1/2^i$ for $i = 1, 2, 3, \ldots, 10$.

**31.** Find the probability that a family with five children does not have a boy, if the sexes of children are independent and if

  **a)** a boy and a girl are equally likely.

  **b)** the probability of a boy is 0.51.

  **c)** the probability that the $i$th child is a boy is $0.51 - (i/100)$.

**32.** Find the probability that a randomly generated bit string of length 10 begins with a 1 or ends with a 00 for the same conditions as in parts (a), (b), and (c) of Exercise 30, if bits are generated independently.

**33.** Find the probability that the first child of a family with five children is a boy or that the last two children of the family are girls, for the same conditions as in parts (a), (b), and (c) of Exercise 31.

**34.** Find each of the following probabilities when $n$ independent Bernoulli trials are carried out with probability of success $p$.

  **a)** the probability of no successes

  **b)** the probability of at least one success

  **c)** the probability of at most one success

  **d)** the probability of at least two successes

**35.** Find each of the following probabilities when $n$ independent Bernoulli trials are carried out with probability of success $p$.

  **a)** the probability of no failures

  **b)** the probability of at least one failure

  **c)** the probability of at most one failure

  **d)** the probability of at least two failures

**36.** Use mathematical induction to prove that if $E_1, E_2, \ldots, E_n$ is a sequence of $n$ pairwise disjoint events in a sample space $S$, where $n$ is a positive integer, then $p(\bigcup_{i=1}^{n} E_i) = \sum_{i=1}^{n} p(E_i)$.

**∗37.** (*Requires calculus*) Show that if $E_1, E_2, \ldots$ is an infinite sequence of pairwise disjoint events in a sample space $S$, then $p(\bigcup_{i=1}^{\infty} E_i) = \sum_{i=1}^{\infty} p(E_i)$. [*Hint:* Use Exercise 36 and take limits.]

**38.** A pair of dice is rolled in a remote location and when you ask an honest observer whether at least one die came up six, this honest observer answers in the affirmative.

  **a)** What is the probability that the sum of the numbers that came up on the two dice is seven, given the information provided by the honest observer?

  **b)** Suppose that the honest observer tells us that at least one die came up five. What is the probability the sum of the numbers that came up on the dice is seven, given this information?

**∗∗39.** This exercise employs the probabilistic method to prove a result about round-robin tournaments. In a **round-robin tournament** with $m$ players, every two players play one game in which one player wins and the other loses.

  We want to find conditions on positive integers $m$ and $k$ with $k < m$ such that it is possible for the outcomes of the tournament to have the property that for every set of $k$ players, there is a player who beats every member in this set. So that we can use probabilistic reasoning to draw conclusions about round-robin tournaments, we assume that when two players compete it is equally likely that either player wins the game and we assume that the outcomes of different games are independent. Let $E$ be the event that for every set $S$ with $k$ players, where $k$ is a positive integer less than $m$, there is a player who has beaten all $k$ players in $S$.

  **a)** Show that $p(\overline{E}) \leq \sum_{j=1}^{\binom{m}{k}} p(F_j)$, where $F_j$ is the event that there is no player who beats all $k$ players from the $j$th set in a list of the $\binom{m}{k}$ sets of $k$ players.

  **b)** Show that the probability of $F_j$ is $(1 - 2^{-k})^{m-k}$.

  **c)** Conclude from parts (a) and (b) that $p(\overline{E}) \leq \binom{m}{k}(1 - 2^{-k})^{m-k}$ and, therefore, that there must be a tournament with the described property if $\binom{m}{k}(1 - 2^{-k})^{m-k} < 1$.

  **d)** Use part (c) to find values of $m$ such that there is a tournament with $m$ players such that for every set $S$ of two players, there is a player who has beaten both players in $S$. Repeat for sets of three players.

**∗40.** Devise a Monte Carlo algorithm that determines whether a permutation of the integers 1 through $n$ has already been sorted (that is, it is in increasing order), or instead, is a random permutation. A step of the algorithm should answer "true" if it determines the list is not sorted and "unknown" otherwise. After $k$ steps, the algorithm decides that the integers are sorted if the answer is "unknown" in each step. Show that as the number of steps increases, the probability that the algorithm produces an incorrect answer is extremely small. [*Hint:* For each step, test whether certain elements are in the correct order. Make sure these tests are independent.]

**41.** Use pseudocode to write out the probabilistic primality test described in Example 16.

# 7.3   Bayes' Theorem

## Introduction

There are many times when we want to assess the probability that a particular event occurs on the basis of partial evidence. For example, suppose we know the percentage of people who have a particular disease for which there is a very accurate diagnostic test. People who test positive for

# 9

# Relations

**R**elationships between elements of sets occur in many contexts. Every day we deal with relationships such as those between a business and its telephone number, an employee and his or her salary, a person and a relative, and so on. In mathematics we study relationships such as those between a positive integer and one that it divides, an integer and one that it is congruent to modulo 5, a real number and one that is larger than it, a real number $x$ and the value $f(x)$ where $f$ is a function, and so on. Relationships such as that between a program and a variable it uses, and that between a computer language and a valid statement in this language often arise in computer science.

Relationships between elements of sets are represented using the structure called a relation, which is just a subset of the Cartesian product of the sets. Relations can be used to solve problems such as determining which pairs of cities are linked by airline flights in a network, finding a viable order for the different phases of a complicated project, or producing a useful way to store information in computer databases.

In some computer languages, only the first 31 characters of the name of a variable matter. The relation consisting of ordered pairs of strings where the first string has the same initial 31 characters as the second string is an example of a special type of relation, known as an equivalence relation. Equivalence relations arise throughout mathematics and computer science. We will study equivalence relations, and other special types of relations, in this chapter.

## 9.1 Relations and Their Properties

### Introduction

The most direct way to express a relationship between elements of two sets is to use ordered pairs made up of two related elements. For this reason, sets of ordered pairs are called binary relations. In this section we introduce the basic terminology used to describe binary relations. Later in this chapter we will use relations to solve problems involving communications networks, project scheduling, and identifying elements in sets with common properties.

Links

**DEFINITION 1**   Let $A$ and $B$ be sets. A *binary relation from $A$ to $B$* is a subset of $A \times B$.

In other words, a binary relation from $A$ to $B$ is a set $R$ of ordered pairs where the first element of each ordered pair comes from $A$ and the second element comes from $B$. We use the notation $a\,R\,b$ to denote that $(a, b) \in R$ and $a\,\cancel{R}\,b$ to denote that $(a, b) \notin R$. Moreover, when $(a, b)$ belongs to $R$, $a$ is said to be **related to** $b$ by $R$.

Binary relations represent relationships between the elements of two sets. We will introduce *n*-ary relations, which express relationships among elements of more than two sets, later in this chapter. We will omit the word *binary* when there is no danger of confusion.

Examples 1–3 illustrate the notion of a relation.

**EXAMPLE 1**   Let $A$ be the set of students in your school, and let $B$ be the set of courses. Let $R$ be the relation that consists of those pairs $(a, b)$, where $a$ is a student enrolled in course $b$. For instance, if Jason Goodfriend and Deborah Sherman are enrolled in CS518, the pairs

(Jason Goodfriend, CS518) and (Deborah Sherman, CS518) belong to $R$. If Jason Goodfriend is also enrolled in CS510, then the pair (Jason Goodfriend, CS510) is also in $R$. However, if Deborah Sherman is not enrolled in CS510, then the pair (Deborah Sherman, CS510) is not in $R$.

Note that if a student is not currently enrolled in any courses there will be no pairs in $R$ that have this student as the first element. Similarly, if a course is not currently being offered there will be no pairs in $R$ that have this course as their second element. ◄

**EXAMPLE 2**  Let $A$ be the set of cities in the U.S.A., and let $B$ be the set of the 50 states in the U.S.A. Define the relation $R$ by specifying that $(a, b)$ belongs to $R$ if a city with name $a$ is in the state $b$. For instance, (Boulder, Colorado), (Bangor, Maine), (Ann Arbor, Michigan), (Middletown, New Jersey), (Middletown, New York), (Cupertino, California), and (Red Bank, New Jersey) are in $R$. ◄

**EXAMPLE 3**  Let $A = \{0, 1, 2\}$ and $B = \{a, b\}$. Then $\{(0, a), (0, b), (1, a), (2, b)\}$ is a relation from $A$ to $B$. This means, for instance, that $0 \, R \, a$, but that $1 \, \not{R} \, b$. Relations can be represented graphically, as shown in Figure 1, using arrows to represent ordered pairs. Another way to represent this relation is to use a table, which is also done in Figure 1. We will discuss representations of relations in more detail in Section 9.3. ◄

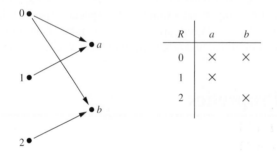

| $R$ | $a$ | $b$ |
|-----|-----|-----|
| 0 | × | × |
| 1 | × | |
| 2 | | × |

**FIGURE 1**  **Displaying the Ordered Pairs in the Relation $R$ from Example 3.**

## Functions as Relations

Recall that a function $f$ from a set $A$ to a set $B$ (as defined in Section 2.3) assigns exactly one element of $B$ to each element of $A$. The graph of $f$ is the set of ordered pairs $(a, b)$ such that $b = f(a)$. Because the graph of $f$ is a subset of $A \times B$, it is a relation from $A$ to $B$. Moreover, the graph of a function has the property that every element of $A$ is the first element of exactly one ordered pair of the graph.

Conversely, if $R$ is a relation from $A$ to $B$ such that every element in $A$ is the first element of exactly one ordered pair of $R$, then a function can be defined with $R$ as its graph. This can be done by assigning to an element $a$ of $A$ the unique element $b \in B$ such that $(a, b) \in R$. (Note that the relation $R$ in Example 2 is not the graph of a function because Middletown occurs more than once as the first element of an ordered pair in $R$.)

A relation can be used to express a one-to-many relationship between the elements of the sets $A$ and $B$ (as in Example 2), where an element of $A$ may be related to more than one element of $B$. A function represents a relation where exactly one element of $B$ is related to each element of $A$.

Relations are a generalization of graphs of functions; they can be used to express a much wider class of relationships between sets. (Recall that the graph of the function $f$ from $A$ to $B$ is the set of ordered pairs $(a, f(a))$ for $a \in A$.)

## Relations on a Set

Relations from a set $A$ to itself are of special interest.

**DEFINITION 2**  A *relation on a set* $A$ is a relation from $A$ to $A$.

In other words, a relation on a set $A$ is a subset of $A \times A$.

**EXAMPLE 4**  Let $A$ be the set $\{1, 2, 3, 4\}$. Which ordered pairs are in the relation $R = \{(a, b) \mid a$ divides $b\}$?

*Solution:* Because $(a, b)$ is in $R$ if and only if $a$ and $b$ are positive integers not exceeding 4 such that $a$ divides $b$, we see that

$$R = \{(1, 1), (1, 2), (1, 3), (1, 4), (2, 2), (2, 4), (3, 3), (4, 4)\}.$$

The pairs in this relation are displayed both graphically and in tabular form in Figure 2.  ◀

Next, some examples of relations on the set of integers will be given in Example 5.

**EXAMPLE 5**  Consider these relations on the set of integers:

$$R_1 = \{(a, b) \mid a \leq b\},$$
$$R_2 = \{(a, b) \mid a > b\},$$
$$R_3 = \{(a, b) \mid a = b \text{ or } a = -b\},$$
$$R_4 = \{(a, b) \mid a = b\},$$
$$R_5 = \{(a, b) \mid a = b + 1\},$$
$$R_6 = \{(a, b) \mid a + b \leq 3\}.$$

Which of these relations contain each of the pairs $(1, 1)$, $(1, 2)$, $(2, 1)$, $(1, -1)$, and $(2, 2)$?

*Remark:* Unlike the relations in Examples 1–4, these are relations on an infinite set.

*Solution:* The pair $(1, 1)$ is in $R_1$, $R_3$, $R_4$, and $R_6$; $(1, 2)$ is in $R_1$ and $R_6$; $(2, 1)$ is in $R_2$, $R_5$, and $R_6$; $(1, -1)$ is in $R_2$, $R_3$, and $R_6$; and finally, $(2, 2)$ is in $R_1$, $R_3$, and $R_4$.  ◀

It is not hard to determine the number of relations on a finite set, because a relation on a set $A$ is simply a subset of $A \times A$.

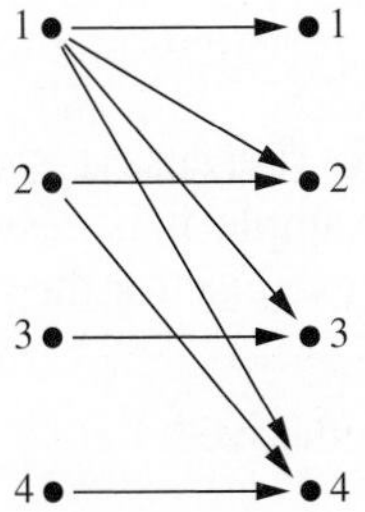

| $R$ | 1 | 2 | 3 | 4 |
|-----|---|---|---|---|
| 1 | × | × | × | × |
| 2 |   | × |   | × |
| 3 |   |   | × |   |
| 4 |   |   |   | × |

**FIGURE 2**  **Displaying the Ordered Pairs in the Relation $R$ from Example 4.**

**EXAMPLE 6**   How many relations are there on a set with $n$ elements?

*Solution:* A relation on a set $A$ is a subset of $A \times A$. Because $A \times A$ has $n^2$ elements when $A$ has $n$ elements, and a set with $m$ elements has $2^m$ subsets, there are $2^{n^2}$ subsets of $A \times A$. Thus, there are $2^{n^2}$ relations on a set with $n$ elements. For example, there are $2^{3^2} = 2^9 = 512$ relations on the set $\{a, b, c\}$. ◄

## Properties of Relations

There are several properties that are used to classify relations on a set. We will introduce the most important of these here.

In some relations an element is always related to itself. For instance, let $R$ be the relation on the set of all people consisting of pairs $(x, y)$ where $x$ and $y$ have the same mother and the same father. Then $x R x$ for every person $x$.

**DEFINITION 3**   A relation $R$ on a set $A$ is called *reflexive* if $(a, a) \in R$ for every element $a \in A$.

*Remark:* Using quantifiers we see that the relation $R$ on the set $A$ is reflexive if $\forall a((a, a) \in R)$, where the universe of discourse is the set of all elements in $A$.

We see that a relation on $A$ is reflexive if every element of $A$ is related to itself. Examples 7–9 illustrate the concept of a reflexive relation.

**EXAMPLE 7**   Consider the following relations on $\{1, 2, 3, 4\}$:

$R_1 = \{(1, 1), (1, 2), (2, 1), (2, 2), (3, 4), (4, 1), (4, 4)\}$,
$R_2 = \{(1, 1), (1, 2), (2, 1)\}$,
$R_3 = \{(1, 1), (1, 2), (1, 4), (2, 1), (2, 2), (3, 3), (4, 1), (4, 4)\}$,
$R_4 = \{(2, 1), (3, 1), (3, 2), (4, 1), (4, 2), (4, 3)\}$,
$R_5 = \{(1, 1), (1, 2), (1, 3), (1, 4), (2, 2), (2, 3), (2, 4), (3, 3), (3, 4), (4, 4)\}$,
$R_6 = \{(3, 4)\}$.

Which of these relations are reflexive?

*Solution:* The relations $R_3$ and $R_5$ are reflexive because they both contain all pairs of the form $(a, a)$, namely, $(1, 1)$, $(2, 2)$, $(3, 3)$, and $(4, 4)$. The other relations are not reflexive because they do not contain all of these ordered pairs. In particular, $R_1$, $R_2$, $R_4$, and $R_6$ are not reflexive because $(3, 3)$ is not in any of these relations. ◄

**EXAMPLE 8**   Which of the relations from Example 5 are reflexive?

*Solution:* The reflexive relations from Example 5 are $R_1$ (because $a \leq a$ for every integer $a$), $R_3$, and $R_4$. For each of the other relations in this example it is easy to find a pair of the form $(a, a)$ that is not in the relation. (This is left as an exercise for the reader.) ◄

**EXAMPLE 9**   Is the "divides" relation on the set of positive integers reflexive?

*Solution:* Because $a \mid a$ whenever $a$ is a positive integer, the "divides" relation is reflexive. (Note that if we replace the set of positive integers with the set of all integers the relation is not reflexive because by definition 0 does not divide 0.) ◄

In some relations an element is related to a second element if and only if the second element is also related to the first element. The relation consisting of pairs $(x, y)$, where $x$ and $y$ are students at your school with at least one common class has this property. Other relations have the property that if an element is related to a second element, then this second element is not related to the first. The relation consisting of the pairs $(x, y)$, where $x$ and $y$ are students at your school, where $x$ has a higher grade point average than $y$ has this property.

**DEFINITION 4**    A relation $R$ on a set $A$ is called *symmetric* if $(b, a) \in R$ whenever $(a, b) \in R$, for all $a, b \in A$. A relation $R$ on a set $A$ such that for all $a, b \in A$, if $(a, b) \in R$ and $(b, a) \in R$, then $a = b$ is called *antisymmetric*.

*Remark:* Using quantifiers, we see that the relation $R$ on the set $A$ is symmetric if $\forall a \forall b ((a, b) \in R \rightarrow (b, a) \in R)$. Similarly, the relation $R$ on the set $A$ is antisymmetric if $\forall a \forall b (((a, b) \in R \land (b, a) \in R) \rightarrow (a = b))$.

That is, a relation is symmetric if and only if $a$ is related to $b$ implies that $b$ is related to $a$. A relation is antisymmetric if and only if there are no pairs of distinct elements $a$ and $b$ with $a$ related to $b$ and $b$ related to $a$. That is, the only way to have $a$ related to $b$ and $b$ related to $a$ is for $a$ and $b$ to be the same element. The terms *symmetric* and *antisymmetric* are not opposites, because a relation can have both of these properties or may lack both of them (see Exercise 10). A relation cannot be both symmetric and antisymmetric if it contains some pair of the form $(a, b)$, where $a \neq b$.

*Remark:* Although relatively few of the $2^{n^2}$ relations on a set with $n$ elements are symmetric or antisymmetric, as counting arguments can show, many important relations have one of these properties. (See Exercise 47.)

**EXAMPLE 10**    Which of the relations from Example 7 are symmetric and which are antisymmetric?

Extra
Examples

*Solution:* The relations $R_2$ and $R_3$ are symmetric, because in each case $(b, a)$ belongs to the relation whenever $(a, b)$ does. For $R_2$, the only thing to check is that both $(2, 1)$ and $(1, 2)$ are in the relation. For $R_3$, it is necessary to check that both $(1, 2)$ and $(2, 1)$ belong to the relation, and $(1, 4)$ and $(4, 1)$ belong to the relation. The reader should verify that none of the other relations is symmetric. This is done by finding a pair $(a, b)$ such that it is in the relation but $(b, a)$ is not.

$R_4$, $R_5$, and $R_6$ are all antisymmetric. For each of these relations there is no pair of elements $a$ and $b$ with $a \neq b$ such that both $(a, b)$ and $(b, a)$ belong to the relation. The reader should verify that none of the other relations is antisymmetric. This is done by finding a pair $(a, b)$ with $a \neq b$ such that $(a, b)$ and $(b, a)$ are both in the relation. ◀

**EXAMPLE 11**    Which of the relations from Example 5 are symmetric and which are antisymmetric?

*Solution:* The relations $R_3$, $R_4$, and $R_6$ are symmetric. $R_3$ is symmetric, for if $a = b$ or $a = -b$, then $b = a$ or $b = -a$. $R_4$ is symmetric because $a = b$ implies that $b = a$. $R_6$ is symmetric because $a + b \leq 3$ implies that $b + a \leq 3$. The reader should verify that none of the other relations is symmetric.

The relations $R_1$, $R_2$, $R_4$, and $R_5$ are antisymmetric. $R_1$ is antisymmetric because the inequalities $a \leq b$ and $b \leq a$ imply that $a = b$. $R_2$ is antisymmetric because it is impossible that $a > b$ and $b > a$. $R_4$ is antisymmetric, because two elements are related with respect to $R_4$ if and only if they are equal. $R_5$ is antisymmetric because it is impossible that $a = b + 1$ and $b = a + 1$. The reader should verify that none of the other relations is antisymmetric. ◀

**EXAMPLE 12**    Is the "divides" relation on the set of positive integers symmetric? Is it antisymmetric?

*Solution:* This relation is not symmetric because $1 \mid 2$, but $2 \nmid 1$. It is antisymmetric, for if $a$ and $b$ are positive integers with $a \mid b$ and $b \mid a$, then $a = b$ (the verification of this is left as an exercise for the reader).    ◄

Let $R$ be the relation consisting of all pairs $(x, y)$ of students at your school, where $x$ has taken more credits than $y$. Suppose that $x$ is related to $y$ and $y$ is related to $z$. This means that $x$ has taken more credits than $y$ and $y$ has taken more credits than $z$. We can conclude that $x$ has taken more credits than $z$, so that $x$ is related to $z$. What we have shown is that $R$ has the transitive property, which is defined as follows.

**DEFINITION 5**    A relation $R$ on a set $A$ is called *transitive* if whenever $(a, b) \in R$ and $(b, c) \in R$, then $(a, c) \in R$, for all $a, b, c \in A$.

*Remark:* Using quantifiers we see that the relation $R$ on a set $A$ is transitive if we have $\forall a \forall b \forall c (((a, b) \in R \wedge (b, c) \in R) \rightarrow (a, c) \in R)$.

**EXAMPLE 13**    Which of the relations in Example 7 are transitive?

*Solution:* $R_4$, $R_5$, and $R_6$ are transitive. For each of these relations, we can show that it is transitive by verifying that if $(a, b)$ and $(b, c)$ belong to this relation, then $(a, c)$ also does. For instance, $R_4$ is transitive, because $(3, 2)$ and $(2, 1)$, $(4, 2)$ and $(2, 1)$, $(4, 3)$ and $(3, 1)$, and $(4, 3)$ and $(3, 2)$ are the only such sets of pairs, and $(3, 1)$, $(4, 1)$, and $(4, 2)$ belong to $R_4$. The reader should verify that $R_5$ and $R_6$ are transitive.

$R_1$ is not transitive because $(3, 4)$ and $(4, 1)$ belong to $R_1$, but $(3, 1)$ does not. $R_2$ is not transitive because $(2, 1)$ and $(1, 2)$ belong to $R_2$, but $(2, 2)$ does not. $R_3$ is not transitive because $(4, 1)$ and $(1, 2)$ belong to $R_3$, but $(4, 2)$ does not.    ◄

**EXAMPLE 14**    Which of the relations in Example 5 are transitive?

*Solution:* The relations $R_1$, $R_2$, $R_3$, and $R_4$ are transitive. $R_1$ is transitive because $a \leq b$ and $b \leq c$ imply that $a \leq c$. $R_2$ is transitive because $a > b$ and $b > c$ imply that $a > c$. $R_3$ is transitive because $a = \pm b$ and $b = \pm c$ imply that $a = \pm c$. $R_4$ is clearly transitive, as the reader should verify. $R_5$ is not transitive because $(2, 1)$ and $(1, 0)$ belong to $R_5$, but $(2, 0)$ does not. $R_6$ is not transitive because $(2, 1)$ and $(1, 2)$ belong to $R_6$, but $(2, 2)$ does not.    ◄

**EXAMPLE 15**    Is the "divides" relation on the set of positive integers transitive?

*Solution:* Suppose that $a$ divides $b$ and $b$ divides $c$. Then there are positive integers $k$ and $l$ such that $b = ak$ and $c = bl$. Hence, $c = a(kl)$, so $a$ divides $c$. It follows that this relation is transitive.    ◄

We can use counting techniques to determine the number of relations with specific properties. Finding the number of relations with a particular property provides information about how common this property is in the set of all relations on a set with $n$ elements.

**EXAMPLE 16**    How many reflexive relations are there on a set with $n$ elements?

*Solution:* A relation $R$ on a set $A$ is a subset of $A \times A$. Consequently, a relation is determined by specifying whether each of the $n^2$ ordered pairs in $A \times A$ is in $R$. However, if $R$ is reflexive, each of the $n$ ordered pairs $(a, a)$ for $a \in A$ must be in $R$. Each of the other $n(n-1)$ ordered pairs of the form $(a, b)$, where $a \neq b$, may or may not be in $R$. Hence, by the product rule for counting, there are $2^{n(n-1)}$ reflexive relations [this is the number of ways to choose whether each element $(a, b)$, with $a \neq b$, belongs to $R$]. ◀

Formulas for the number of symmetric relations and the number of antisymmetric relations on a set with $n$ elements can be found using reasoning similar to that in Example 16 (see Exercise 47). However, no general formula is known that counts the transitive relations on a set with $n$ elements. Currently, $T(n)$, the number of transitive relations on a set with $n$ elements, is known only for $n \leq 17$. For example, $T(4) = 3,994$, $T(5) = 154,303$, and $T(6) = 9,415,189$.

## Combining Relations

Because relations from $A$ to $B$ are subsets of $A \times B$, two relations from $A$ to $B$ can be combined in any way two sets can be combined. Consider Examples 17–19.

**EXAMPLE 17**   Let $A = \{1, 2, 3\}$ and $B = \{1, 2, 3, 4\}$. The relations $R_1 = \{(1, 1), (2, 2), (3, 3)\}$ and $R_2 = \{(1, 1), (1, 2), (1, 3), (1, 4)\}$ can be combined to obtain

$R_1 \cup R_2 = \{(1, 1), (1, 2), (1, 3), (1, 4), (2, 2), (3, 3)\}$,
$R_1 \cap R_2 = \{(1, 1)\}$,
$R_1 - R_2 = \{(2, 2), (3, 3)\}$,
$R_2 - R_1 = \{(1, 2), (1, 3), (1, 4)\}$. ◀

**EXAMPLE 18**   Let $A$ and $B$ be the set of all students and the set of all courses at a school, respectively. Suppose that $R_1$ consists of all ordered pairs $(a, b)$, where $a$ is a student who has taken course $b$, and $R_2$ consists of all ordered pairs $(a, b)$, where $a$ is a student who requires course $b$ to graduate. What are the relations $R_1 \cup R_2$, $R_1 \cap R_2$, $R_1 \oplus R_2$, $R_1 - R_2$, and $R_2 - R_1$?

*Solution:* The relation $R_1 \cup R_2$ consists of all ordered pairs $(a, b)$, where $a$ is a student who either has taken course $b$ or needs course $b$ to graduate, and $R_1 \cap R_2$ is the set of all ordered pairs $(a, b)$, where $a$ is a student who has taken course $b$ and needs this course to graduate. Also, $R_1 \oplus R_2$ consists of all ordered pairs $(a, b)$, where student $a$ has taken course $b$ but does not need it to graduate or needs course $b$ to graduate but has not taken it. $R_1 - R_2$ is the set of ordered pairs $(a, b)$, where $a$ has taken course $b$ but does not need it to graduate; that is, $b$ is an elective course that $a$ has taken. $R_2 - R_1$ is the set of all ordered pairs $(a, b)$, where $b$ is a course that $a$ needs to graduate but has not taken. ◀

**EXAMPLE 19**   Let $R_1$ be the "less than" relation on the set of real numbers and let $R_2$ be the "greater than" relation on the set of real numbers, that is, $R_1 = \{(x, y) \mid x < y\}$ and $R_2 = \{(x, y) \mid x > y\}$. What are $R_1 \cup R_2$, $R_1 \cap R_2$, $R_1 - R_2$, $R_2 - R_1$, and $R_1 \oplus R_2$?

*Solution:* We note that $(x, y) \in R_1 \cup R_2$ if and only if $(x, y) \in R_1$ or $(x, y) \in R_2$. Hence, $(x, y) \in R_1 \cup R_2$ if and only if $x < y$ or $x > y$. Because the condition $x < y$ or $x > y$ is the same as the condition $x \neq y$, it follows that $R_1 \cup R_2 = \{(x, y) \mid x \neq y\}$. In other words, the union of the "less than" relation and the "greater than" relation is the "not equals" relation.

Next, note that it is impossible for a pair $(x, y)$ to belong to both $R_1$ and $R_2$ because it is impossible that $x < y$ and $x > y$. It follows that $R_1 \cap R_2 = \emptyset$. We also see that $R_1 - R_2 = R_1$, $R_2 - R_1 = R_2$, and $R_1 \oplus R_2 = R_1 \cup R_2 - R_1 \cap R_2 = \{(x, y) \mid x \neq y\}$. ◀

There is another way that relations are combined that is analogous to the composition of functions.

**DEFINITION 6**

Let $R$ be a relation from a set $A$ to a set $B$ and $S$ a relation from $B$ to a set $C$. The *composite* of $R$ and $S$ is the relation consisting of ordered pairs $(a, c)$, where $a \in A$, $c \in C$, and for which there exists an element $b \in B$ such that $(a, b) \in R$ and $(b, c) \in S$. We denote the composite of $R$ and $S$ by $S \circ R$.

Computing the composite of two relations requires that we find elements that are the second element of ordered pairs in the first relation and the first element of ordered pairs in the second relation, as Examples 20 and 21 illustrate.

**EXAMPLE 20**

What is the composite of the relations $R$ and $S$, where $R$ is the relation from $\{1, 2, 3\}$ to $\{1, 2, 3, 4\}$ with $R = \{(1, 1), (1, 4), (2, 3), (3, 1), (3, 4)\}$ and $S$ is the relation from $\{1, 2, 3, 4\}$ to $\{0, 1, 2\}$ with $S = \{(1, 0), (2, 0), (3, 1), (3, 2), (4, 1)\}$?

*Solution:* $S \circ R$ is constructed using all ordered pairs in $R$ and ordered pairs in $S$, where the second element of the ordered pair in $R$ agrees with the first element of the ordered pair in $S$. For example, the ordered pairs $(2, 3)$ in $R$ and $(3, 1)$ in $S$ produce the ordered pair $(2, 1)$ in $S \circ R$. Computing all the ordered pairs in the composite, we find

$$S \circ R = \{(1, 0), (1, 1), (2, 1), (2, 2), (3, 0), (3, 1)\}.$$

◄

**EXAMPLE 21**

**Composing the Parent Relation with Itself**  Let $R$ be the relation on the set of all people such that $(a, b) \in R$ if person $a$ is a parent of person $b$. Then $(a, c) \in R \circ R$ if and only if there is a person $b$ such that $(a, b) \in R$ and $(b, c) \in R$, that is, if and only if there is a person $b$ such that $a$ is a parent of $b$ and $b$ is a parent of $c$. In other words, $(a, c) \in R \circ R$ if and only if $a$ is a grandparent of $c$. ◄

The powers of a relation $R$ can be recursively defined from the definition of a composite of two relations.

**DEFINITION 7**

Let $R$ be a relation on the set $A$. The powers $R^n$, $n = 1, 2, 3, \ldots$, are defined recursively by

$$R^1 = R \qquad \text{and} \qquad R^{n+1} = R^n \circ R.$$

The definition shows that $R^2 = R \circ R$, $R^3 = R^2 \circ R = (R \circ R) \circ R$, and so on.

**EXAMPLE 22**

Let $R = \{(1, 1), (2, 1), (3, 2), (4, 3)\}$. Find the powers $R^n$, $n = 2, 3, 4, \ldots$.

*Solution:* Because $R^2 = R \circ R$, we find that $R^2 = \{(1, 1), (2, 1), (3, 1), (4, 2)\}$. Furthermore, because $R^3 = R^2 \circ R$, $R^3 = \{(1, 1), (2, 1), (3, 1), (4, 1)\}$. Additional computation shows that $R^4$ is the same as $R^3$, so $R^4 = \{(1, 1), (2, 1), (3, 1), (4, 1)\}$. It also follows that $R^n = R^3$ for $n = 5, 6, 7, \ldots$. The reader should verify this. ◄

The following theorem shows that the powers of a transitive relation are subsets of this relation. It will be used in Section 9.4.

**THEOREM 1**

The relation $R$ on a set $A$ is transitive if and only if $R^n \subseteq R$ for $n = 1, 2, 3, \ldots$.

*Proof:* We first prove the "if" part of the theorem. We suppose that $R^n \subseteq R$ for $n = 1$, $2, 3, \ldots,$. In particular, $R^2 \subseteq R$. To see that this implies $R$ is transitive, note that if $(a, b) \in R$ and $(b, c) \in R$, then by the definition of composition, $(a, c) \in R^2$. Because $R^2 \subseteq R$, this means that $(a, c) \in R$. Hence, $R$ is transitive.

We will use mathematical induction to prove the only if part of the theorem. Note that this part of the theorem is trivially true for $n = 1$.

Assume that $R^n \subseteq R$, where $n$ is a positive integer. This is the inductive hypothesis. To complete the inductive step we must show that this implies that $R^{n+1}$ is also a subset of $R$. To show this, assume that $(a, b) \in R^{n+1}$. Then, because $R^{n+1} = R^n \circ R$, there is an element $x$ with $x \in A$ such that $(a, x) \in R$ and $(x, b) \in R^n$. The inductive hypothesis, namely, that $R^n \subseteq R$, implies that $(x, b) \in R$. Furthermore, because $R$ is transitive, and $(a, x) \in R$ and $(x, b) \in R$, it follows that $(a, b) \in R$. This shows that $R^{n+1} \subseteq R$, completing the proof. ◁

# Exercises

**1.** List the ordered pairs in the relation $R$ from $A = \{0, 1, 2, 3, 4\}$ to $B = \{0, 1, 2, 3\}$, where $(a, b) \in R$ if and only if

**a)** $a = b$.　　　　**b)** $a + b = 4$.

**c)** $a > b$.　　　　**d)** $a \mid b$.

**e)** $\gcd(a, b) = 1$.　**f)** $\text{lcm}(a, b) = 2$.

**2. a)** List all the ordered pairs in the relation $R = \{(a, b) \mid a \text{ divides } b\}$ on the set $\{1, 2, 3, 4, 5, 6\}$.

**b)** Display this relation graphically, as was done in Example 4.

**c)** Display this relation in tabular form, as was done in Example 4.

**3.** For each of these relations on the set $\{1, 2, 3, 4\}$, decide whether it is reflexive, whether it is symmetric, whether it is antisymmetric, and whether it is transitive.

**a)** $\{(2, 2), (2, 3), (2, 4), (3, 2), (3, 3), (3, 4)\}$

**b)** $\{(1, 1), (1, 2), (2, 1), (2, 2), (3, 3), (4, 4)\}$

**c)** $\{(2, 4), (4, 2)\}$

**d)** $\{(1, 2), (2, 3), (3, 4)\}$

**e)** $\{(1, 1), (2, 2), (3, 3), (4, 4)\}$

**f)** $\{(1, 3), (1, 4), (2, 3), (2, 4), (3, 1), (3, 4)\}$

**4.** Determine whether the relation $R$ on the set of all people is reflexive, symmetric, antisymmetric, and/or transitive, where $(a, b) \in R$ if and only if

**a)** $a$ is taller than $b$.

**b)** $a$ and $b$ were born on the same day.

**c)** $a$ has the same first name as $b$.

**d)** $a$ and $b$ have a common grandparent.

**5.** Determine whether the relation $R$ on the set of all Web pages is reflexive, symmetric, antisymmetric, and/or transitive, where $(a, b) \in R$ if and only if

**a)** everyone who has visited Web page $a$ has also visited Web page $b$.

**b)** there are no common links found on both Web page $a$ and Web page $b$.

**c)** there is at least one common link on Web page $a$ and Web page $b$.

**d)** there is a Web page that includes links to both Web page $a$ and Web page $b$.

**6.** Determine whether the relation $R$ on the set of all real numbers is reflexive, symmetric, antisymmetric, and/or transitive, where $(x, y) \in R$ if and only if

**a)** $x + y = 0$.　　　　**b)** $x = \pm y$.

**c)** $x - y$ is a rational number.

**d)** $x = 2y$.　　　　**e)** $xy \geq 0$.

**f)** $xy = 0$.　　　　**g)** $x = 1$.

**h)** $x = 1$ or $y = 1$.

**7.** Determine whether the relation $R$ on the set of all integers is reflexive, symmetric, antisymmetric, and/or transitive, where $(x, y) \in R$ if and only if

**a)** $x \neq y$.　　　　**b)** $xy \geq 1$.

**c)** $x = y + 1$ or $x = y - 1$.

**d)** $x \equiv y \pmod 7$.　**e)** $x$ is a multiple of $y$.

**f)** $x$ and $y$ are both negative or both nonnegative.

**g)** $x = y^2$.　　　　**h)** $x \geq y^2$.

**8.** Show that the relation $R = \emptyset$ on a nonempty set $S$ is symmetric and transitive, but not reflexive.

**9.** Show that the relation $R = \emptyset$ on the empty set $S = \emptyset$ is reflexive, symmetric, and transitive.

**10.** Give an example of a relation on a set that is

**a)** both symmetric and antisymmetric.

**b)** neither symmetric nor antisymmetric.

A relation $R$ on the set $A$ is **irreflexive** if for every $a \in A$, $(a, a) \notin R$. That is, $R$ is irreflexive if no element in $A$ is related to itself.

**11.** Which relations in Exercise 3 are irreflexive?

**12.** Which relations in Exercise 4 are irreflexive?

**13.** Which relations in Exercise 5 are irreflexive?

**14.** Which relations in Exercise 6 are irreflexive?

**15.** Can a relation on a set be neither reflexive nor irreflexive?

**16.** Use quantifiers to express what it means for a relation to be irreflexive.

**17.** Give an example of an irreflexive relation on the set of all people.

A relation $R$ is called **asymmetric** if $(a, b) \in R$ implies that $(b, a) \notin R$. Exercises 18–24 explore the notion of an asymmetric relation. Exercise 22 focuses on the difference between asymmetry and antisymmetry.

**18.** Which relations in Exercise 3 are asymmetric?

**19.** Which relations in Exercise 4 are asymmetric?

**20.** Which relations in Exercise 5 are asymmetric?

**21.** Which relations in Exercise 6 are asymmetric?

**22.** Must an asymmetric relation also be antisymmetric? Must an antisymmetric relation be asymmetric? Give reasons for your answers.

**23.** Use quantifiers to express what it means for a relation to be asymmetric.

**24.** Give an example of an asymmetric relation on the set of all people.

**25.** How many different relations are there from a set with $m$ elements to a set with $n$ elements?

☞ Let $R$ be a relation from a set $A$ to a set $B$. The **inverse relation** from $B$ to $A$, denoted by $R^{-1}$, is the set of ordered pairs $\{(b, a) \mid (a, b) \in R\}$. The **complementary relation** $\overline{R}$ is the set of ordered pairs $\{(a, b) \mid (a, b) \notin R\}$.

**26.** Let $R$ be the relation $R = \{(a, b) \mid a < b\}$ on the set of integers. Find
   **a)** $R^{-1}$.          **b)** $\overline{R}$.

**27.** Let $R$ be the relation $R = \{(a, b) \mid a \text{ divides } b\}$ on the set of positive integers. Find
   **a)** $R^{-1}$.          **b)** $\overline{R}$.

**28.** Let $R$ be the relation on the set of all states in the United States consisting of pairs $(a, b)$ where state $a$ borders state $b$. Find
   **a)** $R^{-1}$.          **b)** $\overline{R}$.

**29.** Suppose that the function $f$ from $A$ to $B$ is a one-to-one correspondence. Let $R$ be the relation that equals the graph of $f$. That is, $R = \{(a, f(a)) \mid a \in A\}$. What is the inverse relation $R^{-1}$?

**30.** Let $R_1 = \{(1, 2), (2, 3), (3, 4)\}$ and $R_2 = \{(1, 1), (1, 2), (2, 1), (2, 2), (2, 3), (3, 1), (3, 2), (3, 3), (3, 4)\}$ be relations from $\{1, 2, 3\}$ to $\{1, 2, 3, 4\}$. Find
   **a)** $R_1 \cup R_2$.          **b)** $R_1 \cap R_2$.
   **c)** $R_1 - R_2$.          **d)** $R_2 - R_1$.

**31.** Let $A$ be the set of students at your school and $B$ the set of books in the school library. Let $R_1$ and $R_2$ be the relations consisting of all ordered pairs $(a, b)$, where student $a$ is required to read book $b$ in a course, and where student $a$ has read book $b$, respectively. Describe the ordered pairs in each of these relations.
   **a)** $R_1 \cup R_2$          **b)** $R_1 \cap R_2$
   **c)** $R_1 \oplus R_2$          **d)** $R_1 - R_2$
   **e)** $R_2 - R_1$

**32.** Let $R$ be the relation $\{(1, 2), (1, 3), (2, 3), (2, 4), (3, 1)\}$, and let $S$ be the relation $\{(2, 1), (3, 1), (3, 2), (4, 2)\}$. Find $S \circ R$.

**33.** Let $R$ be the relation on the set of people consisting of pairs $(a, b)$, where $a$ is a parent of $b$. Let $S$ be the relation on the set of people consisting of pairs $(a, b)$, where $a$ and $b$ are siblings (brothers or sisters). What are $S \circ R$ and $R \circ S$?

Exercises 34–37 deal with these relations on the set of real numbers:

$R_1 = \{(a, b) \in \mathbf{R}^2 \mid a > b\}$, the "greater than" relation,

$R_2 = \{(a, b) \in \mathbf{R}^2 \mid a \geq b\}$, the "greater than or equal to" relation,

$R_3 = \{(a, b) \in \mathbf{R}^2 \mid a < b\}$, the "less than" relation,

$R_4 = \{(a, b) \in \mathbf{R}^2 \mid a \leq b\}$, the "less than or equal to" relation,

$R_5 = \{(a, b) \in \mathbf{R}^2 \mid a = b\}$, the "equal to" relation,

$R_6 = \{(a, b) \in \mathbf{R}^2 \mid a \neq b\}$, the "unequal to" relation.

**34.** Find
   **a)** $R_1 \cup R_3$.          **b)** $R_1 \cup R_5$.
   **c)** $R_2 \cap R_4$.          **d)** $R_3 \cap R_5$.
   **e)** $R_1 - R_2$.          **f)** $R_2 - R_1$.
   **g)** $R_1 \oplus R_3$.          **h)** $R_2 \oplus R_4$.

**35.** Find
   **a)** $R_2 \cup R_4$.          **b)** $R_3 \cup R_6$.
   **c)** $R_3 \cap R_6$.          **d)** $R_4 \cap R_6$.
   **e)** $R_3 - R_6$.          **f)** $R_6 - R_3$.
   **g)** $R_2 \oplus R_6$.          **h)** $R_3 \oplus R_5$.

**36.** Find
   **a)** $R_1 \circ R_1$.          **b)** $R_1 \circ R_2$.
   **c)** $R_1 \circ R_3$.          **d)** $R_1 \circ R_4$.
   **e)** $R_1 \circ R_5$.          **f)** $R_1 \circ R_6$.
   **g)** $R_2 \circ R_3$.          **h)** $R_3 \circ R_3$.

**37.** Find
   **a)** $R_2 \circ R_1$.          **b)** $R_2 \circ R_2$.
   **c)** $R_3 \circ R_5$.          **d)** $R_4 \circ R_1$.
   **e)** $R_5 \circ R_3$.          **f)** $R_3 \circ R_6$.
   **g)** $R_4 \circ R_6$.          **h)** $R_6 \circ R_6$.

**38.** Let $R$ be the parent relation on the set of all people (see Example 21). When is an ordered pair in the relation $R^3$?

**39.** Let $R$ be the relation on the set of people with doctorates such that $(a, b) \in R$ if and only if $a$ was the thesis advisor of $b$. When is an ordered pair $(a, b)$ in $R^2$? When is an ordered pair $(a, b)$ in $R^n$, when $n$ is a positive integer? (Assume that every person with a doctorate has a thesis advisor.)

**40.** Let $R_1$ and $R_2$ be the "divides" and "is a multiple of" relations on the set of all positive integers, respectively. That is, $R_1 = \{(a, b) \mid a \text{ divides } b\}$ and $R_2 = \{(a, b) \mid a \text{ is a multiple of } b\}$. Find
   **a)** $R_1 \cup R_2$.          **b)** $R_1 \cap R_2$.
   **c)** $R_1 - R_2$.          **d)** $R_2 - R_1$.
   **e)** $R_1 \oplus R_2$.

**41.** Let $R_1$ and $R_2$ be the "congruent modulo 3" and the "congruent modulo 4" relations, respectively, on the set of integers. That is, $R_1 = \{(a, b) \mid a \equiv b \pmod 3\}$ and $R_2 = \{(a, b) \mid a \equiv b \pmod 4\}$. Find

**a)** $R_1 \cup R_2$.     **b)** $R_1 \cap R_2$.
**c)** $R_1 - R_2$.     **d)** $R_2 - R_1$.
**e)** $R_1 \oplus R_2$.

**42.** List the 16 different relations on the set $\{0, 1\}$.

**43.** How many of the 16 different relations on $\{0, 1\}$ contain the pair $(0, 1)$?

**44.** Which of the 16 relations on $\{0, 1\}$, which you listed in Exercise 42, are

**a)** reflexive?     **b)** irreflexive?
**c)** symmetric?     **d)** antisymmetric?
**e)** asymmetric?     **f)** transitive?

**45. a)** How many relations are there on the set $\{a, b, c, d\}$?
**b)** How many relations are there on the set $\{a, b, c, d\}$ that contain the pair $(a, a)$?

**46.** Let $S$ be a set with $n$ elements and let $a$ and $b$ be distinct elements of $S$. How many relations $R$ are there on $S$ such that

**a)** $(a, b) \in R$?     **b)** $(a, b) \notin R$?
**c)** no ordered pair in $R$ has $a$ as its first element?
**d)** at least one ordered pair in $R$ has $a$ as its first element?
**e)** no ordered pair in $R$ has $a$ as its first element or $b$ as its second element?
**f)** at least one ordered pair in $R$ either has $a$ as its first element or has $b$ as its second element?

**\*47.** How many relations are there on a set with $n$ elements that are

**a)** symmetric?     **b)** antisymmetric?
**c)** asymmetric?     **d)** irreflexive?
**e)** reflexive and symmetric?
**f)** neither reflexive nor irreflexive?

**\*48.** How many transitive relations are there on a set with $n$ elements if

**a)** $n = 1$?     **b)** $n = 2$?     **c)** $n = 3$?

**49.** Find the error in the "proof" of the following "theorem."

"*Theorem*": Let $R$ be a relation on a set $A$ that is symmetric and transitive. Then $R$ is reflexive.

"*Proof*": Let $a \in A$. Take an element $b \in A$ such that $(a, b) \in R$. Because $R$ is symmetric, we also have $(b, a) \in R$. Now using the transitive property, we can conclude that $(a, a) \in R$ because $(a, b) \in R$ and $(b, a) \in R$.

**50.** Suppose that $R$ and $S$ are reflexive relations on a set $A$. Prove or disprove each of these statements.

**a)** $R \cup S$ is reflexive.
**b)** $R \cap S$ is reflexive.
**c)** $R \oplus S$ is irreflexive.
**d)** $R - S$ is irreflexive.
**e)** $S \circ R$ is reflexive.

**51.** Show that the relation $R$ on a set $A$ is symmetric if and only if $R = R^{-1}$, where $R^{-1}$ is the inverse relation.

**52.** Show that the relation $R$ on a set $A$ is antisymmetric if and only if $R \cap R^{-1}$ is a subset of the diagonal relation $\Delta = \{(a, a) \mid a \in A\}$.

**53.** Show that the relation $R$ on a set $A$ is reflexive if and only if the inverse relation $R^{-1}$ is reflexive.

**54.** Show that the relation $R$ on a set $A$ is reflexive if and only if the complementary relation $\overline{R}$ is irreflexive.

**55.** Let $R$ be a relation that is reflexive and transitive. Prove that $R^n = R$ for all positive integers $n$.

**56.** Let $R$ be the relation on the set $\{1, 2, 3, 4, 5\}$ containing the ordered pairs $(1, 1), (1, 2), (1, 3), (2, 3), (2, 4), (3, 1)$, $(3, 4)$, $(3, 5)$, $(4, 2)$, $(4, 5)$, $(5, 1)$, $(5, 2)$, and $(5, 4)$. Find

**a)** $R^2$.     **b)** $R^3$.     **c)** $R^4$.     **d)** $R^5$.

**57.** Let $R$ be a reflexive relation on a set $A$. Show that $R^n$ is reflexive for all positive integers $n$.

**\*58.** Let $R$ be a symmetric relation. Show that $R^n$ is symmetric for all positive integers $n$.

**59.** Suppose that the relation $R$ is irreflexive. Is $R^2$ necessarily irreflexive? Give a reason for your answer.

# 9.2   *n*-ary Relations and Their Applications

## Introduction

Relationships among elements of more than two sets often arise. For instance, there is a relationship involving the name of a student, the student's major, and the student's grade point average. Similarly, there is a relationship involving the airline, flight number, starting point, destination, departure time, and arrival time of a flight. An example of such a relationship in mathematics involves three integers, where the first integer is larger than the second integer, which is larger than the third. Another example is the betweenness relationship involving points on a line, such that three points are related when the second point is between the first and the third.

We will study relationships among elements from more than two sets in this section. These relationships are called ***n*-ary relations**. These relations are used to represent computer databases. These representations help us answer queries about the information stored in databases, such as: Which flights land at O'Hare Airport between 3 A.M. and 4 A.M.? Which students at your school are sophomores majoring in mathematics or computer science and have greater than a 3.0 average? Which employees of a company have worked for the company less than 5 years and make more than $50,000?

## *n*-ary Relations

We begin with the basic definition on which the theory of relational databases rests.

**DEFINITION 1**

Let $A_1, A_2, \ldots, A_n$ be sets. An *n-ary relation* on these sets is a subset of $A_1 \times A_2 \times \cdots \times A_n$. The sets $A_1, A_2, \ldots, A_n$ are called the *domains* of the relation, and $n$ is called its *degree*.

**EXAMPLE 1** Let $R$ be the relation on $\mathbf{N} \times \mathbf{N} \times \mathbf{N}$ consisting of triples $(a, b, c)$, where $a$, $b$, and $c$ are integers with $a < b < c$. Then $(1, 2, 3) \in R$, but $(2, 4, 3) \notin R$. The degree of this relation is 3. Its domains are all equal to the set of natural numbers. ◀

**EXAMPLE 2** Let $R$ be the relation on $\mathbf{Z} \times \mathbf{Z} \times \mathbf{Z}$ consisting of all triples of integers $(a, b, c)$ in which $a$, $b$, and $c$ form an arithmetic progression. That is, $(a, b, c) \in R$ if and only if there is an integer $k$ such that $b = a + k$ and $c = a + 2k$, or equivalently, such that $b - a = k$ and $c - b = k$. Note that $(1, 3, 5) \in R$ because $3 = 1 + 2$ and $5 = 1 + 2 \cdot 2$, but $(2, 5, 9) \notin R$ because $5 - 2 = 3$ while $9 - 5 = 4$. This relation has degree 3 and its domains are all equal to the set of integers. ◀

**EXAMPLE 3** Let $R$ be the relation on $\mathbf{Z} \times \mathbf{Z} \times \mathbf{Z}^+$ consisting of triples $(a, b, m)$, where $a$, $b$, and $m$ are integers with $m \geq 1$ and $a \equiv b \pmod{m}$. Then $(8, 2, 3)$, $(-1, 9, 5)$, and $(14, 0, 7)$ all belong to $R$, but $(7, 2, 3), (-2, -8, 5)$, and $(11, 0, 6)$ do not belong to $R$ because $8 \equiv 2 \pmod 3$, $-1 \equiv 9 \pmod 5$, and $14 \equiv 0 \pmod 7$, but $7 \not\equiv 2 \pmod 3$, $-2 \not\equiv -8 \pmod 5$, and $11 \not\equiv 0 \pmod 6$. This relation has degree 3 and its first two domains are the set of all integers and its third domain is the set of positive integers. ◀

**EXAMPLE 4** Let $R$ be the relation consisting of 5-tuples $(A, N, S, D, T)$ representing airplane flights, where $A$ is the airline, $N$ is the flight number, $S$ is the starting point, $D$ is the destination, and $T$ is the departure time. For instance, if Nadir Express Airlines has flight 963 from Newark to Bangor at 15:00, then (Nadir, 963, Newark, Bangor, 15:00) belongs to $R$. The degree of this relation is 5, and its domains are the set of all airlines, the set of flight numbers, the set of cities, the set of cities (again), and the set of times. ◀

## Databases and Relations

The time required to manipulate information in a database depends on how this information is stored. The operations of adding and deleting records, updating records, searching for records, and combining records from overlapping databases are performed millions of times each day in a large database. Because of the importance of these operations, various methods for representing databases have been developed. We will discuss one of these methods, called the **relational data model**, based on the concept of a relation.

 Links

A database consists of **records**, which are *n*-tuples, made up of **fields**. The fields are the entries of the *n*-tuples. For instance, a database of student records may be made up of fields containing the name, student number, major, and grade point average of the student. The relational data model represents a database of records as an *n*-ary relation. Thus, student records

# 9.3    Representing Relations

## Introduction

In this section, and in the remainder of this chapter, all relations we study will be binary relations. Because of this, in this section and in the rest of this chapter, the word relation will always refer to a binary relation. There are many ways to represent a relation between finite sets. As we have seen in Section 9.1, one way is to list its ordered pairs. Another way to represent a relation is to use a table, as we did in Example 3 in Section 9.1. In this section we will discuss two alternative methods for representing relations. One method uses zero–one matrices. The other method uses pictorial representations called directed graphs, which we will discuss later in this section.

Generally, matrices are appropriate for the representation of relations in computer programs. On the other hand, people often find the representation of relations using directed graphs useful for understanding the properties of these relations.

## Representing Relations Using Matrices

A relation between finite sets can be represented using a zero–one matrix. Suppose that $R$ is a relation from $A = \{a_1, a_2, \ldots, a_m\}$ to $B = \{b_1, b_2, \ldots, b_n\}$. (Here the elements of the sets $A$ and $B$ have been listed in a particular, but arbitrary, order. Furthermore, when $A = B$ we use the same ordering for $A$ and $B$.) The relation $R$ can be represented by the matrix $\mathbf{M}_R = [m_{ij}]$, where

$$m_{ij} = \begin{cases} 1 \text{ if } (a_i, b_j) \in R, \\ 0 \text{ if } (a_i, b_j) \notin R. \end{cases}$$

In other words, the zero–one matrix representing $R$ has a 1 as its $(i, j)$ entry when $a_i$ is related to $b_j$, and a 0 in this position if $a_i$ is not related to $b_j$. (Such a representation depends on the orderings used for $A$ and $B$.)

The use of matrices to represent relations is illustrated in Examples 1–6.

**EXAMPLE 1**    Suppose that $A = \{1, 2, 3\}$ and $B = \{1, 2\}$. Let $R$ be the relation from $A$ to $B$ containing $(a, b)$ if $a \in A$, $b \in B$, and $a > b$. What is the matrix representing $R$ if $a_1 = 1$, $a_2 = 2$, and $a_3 = 3$, and $b_1 = 1$ and $b_2 = 2$?

*Solution:* Because $R = \{(2, 1), (3, 1), (3, 2)\}$, the matrix for $R$ is

$$\mathbf{M}_R = \begin{bmatrix} 0 & 0 \\ 1 & 0 \\ 1 & 1 \end{bmatrix}.$$

The 1s in $\mathbf{M}_R$ show that the pairs $(2, 1)$, $(3, 1)$, and $(3, 2)$ belong to $R$. The 0s show that no other pairs belong to $R$.    ◀

**EXAMPLE 2**    Let $A = \{a_1, a_2, a_3\}$ and $B = \{b_1, b_2, b_3, b_4, b_5\}$. Which ordered pairs are in the relation $R$ represented by the matrix

$$\mathbf{M}_R = \begin{bmatrix} 0 & 1 & 0 & 0 & 0 \\ 1 & 0 & 1 & 1 & 0 \\ 1 & 0 & 1 & 0 & 1 \end{bmatrix}?$$

*Solution:* Because $R$ consists of those ordered pairs $(a_i, b_j)$ with $m_{ij} = 1$, it follows that

$$R = \{(a_1, b_2), (a_2, b_1), (a_2, b_3), (a_2, b_4), (a_3, b_1), (a_3, b_3), (a_3, b_5)\}. \quad \blacktriangleleft$$

The matrix of a relation on a set, which is a square matrix, can be used to determine whether the relation has certain properties. Recall that a relation $R$ on $A$ is reflexive if $(a, a) \in R$ whenever $a \in A$. Thus, $R$ is reflexive if and only if $(a_i, a_i) \in R$ for $i = 1, 2, \ldots, n$. Hence, $R$ is reflexive if and only if $m_{ii} = 1$, for $i = 1, 2, \ldots, n$. In other words, $R$ is reflexive if all the elements on the main diagonal of $\mathbf{M}_R$ are equal to 1, as shown in Figure 1. Note that the elements off the main diagonal can be either 0 or 1.

The relation $R$ is symmetric if $(a, b) \in R$ implies that $(b, a) \in R$. Consequently, the relation $R$ on the set $A = \{a_1, a_2, \ldots, a_n\}$ is symmetric if and only if $(a_j, a_i) \in R$ whenever $(a_i, a_j) \in R$. In terms of the entries of $\mathbf{M}_R$, $R$ is symmetric if and only if $m_{ji} = 1$ whenever $m_{ij} = 1$. This also means $m_{ji} = 0$ whenever $m_{ij} = 0$. Consequently, $R$ is symmetric if and only if $m_{ij} = m_{ji}$, for all pairs of integers $i$ and $j$ with $i = 1, 2, \ldots, n$ and $j = 1, 2, \ldots, n$. Recalling the definition of the transpose of a matrix from Section 2.6, we see that $R$ is symmetric if and only if

$$\mathbf{M}_R = (\mathbf{M}_R)^t,$$

that is, if $\mathbf{M}_R$ is a symmetric matrix. The form of the matrix for a symmetric relation is illustrated in Figure 2(a).

The relation $R$ is antisymmetric if and only if $(a, b) \in R$ and $(b, a) \in R$ imply that $a = b$. Consequently, the matrix of an antisymmetric relation has the property that if $m_{ij} = 1$ with $i \neq j$, then $m_{ji} = 0$. Or, in other words, either $m_{ij} = 0$ or $m_{ji} = 0$ when $i \neq j$. The form of the matrix for an antisymmetric relation is illustrated in Figure 2(b).

**FIGURE 1   The Zero–One Matrix for a Reflexive Relation. (Off Diagonal Elements Can Be 0 or 1.)**

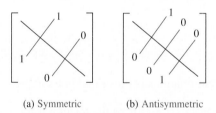

(a) Symmetric      (b) Antisymmetric

**FIGURE 2   The Zero–One Matrices for Symmetric and Antisymmetric Relations.**

**EXAMPLE 3**   Suppose that the relation $R$ on a set is represented by the matrix

$$\mathbf{M}_R = \begin{bmatrix} 1 & 1 & 0 \\ 1 & 1 & 1 \\ 0 & 1 & 1 \end{bmatrix}.$$

Is $R$ reflexive, symmetric, and/or antisymmetric?

*Solution:* Because all the diagonal elements of this matrix are equal to 1, $R$ is reflexive. Moreover, because $\mathbf{M}_R$ is symmetric, it follows that $R$ is symmetric. It is also easy to see that $R$ is not antisymmetric. $\quad \blacktriangleleft$

The Boolean operations join and meet (discussed in Section 2.6) can be used to find the matrices representing the union and the intersection of two relations. Suppose that $R_1$ and $R_2$ are relations on a set $A$ represented by the matrices $\mathbf{M}_{R_1}$ and $\mathbf{M}_{R_2}$, respectively. The matrix representing the union of these relations has a 1 in the positions where either $\mathbf{M}_{R_1}$ or $\mathbf{M}_{R_2}$ has a 1. The matrix representing the intersection of these relations has a 1 in the positions where both $\mathbf{M}_{R_1}$ and $\mathbf{M}_{R_2}$ have a 1. Thus, the matrices representing the union and intersection of these relations are

$$\mathbf{M}_{R_1 \cup R_2} = \mathbf{M}_{R_1} \vee \mathbf{M}_{R_2} \quad \text{and} \quad \mathbf{M}_{R_1 \cap R_2} = \mathbf{M}_{R_1} \wedge \mathbf{M}_{R_2}.$$

**EXAMPLE 4** Suppose that the relations $R_1$ and $R_2$ on a set $A$ are represented by the matrices

$$\mathbf{M}_{R_1} = \begin{bmatrix} 1 & 0 & 1 \\ 1 & 0 & 0 \\ 0 & 1 & 0 \end{bmatrix} \quad \text{and} \quad \mathbf{M}_{R_2} = \begin{bmatrix} 1 & 0 & 1 \\ 0 & 1 & 1 \\ 1 & 0 & 0 \end{bmatrix}.$$

What are the matrices representing $R_1 \cup R_2$ and $R_1 \cap R_2$?

*Solution:* The matrices of these relations are

$$\mathbf{M}_{R_1 \cup R_2} = \mathbf{M}_{R_1} \vee \mathbf{M}_{R_2} = \begin{bmatrix} 1 & 0 & 1 \\ 1 & 1 & 1 \\ 1 & 1 & 0 \end{bmatrix},$$

$$\mathbf{M}_{R_1 \cap R_2} = \mathbf{M}_{R_1} \wedge \mathbf{M}_{R_2} = \begin{bmatrix} 1 & 0 & 1 \\ 0 & 0 & 0 \\ 0 & 0 & 0 \end{bmatrix}.$$
◀

We now turn our attention to determining the matrix for the composite of relations. This matrix can be found using the Boolean product of the matrices (discussed in Section 2.6) for these relations. In particular, suppose that $R$ is a relation from $A$ to $B$ and $S$ is a relation from $B$ to $C$. Suppose that $A$, $B$, and $C$ have $m$, $n$, and $p$ elements, respectively. Let the zero–one matrices for $S \circ R$, $R$, and $S$ be $\mathbf{M}_{S \circ R} = [t_{ij}]$, $\mathbf{M}_R = [r_{ij}]$, and $\mathbf{M}_S = [s_{ij}]$, respectively (these matrices have sizes $m \times p$, $m \times n$, and $n \times p$, respectively). The ordered pair $(a_i, c_j)$ belongs to $S \circ R$ if and only if there is an element $b_k$ such that $(a_i, b_k)$ belongs to $R$ and $(b_k, c_j)$ belongs to $S$. It follows that $t_{ij} = 1$ if and only if $r_{ik} = s_{kj} = 1$ for some $k$. From the definition of the Boolean product, this means that

$$\mathbf{M}_{S \circ R} = \mathbf{M}_R \odot \mathbf{M}_S.$$

**EXAMPLE 5** Find the matrix representing the relations $S \circ R$, where the matrices representing $R$ and $S$ are

$$\mathbf{M}_R = \begin{bmatrix} 1 & 0 & 1 \\ 1 & 1 & 0 \\ 0 & 0 & 0 \end{bmatrix} \quad \text{and} \quad \mathbf{M}_S = \begin{bmatrix} 0 & 1 & 0 \\ 0 & 0 & 1 \\ 1 & 0 & 1 \end{bmatrix}.$$

*Solution:* The matrix for $S \circ R$ is

$$\mathbf{M}_{S \circ R} = \mathbf{M}_R \odot \mathbf{M}_S = \begin{bmatrix} 1 & 1 & 1 \\ 0 & 1 & 1 \\ 0 & 0 & 0 \end{bmatrix}.$$
◀

The matrix representing the composite of two relations can be used to find the matrix for $\mathbf{M}_{R^n}$. In particular,

$$\mathbf{M}_{R^n} = \mathbf{M}_R^{[n]},$$

from the definition of Boolean powers. Exercise 35 asks for a proof of this formula.

**EXAMPLE 6**    Find the matrix representing the relation $R^2$, where the matrix representing $R$ is

$$\mathbf{M}_R = \begin{bmatrix} 0 & 1 & 0 \\ 0 & 1 & 1 \\ 1 & 0 & 0 \end{bmatrix}.$$

*Solution:* The matrix for $R^2$ is

$$\mathbf{M}_{R^2} = \mathbf{M}_R^{[2]} = \begin{bmatrix} 0 & 1 & 1 \\ 1 & 1 & 1 \\ 0 & 1 & 0 \end{bmatrix}.$$

◀

## Representing Relations Using Digraphs

We have shown that a relation can be represented by listing all of its ordered pairs or by using a zero–one matrix. There is another important way of representing a relation using a pictorial representation. Each element of the set is represented by a point, and each ordered pair is represented using an arc with its direction indicated by an arrow. We use such pictorial representations when we think of relations on a finite set as **directed graphs**, or **digraphs**.

**DEFINITION 1**    A *directed graph*, or *digraph*, consists of a set $V$ of *vertices* (or *nodes*) together with a set $E$ of ordered pairs of elements of $V$ called *edges* (or *arcs*). The vertex $a$ is called the *initial vertex* of the edge $(a, b)$, and the vertex $b$ is called the *terminal vertex* of this edge.

An edge of the form $(a, a)$ is represented using an arc from the vertex $a$ back to itself. Such an edge is called a **loop**.

**EXAMPLE 7**    The directed graph with vertices $a$, $b$, $c$, and $d$, and edges $(a, b)$, $(a, d)$, $(b, b)$, $(b, d)$, $(c, a)$, $(c, b)$, and $(d, b)$ is displayed in Figure 3.    ◀

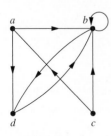

**FIGURE 3**
**A Directed Graph.**

The relation $R$ on a set $A$ is represented by the directed graph that has the elements of $A$ as its vertices and the ordered pairs $(a, b)$, where $(a, b) \in R$, as edges. This assignment sets up a one-to-one correspondence between the relations on a set $A$ and the directed graphs with $A$ as their set of vertices. Thus, every statement about relations corresponds to a statement about directed graphs, and vice versa. Directed graphs give a visual display of information about relations. As such, they are often used to study relations and their properties. (Note that relations from a set $A$ to a set $B$ can be represented by a directed graph where there is a vertex for each element of $A$ and a vertex for each element of $B$, as shown in Section 9.1. However, when $A = B$, such representation provides much less insight than the digraph representations described here.) The use of directed graphs to represent relations on a set is illustrated in Examples 8–10.

**EXAMPLE 8**    The directed graph of the relation

$$R = \{(1, 1), (1, 3), (2, 1), (2, 3), (2, 4), (3, 1), (3, 2), (4, 1)\}$$

on the set $\{1, 2, 3, 4\}$ is shown in Figure 4.    ◄

**EXAMPLE 9**    What are the ordered pairs in the relation $R$ represented by the directed graph shown in Figure 5?

*Solution:* The ordered pairs $(x, y)$ in the relation are

$$R = \{(1, 3), (1, 4), (2, 1), (2, 2), (2, 3), (3, 1), (3, 3), (4, 1), (4, 3)\}.$$

Each of these pairs corresponds to an edge of the directed graph, with $(2, 2)$ and $(3, 3)$ corresponding to loops.    ◄

We will study directed graphs extensively in Chapter 10.

The directed graph representing a relation can be used to determine whether the relation has various properties. For instance, a relation is reflexive if and only if there is a loop at every vertex of the directed graph, so that every ordered pair of the form $(x, x)$ occurs in the relation. A relation is symmetric if and only if for every edge between distinct vertices in its digraph there is an edge in the opposite direction, so that $(y, x)$ is in the relation whenever $(x, y)$ is in the relation. Similarly, a relation is antisymmetric if and only if there are never two edges in opposite directions between distinct vertices. Finally, a relation is transitive if and only if whenever there is an edge from a vertex $x$ to a vertex $y$ and an edge from a vertex $y$ to a vertex $z$, there is an edge from $x$ to $z$ (completing a triangle where each side is a directed edge with the correct direction).

***Remark:*** Note that a symmetric relation can be represented by an undirected graph, which is a graph where edges do not have directions. We will study undirected graphs in Chapter 10.

**EXAMPLE 10**    Determine whether the relations for the directed graphs shown in Figure 6 are reflexive, symmetric, antisymmetric, and/or transitive.

*Solution:* Because there are loops at every vertex of the directed graph of $R$, it is reflexive. $R$ is neither symmetric nor antisymmetric because there is an edge from $a$ to $b$ but not one from $b$ to $a$, but there are edges in both directions connecting $b$ and $c$. Finally, $R$ is not transitive because there is an edge from $a$ to $b$ and an edge from $b$ to $c$, but no edge from $a$ to $c$.

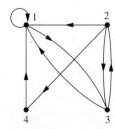

**FIGURE 4    The Directed Graph of the Relation $R$.**

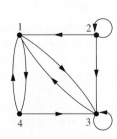

**FIGURE 5    The Directed Graph of the Relation $R$.**

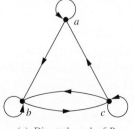

(a) Directed graph of $R$

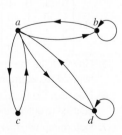

(b) Directed graph of $S$

**FIGURE 6    The Directed Graphs of the Relations $R$ and $S$.**

Because loops are not present at all the vertices of the directed graph of $S$, this relation is not reflexive. It is symmetric and not antisymmetric, because every edge between distinct vertices is accompanied by an edge in the opposite direction. It is also not hard to see from the directed graph that $S$ is not transitive, because $(c, a)$ and $(a, b)$ belong to $S$, but $(c, b)$ does not belong to $S$.   ◀

## Exercises

1. Represent each of these relations on $\{1, 2, 3\}$ with a matrix (with the elements of this set listed in increasing order).
   a) $\{(1, 1), (1, 2), (1, 3)\}$
   b) $\{(1, 2), (2, 1), (2, 2), (3, 3)\}$
   c) $\{(1, 1), (1, 2), (1, 3), (2, 2), (2, 3), (3, 3)\}$
   d) $\{(1, 3), (3, 1)\}$

2. Represent each of these relations on $\{1, 2, 3, 4\}$ with a matrix (with the elements of this set listed in increasing order).
   a) $\{(1, 2), (1, 3), (1, 4), (2, 3), (2, 4), (3, 4)\}$
   b) $\{(1, 1), (1, 4), (2, 2), (3, 3), (4, 1)\}$
   c) $\{(1, 2), (1, 3), (1, 4), (2, 1), (2, 3), (2, 4), (3, 1), (3, 2), (3, 4), (4, 1), (4, 2), (4, 3)\}$
   d) $\{(2, 4), (3, 1), (3, 2), (3, 4)\}$

3. List the ordered pairs in the relations on $\{1, 2, 3\}$ corresponding to these matrices (where the rows and columns correspond to the integers listed in increasing order).

   a) $\begin{bmatrix} 1 & 0 & 1 \\ 0 & 1 & 0 \\ 1 & 0 & 1 \end{bmatrix}$   b) $\begin{bmatrix} 0 & 1 & 0 \\ 0 & 1 & 0 \\ 0 & 1 & 0 \end{bmatrix}$

   c) $\begin{bmatrix} 1 & 1 & 1 \\ 1 & 0 & 1 \\ 1 & 1 & 1 \end{bmatrix}$

4. List the ordered pairs in the relations on $\{1, 2, 3, 4\}$ corresponding to these matrices (where the rows and columns correspond to the integers listed in increasing order).

   a) $\begin{bmatrix} 1 & 1 & 0 & 1 \\ 1 & 0 & 1 & 0 \\ 0 & 1 & 1 & 1 \\ 1 & 0 & 1 & 1 \end{bmatrix}$   b) $\begin{bmatrix} 1 & 1 & 1 & 0 \\ 0 & 1 & 0 & 0 \\ 0 & 0 & 1 & 1 \\ 1 & 0 & 0 & 1 \end{bmatrix}$

   c) $\begin{bmatrix} 0 & 1 & 0 & 1 \\ 1 & 0 & 1 & 0 \\ 0 & 1 & 0 & 1 \\ 1 & 0 & 1 & 0 \end{bmatrix}$

5. How can the matrix representing a relation $R$ on a set $A$ be used to determine whether the relation is irreflexive?

6. How can the matrix representing a relation $R$ on a set $A$ be used to determine whether the relation is asymmetric?

7. Determine whether the relations represented by the matrices in Exercise 3 are reflexive, irreflexive, symmetric, antisymmetric, and/or transitive.

8. Determine whether the relations represented by the matrices in Exercise 4 are reflexive, irreflexive, symmetric, antisymmetric, and/or transitive.

9. How many nonzero entries does the matrix representing the relation $R$ on $A = \{1, 2, 3, \ldots, 100\}$ consisting of the first 100 positive integers have if $R$ is
   a) $\{(a, b) \mid a > b\}$?   b) $\{(a, b) \mid a \neq b\}$?
   c) $\{(a, b) \mid a = b + 1\}$?   d) $\{(a, b) \mid a = 1\}$?
   e) $\{(a, b) \mid ab = 1\}$?

10. How many nonzero entries does the matrix representing the relation $R$ on $A = \{1, 2, 3, \ldots, 1000\}$ consisting of the first 1000 positive integers have if $R$ is
   a) $\{(a, b) \mid a \leq b\}$?
   b) $\{(a, b) \mid a = b \pm 1\}$?
   c) $\{(a, b) \mid a + b = 1000\}$?
   d) $\{(a, b) \mid a + b \leq 1001\}$?
   e) $\{(a, b) \mid a \neq 0\}$?

11. How can the matrix for $\overline{R}$, the complement of the relation $R$, be found from the matrix representing $R$, when $R$ is a relation on a finite set $A$?

12. How can the matrix for $R^{-1}$, the inverse of the relation $R$, be found from the matrix representing $R$, when $R$ is a relation on a finite set $A$?

13. Let $R$ be the relation represented by the matrix

$$\mathbf{M}_R = \begin{bmatrix} 0 & 1 & 1 \\ 1 & 1 & 0 \\ 1 & 0 & 1 \end{bmatrix}.$$

   Find the matrix representing
   a) $R^{-1}$.   b) $\overline{R}$.   c) $R^2$.

14. Let $R_1$ and $R_2$ be relations on a set $A$ represented by the matrices

$$\mathbf{M}_{R_1} = \begin{bmatrix} 0 & 1 & 0 \\ 1 & 1 & 1 \\ 1 & 0 & 0 \end{bmatrix} \quad \text{and} \quad \mathbf{M}_{R_2} = \begin{bmatrix} 0 & 1 & 0 \\ 0 & 1 & 1 \\ 1 & 1 & 1 \end{bmatrix}.$$

   Find the matrices that represent
   a) $R_1 \cup R_2$.   b) $R_1 \cap R_2$.   c) $R_2 \circ R_1$.
   d) $R_1 \circ R_1$.   e) $R_1 \oplus R_2$.

15. Let $R$ be the relation represented by the matrix

$$\mathbf{M}_R = \begin{bmatrix} 0 & 1 & 0 \\ 0 & 0 & 1 \\ 1 & 1 & 0 \end{bmatrix}.$$

   Find the matrices that represent
   a) $R^2$.   b) $R^3$.   c) $R^4$.

16. Let $R$ be a relation on a set $A$ with $n$ elements. If there are $k$ nonzero entries in $\mathbf{M}_R$, the matrix representing $R$, how many nonzero entries are there in $\mathbf{M}_{R^{-1}}$, the matrix representing $R^{-1}$, the inverse of $R$?

17. Let $R$ be a relation on a set $A$ with $n$ elements. If there are $k$ nonzero entries in $\mathbf{M}_R$, the matrix representing $R$, how many nonzero entries are there in $\mathbf{M}_{\overline{R}}$, the matrix representing $\overline{R}$, the complement of $R$?

18. Draw the directed graphs representing each of the relations from Exercise 1.

19. Draw the directed graphs representing each of the relations from Exercise 2.

20. Draw the directed graph representing each of the relations from Exercise 3.

21. Draw the directed graph representing each of the relations from Exercise 4.

22. Draw the directed graph that represents the relation $\{(a, a), (a, b), (b, c), (c, b), (c, d), (d, a), (d, b)\}$.

In Exercises 23–28 list the ordered pairs in the relations represented by the directed graphs.

23.

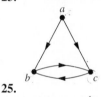

24.

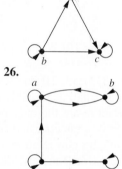

25.

26.

27.

28.

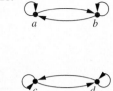

29. How can the directed graph of a relation $R$ on a finite set $A$ be used to determine whether a relation is asymmetric?

30. How can the directed graph of a relation $R$ on a finite set $A$ be used to determine whether a relation is irreflexive?

31. Determine whether the relations represented by the directed graphs shown in Exercises 23–25 are reflexive, irreflexive, symmetric, antisymmetric, and/or transitive.

32. Determine whether the relations represented by the directed graphs shown in Exercises 26–28 are reflexive, irreflexive, symmetric, antisymmetric, asymmetric, and/or transitive.

33. Let $R$ be a relation on a set $A$. Explain how to use the directed graph representing $R$ to obtain the directed graph representing the inverse relation $R^{-1}$.

34. Let $R$ be a relation on a set $A$. Explain how to use the directed graph representing $R$ to obtain the directed graph representing the complementary relation $\overline{R}$.

35. Show that if $\mathbf{M}_R$ is the matrix representing the relation $R$, then $\mathbf{M}_R^{[n]}$ is the matrix representing the relation $R^n$.

36. Given the directed graphs representing two relations, how can the directed graph of the union, intersection, symmetric difference, difference, and composition of these relations be found?

# 9.4 Closures of Relations

## Introduction

A computer network has data centers in Boston, Chicago, Denver, Detroit, New York, and San Diego. There are direct, one-way telephone lines from Boston to Chicago, from Boston to Detroit, from Chicago to Detroit, from Detroit to Denver, and from New York to San Diego. Let $R$ be the relation containing $(a, b)$ if there is a telephone line from the data center in $a$ to that in $b$. How can we determine if there is some (possibly indirect) link composed of one or more telephone lines from one center to another? Because not all links are direct, such as the link from Boston to Denver that goes through Detroit, $R$ cannot be used directly to answer this. In the language of relations, $R$ is not transitive, so it does not contain all the pairs that can be linked. As we will show in this section, we can find all pairs of data centers that have a link by constructing a transitive relation $S$ containing $R$ such that $S$ is a subset of every transitive relation containing $R$. Here, $S$ is the smallest transitive relation that contains $R$. This relation is called the **transitive closure** of $R$.

In general, let $R$ be a relation on a set $A$. $R$ may or may not have some property **P**, such as reflexivity, symmetry, or transitivity. If there is a relation $S$ with property **P** containing $R$ such that $S$ is a subset of every relation with property **P** containing $R$, then $S$ is called the **closure** of $R$ with respect to **P**. (Note that the closure of a relation with respect to a property may not exist; see Exercises 15 and 35.) We will show how reflexive, symmetric, and transitive closures of relations can be found.

## Closures

The relation $R = \{(1, 1), (1, 2), (2, 1), (3, 2)\}$ on the set $A = \{1, 2, 3\}$ is not reflexive. How can we produce a reflexive relation containing $R$ that is as small as possible? This can be done by adding $(2, 2)$ and $(3, 3)$ to $R$, because these are the only pairs of the form $(a, a)$ that are not in $R$. Clearly, this new relation contains $R$. Furthermore, *any* reflexive relation that contains $R$ must also contain $(2, 2)$ and $(3, 3)$. Because this relation contains $R$, is reflexive, and is contained within every reflexive relation that contains $R$, it is called the **reflexive closure** of $R$.

As this example illustrates, given a relation $R$ on a set $A$, the reflexive closure of $R$ can be formed by adding to $R$ all pairs of the form $(a, a)$ with $a \in A$, not already in $R$. The addition of these pairs produces a new relation that is reflexive, contains $R$, and is contained within any reflexive relation containing $R$. We see that the reflexive closure of $R$ equals $R \cup \Delta$, where $\Delta = \{(a, a) \mid a \in A\}$ is the **diagonal relation** on $A$. (The reader should verify this.)

**EXAMPLE 1**    What is the reflexive closure of the relation $R = \{(a, b) \mid a < b\}$ on the set of integers?

*Solution:* The reflexive closure of $R$ is

$$R \cup \Delta = \{(a, b) \mid a < b\} \cup \{(a, a) \mid a \in \mathbf{Z}\} = \{(a, b) \mid a \leq b\}. \qquad \blacktriangleleft$$

The relation $\{(1, 1), (1, 2), (2, 2), (2, 3), (3, 1), (3, 2)\}$ on $\{1, 2, 3\}$ is not symmetric. How can we produce a symmetric relation that is as small as possible and contains $R$? To do this, we need only add $(2, 1)$ and $(1, 3)$, because these are the only pairs of the form $(b, a)$ with $(a, b) \in R$ that are not in $R$. This new relation is symmetric and contains $R$. Furthermore, *any* symmetric relation that contains $R$ must contain this new relation, because a symmetric relation that contains $R$ must contain $(2, 1)$ and $(1, 3)$. Consequently, this new relation is called the **symmetric closure** of $R$.

As this example illustrates, the symmetric closure of a relation $R$ can be constructed by adding all ordered pairs of the form $(b, a)$, where $(a, b)$ is in the relation, that are not already present in $R$. Adding these pairs produces a relation that is symmetric, that contains $R$, and that is contained in any symmetric relation that contains $R$. The symmetric closure of a relation can be constructed by taking the union of a relation with its inverse (defined in the preamble of Exercise 26 in Section 9.1); that is, $R \cup R^{-1}$ is the symmetric closure of $R$, where $R^{-1} = \{(b, a) \mid (a, b) \in R\}$. The reader should verify this statement.

**EXAMPLE 2**    What is the symmetric closure of the relation $R = \{(a, b) \mid a > b\}$ on the set of positive integers?

*Solution:* The symmetric closure of $R$ is the relation

$$R \cup R^{-1} = \{(a, b) \mid a > b\} \cup \{(b, a) \mid a > b\} = \{(a, b) \mid a \neq b\}.$$

This last equality follows because $R$ contains all ordered pairs of positive integers where the first element is greater than the second element and $R^{-1}$ contains all ordered pairs of positive integers where the first element is less than the second.    $\blacktriangleleft$

Suppose that a relation $R$ is not transitive. How can we produce a transitive relation that contains $R$ such that this new relation is contained within any transitive relation that contains $R$? Can the transitive closure of a relation $R$ be produced by adding all the pairs of the form $(a, c)$, where $(a, b)$ and $(b, c)$ are already in the relation? Consider the relation

**13.** Suppose that the relation $R$ on the finite set $A$ is represented by the matrix $\mathbf{M}_R$. Show that the matrix that represents the symmetric closure of $R$ is $\mathbf{M}_R \vee \mathbf{M}_R^t$.

**14.** Show that the closure of a relation $R$ with respect to a property **P**, if it exists, is the intersection of all the relations with property **P** that contain $R$.

**15.** When is it possible to define the "irreflexive closure" of a relation $R$, that is, a relation that contains $R$, is irreflexive, and is contained in every irreflexive relation that contains $R$?

**16.** Determine whether these sequences of vertices are paths in this directed graph.

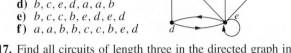

**a)** $a, b, c, e$
**b)** $b, e, c, b, e$
**c)** $a, a, b, e, d, e$
**d)** $b, c, e, d, a, a, b$
**e)** $b, c, c, b, e, d, e, d$
**f)** $a, a, b, b, c, c, b, e, d$

**17.** Find all circuits of length three in the directed graph in Exercise 16.

**18.** Determine whether there is a path in the directed graph in Exercise 16 beginning at the first vertex given and ending at the second vertex given.

**a)** $a, b$      **b)** $b, a$      **c)** $b, b$
**d)** $a, e$      **e)** $b, d$      **f)** $c, d$
**g)** $d, d$      **h)** $e, a$      **i)** $e, c$

**19.** Let $R$ be the relation on the set $\{1, 2, 3, 4, 5\}$ containing the ordered pairs $(1, 3), (2, 4), (3, 1), (3, 5), (4, 3), (5, 1)$, $(5, 2)$, and $(5, 4)$. Find

**a)** $R^2$.      **b)** $R^3$.      **c)** $R^4$.
**d)** $R^5$.      **e)** $R^6$.      **f)** $R^*$.

**20.** Let $R$ be the relation that contains the pair $(a, b)$ if $a$ and $b$ are cities such that there is a direct non-stop airline flight from $a$ to $b$. When is $(a, b)$ in

**a)** $R^2$?      **b)** $R^3$?      **c)** $R^*$?

**21.** Let $R$ be the relation on the set of all students containing the ordered pair $(a, b)$ if $a$ and $b$ are in at least one common class and $a \neq b$. When is $(a, b)$ in

**a)** $R^2$?      **b)** $R^3$?      **c)** $R^*$?

**22.** Suppose that the relation $R$ is reflexive. Show that $R^*$ is reflexive.

**23.** Suppose that the relation $R$ is symmetric. Show that $R^*$ is symmetric.

**24.** Suppose that the relation $R$ is irreflexive. Is the relation $R^2$ necessarily irreflexive?

**25.** Use Algorithm 1 to find the transitive closures of these relations on $\{1, 2, 3, 4\}$.

**a)** $\{(1, 2), (2, 1), (2, 3), (3, 4), (4, 1)\}$
**b)** $\{(2, 1), (2, 3), (3, 1), (3, 4), (4, 1), (4, 3)\}$
**c)** $\{(1, 2), (1, 3), (1, 4), (2, 3), (2, 4), (3, 4)\}$
**d)** $\{(1, 1), (1, 4), (2, 1), (2, 3), (3, 1), (3, 2), (3, 4), (4, 2)\}$

**26.** Use Algorithm 1 to find the transitive closures of these relations on $\{a, b, c, d, e\}$.

**a)** $\{(a, c), (b, d), (c, a), (d, b), (e, d)\}$
**b)** $\{(b, c), (b, e), (c, e), (d, a), (e, b), (e, c)\}$
**c)** $\{(a, b), (a, c), (a, e), (b, a), (b, c), (c, a), (c, b), (d, a),$ $(e, d)\}$
**d)** $\{(a, e), (b, a), (b, d), (c, d), (d, a), (d, c), (e, a), (e, b),$ $(e, c), (e, e)\}$

**27.** Use Warshall's algorithm to find the transitive closures of the relations in Exercise 25.

**28.** Use Warshall's algorithm to find the transitive closures of the relations in Exercise 26.

**29.** Find the smallest relation containing the relation $\{(1, 2), (1, 4), (3, 3), (4, 1)\}$ that is

**a)** reflexive and transitive.
**b)** symmetric and transitive.
**c)** reflexive, symmetric, and transitive.

**30.** Finish the proof of the case when $a \neq b$ in Lemma 1.

**31.** Algorithms have been devised that use $O(n^{2.8})$ bit operations to compute the Boolean product of two $n \times n$ zero–one matrices. Assuming that these algorithms can be used, give big-$O$ estimates for the number of bit operations using Algorithm 1 and using Warshall's algorithm to find the transitive closure of a relation on a set with $n$ elements.

**∗32.** Devise an algorithm using the concept of interior vertices in a path to find the length of the shortest path between two vertices in a directed graph, if such a path exists.

**33.** Adapt Algorithm 1 to find the reflexive closure of the transitive closure of a relation on a set with $n$ elements.

**34.** Adapt Warshall's algorithm to find the reflexive closure of the transitive closure of a relation on a set with $n$ elements.

**35.** Show that the closure with respect to the property **P** of the relation $R = \{(0, 0), (0, 1), (1, 1), (2, 2)\}$ on the set $\{0, 1, 2\}$ does not exist if **P** is the property

**a)** "is not reflexive."
**b)** "has an odd number of elements."

# 9.5  Equivalence Relations

## Introduction

In some programming languages the names of variables can contain an unlimited number of characters. However, there is a limit on the number of characters that are checked when a compiler determines whether two variables are equal. For instance, in traditional C, only the first eight characters of a variable name are checked by the compiler. (These characters are uppercase or lowercase letters, digits, or underscores.) Consequently, the compiler considers strings longer than eight characters that agree in their first eight characters the same. Let $R$ be the relation on the set of strings of characters such that $s R t$, where $s$ and $t$ are two strings, if $s$ and $t$ are at least eight characters long and the first eight characters of $s$ and $t$ agree, or $s = t$. It is easy to see that $R$ is reflexive, symmetric, and transitive. Moreover, $R$ divides the set of all strings into classes, where all strings in a particular class are considered the same by a compiler for traditional C.

The integers $a$ and $b$ are related by the "congruence modulo 4" relation when 4 divides $a - b$. We will show later that this relation is reflexive, symmetric, and transitive. It is not hard to see that $a$ is related to $b$ if and only if $a$ and $b$ have the same remainder when divided by 4. It follows that this relation splits the set of integers into four different classes. When we care only what remainder an integer leaves when it is divided by 4, we need only know which class it is in, not its particular value.

These two relations, $R$ and congruence modulo 4, are examples of equivalence relations, namely, relations that are reflexive, symmetric, and transitive. In this section we will show that such relations split sets into disjoint classes of equivalent elements. Equivalence relations arise whenever we care only whether an element of a set is in a certain class of elements, instead of caring about its particular identity.

## Equivalence Relations

**Links**

In this section we will study relations with a particular combination of properties that allows them to be used to relate objects that are similar in some way.

**DEFINITION 1**

> A relation on a set $A$ is called an *equivalence relation* if it is reflexive, symmetric, and transitive.

*Equivalence relations are important in every branch of mathematics!*

Equivalence relations are important throughout mathematics and computer science. One reason for this is that in an equivalence relation, when two elements are related it makes sense to say they are equivalent.

**DEFINITION 2**

> Two elements $a$ and $b$ that are related by an equivalence relation are called *equivalent*. The notation $a \sim b$ is often used to denote that $a$ and $b$ are equivalent elements with respect to a particular equivalence relation.

For the notion of equivalent elements to make sense, every element should be equivalent to itself, as the reflexive property guarantees for an equivalence relation. It makes sense to say that $a$ and $b$ are related (not just that $a$ is related to $b$) by an equivalence relation, because when $a$ is related to $b$, by the symmetric property, $b$ is related to $a$. Furthermore, because an equivalence relation is transitive, if $a$ and $b$ are equivalent and $b$ and $c$ are equivalent, it follows that $a$ and $c$ are equivalent.

Examples 1–5 illustrate the notion of an equivalence relation.

**EXAMPLE 1**    Let $R$ be the relation on the set of integers such that $a R b$ if and only if $a = b$ or $a = -b$. In Section 9.1 we showed that $R$ is reflexive, symmetric, and transitive. It follows that $R$ is an equivalence relation. ◄

**EXAMPLE 2**    Let $R$ be the relation on the set of real numbers such that $a R b$ if and only if $a - b$ is an integer. Is $R$ an equivalence relation?

Extra
Examples

*Solution:* Because $a - a = 0$ is an integer for all real numbers $a$, $aRa$ for all real numbers $a$. Hence, $R$ is reflexive. Now suppose that $aRb$. Then $a - b$ is an integer, so $b - a$ is also an integer. Hence, $bRa$. It follows that $R$ is symmetric. If $aRb$ and $bRc$, then $a - b$ and $b - c$ are integers. Therefore, $a - c = (a - b) + (b - c)$ is also an integer. Hence, $aRc$. Thus, $R$ is transitive. Consequently, $R$ is an equivalence relation. ◄

One of the most widely used equivalence relations is congruence modulo $m$, where $m$ is an integer greater than 1.

**EXAMPLE 3**   **Congruence Modulo $m$**   Let $m$ be an integer with $m > 1$. Show that the relation

$$R = \{(a, b) \mid a \equiv b \pmod{m}\}$$

is an equivalence relation on the set of integers.

*Solution:* Recall from Section 4.1 that $a \equiv b \pmod{m}$ if and only if $m$ divides $a - b$. Note that $a - a = 0$ is divisible by $m$, because $0 = 0 \cdot m$. Hence, $a \equiv a \pmod{m}$, so congruence modulo $m$ is reflexive. Now suppose that $a \equiv b \pmod{m}$. Then $a - b$ is divisible by $m$, so $a - b = km$, where $k$ is an integer. It follows that $b - a = (-k)m$, so $b \equiv a \pmod{m}$. Hence, congruence modulo $m$ is symmetric. Next, suppose that $a \equiv b \pmod{m}$ and $b \equiv c \pmod{m}$. Then $m$ divides both $a - b$ and $b - c$. Therefore, there are integers $k$ and $l$ with $a - b = km$ and $b - c = lm$. Adding these two equations shows that $a - c = (a - b) + (b - c) = km + lm = (k + l)m$. Thus, $a \equiv c \pmod{m}$. Therefore, congruence modulo $m$ is transitive. It follows that congruence modulo $m$ is an equivalence relation. ◄

**EXAMPLE 4**   Suppose that $R$ is the relation on the set of strings of English letters such that $aRb$ if and only if $l(a) = l(b)$, where $l(x)$ is the length of the string $x$. Is $R$ an equivalence relation?

*Solution:* Because $l(a) = l(a)$, it follows that $aRa$ whenever $a$ is a string, so that $R$ is reflexive. Next, suppose that $aRb$, so that $l(a) = l(b)$. Then $bRa$, because $l(b) = l(a)$. Hence, $R$ is symmetric. Finally, suppose that $aRb$ and $bRc$. Then $l(a) = l(b)$ and $l(b) = l(c)$. Hence, $l(a) = l(c)$, so $aRc$. Consequently, $R$ is transitive. Because $R$ is reflexive, symmetric, and transitive, it is an equivalence relation. ◄

**EXAMPLE 5**   Let $n$ be a positive integer and $S$ a set of strings. Suppose that $R_n$ is the relation on $S$ such that $sR_n t$ if and only if $s = t$, or both $s$ and $t$ have at least $n$ characters and the first $n$ characters of $s$ and $t$ are the same. That is, a string of fewer than $n$ characters is related only to itself; a string $s$ with at least $n$ characters is related to a string $t$ if and only if $t$ has at least $n$ characters and $t$ begins with the $n$ characters at the start of $s$. For example, let $n = 3$ and let $S$ be the set of all bit strings. Then $sR_3 t$ either when $s = t$ or both $s$ and $t$ are bit strings of length 3 or more that begin with the same three bits. For instance, $01 R_3 01$ and $00111 R_3 00101$, but $01 \not R_3 010$ and $01011 \not R_3 01110$.

Show that for every set $S$ of strings and every positive integer $n$, $R_n$ is an equivalence relation on $S$.

*Solution:* The relation $R_n$ is reflexive because $s = s$, so that $sR_n s$ whenever $s$ is a string in $S$. If $sR_n t$, then either $s = t$ or $s$ and $t$ are both at least $n$ characters long that begin with the same $n$ characters. This means that $tR_n s$. We conclude that $R_n$ is symmetric.

Now suppose that $sR_n t$ and $tR_n u$. Then either $s = t$ or $s$ and $t$ are at least $n$ characters long and $s$ and $t$ begin with the same $n$ characters, and either $t = u$ or $t$ and $u$ are at least $n$ characters long and $t$ and $u$ begin with the same $n$ characters. From this, we can deduce that either $s = u$ or both $s$ and $u$ are $n$ characters long and $s$ and $u$ begin with the same $n$ characters (because in this case we know that $s$, $t$, and $u$ are all at least $n$ characters long and both $s$ and $u$ begin with the same $n$ characters as $t$ does). Consequently, $R_n$ is transitive. It follows that $R_n$ is an equivalence relation. ◄

In Examples 6 and 7 we look at two relations that are not equivalence relations.

**EXAMPLE 6**   Show that the "divides" relation is the set of positive integers in not an equivalence relation.

*Solution:* By Examples 9 and 15 in Section 9.1, we know that the "divides" relation is reflexive and transitive. However, by Example 12 in Section 9.1, we know that this relation is not symmetric (for instance, $2 \mid 4$ but $4 \nmid 2$). We conclude that the "divides" relation on the set of positive integers is not an equivalence relation.   ◄

**EXAMPLE 7**   Let $R$ be the relation on the set of real numbers such that $x R y$ if and only if $x$ and $y$ are real numbers that differ by less than 1, that is $|x - y| < 1$. Show that $R$ is not an equivalence relation.

*Solution:* $R$ is reflexive because $|x - x| = 0 < 1$ whenever $x \in \mathbf{R}$. $R$ is symmetric, for if $x R y$, where $x$ and $y$ are real numbers, then $|x - y| < 1$, which tells us that $|y - x| = |x - y| < 1$, so that $y R x$. However, $R$ is not an equivalence relation because it is not transitive. Take $x = 2.8$, $y = 1.9$, and $z = 1.1$, so that $|x - y| = |2.8 - 1.9| = 0.9 < 1$, $|y - z| = |1.9 - 1.1| = 0.8 < 1$, but $|x - z| = |2.8 - 1.1| = 1.7 > 1$. That is, $2.8 R 1.9$, $1.9 R 1.1$, but $2.8 \not R 1.1$.   ◄

## Equivalence Classes

Let $A$ be the set of all students in your school who graduated from high school. Consider the relation $R$ on $A$ that consists of all pairs $(x, y)$, where $x$ and $y$ graduated from the same high school. Given a student $x$, we can form the set of all students equivalent to $x$ with respect to $R$. This set consists of all students who graduated from the same high school as $x$ did. This subset of $A$ is called an equivalence class of the relation.

**DEFINITION 3**   Let $R$ be an equivalence relation on a set $A$. The set of all elements that are related to an element $a$ of $A$ is called the *equivalence class* of $a$. The equivalence class of $a$ with respect to $R$ is denoted by $[a]_R$. When only one relation is under consideration, we can delete the subscript $R$ and write $[a]$ for this equivalence class.

In other words, if $R$ is an equivalence relation on a set $A$, the equivalence class of the element $a$ is

$$[a]_R = \{s \mid (a, s) \in R\}.$$

If $b \in [a]_R$, then $b$ is called a **representative** of this equivalence class. Any element of a class can be used as a representative of this class. That is, there is nothing special about the particular element chosen as the representative of the class.

**EXAMPLE 8**   What is the equivalence class of an integer for the equivalence relation of Example 1?

*Solution:* Because an integer is equivalent to itself and its negative in this equivalence relation, it follows that $[a] = \{-a, a\}$. This set contains two distinct integers unless $a = 0$. For instance, $[7] = \{-7, 7\}$, $[-5] = \{-5, 5\}$, and $[0] = \{0\}$.   ◄

**EXAMPLE 9**   What are the equivalence classes of 0 and 1 for congruence modulo 4?

*Solution:* The equivalence class of 0 contains all integers $a$ such that $a \equiv 0 \pmod 4$. The integers in this class are those divisible by 4. Hence, the equivalence class of 0 for this relation is

$$[0] = \{\ldots, -8, -4, 0, 4, 8, \ldots\}.$$

The equivalence class of 1 contains all the integers $a$ such that $a \equiv 1 \pmod 4$. The integers in this class are those that have a remainder of 1 when divided by 4. Hence, the equivalence class of 1 for this relation is

$$[1] = \{\ldots, -7, -3, 1, 5, 9, \ldots\}. \qquad \blacktriangleleft$$

In Example 9 the equivalence classes of 0 and 1 with respect to congruence modulo 4 were found. Example 9 can easily be generalized, replacing 4 with any positive integer $m$. The equivalence classes of the relation congruence modulo $m$ are called the **congruence classes modulo** $m$. The congruence class of an integer $a$ modulo $m$ is denoted by $[a]_m$, so $[a]_m = \{\ldots, a - 2m, a - m, a, a + m, a + 2m, \ldots\}$. For instance, from Example 9 it follows that $[0]_4 = \{\ldots, -8, -4, 0, 4, 8, \ldots\}$ and $[1]_4 = \{\ldots, -7, -3, 1, 5, 9, \ldots\}$.

**EXAMPLE 10**    What is the equivalence class of the string 0111 with respect to the equivalence relation $R_3$ from Example 5 on the set of all bit strings? (Recall that $s R_3 t$ if and only if $s$ and $t$ are bit strings with $s = t$ or $s$ and $t$ are strings of at least three bits that start with the same three bits.)

*Solution:* The bit strings equivalent to 0111 are the bit strings with at least three bits that begin with 011. These are the bit strings 011, 0110, 0111, 01100, 01101, 01110, 01111, and so on. Consequently,

$$[011]_{R_3} = \{011, 0110, 0111, 01100, 01101, 01110, 01111, \ldots\}. \qquad \blacktriangleleft$$

**EXAMPLE 11**    **Identifiers in the C Programming Language**    In the C programming language, an **identifier** is the name of a variable, a function, or another type of entity. Each identifier is a nonempty string of characters where each character is a lowercase or an uppercase English letter, a digit, or an underscore, and the first character is a lowercase or an uppercase English letter. Identifiers can be any length. This allows developers to use as many characters as they want to name an entity, such as a variable. However, for compilers for some versions of C, there is a limit on the number of characters checked when two names are compared to see whether they refer to the same thing. For example, Standard C compilers consider two identifiers the same when they agree in their first 31 characters. Consequently, developers must be careful not to use identifiers with the same initial 31 characters for different things. We see that two identifiers are considered the same when they are related by the relation $R_{31}$ in Example 5. Using Example 5, we know that $R_{31}$, on the set of all identifiers in Standard C, is an equivalence relation.

What are the equivalence classes of each of the identifiers Number_of_tropical_storms, Number_of_named_tropical_storms, and Number_of_named_tropical_storms_in_the_Atlantic_in_2005?

*Solution:* Note that when an identifier is less than 31 characters long, by the definition of $R_{31}$, its equivalence class contains only itself. Because the identifier Number_of_tropical_storms is 25 characters long, its equivalence class contains exactly one element, namely, itself.

The identifier Number_of_named_tropical_storms is exactly 31 characters long. An identifier is equivalent to it when it starts with these same 31 characters. Consequently, every identifier at least 31 characters long that starts with Number_of_named_tropical_storms is equivalent to this identifier. It follows that the equivalence class of Number_of_named_tropical_storms is the set of all identifiers that begin with the 31 characters Number_of_named_tropical_storms.

An identifier is equivalent to the Number_of_named_tropical_storms_in_the_Atlantic_in_2005 if and only if it begins with its first 31 characters. Because these characters are Number_of_named_tropical_storms, we see that an identifier is equivalent to Number_of_named_tropical_storms_in_the_Atlantic_in_2005 if and only if it is equivalent to Number_of_named_tropical_storms. It follows that these last two identifiers have the same equivalence class. $\qquad \blacktriangleleft$

## Equivalence Classes and Partitions

Let $A$ be the set of students at your school who are majoring in exactly one subject, and let $R$ be the relation on $A$ consisting of pairs $(x, y)$, where $x$ and $y$ are students with the same major. Then $R$ is an equivalence relation, as the reader should verify. We can see that $R$ splits all students in $A$ into a collection of disjoint subsets, where each subset contains students with a specified major. For instance, one subset contains all students majoring (just) in computer science, and a second subset contains all students majoring in history. Furthermore, these subsets are equivalence classes of $R$. This example illustrates how the equivalence classes of an equivalence relation partition a set into disjoint, nonempty subsets. We will make these notions more precise in the following discussion.

Let $R$ be a relation on the set $A$. Theorem 1 shows that the equivalence classes of two elements of $A$ are either identical or disjoint.

**THEOREM 1**    Let $R$ be an equivalence relation on a set $A$. These statements for elements $a$ and $b$ of $A$ are equivalent:

   (*i*)  $aRb$      (*ii*)  $[a] = [b]$      (*iii*)  $[a] \cap [b] \neq \emptyset$

*Proof:* We first show that (*i*) implies (*ii*). Assume that $aRb$. We will prove that $[a] = [b]$ by showing $[a] \subseteq [b]$ and $[b] \subseteq [a]$. Suppose $c \in [a]$. Then $aRc$. Because $aRb$ and $R$ is symmetric, we know that $bRa$. Furthermore, because $R$ is transitive and $bRa$ and $aRc$, it follows that $bRc$. Hence, $c \in [b]$. This shows that $[a] \subseteq [b]$. The proof that $[b] \subseteq [a]$ is similar; it is left as an exercise for the reader.

Second, we will show that (*ii*) implies (*iii*). Assume that $[a] = [b]$. It follows that $[a] \cap [b] \neq \emptyset$ because $[a]$ is nonempty (because $a \in [a]$ because $R$ is reflexive).

Next, we will show that (*iii*) implies (*i*). Suppose that $[a] \cap [b] \neq \emptyset$. Then there is an element $c$ with $c \in [a]$ and $c \in [b]$. In other words, $aRc$ and $bRc$. By the symmetric property, $cRb$. Then by transitivity, because $aRc$ and $cRb$, we have $aRb$.

Because (*i*) implies (*ii*), (*ii*) implies (*iii*), and (*iii*) implies (*i*), the three statements, (*i*), (*ii*), and (*iii*), are equivalent.                                                                              ◁

We are now in a position to show how an equivalence relation *partitions* a set. Let $R$ be an equivalence relation on a set $A$. The union of the equivalence classes of $R$ is all of $A$, because an element $a$ of $A$ is in its own equivalence class, namely, $[a]_R$. In other words,

$$\bigcup_{a \in A} [a]_R = A.$$

In addition, from Theorem 1, it follows that these equivalence classes are either equal or disjoint, so

$$[a]_R \cap [b]_R = \emptyset,$$

when $[a]_R \neq [b]_R$.

Recall that an *index set* is a set whose members label, or index, the elements of a set.

These two observations show that the equivalence classes form a partition of $A$, because they split $A$ into disjoint subsets. More precisely, a **partition** of a set $S$ is a collection of disjoint nonempty subsets of $S$ that have $S$ as their union. In other words, the collection of subsets $A_i$, $i \in I$ (where $I$ is an index set) forms a partition of $S$ if and only if

$$A_i \neq \emptyset \text{ for } i \in I,$$

$$A_i \cap A_j = \emptyset \text{ when } i \neq j,$$

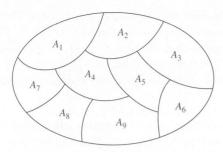

**FIGURE 1   A Partition of a Set.**

and

$$\bigcup_{i \in I} A_i = S.$$

(Here the notation $\bigcup_{i \in I} A_i$ represents the union of the sets $A_i$ for all $i \in I$.) Figure 1 illustrates the concept of a partition of a set.

**EXAMPLE 12**   Suppose that $S = \{1, 2, 3, 4, 5, 6\}$. The collection of sets $A_1 = \{1, 2, 3\}$, $A_2 = \{4, 5\}$, and $A_3 = \{6\}$ forms a partition of $S$, because these sets are disjoint and their union is $S$.   ◀

We have seen that the equivalence classes of an equivalence relation on a set form a partition of the set. The subsets in this partition are the equivalence classes. Conversely, every partition of a set can be used to form an equivalence relation. Two elements are equivalent with respect to this relation if and only if they are in the same subset of the partition.

To see this, assume that $\{A_i \mid i \in I\}$ is a partition on $S$. Let $R$ be the relation on $S$ consisting of the pairs $(x, y)$, where $x$ and $y$ belong to the same subset $A_i$ in the partition. To show that $R$ is an equivalence relation we must show that $R$ is reflexive, symmetric, and transitive.

We see that $(a, a) \in R$ for every $a \in S$, because $a$ is in the same subset as itself. Hence, $R$ is reflexive. If $(a, b) \in R$, then $b$ and $a$ are in the same subset of the partition, so that $(b, a) \in R$ as well. Hence, $R$ is symmetric. If $(a, b) \in R$ and $(b, c) \in R$, then $a$ and $b$ are in the same subset $X$ in the partition, and $b$ and $c$ are in the same subset $Y$ of the partition. Because the subsets of the partition are disjoint and $b$ belongs to $X$ and $Y$, it follows that $X = Y$. Consequently, $a$ and $c$ belong to the same subset of the partition, so $(a, c) \in R$. Thus, $R$ is transitive.

It follows that $R$ is an equivalence relation. The equivalence classes of $R$ consist of subsets of $S$ containing related elements, and by the definition of $R$, these are the subsets of the partition. Theorem 2 summarizes the connections we have established between equivalence relations and partitions.

**THEOREM 2**   Let $R$ be an equivalence relation on a set $S$. Then the equivalence classes of $R$ form a partition of $S$. Conversely, given a partition $\{A_i \mid i \in I\}$ of the set $S$, there is an equivalence relation $R$ that has the sets $A_i$, $i \in I$, as its equivalence classes.

Example 13 shows how to construct an equivalence relation from a partition.

**EXAMPLE 13**   List the ordered pairs in the equivalence relation $R$ produced by the partition $A_1 = \{1, 2, 3\}$, $A_2 = \{4, 5\}$, and $A_3 = \{6\}$ of $S = \{1, 2, 3, 4, 5, 6\}$, given in Example 12.

*Solution:* The subsets in the partition are the equivalence classes of $R$. The pair $(a, b) \in R$ if and only if $a$ and $b$ are in the same subset of the partition. The pairs $(1, 1), (1, 2), (1, 3), (2, 1), (2, 2)$, $(2, 3), (3, 1), (3, 2)$, and $(3, 3)$ belong to $R$ because $A_1 = \{1, 2, 3\}$ is an equivalence class; the pairs $(4, 4), (4, 5), (5, 4)$, and $(5, 5)$ belong to $R$ because $A_2 = \{4, 5\}$ is an equivalence class; and finally the pair $(6, 6)$ belongs to $R$ because $\{6\}$ is an equivalence class. No pair other than those listed belongs to $R$.    ◀

The congruence classes modulo $m$ provide a useful illustration of Theorem 2. There are $m$ different congruence classes modulo $m$, corresponding to the $m$ different remainders possible when an integer is divided by $m$. These $m$ congruence classes are denoted by $[0]_m, [1]_m, \ldots, [m - 1]_m$. They form a partition of the set of integers.

**EXAMPLE 14**    What are the sets in the partition of the integers arising from congruence modulo 4?

*Solution:* There are four congruence classes, corresponding to $[0]_4, [1]_4, [2]_4$, and $[3]_4$. They are the sets

$$[0]_4 = \{\ldots, -8, -4, 0, 4, 8, \ldots\},$$
$$[1]_4 = \{\ldots, -7, -3, 1, 5, 9, \ldots\},$$
$$[2]_4 = \{\ldots, -6, -2, 2, 6, 10, \ldots\},$$
$$[3]_4 = \{\ldots, -5, -1, 3, 7, 11, \ldots\}.$$

These congruence classes are disjoint, and every integer is in exactly one of them. In other words, as Theorem 2 says, these congruence classes form a partition.    ◀

We now provide an example of a partition of the set of all strings arising from an equivalence relation on this set.

**EXAMPLE 15**    Let $R_3$ be the relation from Example 5. What are the sets in the partition of the set of all bit strings arising from the relation $R_3$ on the set of all bit strings? (Recall that $s R_3 t$, where $s$ and $t$ are bit strings, if $s = t$ or $s$ and $t$ are bit strings with at least three bits that agree in their first three bits.)

*Solution:* Note that every bit string of length less than three is equivalent only to itself. Hence $[\lambda]_{R_3} = \{\lambda\}, [0]_{R_3} = \{0\}, [1]_{R_3} = \{1\}, [00]_{R_3} = \{00\}, [01]_{R_3} = \{01\}, [10]_{R_3} = \{10\}$, and $[11]_{R_3} = \{11\}$. Note that every bit string of length three or more is equivalent to one of the eight bit strings 000, 001, 010, 011, 100, 101, 110, and 111. We have

$$[000]_{R_3} = \{000, 0000, 0001, 00000, 00001, 00010, 00011, \ldots\},$$

$$[001]_{R_3} = \{001, 0010, 0011, 00100, 00101, 00110, 00111, \ldots\},$$

$$[010]_{R_3} = \{010, 0100, 0101, 01000, 01001, 01010, 01011, \ldots\},$$

$$[011]_{R_3} = \{011, 0110, 0111, 01100, 01101, 01110, 01111, \ldots\},$$

$$[100]_{R_3} = \{100, 1000, 1001, 10000, 10001, 10010, 10011, \ldots\},$$

$$[101]_{R_3} = \{101, 1010, 1011, 10100, 10101, 10110, 10111, \ldots\},$$

$$[110]_{R_3} = \{110, 1100, 1101, 11000, 11001, 11010, 11011, \ldots\},$$

$$[111]_{R_3} = \{111, 1110, 1111, 11100, 11101, 11110, 11111, \ldots\}.$$

These 15 equivalence classes are disjoint and every bit string is in exactly one of them. As Theorem 2 tells us, these equivalence classes partition the set of all bit strings.    ◀

# Exercises

**1.** Which of these relations on $\{0, 1, 2, 3\}$ are equivalence relations? Determine the properties of an equivalence relation that the others lack.
   **a)** $\{(0,0), (1,1), (2,2), (3,3)\}$
   **b)** $\{(0,0), (0,2), (2,0), (2,2), (2,3), (3,2), (3,3)\}$
   **c)** $\{(0,0), (1,1), (1,2), (2,1), (2,2), (3,3)\}$
   **d)** $\{(0,0), (1,1), (1,3), (2,2), (2,3), (3,1), (3,2),$ $(3,3)\}$
   **e)** $\{(0,0), (0,1), (0,2), (1,0), (1,1), (1,2), (2,0),$ $(2,2), (3,3)\}$

**2.** Which of these relations on the set of all people are equivalence relations? Determine the properties of an equivalence relation that the others lack.
   **a)** $\{(a,b) \mid a \text{ and } b \text{ are the same age}\}$
   **b)** $\{(a,b) \mid a \text{ and } b \text{ have the same parents}\}$
   **c)** $\{(a,b) \mid a \text{ and } b \text{ share a common parent}\}$
   **d)** $\{(a,b) \mid a \text{ and } b \text{ have met}\}$
   **e)** $\{(a,b) \mid a \text{ and } b \text{ speak a common language}\}$

**3.** Which of these relations on the set of all functions from $\mathbf{Z}$ to $\mathbf{Z}$ are equivalence relations? Determine the properties of an equivalence relation that the others lack.
   **a)** $\{(f,g) \mid f(1) = g(1)\}$
   **b)** $\{(f,g) \mid f(0) = g(0) \text{ or } f(1) = g(1)\}$
   **c)** $\{(f,g) \mid f(x) - g(x) = 1 \text{ for all } x \in \mathbf{Z}\}$
   **d)** $\{(f,g) \mid \text{for some } C \in \mathbf{Z}, \text{ for all } x \in \mathbf{Z}, f(x) - g(x) = C\}$
   **e)** $\{(f,g) \mid f(0) = g(1) \text{ and } f(1) = g(0)\}$

**4.** Define three equivalence relations on the set of students in your discrete mathematics class different from the relations discussed in the text. Determine the equivalence classes for each of these equivalence relations.

**5.** Define three equivalence relations on the set of buildings on a college campus. Determine the equivalence classes for each of these equivalence relations.

**6.** Define three equivalence relations on the set of classes offered at your school. Determine the equivalence classes for each of these equivalence relations.

**7.** Show that the relation of logical equivalence on the set of all compound propositions is an equivalence relation. What are the equivalence classes of **F** and of **T**?

**8.** Let $R$ be the relation on the set of all sets of real numbers such that $S \, R \, T$ if and only if $S$ and $T$ have the same cardinality. Show that $R$ is an equivalence relation. What are the equivalence classes of the sets $\{0, 1, 2\}$ and $\mathbf{Z}$?

**9.** Suppose that $A$ is a nonempty set, and $f$ is a function that has $A$ as its domain. Let $R$ be the relation on $A$ consisting of all ordered pairs $(x, y)$ such that $f(x) = f(y)$.
   **a)** Show that $R$ is an equivalence relation on $A$.
   **b)** What are the equivalence classes of $R$?

**10.** Suppose that $A$ is a nonempty set and $R$ is an equivalence relation on $A$. Show that there is a function $f$ with $A$ as its domain such that $(x, y) \in R$ if and only if $f(x) = f(y)$.

**11.** Show that the relation $R$ consisting of all pairs $(x, y)$ such that $x$ and $y$ are bit strings of length three or more that agree in their first three bits is an equivalence relation on the set of all bit strings of length three or more.

**12.** Show that the relation $R$ consisting of all pairs $(x, y)$ such that $x$ and $y$ are bit strings of length three or more that agree except perhaps in their first three bits is an equivalence relation on the set of all bit strings of length three or more.

**13.** Show that the relation $R$ consisting of all pairs $(x, y)$ such that $x$ and $y$ are bit strings that agree in their first and third bits is an equivalence relation on the set of all bit strings of length three or more.

**14.** Let $R$ be the relation consisting of all pairs $(x, y)$ such that $x$ and $y$ are strings of uppercase and lowercase English letters with the property that for every positive integer $n$, the $n$th characters in $x$ and $y$ are the same letter, either uppercase or lowercase. Show that $R$ is an equivalence relation.

**15.** Let $R$ be the relation on the set of ordered pairs of positive integers such that $((a, b), (c, d)) \in R$ if and only if $a + d = b + c$. Show that $R$ is an equivalence relation.

**16.** Let $R$ be the relation on the set of ordered pairs of positive integers such that $((a, b), (c, d)) \in R$ if and only if $ad = bc$. Show that $R$ is an equivalence relation.

**17.** (*Requires calculus*)
   **a)** Show that the relation $R$ on the set of all differentiable functions from $\mathbf{R}$ to $\mathbf{R}$ consisting of all pairs $(f, g)$ such that $f'(x) = g'(x)$ for all real numbers $x$ is an equivalence relation.
   **b)** Which functions are in the same equivalence class as the function $f(x) = x^2$?

**18.** (*Requires calculus*)
   **a)** Let $n$ be a positive integer. Show that the relation $R$ on the set of all polynomials with real-valued coefficients consisting of all pairs $(f, g)$ such that $f^{(n)}(x) = g^{(n)}(x)$ is an equivalence relation. [Here $f^{(n)}(x)$ is the $n$th derivative of $f(x)$.]
   **b)** Which functions are in the same equivalence class as the function $f(x) = x^4$, where $n = 3$?

**19.** Let $R$ be the relation on the set of all URLs (or Web addresses) such that $x \, R \, y$ if and only if the Web page at $x$ is the same as the Web page at $y$. Show that $R$ is an equivalence relation.

**20.** Let $R$ be the relation on the set of all people who have visited a particular Web page such that $x \, R \, y$ if and only if person $x$ and person $y$ have followed the same set of links starting at this Web page (going from Web page to Web page until they stop using the Web). Show that $R$ is an equivalence relation.

In Exercises 21–23 determine whether the relation with the directed graph shown is an equivalence relation.

**21.** 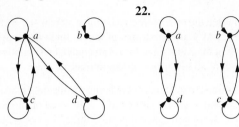 **22.**

**23.**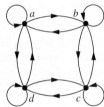

**24.** Determine whether the relations represented by these zero–one matrices are equivalence relations.

a) $\begin{bmatrix} 1 & 1 & 1 \\ 0 & 1 & 1 \\ 1 & 1 & 1 \end{bmatrix}$   b) $\begin{bmatrix} 1 & 0 & 1 & 0 \\ 0 & 1 & 0 & 1 \\ 1 & 0 & 1 & 0 \\ 0 & 1 & 0 & 1 \end{bmatrix}$   c) $\begin{bmatrix} 1 & 1 & 1 & 0 \\ 1 & 1 & 1 & 0 \\ 1 & 1 & 1 & 0 \\ 0 & 0 & 0 & 1 \end{bmatrix}$

**25.** Show that the relation $R$ on the set of all bit strings such that $s\,R\,t$ if and only if $s$ and $t$ contain the same number of 1s is an equivalence relation.

**26.** What are the equivalence classes of the equivalence relations in Exercise 1?

**27.** What are the equivalence classes of the equivalence relations in Exercise 2?

**28.** What are the equivalence classes of the equivalence relations in Exercise 3?

**29.** What is the equivalence class of the bit string 011 for the equivalence relation in Exercise 25?

**30.** What are the equivalence classes of these bit strings for the equivalence relation in Exercise 11?

a) 010     b) 1011     c) 11111     d) 01010101

**31.** What are the equivalence classes of the bit strings in Exercise 30 for the equivalence relation from Exercise 12?

**32.** What are the equivalence classes of the bit strings in Exercise 30 for the equivalence relation from Exercise 13?

**33.** What are the equivalence classes of the bit strings in Exercise 30 for the equivalence relation $R_4$ from Example 5 on the set of all bit strings? (Recall that bit strings $s$ and $t$ are equivalent under $R_4$ if and only if they are equal or they are both at least four bits long and agree in their first four bits.)

**34.** What are the equivalence classes of the bit strings in Exercise 30 for the equivalence relation $R_5$ from Example 5 on the set of all bit strings? (Recall that bit strings $s$ and $t$ are equivalent under $R_5$ if and only if they are equal or they are both at least five bits long and agree in their first five bits.)

**35.** What is the congruence class $[n]_5$ (that is, the equivalence class of $n$ with respect to congruence modulo 5) when $n$ is

a) 2?     b) 3?     c) 6?     d) $-3$?

**36.** What is the congruence class $[4]_m$ when $m$ is

a) 2?     b) 3?     c) 6?     d) 8?

**37.** Give a description of each of the congruence classes modulo 6.

**38.** What is the equivalence class of each of these strings with respect to the equivalence relation in Exercise 14?

a) *No*     b) *Yes*     c) *Help*

**39.** a) What is the equivalence class of $(1, 2)$ with respect to the equivalence relation in Exercise 15?
b) Give an interpretation of the equivalence classes for the equivalence relation $R$ in Exercise 15. [*Hint:* Look at the difference $a - b$ corresponding to $(a, b)$.]

**40.** a) What is the equivalence class of $(1, 2)$ with respect to the equivalence relation in Exercise 16?
b) Give an interpretation of the equivalence classes for the equivalence relation $R$ in Exercise 16. [*Hint:* Look at the ratio $a/b$ corresponding to $(a, b)$.]

**41.** Which of these collections of subsets are partitions of $\{1, 2, 3, 4, 5, 6\}$?

a) $\{1, 2\}, \{2, 3, 4\}, \{4, 5, 6\}$   b) $\{1\}, \{2, 3, 6\}, \{4\}, \{5\}$
c) $\{2, 4, 6\}, \{1, 3, 5\}$   d) $\{1, 4, 5\}, \{2, 6\}$

**42.** Which of these collections of subsets are partitions of $\{-3, -2, -1, 0, 1, 2, 3\}$?

a) $\{-3, -1, 1, 3\}, \{-2, 0, 2\}$
b) $\{-3, -2, -1, 0\}, \{0, 1, 2, 3\}$
c) $\{-3, 3\}, \{-2, 2\}, \{-1, 1\}, \{0\}$
d) $\{-3, -2, 2, 3\}, \{-1, 1\}$

**43.** Which of these collections of subsets are partitions of the set of bit strings of length 8?

a) the set of bit strings that begin with 1, the set of bit strings that begin with 00, and the set of bit strings that begin with 01
b) the set of bit strings that contain the string 00, the set of bit strings that contain the string 01, the set of bit strings that contain the string 10, and the set of bit strings that contain the string 11
c) the set of bit strings that end with 00, the set of bit strings that end with 01, the set of bit strings that end with 10, and the set of bit strings that end with 11
d) the set of bit strings that end with 111, the set of bit strings that end with 011, and the set of bit strings that end with 00
e) the set of bit strings that contain $3k$ ones for some nonnegative integer $k$; the set of bit strings that contain $3k + 1$ ones for some nonnegative integer $k$; and the set of bit strings that contain $3k + 2$ ones for some nonnegative integer $k$.

**44.** Which of these collections of subsets are partitions of the set of integers?

a) the set of even integers and the set of odd integers
b) the set of positive integers and the set of negative integers

c) the set of integers divisible by 3, the set of integers leaving a remainder of 1 when divided by 3, and the set of integers leaving a remainder of 2 when divided by 3

d) the set of integers less than $-100$, the set of integers with absolute value not exceeding 100, and the set of integers greater than 100

e) the set of integers not divisible by 3, the set of even integers, and the set of integers that leave a remainder of 3 when divided by 6

**45.** Which of these are partitions of the set $\mathbf{Z} \times \mathbf{Z}$ of ordered pairs of integers?

a) the set of pairs $(x, y)$, where $x$ or $y$ is odd; the set of pairs $(x, y)$, where $x$ is even; and the set of pairs $(x, y)$, where $y$ is even

b) the set of pairs $(x, y)$, where both $x$ and $y$ are odd; the set of pairs $(x, y)$, where exactly one of $x$ and $y$ is odd; and the set of pairs $(x, y)$, where both $x$ and $y$ are even

c) the set of pairs $(x, y)$, where $x$ is positive; the set of pairs $(x, y)$, where $y$ is positive; and the set of pairs $(x, y)$, where both $x$ and $y$ are negative

d) the set of pairs $(x, y)$, where $3 \mid x$ and $3 \mid y$; the set of pairs $(x, y)$, where $3 \mid x$ and $3 \nmid y$; the set of pairs $(x, y)$, where $3 \nmid x$ and $3 \mid y$; and the set of pairs $(x, y)$, where $3 \nmid x$ and $3 \nmid y$

e) the set of pairs $(x, y)$, where $x > 0$ and $y > 0$; the set of pairs $(x, y)$, where $x > 0$ and $y \leq 0$; the set of pairs $(x, y)$, where $x \leq 0$ and $y > 0$; and the set of pairs $(x, y)$, where $x \leq 0$ and $y \leq 0$

f) the set of pairs $(x, y)$, where $x \neq 0$ and $y \neq 0$; the set of pairs $(x, y)$, where $x = 0$ and $y \neq 0$; and the set of pairs $(x, y)$, where $x \neq 0$ and $y = 0$

**46.** Which of these are partitions of the set of real numbers?

a) the negative real numbers, $\{0\}$, the positive real numbers

b) the set of irrational numbers, the set of rational numbers

c) the set of intervals $[k, k + 1], k = \ldots, -2, -1, 0, 1, 2, \ldots$

d) the set of intervals $(k, k + 1), k = \ldots, -2, -1, 0, 1, 2, \ldots$

e) the set of intervals $(k, k + 1], k = \ldots, -2, -1, 0, 1, 2, \ldots$

f) the sets $\{x + n \mid n \in \mathbf{Z}\}$ for all $x \in [0, 1)$

**47.** List the ordered pairs in the equivalence relations produced by these partitions of $\{0, 1, 2, 3, 4, 5\}$.

a) $\{0\}, \{1, 2\}, \{3, 4, 5\}$

b) $\{0, 1\}, \{2, 3\}, \{4, 5\}$

c) $\{0, 1, 2\}, \{3, 4, 5\}$

d) $\{0\}, \{1\}, \{2\}, \{3\}, \{4\}, \{5\}$

**48.** List the ordered pairs in the equivalence relations produced by these partitions of $\{a, b, c, d, e, f, g\}$.

a) $\{a, b\}, \{c, d\}, \{e, f, g\}$

b) $\{a\}, \{b\}, \{c, d\}, \{e, f\}, \{g\}$

c) $\{a, b, c, d\}, \{e, f, g\}$

d) $\{a, c, e, g\}, \{b, d\}, \{f\}$

A partition $P_1$ is called a **refinement** of the partition $P_2$ if every set in $P_1$ is a subset of one of the sets in $P_2$.

**49.** Show that the partition formed from congruence classes modulo 6 is a refinement of the partition formed from congruence classes modulo 3.

**50.** Show that the partition of the set of people living in the United States consisting of subsets of people living in the same county (or parish) and same state is a refinement of the partition consisting of subsets of people living in the same state.

**51.** Show that the partition of the set of bit strings of length 16 formed by equivalence classes of bit strings that agree on the last eight bits is a refinement of the partition formed from the equivalence classes of bit strings that agree on the last four bits.

In Exercises 52 and 53, $R_n$ refers to the family of equivalence relations defined in Example 5. Recall that $s \, R_n \, t$, where $s$ and $t$ are two strings if $s = t$ or $s$ and $t$ are strings with at least $n$ characters that agree in their first $n$ characters.

**52.** Show that the partition of the set of all bit strings formed by equivalence classes of bit strings with respect to the equivalence relation $R_4$ is a refinement of the partition formed by equivalence classes of bit strings with respect to the equivalence relation $R_3$.

**53.** Show that the partition of the set of all identifiers in C formed by the equivalence classes of identifiers with respect to the equivalence relation $R_{31}$ is a refinement of the partition formed by equivalence classes of identifiers with respect to the equivalence relation $R_8$. (Compilers for "old" C consider identifiers the same when their names agree in their first eight characters, while compilers in standard C consider identifiers the same when their names agree in their first 31 characters.)

**54.** Suppose that $R_1$ and $R_2$ are equivalence relations on a set $A$. Let $P_1$ and $P_2$ be the partitions that correspond to $R_1$ and $R_2$, respectively. Show that $R_1 \subseteq R_2$ if and only if $P_1$ is a refinement of $P_2$.

**55.** Find the smallest equivalence relation on the set $\{a, b, c, d, e\}$ containing the relation $\{(a, b), (a, c), (d, e)\}$.

**56.** Suppose that $R_1$ and $R_2$ are equivalence relations on the set $S$. Determine whether each of these combinations of $R_1$ and $R_2$ must be an equivalence relation.

a) $R_1 \cup R_2$  　　b) $R_1 \cap R_2$  　　c) $R_1 \oplus R_2$

**57.** Consider the equivalence relation from Example 2, namely, $R = \{(x, y) \mid x - y \text{ is an integer}\}$.

a) What is the equivalence class of 1 for this equivalence relation?

b) What is the equivalence class of 1/2 for this equivalence relation?

**\*58.** Each bead on a bracelet with three beads is either red, white, or blue, as illustrated in the figure shown.

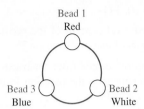

Bead 1
Red

Bead 3
Blue

Bead 2
White

Define the relation $R$ between bracelets as: $(B_1, B_2)$, where $B_1$ and $B_2$ are bracelets, belongs to $R$ if and only if $B_2$ can be obtained from $B_1$ by rotating it or rotating it and then reflecting it.

**a)** Show that $R$ is an equivalence relation.

**b)** What are the equivalence classes of $R$?

**\*59.** Let $R$ be the relation on the set of all colorings of the $2 \times 2$ checkerboard where each of the four squares is colored either red or blue so that $(C_1, C_2)$, where $C_1$ and $C_2$ are $2 \times 2$ checkerboards with each of their four squares colored blue or red, belongs to $R$ if and only if $C_2$ can be obtained from $C_1$ either by rotating the checkerboard or by rotating it and then reflecting it.

**a)** Show that $R$ is an equivalence relation.

**b)** What are the equivalence classes of $R$?

**60. a)** Let $R$ be the relation on the set of functions from $\mathbf{Z}^+$ to $\mathbf{Z}^+$ such that $(f, g)$ belongs to $R$ if and only if $f$ is $\Theta(g)$ (see Section 3.2). Show that $R$ is an equivalence relation.

**b)** Describe the equivalence class containing $f(n) = n^2$ for the equivalence relation of part (a).

**61.** Determine the number of different equivalence relations on a set with three elements by listing them.

**62.** Determine the number of different equivalence relations on a set with four elements by listing them.

**\*63.** Do we necessarily get an equivalence relation when we form the transitive closure of the symmetric closure of the reflexive closure of a relation?

**\*64.** Do we necessarily get an equivalence relation when we form the symmetric closure of the reflexive closure of the transitive closure of a relation?

**65.** Suppose we use Theorem 2 to form a partition $P$ from an equivalence relation $R$. What is the equivalence relation $R'$ that results if we use Theorem 2 again to form an equivalence relation from $P$?

**66.** Suppose we use Theorem 2 to form an equivalence relation $R$ from a partition $P$. What is the partition $P'$ that results if we use Theorem 2 again to form a partition from $R$?

**67.** Devise an algorithm to find the smallest equivalence relation containing a given relation.

**\*68.** Let $p(n)$ denote the number of different equivalence relations on a set with $n$ elements (and by Theorem 2 the number of partitions of a set with $n$ elements). Show that $p(n)$ satisfies the recurrence relation $p(n) = \sum_{j=0}^{n-1} C(n-1, j) p(n-j-1)$ and the initial condition $p(0) = 1$. (*Note:* The numbers $p(n)$ are called **Bell numbers** after the American mathematician E. T. Bell.)

**69.** Use Exercise 68 to find the number of different equivalence relations on a set with $n$ elements, where $n$ is a positive integer not exceeding 10.

# 9.6  Partial Orderings

## Introduction

Links

We often use relations to order some or all of the elements of sets. For instance, we order words using the relation containing pairs of words $(x, y)$, where $x$ comes before $y$ in the dictionary. We schedule projects using the relation consisting of pairs $(x, y)$, where $x$ and $y$ are tasks in a project such that $x$ must be completed before $y$ begins. We order the set of integers using the relation containing the pairs $(x, y)$, where $x$ is less than $y$. When we add all of the pairs of the form $(x, x)$ to these relations, we obtain a relation that is reflexive, antisymmetric, and transitive. These are properties that characterize relations used to order the elements of sets.

**DEFINITION 1**   A relation $R$ on a set $S$ is called a *partial ordering* or *partial order* if it is reflexive, antisymmetric, and transitive. A set $S$ together with a partial ordering $R$ is called a *partially ordered set*, or *poset*, and is denoted by $(S, R)$. Members of $S$ are called *elements* of the poset.

We give examples of posets in Examples 1–3.

**EXAMPLE 1**   Show that the "greater than or equal" relation ($\geq$) is a partial ordering on the set of integers.

# Axioms for the Real Numbers and the Positive Integers

I n this book we have assumed an explicit set of axioms for the set of real numbers and for the set of positive integers. In this appendix we will list these axioms and we will illustrate how basic facts, also used without proof in the text, can be derived using them.

## Axioms for Real Numbers

The standard axioms for real numbers include both the **field** (or **algebraic**) **axioms**, used to specify rules for basic arithmetic operations, and the **order axioms**, used to specify properties of the ordering of real numbers.

THE FIELD AXIOMS   We begin with the field axioms. As usual, we denote the sum and product of two real numbers $x$ and $y$ by $x + y$ and $x \cdot y$, respectively. (Note that the product of $x$ and $y$ is often denoted by $xy$ without the use of the dot to indicate multiplication. We will not use this abridged notation in this appendix, but will within the text.) Also, by convention, we perform multiplications before additions unless parentheses are used. Although these statements are axioms, they are commonly called *laws* or *rules*. The first two of these axioms tell us that when we add or multiply two real numbers, the result is again a real number; these are the *closure laws*.

- **Closure law for addition**   For all real numbers $x$ and $y$, $x + y$ is a real number.
- **Closure law for multiplication**   For all real numbers $x$ and $y$, $x \cdot y$ is a real number.

The next two axioms tell us that when we add or multiply three real numbers, we get the same result regardless of the order of operations; these are the *associative laws*.

- **Associative law for addition**   For all real numbers $x$, $y$, and $z$, $(x + y) + z = x + (y + z)$.
- **Associative law for multiplication**   For all real numbers $x$, $y$, and $z$, $(x \cdot y) \cdot z = x \cdot (y \cdot z)$.

Two additional algebraic axioms tell us that the order in which we add or multiply two numbers does not matter; these are the *commutative laws*.

- **Commutative law for addition**   For all real numbers $x$ and $y$, $x + y = y + x$.
- **Commutative law for multiplication**   For all real numbers $x$ and $y$, $x \cdot y = y \cdot x$.

The next two axioms tell us that 0 and 1 are additive and multiplicative identities for the set of real numbers. That is, when we add 0 to a real number or multiply a real number by 1 we do not change this real number. These laws are called *identity laws*.

- **Additive identity law**   For every real number $x$, $x + 0 = 0 + x = x$.
- **Multiplicative identity law**   For every real number $x$, $x \cdot 1 = 1 \cdot x = x$.

Although it seems obvious, we also need the following axiom.

- **Identity elements axiom**   The additive identity 0 and the multiplicative identity 1 are distinct, that is $0 \neq 1$.

Two additional axioms tell us that for every real number, there is a real number that can be added to this number to produce 0, and for every nonzero real number, there is a real number by which it can be multiplied to produce 1. These are the *inverse laws*.

- **Inverse law for addition**    For every real number $x$, there exists a real number $-x$ (called the *additive inverse* of $x$) such that $x + (-x) = (-x) + x = 0$.
- **Inverse law for multiplication**    For every nonzero real number $x$, there exists a real number $1/x$ (called the *multiplicative inverse* of $x$) such that $x \cdot (1/x) = (1/x) \cdot x = 1$.

The final algebraic axioms for real numbers are the *distributive laws*, which tell us that multiplication distributes over addition; that is, that we obtain the same result when we first add a pair of real numbers and then multiply by a third real number or when we multiply each of these two real numbers by the third real number and then add the two products.

- **Distributive laws**    For all real numbers $x$, $y$, and $z$, $x \cdot (y + z) = x \cdot y + x \cdot z$ and $(x + y) \cdot z = x \cdot z + y \cdot z$.

ORDER AXIOMS    Next, we will state the *order axioms* for the real numbers, which specify properties of the "greater than" relation, denoted by $>$, on the set of real numbers. We write $x > y$ (and $y < x$) when $x$ is greater than $y$, and we write $x \geq y$ (and $y \leq x$) when $x > y$ or $x = y$. The first of these axioms tells us that given two real numbers, exactly one of three possibilities occurs: the two numbers are equal, the first is greater than the second, or the second is greater than the first. This rule is called the *trichotomy law*.

- **Trichotomy law**    For all real numbers $x$ and $y$, exactly one of $x = y$, $x > y$, or $y > x$ is true.

Next, we have an axiom, called *the transitivity law*, that tells us that if one number is greater than a second number and this second number is greater than a third, then the first number is greater than the third.

- **Transitivity law**    For all real numbers $x$, $y$, and $z$, if $x > y$ and $y > z$, then $x > z$.

We also have two *compatibility laws*, which tell us that when we add a number to both sides in a greater than relationship, the greater than relationship is preserved and when we multiply both sides of a greater than relationship by a *positive real number* (that is, a real number $x$ with $x > 0$), the greater than relationship is preserved.

- **Additive compatibility law**    For all real numbers $x$, $y$, and $z$, if $x > y$, then $x + z > y + z$.
- **Multiplicative compatibility law**    For all real numbers $x$, $y$, and $z$, if $x > y$ and $z > 0$, then $x \cdot z > y \cdot z$.

We leave it to the reader (see Exercise 15) to prove that for all real numbers $x$, $y$, and $z$, if $x > y$ and $z < 0$, then $x \cdot z < y \cdot z$. That is, multiplication of an inequality by a negative real number reverses the direction of the inequality.

The final axiom for the set of real numbers is the *completeness property*. Before we state this axiom, we need some definitions. First, given a nonempty set $A$ of real numbers, we say that the real number $b$ is an **upper bound** of $A$ if for every real number $a$ in $A$, $b \geq a$. A real number $s$ is a **least upper bound** of $A$ if $s$ is an upper bound of $A$ and whenever $t$ is an upper bound of $A$, then we have $s \leq t$.

- **Completeness property**    Every nonempty set of real numbers that is bounded above has a least upper bound.

# Using Axioms to Prove Basic Facts

The axioms we have listed can be used to prove many properties that are often used without explicit mention. We give several examples of results we can prove using axioms and leave the proof of a variety of other properties as exercises. Although the results we will prove seem quite obvious, proving them using only the axioms we have stated can be challenging.

| THEOREM 1 | The additive identity element 0 of the real numbers is unique. |
|---|---|

*Proof:* To show that the additive identity element 0 of the real numbers is unique, suppose that $0'$ is also an additive identity for the real numbers. This means that $0' + x = x + 0' = x$ whenever $x$ is a real number. By the additive identity law, it follows that $0 + 0' = 0'$. Because $0'$ is an additive identity, we know that $0 + 0' = 0$. It follows that $0 = 0'$, because both equal $0 + 0'$. This shows that 0 is the unique additive identity for the real numbers.                                   ◁

| THEOREM 2 | The additive inverse of a real number $x$ is unique. |
|---|---|

*Proof:* Let $x$ be a real number. Suppose that $y$ and $z$ are both additive inverses of $x$. Then,

$$
\begin{aligned}
y &= 0 + y && \text{by the additive identity law} \\
  &= (z + x) + y && \text{because } z \text{ is an additive inverse of } x \\
  &= z + (x + y) && \text{by the associative law for addition} \\
  &= z + 0 && \text{because } y \text{ is an additive inverse of } x \\
  &= z && \text{by the additive identity law.}
\end{aligned}
$$

It follows that $y = z$.                                   ◁

Theorems 1 and 2 tell us that the additive identity and additive inverses are unique. Theorems 3 and 4 tell us that the multiplicative identity and multiplicative inverses of nonzero real numbers are also unique. We leave their proofs as exercises.

| THEOREM 3 | The multiplicative identity element 1 of the real numbers is unique. |
|---|---|

| THEOREM 4 | The multiplicative inverse of a nonzero real number $x$ is unique. |
|---|---|

| THEOREM 5 | For every real number $x$, $x \cdot 0 = 0$. |
|---|---|

*Proof:* Suppose that $x$ is a real number. By the additive inverse law, there is a real number $y$ that is the additive inverse of $x \cdot 0$, so we have $x \cdot 0 + y = 0$. By the additive identity law, $0 + 0 = 0$. Using the distributive law, we see that $x \cdot 0 = x \cdot (0 + 0) = x \cdot 0 + x \cdot 0$. It follows that

$$0 = x \cdot 0 + y = (x \cdot 0 + x \cdot 0) + y.$$

Next, note that by the associative law for addition and because $x \cdot 0 + y = 0$, it follows that

$$(x \cdot 0 + x \cdot 0) + y = x \cdot 0 + (x \cdot 0 + y) = x \cdot 0 + 0.$$

Finally, by the additive identity law, we know that $x \cdot 0 + 0 = x \cdot 0$. Consequently, $x \cdot 0 = 0$. ◁

**THEOREM 6**   For all real numbers $x$ and $y$, if $x \cdot y = 0$, then $x = 0$ or $y = 0$.

*Proof:* Suppose that $x$ and $y$ are real numbers and $x \cdot y = 0$. If $x \neq 0$, then, by the multiplicative inverse law, $x$ has a multiplicative inverse $1/x$, such that $x \cdot (1/x) = (1/x) \cdot x = 1$. Because $x \cdot y = 0$, we have $(1/x) \cdot (x \cdot y) = (1/x) \cdot 0 = 0$ by Theorem 5. Using the associate law for multiplication, we have $((1/x) \cdot x) \cdot y = 0$. This means that $1 \cdot y = 0$. By the multiplicative identity rule, we see that $1 \cdot y = y$, so $y = 0$. Consequently, either $x = 0$ or $y = 0$. ◁

**THEOREM 7**   The multiplicative identity element 1 in the set of real numbers is greater than the additive identity element 0.

*Proof:* By the trichotomy law, either $0 = 1$, $0 > 1$, or $1 > 0$. We know by the identity elements axiom that $0 \neq 1$.

So, assume that $0 > 1$. We will show that this assumption leads to a contradiction. By the additive inverse law, 1 has an additive inverse $-1$ with $1 + (-1) = 0$. The additive compatibility law tells us that $0 + (-1) > 1 + (-1) = 0$; the additive identity law tells us that $0 + (-1) = -1$. Consequently, $-1 > 0$, and by the multiplicative compatibility law, $(-1) \cdot (-1) > (-1) \cdot 0$. By Theorem 5 the right-hand side of last inequality is 0. By the distributive law, $(-1) \cdot (-1) + (-1) \cdot 1 = (-1) \cdot (-1 + 1) = (-1) \cdot 0 = 0$. Hence, the left-hand side of this last inequality, $(-1) \cdot (-1)$, is the unique additive inverse of $-1$, so this side of the inequality equals 1. Consequently this last inequality becomes $1 > 0$, contradicting the trichotomy law because we had assumed that $0 > 1$.

Because we know that $0 \neq 1$ and that it is impossible for $0 > 1$, by the trichotomy law, we conclude that $1 > 0$. ◁

---

ARCHIMEDES (287 B.C.E.–212 B.C.E.)   Archimedes was one of the greatest scientists and mathematicians of ancient times. He was born in Syracuse, a Greek city-state in Sicily. His father, Phidias, was an astronomer. Archimedes was educated in Alexandria, Egypt. After completing his studies, he returned to Syracuse, where he spent the rest of his life. Little is known about his personal life; we do not know whether he was ever married or had children. Archimedes was killed in 212 B.C.E. by a Roman soldier when the Romans overran Syracuse.

Archimedes made many important discoveries in geometry. His method for computing the area under a curve was described two thousand years before his ideas were re-invented as part of integral calculus. Archimedes also developed a method for expressing large integers inexpressible by the usual Greek method. He discovered a method for computing the volume of a sphere, as well as of other solids, and he calculated an approximation of $\pi$. Archimedes was also an accomplished engineer and inventor; his machine for pumping water, now called *Archimedes' screw*, is still in use today. Perhaps his best known discovery is the *principle of buoyancy*, which tells us that an object submerged in liquid becomes lighter by an amount equal to the weight it displaces. Some histories tell us that Archimedes was an early streaker, running naked through the streets of Syracuse shouting "Eureka" (which means "I have found it") when he made this discovery. He is also known for his clever use of machines that held off Roman forces sieging Syracuse for several years during the Second Punic War.

The next theorem tells us that for every real number there is an integer (where by an *integer*, we mean 0, the sum of any number of 1s, and the additive inverses of these sums) greater than this real number. This result is attributed to the Greek mathematician Archimedes. The result can be found in Book V of Euclid's *Elements*.

**THEOREM 8**    **ARCHIMEDEAN PROPERTY**   For every real number $x$ there exists an integer $n$ such that $n > x$.

*Proof:* Suppose that $x$ is a real number such that $n \leq x$ for every integer $n$. Then $x$ is an upper bound of the set of integers. By the completeness property it follows that the set of integers has a least upper bound $M$. Because $M - 1 < M$ and $M$ is a least upper bound of the set of integers, $M - 1$ is not an upper bound of the set of integers. This means that there is an integer $n$ with $n > M - 1$. This implies that $n + 1 > M$, contradicting the fact that $M$ is an upper bound of the set of integers.                                                                                        ◁

## Axioms for the Set of Positive Integers

The axioms we now list specify the set of positive integers as
    the subset of the set of integers satisfying four key properties. We assume the truth of these axioms in this textbook.

- ■ **Axiom 1**   The number 1 is a positive integer.
- ■ **Axiom 2**    If $n$ is a positive integer, then $n + 1$, the *successor* of $n$, is also a positive integer.
- ■ **Axiom 3**   Every positive integer other than 1 is the successor of a positive integer.
- ■ **Axiom 4**   **The Well-Ordering Property** Every nonempty subset of the set of positive integers has a least element.

In Sections 5.1 and 5.2 it is shown that the well-ordering principle is equivalent to the principle of mathematical induction.

- ■ **Mathematical induction axiom**    If $S$ is a set of positive integers such that $1 \in S$ and for all positive integers $n$ if $n \in S$, then $n + 1 \in S$, then $S$ is the set of positive integers.

Most mathematicians take the real number system as already existing, with the real numbers satisfying the axioms we have listed in this appendix. However, mathematicians in the nineteenth century developed techniques to construct the set of real numbers, starting with more basic sets of numbers. (The process of constructing the real numbers is sometimes studied in advanced undergraduate mathematics classes. A treatment of this can be found in [Mo91], for instance.) The first step in the process is the construction of the set of positive integers using axioms 1–3 and either the well-ordering property or the mathematical induction axiom. Then, the operations of addition and multiplication of positive integers are defined. Once this has been done, the set of integers can be constructed using equivalence classes of pairs of positive integers where $(a, b) \sim (c, d)$ if and only if $a + d = b + c$; addition and multiplication of integers can be defined using these pairs (see Exercise 21). (Equivalence relations and equivalence classes are discussed in Chapter 9.) Next, the set of rational numbers can be constructed using the equivalence classes of pairs of integers where the second integer in the pair is not zero, where $(a, b) \approx (c, d)$ if and only if $a \cdot d = b \cdot c$; addition and multiplication of rational numbers can be defined in terms of these pairs (see Exercise 22). Using infinite sequences, the set of real numbers can then be constructed from the set of rational numbers. The interested reader will find it worthwhile to read through the many details of the steps of this construction.

# Exercises

Use only the axioms and theorems in this appendix in the proofs in your answers to these exercises.

1. Prove Theorem 3, which states that the multiplicative identity element of the real numbers is unique.

2. Prove Theorem 4, which states that for every nonzero real number $x$, the multiplicative inverse of $x$ is unique.

3. Prove that for all real numbers $x$ and $y$, $(-x) \cdot y = x \cdot (-y) = -(x \cdot y)$.

4. Prove that for all real numbers $x$ and $y$, $-(x + y) = (-x) + (-y)$.

5. Prove that for all real numbers $x$ and $y$, $(-x) \cdot (-y) = x \cdot y$.

6. Prove that for all real numbers $x$, $y$, and $z$, if $x + z = y + z$, then $x = y$.

7. Prove that for every real number $x$, $-(-x) = x$.

Define the **difference** $x - y$ of real numbers $x$ and $y$ by $x - y = x + (-y)$, where $-y$ is the additive inverse of $y$, and the **quotient** $x/y$, where $y \neq 0$, by $x/y = x \cdot (1/y)$, where $1/y$ is the multiplicative inverse of $y$.

8. Prove that for all real numbers $x$ and $y$, $x = y$ if and only if $x - y = 0$.

9. Prove that for all real numbers $x$ and $y$, $-x - y = -(x + y)$.

10. Prove that for all nonzero real numbers $x$ and $y$, $1/(x/y) = y/x$, where $1/(x/y)$ is the multiplicative inverse of $x/y$.

11. Prove that for all real numbers $w$, $x$, $y$, and $z$, if $x \neq 0$ and $z \neq 0$, then $(w/x) + (y/z) = (w \cdot z + x \cdot y)/(x \cdot z)$.

12. Prove that for every positive real number $x$, $1/x$ is also a positive real number.

13. Prove that for all positive real numbers $x$ and $y$, $x \cdot y$ is also a positive real number.

14. Prove that for all real numbers $x$ and $y$, if $x > 0$ and $y < 0$, then $x \cdot y < 0$.

15. Prove that for all real numbers $x$, $y$, and $z$, if $x > y$ and $z < 0$, then $x \cdot z < y \cdot z$.

16. Prove that for every real number $x$, $x \neq 0$ if and only if $x^2 > 0$.

17. Prove that for all real numbers $w$, $x$, $y$, and $z$, if $w < x$ and $y < z$, then $w + y < x + z$.

18. Prove that for all positive real numbers $x$ and $y$, if $x < y$, then $1/x > 1/y$.

19. Prove that for every positive real number $x$, there exists a positive integer $n$ such that $n \cdot x > 1$.

*20. Prove that between every two distinct real numbers there is a rational number (that is, a number of the form $x/y$, where $x$ and $y$ are integers with $y \neq 0$).

Exercises 21 and 22 involve the notion of an equivalence relation, discussed in Chapter 9 of the text.

*21. Define a relation $\sim$ on the set of ordered pairs of positive integers by $(w, x) \sim (y, z)$ if and only if $w + z = x + y$. Show that the operations $[(w, x)]_\sim + [(y, z)]_\sim = [(w + y, x + z)]_\sim$ and $[(w, x)]_\sim \cdot [(y, z)]_\sim = [(w \cdot y + x \cdot z, x \cdot y + w \cdot z)]_\sim$ are well-defined, that is, they do not depend on the representative of the equivalence classes chosen for the computation.

*22. Define a relation $\approx$ on ordered pairs of integers with second entry nonzero by $(w, x) \approx (y, z)$ if and only if $w \cdot z = x \cdot y$. Show that the operations $[(w, x)]_\approx + [(y, z)]_\approx = [(w \cdot z + x \cdot y, x \cdot z)]_\approx$ and $[(w, x)]_\approx \cdot [(y, z)]_\approx = [(w \cdot y, x \cdot z)]_\approx$ are well-defined, that is, they do not depend on the representative of the equivalence classes chosen for the computation.

# Answers to Odd-Numbered Exercises

## CHAPTER 1

### Section 1.1

**1. a)** Yes, T **b)** Yes, F **c)** Yes, T **d)** Yes, F **e)** No **f)** No
**3. a)** Mei does not have an MP3 player. **b)** There is pollution in New Jersey. **c)** $2 + 1 \neq 3$. **d)** The summer in Maine is not hot or it is not sunny. **5. a)** Steve does not have more than 100 GB free disk space on his laptop **b)** Zach does not block e-mails from Jennifer, or he does not block texts from Jennifer **c)** $7 \cdot 11 \cdot 13 \neq 999$ **d)** Diane did not ride her bike 100 miles on Sunday **7. a)** F **b)** T **c)** T **d)** T **e)** T **9. a)** Sharks have not been spotted near the shore. **b)** Swimming at the New Jersey shore is allowed, and sharks have been spotted near the shore. **c)** Swimming at the New Jersey shore is not allowed, or sharks have been spotted near the shore. **d)** If swimming at the New Jersey shore is allowed, then sharks have not been spotted near the shore. **e)** If sharks have not been spotted near the shore, then swimming at the New Jersey shore is allowed. **f)** If swimming at the New Jersey shore is not allowed, then sharks have not been spotted near the shore. **g)** Swimming at the New Jersey shore is allowed if and only if sharks have not been spotted near the shore. **h)** Swimming at the New Jersey shore is not allowed, and either swimming at the New Jersey shore is allowed or sharks have not been spotted near the shore. (Note that we were able to incorporate the parentheses by using the word "either" in the second half of the sentence.) **11. a)** $p \wedge q$ **b)** $p \wedge \neg q$ **c)** $\neg p \wedge \neg q$ **d)** $p \vee q$ **e)** $p \rightarrow q$ **f)** $(p \vee q) \wedge (p \rightarrow \neg q)$ **g)** $q \leftrightarrow p$ **13. a)** $\neg p$ **b)** $p \wedge \neg q$ **c)** $p \rightarrow q$ **d)** $\neg p \rightarrow \neg q$ **e)** $p \rightarrow q$ **f)** $q \wedge \neg p$ **g)** $q \rightarrow p$ **15. a)** $r \wedge \neg p$ **b)** $\neg p \wedge q \wedge r$ **c)** $r \rightarrow (q \leftrightarrow \neg p)$ **d)** $\neg q \wedge \neg p \wedge r$ **e)** $(q \rightarrow (\neg r \wedge \neg p)) \wedge \neg((\neg r \wedge \neg p) \rightarrow q)$ **f)** $(p \wedge r) \rightarrow \neg q$ **17. a)** False **b)** True **c)** True **d)** True
**19. a)** Exclusive or: You get only one beverage. **b)** Inclusive or: Long passwords can have any combination of symbols. **c)** Inclusive or: A student with both courses is even more qualified. **d)** Either interpretation possible; a traveler might wish to pay with a mixture of the two currencies, or the store may not allow that. **21. a)** Inclusive or: It is allowable to take discrete mathematics if you have had calculus or computer science, or both. Exclusive or: It is allowable to take discrete mathematics if you have had calculus or computer science, but not if you have had both. Most likely the inclusive or is intended. **b)** Inclusive or: You can take the rebate, or you can get a low-interest loan, or you can get both the rebate and a low-interest loan. Exclusive or: You can take the rebate, or you can get a low-interest loan, but you cannot get both the rebate and a low-interest loan. Most likely the exclusive or is intended. **c)** Inclusive or: You can order two items from column A and none from column B, or three items from column B and none from column A, or five items including two from column A and three from column B. Exclusive or: You can order two items from column A or three items from column B, but not both. Almost certainly the exclusive or is intended. **d)** Inclusive or: More than 2 feet of snow or windchill below $-100$, or both, will close school. Exclusive or: More than 2 feet of snow or windchill below $-100$, but not both, will close school. Certainly the inclusive or is intended. **23. a)** If the wind blows from the northeast, then it snows. **b)** If it stays warm for a week, then the apple trees will bloom. **c)** If the Pistons win the championship, then they beat the Lakers. **d)** If you get to the top of Long's Peak, then you must have walked 8 miles. **e)** If you are world-famous, then you will get tenure as a professor. **f)** If you drive more than 400 miles, then you will need to buy gasoline. **g)** If your guarantee is good, then you must have bought your CD player less than 90 days ago. **h)** If the water is not too cold, then Jan will go swimming. **25. a)** You buy an ice cream cone if and only if it is hot outside. **b)** You win the contest if and only if you hold the only winning ticket. **c)** You get promoted if and only if you have connections. **d)** Your mind will decay if and only if you watch television. **e)** The train runs late if and only if it is a day I take the train. **27. a)** Converse: "I will ski tomorrow only if it snows today." Contrapositive: "If I do not ski tomorrow, then it will not have snowed today." Inverse: "If it does not snow today, then I will not ski tomorrow." **b)** Converse: "If I come to class, then there will be a quiz." Contrapositive: "If I do not come to class, then there will not be a quiz." Inverse: "If there is not going to be a quiz, then I don't come to class." **c)** Converse: "A positive integer is a prime if it has no divisors other than 1 and itself." Contrapositive: "If a positive integer has a divisor other than 1 and itself, then it is not prime." Inverse: "If a positive integer is not prime, then it has a divisor other than 1 and itself." **29. a)** 2 **b)** 16 **c)** 64 **d)** 16

**31. a)**

| $p$ | $\neg p$ | $p \wedge \neg p$ |
|---|---|---|
| T | F | F |
| F | T | F |

**b)**

| $p$ | $\neg p$ | $p \vee \neg p$ |
|---|---|---|
| T | F | T |
| F | T | T |

**c)**

| $p$ | $q$ | $\neg q$ | $p \vee \neg q$ | $(p \vee \neg q) \rightarrow q$ |
|---|---|---|---|---|
| T | T | F | T | T |
| T | F | T | T | F |
| F | T | F | F | T |
| F | F | T | T | F |

**d)**

| $p$ | $q$ | $p \vee q$ | $p \wedge q$ | $(p \vee q) \rightarrow (p \wedge q)$ |
|---|---|---|---|---|
| T | T | T | T | T |
| T | F | T | F | F |
| F | T | T | F | F |
| F | F | F | F | T |

**e)**

| $p$ | $q$ | $p \to q$ | $\neg q$ | $\neg p$ | $\neg q \to \neg p$ | $(p \to q) \leftrightarrow (\neg q \to \neg p)$ |
|-----|-----|-----------|----------|----------|---------------------|-------------------------------------------------|
| T | T | T | F | F | T | T |
| T | F | F | T | F | F | T |
| F | T | T | F | T | T | T |
| F | F | T | T | T | T | T |

**f)**

| $p$ | $q$ | $p \to q$ | $q \to p$ | $(p \to q) \to (q \to p)$ |
|-----|-----|-----------|-----------|---------------------------|
| T | T | T | T | T |
| T | F | F | T | T |
| F | T | T | F | F |
| F | F | T | T | T |

**33.** For parts (a), (b), (c), (d), and (f) we have this table.

| $p$ | $q$ | $(p \vee q) \to (p \oplus q)$ | $(p \oplus q) \to (p \wedge q)$ | $(p \vee q) \oplus (p \wedge q)$ | $(p \leftrightarrow q) \oplus (\neg p \leftrightarrow q)$ | $(p \oplus q) \to (p \oplus \neg q)$ |
|-----|-----|-------------------------------|----------------------------------|-----------------------------------|-----------------------------------------------------------|---------------------------------------|
| T | T | F | T | F | T | T |
| T | F | T | F | T | T | F |
| F | T | T | F | T | T | F |
| F | F | T | T | F | T | T |

For part (e) we have this table.

| $p$ | $q$ | $r$ | $\neg p$ | $\neg r$ | $p \leftrightarrow q$ | $\neg p \leftrightarrow \neg r$ | $(p \leftrightarrow q) \oplus (\neg p \leftrightarrow \neg r)$ |
|-----|-----|-----|----------|----------|------------------------|----------------------------------|----------------------------------------------------------------|
| T | T | T | F | F | T | T | F |
| T | T | F | F | T | T | F | T |
| T | F | T | F | F | F | T | T |
| T | F | F | F | T | F | F | F |
| F | T | T | T | F | F | F | F |
| F | T | F | T | T | F | T | T |
| F | F | T | T | F | T | F | T |
| F | F | F | T | T | T | T | F |

**35.**

| $p$ | $q$ | $p \to \neg q$ | $\neg p \leftrightarrow q$ | $(p \to q) \vee (\neg p \to q)$ | $(p \to q) \wedge (\neg p \to q)$ | $(p \leftrightarrow q) \vee (\neg p \leftrightarrow q)$ | $(\neg p \leftrightarrow \neg q) \leftrightarrow (p \leftrightarrow q)$ |
|-----|-----|----------------|-----------------------------|----------------------------------|------------------------------------|---------------------------------------------------------|--------------------------------------------------------------------------|
| T | T | F | F | T | T | T | T |
| T | F | T | T | T | F | T | T |
| F | T | T | T | T | T | T | T |
| F | F | T | F | T | F | T | T |

**37.**

| $p$ | $q$ | $r$ | $p \to (\neg q \vee r)$ | $\neg p \to (q \to r)$ | $(p \to q) \vee (\neg p \to r)$ | $(p \to q) \wedge (\neg p \to r)$ | $(p \leftrightarrow q) \vee (\neg q \leftrightarrow r)$ | $(\neg p \leftrightarrow \neg q) \leftrightarrow (q \leftrightarrow r)$ |
|-----|-----|-----|--------------------------|-------------------------|----------------------------------|------------------------------------|---------------------------------------------------------|--------------------------------------------------------------------------|
| T | T | T | T | T | T | T | T | T |
| T | T | F | F | T | T | T | T | F |
| T | F | T | T | T | T | F | T | T |
| T | F | F | T | T | T | F | F | F |
| F | T | T | T | T | T | T | F | F |
| F | T | F | T | F | T | F | T | T |
| F | F | T | T | T | T | T | T | F |
| F | F | F | T | T | T | F | T | T |

**39.**

| $p$ | $q$ | $r$ | $s$ | $p \leftrightarrow q$ | $r \leftrightarrow s$ | $(p \leftrightarrow q) \leftrightarrow (r \leftrightarrow s)$ |
|---|---|---|---|---|---|---|
| T | T | T | T | T | T | T |
| T | T | T | F | T | F | F |
| T | T | F | T | T | F | F |
| T | T | F | F | T | T | T |
| T | F | T | T | F | T | F |
| T | F | T | F | F | F | T |
| T | F | F | T | F | F | T |
| T | F | F | F | F | T | F |
| F | T | T | T | F | T | F |
| F | T | T | F | F | F | T |
| F | T | F | T | F | F | T |
| F | T | F | F | F | T | F |
| F | F | T | T | T | T | T |
| F | F | T | F | T | F | F |
| F | F | F | T | T | F | F |
| F | F | F | F | T | T | T |

**41.** The first clause is true if and only if at least one of $p, q$, and $r$ is true. The second clause is true if and only if at least one of the three variables is false. Therefore the entire statement is true if and only if there is at least one T and one F among the truth values of the variables, in other words, that they don't all have the same truth value.  **43. a)** Bitwise *OR* is 111 1111; bitwise *AND* is 000 0000; bitwise *XOR* is 111 1111. **b)** Bitwise *OR* is 1111 1010; bitwise *AND* is 1010 0000; bitwise *XOR* is 0101 1010.  **c)** Bitwise *OR* is 10 0111 1001; bitwise *AND* is 00 0100 0000; bitwise *XOR* is 10 0011 1001.  **d)** Bitwise *OR* is 11 1111 1111; bitwise *AND* is 00 0000 0000; bitwise *XOR* is 11 1111 1111.  **45.** 0.2, 0.6  **47.** 0.8, 0.6  **49. a)** The 99th statement is true and the rest are false.  **b)** Statements 1 through 50 are all true and statements 51 through 100 are all false.  **c)** This cannot happen; it is a paradox, showing that these cannot be statements.

## Section 1.2

**1.** $e \rightarrow a$  **3.** $g \rightarrow (r \wedge (\neg m) \wedge (\neg b))$  **5.** $e \rightarrow (a \wedge (b \vee p) \wedge r)$  **7. a)** $q \rightarrow p$  **b)** $q \wedge \neg p$  **c)** $q \rightarrow p$  **d)** $\neg q \rightarrow \neg p$  **9.** Not consistent  **11.** Consistent  **13.** NEW **AND** JERSEY **AND** BEACHES, (JERSEY **AND** BEACHES) **NOT** NEW  **15.** "If I were to ask you whether the right branch leads to the ruins, would you answer yes?"  **17** If the first professor did not want coffee, then he would know that the answer to the hostess's question was "no." Therefore the hostess and the remaining professors know that the first professor did want coffee. Similarly, the second professor must want coffee. When the third professor said "no," the hostess knows that the third professor does not want coffee.  **19.** $A$ is a knight and $B$ is a knave.  **21.** $A$ is a knight and $B$ is a knight.  **23.** $A$ is a knave and $B$ is a knight.  **25.** $A$ is the knight, $B$ is the spy, $C$ is the knave.  **27.** $A$ is the knight, $B$ is the spy, $C$ is the knave.  **29.** Any of the three can be the knight, any can be the spy, any can be the knave.  **31.** No solutions  **33.** In order of decreasing salary: Fred, Maggie, Janice  **35.** The detective can determine that the butler and cook are lying but cannot determine whether the gardener is telling the truth or whether the handyman is telling the truth.  **37.** The Japanese man owns the zebra, and the Norwegian drinks water.  **39.** One honest, 49 corrupt  **41. a)** $\neg(p \wedge (q \vee \neg r))$ **b)** $((\neg p) \wedge (\neg q)) \vee (p \wedge r)$

**43.**

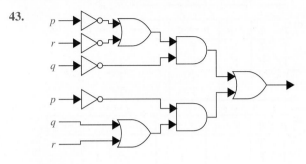

## Section 1.3

**1.** The equivalences follow by showing that the appropriate pairs of columns of this table agree.

| $p$ | $p \wedge T$ | $p \vee F$ | $p \wedge F$ | $p \vee T$ | $p \vee p$ | $p \wedge p$ |
|---|---|---|---|---|---|---|
| T | T | T | F | T | T | T |
| F | F | F | F | T | F | F |

**3. a)**

| $p$ | $q$ | $p \vee q$ | $q \vee p$ |
|---|---|---|---|
| T | T | T | T |
| T | F | T | T |
| F | T | T | T |
| F | F | F | F |

**b)**

| $p$ | $q$ | $p \wedge q$ | $q \wedge p$ |
|---|---|---|---|
| T | T | T | T |
| T | F | F | F |
| F | T | F | F |
| F | F | F | F |

**5.**

| $p$ | $q$ | $r$ | $q \vee r$ | $p \wedge (q \vee r)$ | $p \wedge q$ | $p \wedge r$ | $(p \wedge q) \vee (p \wedge r)$ |
|---|---|---|---|---|---|---|---|
| T | T | T | T | T | T | T | T |
| T | T | F | T | T | T | F | T |
| T | F | T | T | T | F | T | T |
| T | F | F | F | F | F | F | F |
| F | T | T | T | F | F | F | F |
| F | T | F | T | F | F | F | F |
| F | F | T | T | F | F | F | F |
| F | F | F | F | F | F | F | F |

**7. a)** Jan is not rich, or Jan is not happy.  **b)** Carlos will not bicycle tomorrow, and Carlos will not run tomorrow.  **c)** Mei does not walk to class, and Mei does not take the bus to class.  **d)** Ibrahim is not smart, or Ibrahim is not hard working.

**9. a)**

| $p$ | $q$ | $p \wedge q$ | $(p \wedge q) \rightarrow p$ |
|---|---|---|---|
| T | T | T | T |
| T | F | F | T |
| F | T | F | T |
| F | F | F | T |

**b)**

| $p$ | $q$ | $p \lor q$ | $p \to (p \lor q)$ |
|---|---|---|---|
| T | T | T | T |
| T | F | T | T |
| F | T | T | T |
| F | F | F | T |

**c)**

| $p$ | $q$ | $\neg p$ | $p \to q$ | $\neg p \to (p \to q)$ |
|---|---|---|---|---|
| T | T | F | T | T |
| T | F | F | F | T |
| F | T | T | T | T |
| F | F | T | T | T |

**d)**

| $p$ | $q$ | $p \land q$ | $p \to q$ | $(p \land q) \to (p \to q)$ |
|---|---|---|---|---|
| T | T | T | T | T |
| T | F | F | F | T |
| F | T | F | T | T |
| F | F | F | T | T |

**e)**

| $p$ | $q$ | $p \to q$ | $\neg(p \to q)$ | $\neg(p \to q) \to p$ |
|---|---|---|---|---|
| T | T | T | F | T |
| T | F | F | T | T |
| F | T | T | F | T |
| F | F | T | F | T |

**f)**

| $p$ | $q$ | $p \to q$ | $\neg(p \to q)$ | $\neg q$ | $\neg(p \to q) \to \neg q$ |
|---|---|---|---|---|---|
| T | T | T | F | F | T |
| T | F | F | T | T | T |
| F | T | T | F | F | T |
| F | F | T | F | T | T |

**11.** In each case we will show that if the hypothesis is true, then the conclusion is also. **a)** If the hypothesis $p \land q$ is true, then by the definition of conjunction, the conclusion $p$ must also be true. **b)** If the hypothesis $p$ is true, by the definition of disjunction, the conclusion $p \lor q$ is also true. **c)** If the hypothesis $\neg p$ is true, that is, if $p$ is false, then the conclusion $p \to q$ is true. **d)** If the hypothesis $p \land q$ is true, then both $p$ and $q$ are true, so the conclusion $p \to q$ is also true. **e)** If the hypothesis $\neg(p \to q)$ is true, then $p \to q$ is false, so the conclusion $p$ is true (and $q$ is false). **f)** If the hypothesis $\neg(p \to q)$ is true, then $p \to q$ is false, so $p$ is true and $q$ is false. Hence, the conclusion $\neg q$ is true. **13.** That the fourth column of the truth table shown is identical to the first column proves part (a), and that the sixth column is identical to the first column proves part (b).

| $p$ | $q$ | $p \land q$ | $p \lor (p \land q)$ | $p \lor q$ | $p \land (p \lor q)$ |
|---|---|---|---|---|---|
| T | T | T | T | T | T |
| T | F | F | T | T | T |
| F | T | F | F | T | F |
| F | F | F | F | F | F |

**15.** It is a tautology. **17.** Each of these is true precisely when $p$ and $q$ have opposite truth values. **19.** The proposition

$\neg p \leftrightarrow q$ is true when $\neg p$ and $q$ have the same truth values, which means that $p$ and $q$ have different truth values. Similarly, $p \leftrightarrow \neg q$ is true in exactly the same cases. Therefore, these two expressions are logically equivalent. **21.** The proposition $\neg(p \leftrightarrow q)$ is true when $p \leftrightarrow q$ is false, which means that $p$ and $q$ have different truth values. Because this is precisely when $\neg p \leftrightarrow q$ is true, the two expressions are logically equivalent. **23.** For $(p \to r) \land (q \to r)$ to be false, one of the two conditional statements must be false, which happens exactly when $r$ is false and at least one of $p$ and $q$ is true. But these are precisely the cases in which $p \lor q$ is true and $r$ is false, which is precisely when $(p \lor q) \to r$ is false. Because the two propositions are false in exactly the same situations, they are logically equivalent. **25.** For $(p \to r) \lor (q \to r)$ to be false, both of the two conditional statements must be false, which happens exactly when $r$ is false and both $p$ and $q$ are true. But this is precisely the case in which $p \land q$ is true and $r$ is false, which is precisely when $(p \land q) \to r$ is false. Because the two propositions are false in exactly the same situations, they are logically equivalent. **27.** This fact was observed in Section 1 when the biconditional was first defined. Each of these is true precisely when $p$ and $q$ have the same truth values. **29.** The last column is all Ts.

| $p$ | $q$ | $r$ | $p \to q$ | $q \to r$ | $(p \to q) \land (q \to r)$ | $p \to r$ | $(p \to q) \land (q \to r) \to (p \to r)$ |
|---|---|---|---|---|---|---|---|
| T | T | T | T | T | T | T | T |
| T | T | F | T | F | F | F | T |
| T | F | T | F | T | F | T | T |
| T | F | F | F | T | F | F | T |
| F | T | T | T | T | T | T | T |
| F | T | F | T | F | F | T | T |
| F | F | T | T | T | T | T | T |
| F | F | F | T | T | T | T | T |

**31.** These are not logically equivalent because when $p$, $q$, and $r$ are all false, $(p \to q) \to r$ is false, but $p \to (q \to r)$ is true. **33.** Many answers are possible. If we let $r$ be true and $p$, $q$, and $s$ be false, then $(p \to q) \to (r \to s)$ will be false, but $(p \to r) \to (q \to s)$ will be true. **35. a)** $p \lor \neg q \lor \neg r$ **b)** $(p \lor q \lor r) \land s$ **c)** $(p \land T) \lor (q \land F)$ **37.** If we take duals twice, every $\lor$ changes to an $\land$ and then back to an $\lor$, every $\land$ changes to an $\lor$ and then back to an $\land$, every **T** changes to an **F** and then back to a **T**, every **F** changes to a **T** and then back to an **F**. Hence, $(s^*)^* = s$. **39.** Let $p$ and $q$ be equivalent compound propositions involving only the operators $\land$, $\lor$, and $\neg$, and **T** and **F**. Note that $\neg p$ and $\neg q$ are also equivalent. Use De Morgan's laws as many times as necessary to push negations in as far as possible within these compound propositions, changing $\lor$s to $\land$s, and vice versa, and changing **T**s to **F**s, and vice versa. This shows that $\neg p$ and $\neg q$ are the same as $p^*$ and $q^*$ except that each atomic proposition $p_i$ within them is replaced by its negation. From this we can conclude that $p^*$ and $q^*$ are equivalent because $\neg p$ and $\neg q$

are.    **41.** $(p \wedge q \wedge \neg r) \vee (p \wedge \neg q \wedge r) \vee (\neg p \wedge q \wedge r)$
**43.** Given a compound proposition $p$, form its truth table and then write down a proposition $q$ in disjunctive normal form that is logically equivalent to $p$. Because $q$ involves only $\neg$, $\wedge$, and $\vee$, this shows that these three operators form a functionally complete set.    **45.** By Exercise 43, given a compound proposition $p$, we can write down a proposition $q$ that is logically equivalent to $p$ and involves only $\neg$, $\wedge$, and $\vee$. By De Morgan's law we can eliminate all the $\wedge$s by replacing each occurrence of $p_1 \wedge p_2 \wedge \cdots \wedge p_n$ with $\neg(\neg p_1 \vee \neg p_2 \vee \cdots \vee \neg p_n)$.    **47.** $\neg(p \wedge q)$ is true when either $p$ or $q$, or both, are false, and is false when both $p$ and $q$ are true. Because this was the definition of $p \mid q$, the two compound propositions are logically equivalent.    **49.** $\neg(p \vee q)$ is true when both $p$ and $q$ are false, and is false otherwise. Because this was the definition of $p \downarrow q$, the two are logically equivalent.
**51.** $((p \downarrow p) \downarrow q) \downarrow ((p \downarrow p) \downarrow q)$    **53.** This follows immediately from the truth table or definition of $p \mid q$.
**55.** 16    **57.** If the database is open, then either the system is in its initial state or the monitor is put in a closed state.    **59.** All nine    **61. a)** Satisfiable **b)** Not satisfiable **c)** Not satisfiable    **63.** Use the same propositions as were given in the text for a $9 \times 9$ Sudoku puzzle, with the variables indexed from 1 to 4, instead of from 1 to 9, and with a similar change for the propositions for the $2 \times 2$ blocks: $\bigwedge_{r=0}^{1} \bigwedge_{s=0}^{1} \bigwedge_{n=1}^{4} \bigvee_{i=1}^{2} \bigvee_{j=1}^{2} p(2r+i, 2s+j, n)$
**65.** $\bigvee_{i=1}^{9} p(i, j, n)$ asserts that column $j$ contains the number $n$, so $\bigwedge_{n=1}^{9} \bigvee_{i=1}^{9} p(i, j, n)$ asserts that column $j$ contains all 9 numbers; therefore $\bigwedge_{j=1}^{9} \bigwedge_{n=1}^{9} \bigvee_{i=1}^{9} p(i, j, n)$ asserts that every column contains every number.

## Section 1.4

**1. a)** T **b)** T **c)** F    **3. a)** T **b)** F **c)** F **d)** F    **5. a)** There is a student who spends more than 5 hours every weekday in class.   **b)** Every student spends more than 5 hours every weekday in class.   **c)** There is a student who does not spend more than 5 hours every weekday in class.   **d)** No student spends more than 5 hours every weekday in class.
**7. a)** Every comedian is funny.   **b)** Every person is a funny comedian.   **c)** There exists a person such that if she or he is a comedian, then she or he is funny.   **d)** Some comedians are funny.    **9. a)** $\exists x(P(x) \wedge Q(x))$ **b)** $\exists x(P(x) \wedge \neg Q(x))$ **c)** $\forall x(P(x) \vee Q(x))$ **d)** $\forall x \neg(P(x) \vee Q(x))$    **11. a)** T **b)** T **c)** F **d)** F **e)** T **f)** F    **13. a)** T **b)** T **c)** T **d)** T    **15. a)** T **b)** F **c)** T **d)** F    **17. a)** $P(0) \vee P(1) \vee P(2) \vee P(3) \vee P(4)$ **b)** $P(0) \wedge P(1) \wedge P(2) \wedge P(3) \wedge P(4)$ **c)** $\neg P(0) \vee \neg P(1) \vee \neg P(2) \vee \neg P(3) \vee \neg P(4)$    **d)** $\neg P(0) \wedge \neg P(1) \wedge \neg P(2) \wedge \neg P(3) \wedge \neg P(4)$   **e)** $\neg(P(0) \vee P(1) \vee P(2) \vee P(3) \vee P(4))$ **f)** $\neg(P(0) \wedge P(1) \wedge P(2) \wedge P(3) \wedge P(4))$
**19. a)** $P(1) \vee P(2) \vee P(3) \vee P(4) \vee P(5)$   **b)** $P(1) \wedge P(2) \wedge P(3) \wedge P(4) \wedge P(5)$ **c)** $\neg(P(1) \vee P(2) \vee P(3) \vee P(4) \vee P(5))$ **d)** $\neg(P(1) \wedge P(2) \wedge P(3) \wedge P(4) \wedge P(5))$   **e)** $(P(1) \wedge P(2) \wedge P(4) \wedge P(5)) \vee (\neg P(1) \vee \neg P(2) \vee \neg P(3) \vee$

$\neg P(4) \vee \neg P(5))$    **21.** Many answers are possible.   **a)** All students in your discrete mathematics class; all students in the world   **b)** All United States senators; all college football players   **c)** George W. Bush and Jeb Bush; all politicians in the United States   **d)** Bill Clinton and George W. Bush; all politicians in the United States    **23.** Let $C(x)$ be the propositional function "$x$ is in your class." **a)** $\exists x H(x)$ and $\exists x(C(x) \wedge H(x))$, where $H(x)$ is "$x$ can speak Hindi" **b)** $\forall x F(x)$ and $\forall x(C(x) \rightarrow F(x))$, where $F(x)$ is "$x$ is friendly" **c)** $\exists x \neg B(x)$ and $\exists x(C(x) \wedge \neg B(x))$, where $B(x)$ is "$x$ was born in California" **d)** $\exists x M(x)$ and $\exists x(C(x) \wedge M(x))$, where $M(x)$ is "$x$ has been in a movie" **e)** $\forall x \neg L(x)$ and $\forall x(C(x) \rightarrow \neg L(x))$, where $L(x)$ is "$x$ has taken a course in logic programming"    **25.** Let $P(x)$ be "$x$ is perfect"; let $F(x)$ be "$x$ is your friend"; and let the domain be all people. **a)** $\forall x \neg P(x)$ **b)** $\neg \forall x P(x)$ **c)** $\forall x(F(x) \rightarrow P(x))$ **d)** $\exists x(F(x) \wedge P(x))$   **e)** $\forall x(F(x) \wedge P(x))$ or $(\forall x F(x)) \wedge (\forall x P(x))$ **f)** $(\neg \forall x F(x)) \vee (\exists x \neg P(x))$    **27.** Let $Y(x)$ be the propositional function that $x$ is in your school or class, as appropriate. **a)** If we let $V(x)$ be "$x$ has lived in Vietnam," then we have $\exists x V(x)$ if the domain is just your schoolmates, or $\exists x(Y(x) \wedge V(x))$ if the domain is all people. If we let $D(x, y)$ mean that person $x$ has lived in country $y$, then we can rewrite this last one as $\exists x(Y(x) \wedge D(x, \text{Vietnam}))$.   **b)** If we let $H(x)$ be "$x$ can speak Hindi," then we have $\exists x \neg H(x)$ if the domain is just your schoolmates, or $\exists x(Y(x) \wedge \neg H(x))$ if the domain is all people. If we let $S(x, y)$ mean that person $x$ can speak language $y$, then we can rewrite this last one as $\exists x(Y(x) \wedge \neg S(x, \text{Hindi}))$.   **c)** If we let $J(x)$, $P(x)$, and $C(x)$ be the propositional functions asserting $x$'s knowledge of Java, Prolog, and C++, respectively, then we have $\exists x(J(x) \wedge P(x) \wedge C(x))$ if the domain is just your schoolmates, or $\exists x(Y(x) \wedge J(x) \wedge P(x) \wedge C(x))$ if the domain is all people. If we let $K(x, y)$ mean that person $x$ knows programming language $y$, then we can rewrite this last one as $\exists x(Y(x) \wedge K(x, \text{Java}) \wedge K(x, \text{Prolog}) \wedge K(x, \text{C++}))$. **d)** If we let $T(x)$ be "$x$ enjoys Thai food," then we have $\forall x T(x)$ if the domain is just your classmates, or $\forall x(Y(x) \rightarrow T(x))$ if the domain is all people. If we let $E(x, y)$ mean that person $x$ enjoys food of type $y$, then we can rewrite this last one as $\forall x(Y(x) \rightarrow E(x, \text{Thai}))$.   **e)** If we let $H(x)$ be "$x$ plays hockey," then we have $\exists x \neg H(x)$ if the domain is just your classmates, or $\exists x(Y(x) \wedge \neg H(x))$ if the domain is all people. If we let $P(x, y)$ mean that person $x$ plays game $y$, then we can rewrite this last one as $\exists x(Y(x) \wedge \neg P(x, \text{hockey}))$.    **29.** Let $T(x)$ mean that $x$ is a tautology and $C(x)$ mean that $x$ is a contradiction. **a)** $\exists x T(x)$ **b)** $\forall x(C(x) \rightarrow T(\neg x))$ **c)** $\exists x \exists y(\neg T(x) \wedge \neg C(x) \wedge \neg T(y) \wedge \neg C(y) \wedge T(x \vee y))$ **d)** $\forall x \forall y((T(x) \wedge T(y)) \rightarrow T(x \wedge y))$
**31. a)** $Q(0,0,0) \wedge Q(0,1,0)$   **b)** $Q(0,1,1) \vee Q(1, 1, 1) \vee Q(2, 1, 1)$ **c)** $\neg Q(0, 0, 0) \vee \neg Q(0, 0, 1)$ **d)** $\neg Q(0, 0, 1) \vee \neg Q(1, 0, 1) \vee \neg Q(2,0,1)$    **33. a)** Let $T(x)$ be the predicate that $x$ can learn new tricks, and let the domain be old dogs. Original is $\exists x T(x)$. Negation is $\forall x \neg T(x)$: "No old dogs can learn new tricks." **b)** Let $C(x)$ be the predicate that $x$ knows calculus, and let the domain be rabbits. Original is $\neg \exists x C(x)$.

Negation is $\exists x\, C(x)$: "There is a rabbit that knows calculus." **c)** Let $F(x)$ be the predicate that $x$ can fly, and let the domain be birds. Original is $\forall x\, F(x)$. Negation is $\exists x\, \neg F(x)$: "There is a bird who cannot fly." **d)** Let $T(x)$ be the predicate that $x$ can talk, and let the domain be dogs. Original is $\neg\exists x\, T(x)$. Negation is $\exists x\, T(x)$: "There is a dog that talks." **e)** Let $F(x)$ and $R(x)$ be the predicates that $x$ knows French and knows Russian, respectively, and let the domain be people in this class. Original is $\neg\exists x(F(x) \wedge R(x))$. Negation is $\exists x(F(x) \wedge R(x))$: "There is someone in this class who knows French and Russian." **35. a)** There is no counterexample. **b)** $x = 0$ **c)** $x = 2$ **37. a)** $\forall x((F(x, 25{,}000) \vee S(x, 25)) \to E(x))$, where $E(x)$ is "Person $x$ qualifies as an elite flyer in a given year," $F(x, y)$ is "Person $x$ flies more than $y$ miles in a given year," and $S(x, y)$ is "Person $x$ takes more than $y$ flights in a given year" **b)** $\forall x(((M(x) \wedge T(x, 3)) \vee (\neg M(x) \wedge T(x, 3.5))) \to Q(x))$, where $Q(x)$ is "Person $x$ qualifies for the marathon," $M(x)$ is "Person $x$ is a man," and $T(x, y)$ is "Person $x$ has run the marathon in less than $y$ hours" **c)** $M \to ((H(60) \vee (H(45) \wedge T)) \wedge \forall y\, G(B, y))$, where $M$ is the proposition "The student received a masters degree," $H(x)$ is "The student took at least $x$ course hours," $T$ is the proposition "The student wrote a thesis," and $G(x, y)$ is "The person got grade $x$ or higher in course $y$" **d)** $\exists x((T(x, 21) \wedge G(x, 4.0))$, where $T(x, y)$ is "Person $x$ took more than $y$ credit hours" and $G(x, p)$ is "Person $x$ earned grade point average $p$" (we assume that we are talking about one given semester) **39. a)** If there is a printer that is both out of service and busy, then some job has been lost. **b)** If every printer is busy, then there is a job in the queue. **c)** If there is a job that is both queued and lost, then some printer is out of service. **d)** If every printer is busy and every job is queued, then some job is lost. **41. a)** $(\exists x\, F(x, 10)) \to \exists x\, S(x)$, where $F(x, y)$ is "Disk $x$ has more than $y$ kilobytes of free space," and $S(x)$ is "Mail message $x$ can be saved" **b)** $(\exists x\, A(x)) \to \forall x(Q(x) \to T(x))$, where $A(x)$ is "Alert $x$ is active," $Q(x)$ is "Message $x$ is queued," and $T(x)$ is "Message $x$ is transmitted" **c)** $\forall x((x \neq \text{main console}) \to T(x))$, where $T(x)$ is "The diagnostic monitor tracks the status of system $x$" **d)** $\forall x(\neg L(x) \to B(x))$, where $L(x)$ is "The host of the conference call put participant $x$ on a special list" and $B(x)$ is "Participant $x$ was billed" **43.** They are not equivalent. Let $P(x)$ be any propositional function that is sometimes true and sometimes false, and let $Q(x)$ be any propositional function that is always false. Then $\forall x(P(x) \to Q(x))$ is false but $\forall x\, P(x) \to \forall x\, Q(x)$ is true. **45.** Both statements are true precisely when at least one of $P(x)$ and $Q(x)$ is true for at least one value of $x$ in the domain. **47. a)** If $A$ is true, then both sides are logically equivalent to $\forall x\, P(x)$. If $A$ is false, the left-hand side is clearly false. Furthermore, for every $x$, $P(x) \wedge A$ is false, so the right-hand side is false. Hence, the two sides are logically equivalent. **b)** If $A$ is true, then both sides are logically equivalent to $\exists x\, P(x)$. If $A$ is false, the left-hand side is clearly false. Furthermore, for every $x$, $P(x) \wedge A$ is false, so $\exists x(P(x) \wedge A)$ is false. Hence, the two sides are logically equivalent. **49.** We can establish these equivalences by arguing that one side is true if and only if the other side is true. **a)** Suppose that $A$ is true. Then for each $x$, $P(x) \to A$ is true; therefore the left-hand side is always true in this case. By similar reasoning the right-hand side is always true in this case. Therefore, the two propositions are logically equivalent when $A$ is true. On the other hand, suppose that $A$ is false. There are two subcases. If $P(x)$ is false for every $x$, then $P(x) \to A$ is vacuously true, so the left-hand side is vacuously true. The same reasoning shows that the right-hand side is also true, because in this subcase $\exists x\, P(x)$ is false. For the second subcase, suppose that $P(x)$ is true for some $x$. Then for that $x$, $P(x) \to A$ is false, so the left-hand side is false. The right-hand side is also false, because in this subcase $\exists x\, P(x)$ is true but $A$ is false. Thus in all cases, the two propositions have the same truth value. **b)** If $A$ is true, then both sides are trivially true, because the conditional statements have true conclusions. If $A$ is false, then there are two subcases. If $P(x)$ is false for some $x$, then $P(x) \to A$ is vacuously true for that $x$, so the left-hand side is true. The same reasoning shows that the right-hand side is true, because in this subcase $\forall x\, P(x)$ is false. For the second subcase, suppose that $P(x)$ is true for every $x$. Then for every $x$, $P(x) \to A$ is false, so the left-hand side is false (there is no $x$ making the conditional statement true). The right-hand side is also false, because it is a conditional statement with a true hypothesis and a false conclusion. Thus in all cases, the two propositions have the same truth value. **51.** To show these are not logically equivalent, let $P(x)$ be the statement "$x$ is positive," and let $Q(x)$ be the statement "$x$ is negative" with domain the set of integers. Then $\exists x\, P(x) \wedge \exists x\, Q(x)$ is true, but $\exists x(P(x) \wedge Q(x))$ is false. **53. a)** True **b)** False, unless the domain consists of just one element **c)** True **55. a)** Yes **b)** No **c)** juana, kiko **d)** math273, cs301 **e)** juana, kiko **57.** `sibling(X,Y)` `:- mother(M,X), mother(M,Y), father(F,X),` `father(F,Y)` **59. a)** $\forall x(P(x) \to \neg Q(x))$ **b)** $\forall x(Q(x) \to R(x))$ **c)** $\forall x(P(x) \to \neg R(x))$ **d)** The conclusion does not follow. There may be vain professors, because the premises do not rule out the possibility that there are other vain people besides ignorant ones. **61. a)** $\forall x(P(x) \to \neg Q(x))$ **b)** $\forall x(R(x) \to \neg S(x))$ **c)** $\forall x(\neg Q(x) \to S(x))$ **d)** $\forall x(P(x) \to \neg R(x))$ **e)** The conclusion follows. Suppose $x$ is a baby. Then by the first premise, $x$ is illogical, so by the third premise, $x$ is despised. The second premise says that if $x$ could manage a crocodile, then $x$ would not be despised. Therefore, $x$ cannot manage a crocodile.

## Section 1.5

**1. a)** For every real number $x$ there exists a real number $y$ such that $x$ is less than $y$. **b)** For every real number $x$ and real number $y$, if $x$ and $y$ are both nonnegative, then their product is nonnegative. **c)** For every real number $x$ and real number $y$, there exists a real number $z$ such that $xy = z$. **3. a)** There is some student in your class who has sent a message to some student in your class. **b)** There is some student in your class who has sent a message to every student in your class. **c)** Every student in your class has sent a message to at least one student in your class. **d)** There is a student in your class who has been sent a message by every student in your class. **e)** Every student in your class has been sent a message from at least one student in your class. **f)** Every student in the class has sent a message to every student in the class. **5. a)** Sarah Smith has visited www.att.com. **b)** At least one person has visited www.imdb.org. **c)** Jose Orez has visited at least one website. **d)** There is a website that both Ashok Puri and Cindy Yoon have visited. **e)** There is a person besides David Belcher who has visited all the websites that David Belcher has visited. **f)** There are two different people who have visited exactly the same websites. **7. a)** Abdallah Hussein does not like Japanese cuisine. **b)** Some student at your school likes Korean cuisine, and everyone at your school likes Mexican cuisine. **c)** There is some cuisine that either Monique Arsenault or Jay Johnson likes. **d)** For every pair of distinct students at your school, there is some cuisine that at least one them does not like. **e)** There are two students at your school who like exactly the same set of cuisines. **f)** For every pair of students at your school, there is some cuisine about which they have the same opinion (either they both like it or they both do not like it). **9. a)** $\forall x L(x,\text{Jerry})$ **b)** $\forall x \exists y L(x, y)$ **c)** $\exists y \forall x L(x, y)$ **d)** $\forall x \exists y \neg L(x, y)$ **e)** $\exists x \neg L(\text{Lydia}, x)$ **f)** $\exists x \forall y \neg L(y, x)$ **g)** $\exists x (\forall y L(y, x) \wedge \forall z((\forall w L(w, z)) \rightarrow z = x))$ **h)** $\exists x \exists y (x \neq y \wedge L(\text{Lynn}, x) \wedge L(\text{Lynn}, y) \wedge \forall z(L(\text{Lynn}, z) \rightarrow (z = x \vee z = y)))$ **i)** $\forall x L(x, x)$ **j)** $\exists x \forall y (L(x,y) \leftrightarrow x = y)$ **11. a)** $A(\text{Lois, Professor Michaels})$ **b)** $\forall x(S(x) \rightarrow A(x, \text{Professor Gross}))$ **c)** $\forall x(F(x) \rightarrow (A(x, \text{Professor Miller}) \vee A(\text{Professor Miller}, x)))$ **d)** $\exists x(S(x) \wedge \forall y(F(y) \rightarrow \neg A(x, y)))$ **e)** $\exists x(F(x) \wedge \forall y(S(y) \rightarrow \neg A(y,x)))$ **f)** $\forall y(F(y) \rightarrow \exists x(S(x) \wedge A(x,y)))$ **g)** $\exists x(F(x) \wedge \forall y((F(y) \wedge (y \neq x)) \rightarrow A(x,y)))$ **h)** $\exists x(S(x) \wedge \forall y(F(y) \rightarrow \neg A(y, x)))$ **13. a)** $\neg M$(Chou, Koko) **b)** $\neg M$(Arlene, Sarah) $\wedge \neg T$(Arlene, Sarah) **c)** $\neg M$(Deborah, Jose) **d)** $\forall x M(x,\text{Ken})$ **e)** $\forall x \neg T(x, \text{Nina})$ **f)** $\forall x(T - x, \text{Avi}) \vee M(x, \text{Avi})$ **g)** $\exists x \forall y(y \neq x \rightarrow M(x, y))$ **h)** $\exists x \forall y(y \neq x \rightarrow (M(x, y) \vee T(x, y)))$ **i)** $\exists x \exists y(x \neq y \wedge M(x, y) \wedge M(y, x))$ **j)** $\exists x M(x, x)$ **k)** $\exists x \forall y(x \neq y \rightarrow (\neg M(x, y) \wedge \neg T(y, x)))$ **l)** $\forall x(\exists y(x \neq y \wedge (M(y, x) \vee T(y, x))))$ **m)** $\exists x \exists y(x \neq y \wedge M(x, y) \wedge T(y, x))$ **n)** $\exists x \exists y(x \neq y \wedge \forall z((z \neq x \wedge z \neq y) \rightarrow (M(x, z) \vee M(y, z) \vee T(x, z) \vee T(y, z))))$ **15. a)** $\forall x P(x)$, where $P(x)$ is "$x$ needs a course in discrete mathematics" and the domain consists of all computer science students **b)** $\exists x P(x)$, where $P(x)$ is "$x$ owns a personal computer" and the domain consists of all students in this class **c)** $\forall x \exists y P(x, y)$, where $P(x, y)$ is "$x$ has taken $y$," the domain for $x$ consists of all students in this class, and the domain for $y$ consists of all computer science classes **d)** $\exists x \exists y P(x, y)$, where $P(x, y)$ and domains are the same as in part (c) **e)** $\forall x \forall y P(x, y)$, where $P(x, y)$ is "$x$ has been in $y$," the domain for $x$ consists of all students in this class, and the domain for $y$ consists of all buildings on campus **f)** $\exists x \exists y \forall z(P(z, y) \rightarrow Q(x, z))$, where $P(z, y)$ is "$z$ is in

$y$" and $Q(x, z)$ is "$x$ has been in $z$"; the domain for $x$ consists of all students in the class, the domain for $y$ consists of all buildings on campus, and the domain of $z$ consists of all rooms.   **g)** $\forall x \forall y \exists z(P(z, y) \wedge Q(x, z))$, with same environment as in part (f)   **17. a)** $\forall u \exists m(A(u, m) \wedge \forall n(n \neq m \rightarrow \neg A(u, n)))$, where $A(u, m)$ means that user $u$ has access to mailbox $m$   **b)** $\exists p \forall e(H(e) \wedge S(p, \text{running})) \rightarrow S$ (kernel, working correctly), where $H(e)$ means that error condition $e$ is in effect and $S(x, y)$ means that the status of $x$ is $y$   **c)** $\forall u \forall s(E(s, .edu) \rightarrow A(u, s))$, where $E(s, x)$ means that website $s$ has extension $x$, and $A(u, s)$ means that user $u$ can access website $s$   **d)** $\exists x \exists y(x \neq y \wedge \forall z((\forall s \, M(z,s)) \leftrightarrow (z = x \vee z = y)))$, where $M(a, b)$ means that system $a$ monitors remote server $b$   **19. a)** $\forall x \forall y((x < 0) \wedge (y < 0) \rightarrow (x + y < 0))$ **b)** $\neg \forall x \forall y ((x > 0) \wedge (y > 0) \rightarrow (x - y > 0))$ **c)** $\forall x \forall y (x^2 + y^2 \geq (x + y)^2)$ **d)** $\forall x \forall y (|xy| = |x||y|)$   **21.** $\forall x \exists a \exists b \exists c \exists d ((x > 0) \rightarrow x = a^2 + b^2 + c^2 + d^2)$, where the domain consists of all integers   **23. a)** $\forall x \forall y ((x < 0) \wedge (y < 0) \rightarrow (xy > 0))$ **b)** $\forall x(x - x = 0)$ **c)** $\forall x \exists a \exists b(a \neq b \wedge \forall c(c^2 = x \leftrightarrow (c = a \vee c = b)))$ **d)** $\forall x((x < 0) \rightarrow \neg \exists y(x = y^2))$   **25. a)** There is a multiplicative identity for the real numbers. **b)** The product of two negative real numbers is always a positive real number. **c)** There exist real numbers $x$ and $y$ such that $x^2$ exceeds $y$ but $x$ is less than $y$. **d)** The real numbers are closed under the operation of addition.   **27. a)** True **b)** True **c)** True **d)** True **e)** True **f)** False **g)** False **h)** True **i)** False   **29. a)** $P(1,1) \wedge P(1,2) \wedge P(1,3) \wedge P(2,1) \wedge P(2,2) \wedge P(2, 3) \wedge P(3, 1) \wedge P(3, 2) \wedge P(3, 3)$ **b)** $P(1, 1) \vee P(1, 2) \vee P(1, 3) \vee P(2, 1) \vee P(2, 2) \vee P(2, 3) \vee P(3,1) \vee P(3, 2) \vee P(3, 3)$ **c)** $(P(1, 1) \wedge P(1, 2) \wedge P(1, 3)) \vee (P(2, 1) \wedge P(2, 2) \wedge P(2, 3)) \vee (P(3, 1) \wedge P(3, 2) \wedge P(3, 3))$ **d)** $(P(1, 1) \vee P(2, 1) \vee P(3, 1)) \wedge (P(1, 2) \vee P(2, 2) \vee P(3, 2)) \wedge (P(1, 3) \vee P(2, 3) \vee P(3, 3))$ **31. a)** $\exists x \forall y \exists z \neg T(x, y, z)$ **b)** $\exists x \forall y \neg P(x, y) \wedge \exists x \forall y \neg Q(x, y)$ **c)** $\exists x \forall y (\neg P(x, y) \vee \forall z \neg R(x, y, z))$ **d)** $\exists x \forall y(P(x, y) \wedge \neg Q(x, y))$ **33. a)** $\exists x \exists y \neg P(x, y)$ **b)** $\exists y \forall x \neg P(x, y)$ **c)** $\exists y \exists x(\neg P(x, y) \wedge \neg Q(x, y))$ **d)** $(\forall x \forall y P(x, y)) \vee (\exists x \exists y \neg Q(x, y))$ **e)** $\exists x(\forall y \exists z \neg P(x,y,z) \vee \forall z \exists y \neg P(x, y, z))$ **35.** Any domain with four or more members makes the statement true; any domain with three or fewer members makes the statement false. **37. a)** There is someone in this class such that for every two different math courses, these are not the two and only two math courses this person has taken. **b)** Every person has either visited Libya or has not visited a country other than Libya. **c)** Someone has climbed every mountain in the Himalayas. **d)** There is someone who has neither been in a movie with Kevin Bacon nor has been in a movie with someone who has been in a movie with Kevin Bacon. **39. a)** $x = 2, y = -2$ **b)** $x = -4$ **c)** $x = 17, y = -1$ **41.** $\forall x \forall y \forall z((x \cdot y) \cdot z = x \cdot (y \cdot z))$ **43.** $\forall m \forall b(m \neq 0 \rightarrow \exists x(mx + b = 0 \wedge \forall w(mw + b = 0 \rightarrow w = x)))$ **45. a)** True **b)** False **c)** True **47.** $\neg(\exists x \forall y P(x, y)) \leftrightarrow \forall x(\neg \forall y P(x, y)) \leftrightarrow \forall x \exists y \neg P(x,y)$ **49. a)** Suppose that $\forall x P(x) \wedge \exists x Q(x)$ is true. Then $P(x)$ is true for all $x$ and there is an element $y$ for which $Q(y)$ is true. Because $P(x) \wedge Q(y)$ is true for all $x$ and there is a $y$ for which $Q(y)$ is true, $\forall x \exists y (P(x) \wedge Q(y))$ is true. Conversely, suppose that the second proposition is true. Let $x$ be an element in the domain. There is a $y$ such that $Q(y)$ is true, so $\exists x Q(x)$ is true. Because $\forall x P(x)$ is also true, it follows that the first proposition is true.    **b)** Suppose that $\forall x P(x) \vee \exists x Q(x)$ is true. Then either $P(x)$ is true for all $x$, or there exists a $y$ for which $Q(y)$ is true. In the former case, $P(x) \vee Q(y)$ is true for all $x$, so $\forall x \exists y (P(x) \vee Q(y))$ is true. In the latter case, $Q(y)$ is true for a particular $y$, so $P(x) \vee Q(y)$ is true for all $x$ and consequently $\forall x \exists y (P(x) \vee Q(y))$ is true. Conversely, suppose that the second proposition is true. If $P(x)$ is true for all $x$, then the first proposition is true. If not, $P(x)$ is false for some $x$, and for this $x$ there must be a $y$ such that $P(x) \vee Q(y)$ is true. Hence, $Q(y)$ must be true, so $\exists y Q(y)$ is true. It follows that the first proposition must hold.    **51.** We will show how an expression can be put into prenex normal form (PNF) if subexpressions in it can be put into PNF. Then, working from the inside out, any expression can be put in PNF. (To formalize the argument, it is necessary to use the method of structural induction that will be discussed in Section 5.3.) By Exercise 45 of Section 1.4, we can assume that the proposition uses only $\vee$ and $\neg$ as logical connectives. Now note that any proposition with no quantifiers is already in PNF. (This is the basis case of the argument.) Now suppose that the proposition is of the form $Qx P(x)$, where $Q$ is a quantifier. Because $P(x)$ is a shorter expression than the original proposition, we can put it into PNF. Then $Qx$ followed by this PNF is again in PNF and is equivalent to the original proposition. Next, suppose that the proposition is of the form $\neg P$. If $P$ is already in PNF, we slide the negation sign past all the quantifiers using the equivalences in Table 2 in Section 1.4. Finally, assume that proposition is of the form $P \vee Q$, where each of $P$ and $Q$ is in PNF. If only one of $P$ and $Q$ has quantifiers, then we can use Exercise 46 in Section 1.4 to bring the quantifier in front of both. If both $P$ and $Q$ have quantifiers, we can use Exercise 45 in Section 1.4, Exercise 48, or part (b) of Exercise 49 to rewrite $P \vee Q$ with two quantifiers preceding the disjunction of a proposition of the form $R \vee S$, and then put $R \vee S$ into PNF.

## Section 1.6

**1.** Modus ponens; valid; the conclusion is true, because the hypotheses are true.    **3. a)** Addition   **b)** Simplification   **c)** Modus ponens   **d)** Modus tollens   **e)** Hypothetical syllogism    **5.** Let $w$ be "Randy works hard," let $d$ be "Randy is a dull boy," and let $j$ be "Randy will get the job." The hypotheses are $w$, $w \rightarrow d$, and $d \rightarrow \neg j$. Using modus ponens and the first two hypotheses, $d$ follows. Using modus ponens and the last hypothesis, $\neg j$, which is the desired conclusion, "Randy

will not get the job," follows.    **7.** Universal instantiation is used to conclude that "If Socrates is a man, then Socrates is mortal." Modus ponens is then used to conclude that Socrates is mortal.    **9. a)** Valid conclusions are "I did not take Tuesday off," "I took Thursday off," "It rained on Thursday."  **b)** "I did not eat spicy foods and it did not thunder" is a valid conclusion.   **c)** "I am clever" is a valid conclusion.   **d)** "Ralph is not a CS major" is a valid conclusion.   **e)** "That you buy lots of stuff is good for the U.S. and is good for you" is a valid conclusion.   **f)** "Mice gnaw their food" and "Rabbits are not rodents" are valid conclusions.    **11.** Suppose that $p_1, p_2, \ldots, p_n$ are true. We want to establish that $q \rightarrow r$ is true. If $q$ is false, then we are done, vacuously. Otherwise, $q$ is true, so by the validity of the given argument form (that whenever $p_1, p_2, \ldots, p_n, q$ are true, then $r$ must be true), we know that $r$ is true.    **13. a)** Let $c(x)$ be "$x$ is in this class," $j(x)$ be "$x$ knows how to write programs in JAVA," and $h(x)$ be "$x$ can get a high-paying job." The premises are $c(\text{Doug})$, $j(\text{Doug})$, $\forall x (j(x) \rightarrow h(x))$. Using universal instantiation and the last premise, $j(\text{Doug}) \rightarrow h(\text{Doug})$ follows. Applying modus ponens to this conclusion and the second premise, $h(\text{Doug})$ follows. Using conjunction and the first premise, $c(\text{Doug}) \wedge h(\text{Doug})$ follows. Finally, using existential generalization, the desired conclusion, $\exists x (c(x) \wedge h(x))$ follows.   **b)** Let $c(x)$ be "$x$ is in this class," $w(x)$ be "$x$ enjoys whale watching," and $p(x)$ be "$x$ cares about ocean pollution." The premises are $\exists x (c(x) \wedge w(x))$ and $\forall x (w(x) \rightarrow p(x))$. From the first premise, $c(y) \wedge w(y)$ for a particular person $y$. Using simplification, $w(y)$ follows. Using the second premise and universal instantiation, $w(y) \rightarrow p(y)$ follows. Using modus ponens, $p(y)$ follows, and by conjunction, $c(y) \wedge p(y)$ follows. Finally, by existential generalization, the desired conclusion, $\exists x (c(x) \wedge p(x))$, follows.   **c)** Let $c(x)$ be "$x$ is in this class," $p(x)$ be "$x$ owns a PC," and $w(x)$ be "$x$ can use a word-processing program." The premises are $c(\text{Zeke})$, $\forall x (c(x) \rightarrow p(x))$, and $\forall x (p(x) \rightarrow w(x))$. Using the second premise and universal instantiation, $c(\text{Zeke}) \rightarrow p(\text{Zeke})$ follows. Using the first premise and modus ponens, $p(\text{Zeke})$ follows. Using the third premise and universal instantiation, $p(\text{Zeke}) \rightarrow w(\text{Zeke})$ follows. Finally, using modus ponens, $w(\text{Zeke})$, the desired conclusion, follows.   **d)** Let $j(x)$ be "$x$ is in New Jersey," $f(x)$ be "$x$ lives within 50 miles of the ocean," and $s(x)$ be "$x$ has seen the ocean." The premises are $\forall x (j(x) \rightarrow f(x))$ and $\exists x (j(x) \wedge \neg s(x))$. The second hypothesis and existential instantiation imply that $j(y) \wedge \neg s(y)$ for a particular person $y$. By simplification, $j(y)$ for this person $y$. Using universal instantiation and the first premise, $j(y) \rightarrow f(y)$, and by modus ponens, $f(y)$ follows. By simplification, $\neg s(y)$ follows from $j(y) \wedge \neg s(y)$. So $f(y) \wedge \neg s(y)$ follows by conjunction. Finally, the desired conclusion, $\exists x (f(x) \wedge \neg s(x))$, follows by existential generalization.    **15. a)** Correct, using universal instantiation and modus ponens   **b)** Invalid; fallacy of affirming the conclusion   **c)** Invalid; fallacy of denying the hypothesis   **d)** Correct, using universal instantiation and modus tollens    **17.** We know that *some* $x$ exists that makes

$H(x)$ true, but we cannot conclude that Lola is one such $x$.
**19. a)** Fallacy of affirming the conclusion **b)** Fallacy of begging the question **c)** Valid argument using modus tollens **d)** Fallacy of denying the hypothesis **21.** By the second premise, there is some lion that does not drink coffee. Let Leo be such a creature. By simplification we know that Leo is a lion. By modus ponens we know from the first premise that Leo is fierce. Hence, Leo is fierce and does not drink coffee. By the definition of the existential quantifier, there exist fierce creatures that do not drink coffee, that is, some fierce creatures do not drink coffee. **23.** The error occurs in step (5), because we cannot assume, as is being done here, that the $c$ that makes $P$ true is the same as the $c$ that makes $Q$ true. **25.** We are given the premises $\forall x(P(x) \to Q(x))$ and $\neg Q(a)$. We want to show $\neg P(a)$. Suppose, to the contrary, that $\neg P(a)$ is not true. Then $P(a)$ is true. Therefore by universal modus ponens, we have $Q(a)$. But this contradicts the given premise $\neg Q(a)$. Therefore our supposition must have been wrong, and so $\neg P(a)$ is true, as desired.

**27.**

| Step | Reason |
|---|---|
| 1. $\forall x(P(x) \wedge R(x))$ | Premise |
| 2. $P(a) \wedge R(a)$ | Universal instantiation from (1) |
| 3. $P(a)$ | Simplification from (2) |
| 4. $\forall x(P(x) \to$ $(Q(x) \wedge S(x)))$ | Premise |
| 5. $Q(a) \wedge S(a)$ | Universal modus ponens from (3) and (4) |
| 6. $S(a)$ | Simplification from (5) |
| 7. $R(a)$ | Simplification from (2) |
| 8. $R(a) \wedge S(a)$ | Conjunction from (7) and (6) |
| 9. $\forall x(R(x) \wedge S(x))$ | Universal generalization from (5) |

**29.**

| Step | Reason |
|---|---|
| 1. $\exists x \neg P(x)$ | Premise |
| 2. $\neg P(c)$ | Existential instantiation from (1) |
| 3. $\forall x(P(x) \vee Q(x))$ | Premise |
| 4. $P(c) \vee Q(c)$ | Universal instantiation from (3) |
| 5. $Q(c)$ | Disjunctive syllogism from (4) and (2) |
| 6. $\forall x(\neg Q(x) \vee S(x))$ | Premise |
| 7. $\neg Q(c) \vee S(c)$ | Universal instantiation from (6) |
| 8. $S(c)$ | Disjunctive syllogism from (5) and (7) |
| 9. $\forall x(R(x) \to \neg S(x))$ | Premise |
| 10. $R(c) \to \neg S(c)$ | Universal instantiation from (9) |
| 11. $\neg R(c)$ | Modus tollens from (8) and (10) |
| 12. $\exists x \neg R(x)$ | Existential generalization from (11) |

**31.** Let $p$ be "It is raining"; let $q$ be "Yvette has her umbrella"; let $r$ be "Yvette gets wet." Assumptions are $\neg p \vee q$, $\neg q \vee \neg r$, and $p \vee \neg r$. Resolution on the first two gives $\neg p \vee \neg r$. Resolution on this and the third assumption gives $\neg r$, as desired. **33.** Assume that this proposition is satisfiable. Using resolution on the first two clauses enables us to conclude $q \vee q$; in other words, we know that $q$ has to be true. Using resolution on the last two clauses enables us to conclude $\neg q \vee \neg q$; in other words, we know that $\neg q$ has to be true. This is a contradiction. So this proposition is not satisfiable. **35.** Valid

## Section 1.7

**1.** Let $n = 2k + 1$ and $m = 2l + 1$ be odd integers. Then $n + m = 2(k + l + 1)$ is even. **3.** Suppose that $n$ is even. Then $n = 2k$ for some integer $k$. Therefore, $n^2 = (2k)^2 = 4k^2 = 2(2k^2)$. Because we have written $n^2$ as 2 times an integer, we conclude that $n^2$ is even. **5.** Direct proof: Suppose that $m + n$ and $n + p$ are even. Then $m + n = 2s$ for some integer $s$ and $n + p = 2t$ for some integer $t$. If we add these, we get $m + p + 2n = 2s + 2t$. Subtracting $2n$ from both sides and factoring, we have $m + p = 2s + 2t - 2n = 2(s + t - n)$. Because we have written $m + p$ as 2 times an integer, we conclude that $m + p$ is even. **7.** Because $n$ is odd, we can write $n = 2k + 1$ for some integer $k$. Then $(k+1)^2 - k^2 = k^2 + 2k + 1 - k^2 = 2k + 1 = n$. **9.** Suppose that $r$ is rational and $i$ is irrational and $s = r + i$ is rational. Then by Example 7, $s + (-r) = i$ is rational, which is a contradiction. **11.** Because $\sqrt{2} \cdot \sqrt{2} = 2$ is rational and $\sqrt{2}$ is irrational, the product of two irrational numbers is not necessarily irrational. **13.** Proof by contraposition: If $1/x$ were rational, then by definition $1/x = p/q$ for some integers $p$ and $q$ with $q \neq 0$. Because $1/x$ cannot be 0 (if it were, then we'd have the contradiction $1 = x \cdot 0$ by multiplying both sides by $x$), we know that $p \neq 0$. Now $x = 1/(1/x) = 1/(p/q) = q/p$ by the usual rules of algebra and arithmetic. Hence, $x$ can be written as the quotient of two integers with the denominator nonzero. Thus by definition, $x$ is rational. **15.** Assume that it is not true that $x \geq 1$ or $y \geq 1$. Then $x < 1$ and $y < 1$. Adding these two inequalities, we obtain $x + y < 2$, which is the negation of $x + y \geq 2$. **17. a)** Assume that $n$ is odd, so $n = 2k + 1$ for some integer $k$. Then $n^3 + 5 = 2(4k^3 + 6k^2 + 3k + 3)$. Because $n^3 + 5$ is two times some integer, it is even. **b)** Suppose that $n^3 + 5$ is odd and $n$ is odd. Because $n$ is odd and the product of two odd numbers is odd, it follows that $n^2$ is odd and then that $n^3$ is odd. But then $5 = (n^3 + 5) - n^3$ would have to be even because it is the difference of two odd numbers. Therefore, the supposition that $n^3 + 5$ and $n$ were both odd is wrong. **19.** The proposition is vacuously true because 0 is not a positive integer. Vacuous proof. **21.** $P(1)$ is true because $(a + b)^1 = a + b \geq a^1 + b^1 = a + b$. Direct proof. **23.** If we chose 9 or fewer days on each day of the week, this would account for at most $9 \cdot 7 = 63$ days. But we chose 64 days. This contradiction shows that at least 10 of the days we chose must be on the same day of the week. **25.** Suppose by way of contradiction that $a/b$ is a rational root, where $a$ and $b$ are integers and this fraction is in lowest terms (that is, $a$ and $b$ have no common divisor greater than 1). Plug this proposed root into the equation to obtain $a^3/b^3 + a/b + 1 = 0$. Multiply through by $b^3$ to obtain $a^3 + ab^2 + b^3 = 0$. If $a$ and $b$ are both odd, then the left-hand side is the sum of three odd numbers and therefore must be odd. If $a$ is odd and $b$ is even, then the left-hand side is odd + even + even, which is again odd. Similarly, if $a$ is even and $b$ is odd, then the left-hand side is even + even + odd, which is again odd. Because the fraction $a/b$ is in simplest terms, it cannot happen that both $a$ and $b$ are even. Thus in all cases, the left-hand side is odd, and therefore cannot equal 0. This contradiction shows that no such root exists. **27.** First, assume that $n$ is odd, so that $n = 2k+1$ for some integer $k$. Then $5n+6 = 5(2k+1)+6 = 10k+11 = 2(5k+5)+1$. Hence, $5n+6$ is odd. To prove the converse, suppose that $n$ is even, so that $n = 2k$ for some integer $k$. Then $5n+6 = 10k+6 = 2(5k+3)$, so $5n+6$ is even. Hence, $n$ is odd if and only if $5n+6$ is odd. **29.** This proposition is true. Suppose that $m$ is neither 1 nor $-1$. Then $mn$ has a factor $m$ larger than 1. On the other hand, $mn = 1$, and 1 has no such factor. Hence, $m = 1$ or $m = -1$. In the first case $n = 1$, and in the second case $n = -1$, because $n = 1/m$. **31.** We prove that all these are equivalent to $x$ being even. If $x$ is even, then $x = 2k$ for some integer $k$. Therefore $3x+2 = 3 \cdot 2k+2 = 6k+2 = 2(3k+1)$, which is even, because it has been written in the form $2t$, where $t = 3k+1$. Similarly, $x+5 = 2k+5 = 2k+4+1 = 2(k+2)+1$, so $x+5$ is odd; and $x^2 = (2k)^2 = 2(2k^2)$, so $x^2$ is even. For the converses, we will use a proof by contraposition. So assume that $x$ is not even; thus $x$ is odd and we can write $x = 2k+1$ for some integer $k$. Then $3x+2 = 3(2k+1)+2 = 6k+5 = 2(3k+2)+1$, which is odd (i.e., not even), because it has been written in the form $2t+1$, where $t = 3k+2$. Similarly, $x+5 = 2k+1+5 = 2(k+3)$, so $x+5$ is even (i.e., not odd). That $x^2$ is odd was already proved in Example 1. **33.** We give proofs by contraposition of $(i) \rightarrow (ii)$, $(ii) \rightarrow (i)$, $(i) \rightarrow (iii)$, and $(iii) \rightarrow (i)$. For the first of these, suppose that $3x+2$ is rational, namely, equal to $p/q$ for some integers $p$ and $q$ with $q \neq 0$. Then we can write $x = ((p/q)-2)/3 = (p-2q)/(3q)$, where $3q \neq 0$. This shows that $x$ is rational. For the second conditional statement, suppose that $x$ is rational, namely, equal to $p/q$ for some integers $p$ and $q$ with $q \neq 0$. Then we can write $3x+2 = (3p+2q)/q$, where $q \neq 0$. This shows that $3x+2$ is rational. For the third conditional statement, suppose that $x/2$ is rational, namely, equal to $p/q$ for some integers $p$ and $q$ with $q \neq 0$. Then we can write $x = 2p/q$, where $q \neq 0$. This shows that $x$ is rational. And for the fourth conditional statement, suppose that $x$ is rational, namely, equal to $p/q$ for some integers $p$ and $q$ with $q \neq 0$. Then we can write $x/2 = p/(2q)$, where $2q \neq 0$. This shows that $x/2$ is rational. **35.** No Suppose that $p_1 \rightarrow p_4 \rightarrow p_2 \rightarrow p_5 \rightarrow p_3 \rightarrow p_1$. To prove that one of these propositions implies any of the others, just use hypothetical syllogism repeatedly. **39.** We will give a proof by contradiction. Suppose that $a_1, a_2, \ldots, a_n$ are all less than $A$, where $A$ is the average of these numbers. Then $a_1 + a_2 + \cdots + a_n < nA$. Dividing both sides by $n$ shows that $A = (a_1 + a_2 + \cdots + a_n)/n < A$, which is a contradiction. **41.** We will show that the four statements are equivalent by showing that $(i)$ implies $(ii)$, $(ii)$ implies $(iii)$, $(iii)$ implies $(iv)$, and $(iv)$ implies $(i)$. First, assume that $n$ is even. Then $n = 2k$ for some integer $k$. Then $n + 1 = 2k + 1$, so $n + 1$ is odd. This shows that $(i)$ implies $(ii)$. Next, suppose that $n + 1$ is odd, so $n + 1 = 2k + 1$ for some integer $k$. Then $3n + 1 = 2n + (n+1) = 2(n+k) + 1$, which

shows that $3n + 1$ is odd, showing that $(ii)$ implies $(iii)$. Next, suppose that $3n + 1$ is odd, so $3n + 1 = 2k + 1$ for some integer $k$. Then $3n = (2k+1) - 1 = 2k$, so $3n$ is even. This shows that $(iii)$ implies $(iv)$. Finally, suppose that $n$ is not even. Then $n$ is odd, so $n = 2k + 1$ for some integer $k$. Then $3n = 3(2k+1) = 6k+3 = 2(3k+1)+1$, so $3n$ is odd. This completes a proof by contraposition that $(iv)$ implies $(i)$.

## Section 1.8

**1.** $1^2 + 1 = 2 \geq 2 = 2^1$; $2^2 + 1 = 5 \geq 4 = 2^2$; $3^2 + 1 = 10 \geq 8 = 2^3$; $4^2 + 1 = 17 \geq 16 = 2^4$ **3.** If $x \leq y$, then $\max(x, y) + \min(x, y) = y + x = x + y$. If $x \geq y$, then $\max(x, y) + \min(x, y) = x + y$. Because these are the only two cases, the equality always holds. **5.** Because $|x - y| = |y - x|$, the values of $x$ and $y$ are interchangeable. Therefore, without loss of generality, we can assume that $x \geq y$. Then $(x + y - (x - y))/2 = (x + y - x + y)/2 = 2y/2 = y = \min(x, y)$. Similarly, $(x + y + (x - y))/2 = (x + y + x - y)/2 = 2x/2 = x = \max(x, y)$. **7.** There are four cases. *Case 1:* $x \geq 0$ and $y \geq 0$. Then $|x| + |y| = x + y = |x + y|$. *Case 2:* $x < 0$ and $y < 0$. Then $|x| + |y| = -x + (-y) = -(x + y) = |x + y|$ because $x + y < 0$. *Case 3:* $x \geq 0$ and $y < 0$. Then $|x| + |y| = x + (-y)$. If $x \geq -y$, then $|x + y| = x + y$. But because $y < 0$, $-y > y$, so $|x| + |y| = x + (-y) > x + y = |x + y|$. If $x < -y$, then $|x+y| = -(x+y) = -x+(-y)$. But because $x \geq 0$, $x \geq -x$, so $|x|+|y| = x + (-y) \geq -x + (-y) = |x+y|$. *Case 4:* $x < 0$ and $y \geq 0$. Identical to Case 3 with the roles of $x$ and $y$ reversed. **9.** 10,001, 10,002, $\ldots$, 10,100 are all nonsquares, because $100^2 = 10,000$ and $101^2 = 10,201$; constructive. **11.** $8 = 2^3$ and $9 = 3^2$ **13.** Let $x = 2$ and $y = \sqrt{2}$. If $x^y = 2^{\sqrt{2}}$ is irrational, we are done. If not, then let $x = 2^{\sqrt{2}}$ and $y = \sqrt{2}/4$. Then $x^y = (2^{\sqrt{2}})^{\sqrt{2}/4} = 2^{\sqrt{2} \cdot (\sqrt{2})/4} = 2^{1/2} = \sqrt{2}$. **15. a)** This statement asserts the existence of $x$ with a certain property. If we let $y = x$, then we see that $P(x)$ is true. If $y$ is anything other than $x$, then $P(x)$ is not true. Thus, $x$ is the unique element that makes $P$ true. **b)** The first clause here says that there is an element that makes $P$ true. The second clause says that whenever two elements both make $P$ true, they are in fact the same element. Together these say that $P$ is satisfied by exactly one element. **c)** This statement asserts the existence of an $x$ that makes $P$ true and has the further property that whenever we find an element that makes $P$ true, that element is $x$. In other words, $x$ is the unique element that makes $P$ true. **17.** The equation $|a - c| = |b - c|$ is equivalent to the disjunction of two equations: $a - c = b - c$ or $a - c = -b + c$. The first of these is equivalent to $a = b$, which contradicts the assumptions made in this problem, so the original equation is equivalent to $a - c = -b + c$. By adding $b + c$ to both sides and dividing by 2, we see that this equation is equivalent to $c = (a + b)/2$. Thus, there is a unique solution. Furthermore, this $c$ is an integer, because the sum of the odd integers $a$ and $b$ is even.    **19.** We are being asked to solve $n = (k - 2) + (k + 3)$ for $k$. Using the usual, reversible, rules of algebra, we see that this equation is equivalent to $k = (n - 1)/2$. In other words, this is the one and only value of $k$ that makes our equation true. Because $n$ is odd, $n - 1$ is even, so $k$ is an integer.    **21.** If $x$ is itself an integer, then we can take $n = x$ and $\epsilon = 0$. No other solution is possible in this case, because if the integer $n$ is greater than $x$, then $n$ is at least $x + 1$, which would make $\epsilon \geq 1$. If $x$ is not an integer, then round it up to the next integer, and call that integer $n$. Let $\epsilon = n - x$. Clearly $0 \leq \epsilon < 1$; this is the only $\epsilon$ that will work with this $n$, and $n$ cannot be any larger, because $\epsilon$ is constrained to be less than 1.    **23.** The harmonic mean of distinct positive real numbers $x$ and $y$ is always less than their geometric mean. To prove $2xy/(x + y) < \sqrt{xy}$, multiply both sides by $(x + y)/(2\sqrt{xy})$ to obtain the equivalent inequality $\sqrt{xy} < (x + y)/2$, which is proved in Example 14.    **25.** The parity (oddness or evenness) of the sum of the numbers written on the board never changes, because $j + k$ and $|j - k|$ have the same parity (and at each step we reduce the sum by $j + k$ but increase it by $|j - k|$). Therefore the integer at the end of the process must have the same parity as $1 + 2 + \cdots + (2n) = n(2n + 1)$, which is odd because $n$ is odd.    **27.** Without loss of generality we can assume that $n$ is nonnegative, because the fourth power of an integer and the fourth power of its negative are the same. We divide an arbitrary positive integer $n$ by 10, obtaining a quotient $k$ and remainder $l$, whence $n = 10k + l$, and $l$ is an integer between 0 and 9, inclusive. Then we compute $n^4$ in each of these 10 cases. We get the following values, where $X$ is some integer that is a multiple of 10, whose exact value we do not care about. $(10k + 0)^4 = 10{,}000k^4 = 10{,}000k^4 + 0$, $(10k + 1)^4 = 10{,}000k^4 + X \cdot k^3 + X \cdot k^2 + X \cdot k + 1$, $(10k + 2)^4 = 10{,}000k^4 + X \cdot k^3 + X \cdot k^2 + X \cdot k + 16$, $(10k + 3)^4 = 10{,}000k^4 + X \cdot k^3 + X \cdot k^2 + X \cdot k + 81$, $(10k + 4)^4 = 10{,}000k^4 + X \cdot k^3 + X \cdot k^2 + X \cdot k + 256$, $(10k + 5)^4 = 10{,}000k^4 + X \cdot k^3 + X \cdot k^2 + X \cdot k + 625$, $(10k + 6)^4 = 10{,}000k^4 + X \cdot k^3 + X \cdot k^2 + X \cdot k + 1296$, $(10k + 7)^4 = 10{,}000k^4 + X \cdot k^3 + X \cdot k^2 + X \cdot k + 2401$, $(10k + 8)^4 = 10{,}000k^4 + X \cdot k^3 + X \cdot k^2 + X \cdot k + 4096$, $(10k + 9)^4 = 10{,}000k^4 + X \cdot k^3 + X \cdot k^2 + X \cdot k + 6561$. Because each coefficient indicated by $X$ is a multiple of 10, the corresponding term has no effect on the ones digit of the answer. Therefore the ones digits are 0, 1, 6, 1, 6, 5, 6, 1, 6, 1, respectively, so it is always a 0, 1, 5, or 6.    **29.** Because $n^3 > 100$ for all $n > 4$, we need only note that $n = 1$, $n = 2$, $n = 3$, and $n = 4$ do not satisfy $n^2 + n^3 = 100$.    **31.** Because $5^4 = 625$, both $x$ and $y$ must be less than 5. Then $x^4 + y^4 \leq 4^4 + 4^4 = 512 < 625$.    **33.** If it is not true that $a \leq \sqrt[3]{n}$, $b \leq \sqrt[3]{n}$, or $c \leq \sqrt[3]{n}$, then $a > \sqrt[3]{n}$, $b > \sqrt[3]{n}$, and $c > \sqrt[3]{n}$. Multiplying these inequalities of positive numbers together we obtain $abc < (\sqrt[3]{n})^3 = n$, which implies the negation of our hypothesis that $n = abc$.    **35.** By finding a common denominator, we can assume that the given rational numbers are $a/b$ and $c/b$, where $b$ is a pos-

itive integer and $a$ and $c$ are integers with $a < c$. In particular, $(a + 1)/b \leq c/b$. Thus, $x = (a + \frac{1}{2}\sqrt{2})/b$ is between the two given rational numbers, because $0 < \sqrt{2} < 2$. Furthermore, $x$ is irrational, because if $x$ were rational, then $2(bx - a) = \sqrt{2}$ would be as well, in violation of Example 10 in Section 1.7.    **37. a)** Without loss of generality, we can assume that the $x$ sequence is already sorted into nondecreasing order, because we can relabel the indices. There are only a finite number of possible orderings for the $y$ sequence, so if we can show that we can increase the sum (or at least keep it the same) whenever we find $y_i$ and $y_j$ that are out of order (i.e., $i < j$ but $y_i > y_j$) by switching them, then we will have shown that the sum is largest when the $y$ sequence is in nondecreasing order. Indeed, if we perform the swap, then we have added $x_i y_j + x_j y_i$ to the sum and subtracted $x_i y_i + x_j y_j$. The net effect is to have added $x_i y_j + x_j y_i - x_i y_i - x_j y_j = (x_j - x_i)(y_i - y_j)$, which is nonnegative by our ordering assumptions.    **b)** Similar to part (a)    **39. a)** $6 \to 3 \to 10 \to 5 \to 16 \to 8 \to 4 \to 2 \to 1$ **b)** $7 \to 22 \to 11 \to 34 \to 17 \to 52 \to 26 \to 13 \to 40 \to 20 \to 10 \to 5 \to 16 \to 8 \to 4 \to 2 \to 1$    **c)** $17 \to 52 \to 26 \to 13 \to 40 \to 20 \to 10 \to 5 \to 16 \to 8 \to 4 \to 2 \to 1$    **d)** $21 \to 64 \to 32 \to 16 \to 8 \to 4 \to 2 \to 1$    **41.** Without loss of generality, assume that the upper left and upper right corners of the board are removed. Place three dominoes horizontally to fill the remaining portion of the first row, and fill each of the other seven rows with four horizontal dominoes.    **43.** Because there is an even number of squares in all, either there is an even number of squares in each row or there is an even number of squares in each column. In the former case, tile the board in the obvious way by placing the dominoes horizontally, and in the latter case, tile the board in the obvious way by placing the dominoes vertically.    **45.** We can rotate the board if necessary to make the removed squares be 1 and 16. Square 2 must be covered by a domino. If that domino is placed to cover squares 2 and 6, then the following domino placements are forced in succession: 5-9, 13-14, and 10-11, at which point there is no way to cover square 15. Otherwise, square 2 must be covered by a domino placed at 2-3. Then the following domino placements are forced: 4-8, 11-12, 6-7, 5-9, and 10-14, and again there is no way to cover square 15.    **47.** Remove the two black squares adjacent to a white corner, and remove two white squares other than that corner. Then no domino can cover that white corner.

**49. a)**

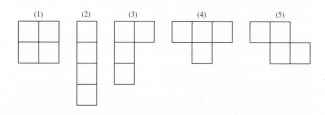

(1)    (2)    (3)    (4)    (5)

**b)** The picture shows tilings for the first four patterns.

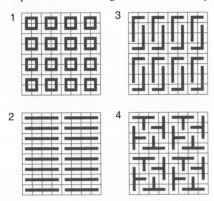

To show that pattern 5 cannot tile the checkerboard, label the squares from 1 to 64, one row at a time from the top, from left to right in each row. Thus, square 1 is the upper left corner, and square 64 is the lower right. Suppose we did have a tiling. By symmetry and without loss of generality, we may suppose that the tile is positioned in the upper left corner, covering squares 1, 2, 10, and 11. This forces a tile to be adjacent to it on the right, covering squares 3, 4, 12, and 13. Continue in this manner and we are forced to have a tile covering squares 6, 7, 15, and 16. This makes it impossible to cover square 8. Thus, no tiling is possible.

## Supplementary Exercises

**1. a)** $q \rightarrow p$  **b)** $q \wedge p$  **c)** $\neg q \vee \neg p$  **d)** $q \leftrightarrow p$   **3. a)** The proposition cannot be false unless $\neg p$ is false, so $p$ is true. If $p$ is true and $q$ is true, then $\neg q \wedge (p \rightarrow q)$ is false, so the conditional statement is true. If $p$ is true and $q$ is false, then $p \rightarrow q$ is false, so $\neg q \wedge (p \rightarrow q)$ is false and the conditional statement is true.  **b)** The proposition cannot be false unless $q$ is false. If $q$ is false and $p$ is true, then $(p \vee q) \wedge \neg p$ is false, and the conditional statement is true. If $q$ is false and $p$ is false, then $(p \vee q) \wedge \neg p$ is false, and the conditional statement is true.  **5.** $\neg q \rightarrow \neg p$; $p \rightarrow q$; $\neg p \rightarrow \neg q$  **7.** $(p \wedge q \wedge r \wedge \neg s) \vee (p \wedge q \wedge \neg r \wedge s) \vee (p \wedge \neg q \wedge r \wedge s) \vee (\neg p \wedge q \wedge r \wedge s)$  **9.** Translating these statements into symbols, using the obvious letters, we have $\neg t \rightarrow \neg g$, $\neg g \rightarrow \neg q$, $r \rightarrow q$, and $\neg t \wedge r$. Assume the statements are consistent. The fourth statement tells us that $\neg t$ must be true. Therefore by modus ponens with the first statement, we know that $\neg g$ is true, hence (from the second statement), that $\neg q$ is true. Also, the fourth statement tells us that $r$ must be true, and so again modus ponens (third statement) makes $q$ true. This is a contradiction: $q \wedge \neg q$. Thus the statements are inconsistent.  **11.** Reject-accept-reject-accept, accept-accept-accept-accept, accept-accept-reject-accept, reject-reject-reject-reject, reject-reject-accept-reject, and reject-accept-accept-accept  **13.** Aaron is a knave and Crystal is a knight; it cannot be determined what Bohan is.  **15.** Brenda  **17.** The premises cannot both be true, because

they are contradictory. Therefore it is (vacuously) true that whenever all the premises are true, the conclusion is also true, which by definition makes this a valid argument. Because the premises are not both true, we cannot conclude that the conclusion is true.  **19.** Use the same propositions as were given in Section 1.3 for a $9 \times 9$ Sudoku puzzle, with the variables indexed from 1 to 16, instead of from 1 to 9, and with a similar change for the propositions for the $4 \times 4$ blocks: $\bigwedge_{r=0}^{3} \bigwedge_{s=0}^{3} \bigwedge_{n=1}^{16} \bigvee_{i=1}^{4} \bigvee_{j=1}^{4} p(4r + i, 4s + j, n)$.  **21. a)** F  **b)** T  **c)** F  **d)** T  **e)** F  **f)** T  **23.** Many answers are possible. One example is United States senators.  **25.** $\forall x \exists y \exists z \, (y \neq z \wedge \forall w (P(w, x) \leftrightarrow (w = y \vee w = z)))$  **27. a)** $\neg \exists x P(x)$  **b)** $\exists x (P(x) \wedge \forall y (P(y) \rightarrow y = x))$  **c)** $\exists x_1 \exists x_2 (P(x_1) \wedge P(x_2) \wedge x_1 \neq x_2 \wedge \forall y (P(y) \rightarrow (y = x_1 \vee y = x_2)))$  **d)** $\exists x_1 \exists x_2 \exists x_3 (P(x_1) \wedge P(x_2) \wedge P(x_3) \wedge x_1 \neq x_2 \wedge x_1 \neq x_3 \wedge x_2 \neq x_3 \wedge \forall y (P(y) \rightarrow (y = x_1 \vee y = x_2 \vee y = x_3)))$  **29.** Suppose that $\exists x (P(x) \rightarrow Q(x))$ is true. Then either $Q(x_0)$ is true for some $x_0$, in which case $\forall x P(x) \rightarrow \exists x \, Q(x)$ is true; or $P(x_0)$ is false for some $x_0$, in which case $\forall x P(x) \rightarrow \exists x Q(x)$ is true. Conversely, suppose that $\exists x (P(x) \rightarrow Q(x))$ is false. That means that $\forall x (P(x) \wedge \neg Q(x))$ is true, which implies $\forall x P(x)$ and $\forall x (\neg Q(x))$. This latter proposition is equivalent to $\neg \exists x Q(x)$. Thus, $\forall x P(x) \rightarrow \exists x Q(x)$ is false.  **31.** No  **33.** $\forall x \, \forall z \, \exists y \, T(x, y, z)$, where $T(x, y, z)$ is the statement that student $x$ has taken class $y$ in department $z$, where the domains are the set of students in the class, the set of courses at this university, and the set of departments in the school of mathematical sciences  **35.** $\exists! x \exists! y \, T(x, y)$ and $\exists x \forall z ((\exists y \forall w (T(z, w) \leftrightarrow w = y)) \leftrightarrow z = x)$, where $T(x, y)$ means that student $x$ has taken class $y$ and the domain is all students in this class  **37.** $P(a) \rightarrow Q(a)$ and $Q(a) \rightarrow R(a)$ by universal instantiation; then $\neg Q(a)$ by modus tollens and $\neg P(a)$ by modus tollens  **39.** We give a proof by contraposition and show that if $\sqrt{x}$ is rational, then $x$ is rational, assuming throughout that $x \geq 0$. Suppose that $\sqrt{x} = p/q$ is rational, $q \neq 0$. Then $x = (\sqrt{x})^2 = p^2/q^2$ is also rational ($q^2$ is again nonzero).  **41.** We can give a constructive proof by letting $m = 10^{500} + 1$. Then $m^2 = (10^{500} + 1)^2 > (10^{500})^2 = 10^{1000}$.  **43.** 23 cannot be written as the sum of eight cubes.  **45.** 223 cannot be written as the sum of 36 fifth powers.

# CHAPTER 2

## Section 2.1

**1. a)** $\{-1, 1\}$  **b)** $\{1, 2, 3, 4, 5, 6, 7, 8, 9, 10, 11\}$  **c)** $\{0, 1, 4, 9, 16, 25, 36, 49, 64, 81\}$  **d)** $\emptyset$  **3. a)** The second is a subset of the first, but the first is not a subset of the second.  **b)** Neither is a subset of the other.  **c)** The first is a subset of the second, but the second is not a subset of the first.  **5. a)** Yes  **b)** No  **c)** No  **7. a)** Yes  **b)** No  **c)** Yes  **d)** No  **e)** No  **f)** No  **9. a)** False  **b)** False  **c)** False  **d)** True  **e)** False  **f)** False  **g)** True  **11. a)** True  **b)** True  **c)** False  **d)** True  **e)** True  **f)** False

**13.**

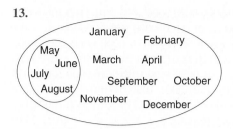

**15.** The dots in certain regions indicate that those regions are not empty.

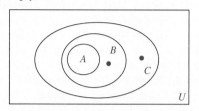

**17.** Suppose that $x \in A$. Because $A \subseteq B$, this implies that $x \in B$. Because $B \subseteq C$, we see that $x \in C$. Because $x \in A$ implies that $x \in C$, it follows that $A \subseteq C$. **19. a)** 1 **b)** 1 **c)** 2 **d)** 3 **21. a)** $\{\emptyset, \{a\}\}$ **b)** $\{\emptyset, \{a\}, \{b\}, \{a, b\}\}$ **c)** $\{\emptyset, \{\emptyset\}, \{\{\emptyset\}\}, \{\emptyset, \{\emptyset\}\}\}$ **23. a)** 8 **b)** 16 **c)** 2 **25.** For the "if" part, given $A \subseteq B$, we want to show that that $\mathcal{P}(A) \subseteq \mathcal{P}(B)$, i.e., if $C \subseteq A$ then $C \subseteq B$. But this follows directly from Exercise 17. For the "only if" part, given that $\mathcal{P}(A) \subseteq \mathcal{P}(B)$, we want to show that $A \subseteq B$. Suppose $a \in A$. Then $\{a\} \subseteq A$, so $\{a\} \in \mathcal{P}(A)$. Since $\mathcal{P}(A) \subseteq \mathcal{P}(B)$, it follows that $\{a\} \in \mathcal{P}(B)$, which means that $\{a\} \subseteq B$. But this implies $a \in B$, as desired. **27. a)** $\{(a, y), (b, y), (c, y), (d, y), (a, z), (b, z), (c, z), (d, z)\}$ **b)** $\{(y, a), (y, b), (y, c), (y, d), (z, a), (z, b), (z, c), (z, d)\}$ **29.** The set of triples $(a, b, c)$, where $a$ is an airline and $b$ and $c$ are cities. A useful subset of this set is the set of triples $(a, b, c)$ for which $a$ flies between $b$ and $c$. **31.** $\emptyset \times A = \{(x, y) \mid x \in \emptyset$ and $y \in A\} = \emptyset = \{(x, y) \mid x \in A$ and $y \in \emptyset\} = A \times \emptyset$ **33. a)** $\{(0, 0), (0, 1), (0, 3), (1, 0), (1, 1), (1, 3), (3, 0), (3, 1), (3, 3)\}$ **b)** $\{(1, 1), (1, 2), (1, a), (1, b), (2, 1), (2, 2), (2, a), (2, b), (a, 1), (a, 2), (a, a), (a, b), (b, 1), (b, 2), (b, a), (b, b)\}$ **35.** $mn$ **37.** $m^n$ **39.** The elements of $A \times B \times C$ consist of 3-tuples $(a, b, c)$, where $a \in A, b \in B$, and $c \in C$, whereas the elements of $(A \times B) \times C$ look like $((a, b), c)$—ordered pairs, the first coordinate of which is again an ordered pair. **41. a)** The square of a real number is never $-1$. True **b)** There exists an integer whose square is 2. False **c)** The square of every integer is positive. False **d)** There is a real number equal to its own square. True **43. a)** $\{-1, 0, 1\}$ **b)** $\mathbf{Z} - \{0, 1\}$ **c)** $\emptyset$ **45.** We must show that $\{\{a\}, \{a, b\}\} = \{\{c\}, \{c, d\}\}$ if and only if $a = c$ and $b = d$. The "if" part is immediate. So assume these two sets are equal. First, consider the case when $a \neq b$. Then $\{\{a\}, \{a, b\}\}$ contains exactly two elements, one of which contains one element. Thus, $\{\{c\}, \{c, d\}\}$ must have the same property, so $c \neq d$ and $\{c\}$ is the element containing exactly one element. Hence, $\{a\} = \{c\}$, which implies that $a = c$. Also, the two-element sets $\{a, b\}$ and $\{c, d\}$ must be equal. Because $a = c$ and $a \neq b$, it follows that $b = d$.

Second, suppose that $a = b$. Then $\{\{a\}, \{a, b\}\} = \{\{a\}\}$, a set with one element. Hence, $\{\{c\}, \{c, d\}\}$ has only one element, which can happen only when $c = d$, and the set is $\{\{c\}\}$. It then follows that $a = c$ and $b = d$. **47.** Let $S = \{a_1, a_2, \ldots, a_n\}$. Represent each subset of $S$ with a bit string of length $n$, where the $i$th bit is 1 if and only if $a_i \in S$. To generate all subsets of $S$, list all $2^n$ bit strings of length $n$ (for instance, in increasing order), and write down the corresponding subsets.

## Section 2.2

**1. a)** The set of students who live within one mile of school and walk to classes **b)** The set of students who live within one mile of school or walk to classes (or do both) **c)** The set of students who live within one mile of school but do not walk to classes **d)** The set of students who walk to classes but live more than one mile away from school **3. a)** $\{0, 1, 2, 3, 4, 5, 6\}$ **b)** $\{3\}$ **c)** $\{1, 2, 4, 5\}$ **d)** $\{0, 6\}$ **5.** $\overline{\overline{A}} = \{x \mid \neg(x \in \overline{A})\} = \{x \mid \neg(\neg x \in A)\} = \{x \mid x \in A\} = A$ **7. a)** $A \cup U = \{x \mid x \in A \lor x \in U\} = \{x \mid x \in A \lor \mathbf{T}\} = \{x \mid \mathbf{T}\} = U$ **b)** $A \cap \emptyset = \{x \mid x \in A \land x \in \emptyset\} = \{x \mid x \in A \land \mathbf{F}\} = \{x \mid \mathbf{F}\} = \emptyset$ **9. a)** $A \cup \overline{A} = \{x \mid x \in A \lor x \notin A\} = U$ **b)** $A \cap \overline{A} = \{x \mid x \in A \land x \notin A\} = \emptyset$ **11. a)** $A \cup B = \{x \mid x \in A \lor x \in B\} = \{x \mid x \in B \lor x \in A\} = B \cup A$ **b)** $A \cap B = \{x \mid x \in A \land x \in B\} = \{x \mid x \in B \land x \in A\} = B \cap A$ **13.** Suppose $x \in A \cap (A \cup B)$. Then $x \in A$ and $x \in A \cup B$ by the definition of intersection. Because $x \in A$, we have proved that the left-hand side is a subset of the right-hand side. Conversely, let $x \in A$. Then by the definition of union, $x \in A \cup B$ as well. Therefore $x \in A \cap (A \cup B)$ by the definition of intersection, so the right-hand side is a subset of the left-hand side. **15. a)** $x \in \overline{A \cup B} \equiv x \notin A \cup B \equiv \neg(x \in A \lor x \in B) \equiv \neg(x \in A) \land \neg(x \in B) \equiv x \notin A \land x \notin B \equiv x \in \overline{A} \land x \in \overline{B} \equiv x \in \overline{A} \cap \overline{B}$

**b)**

| $A$ | $B$ | $A \cup B$ | $\overline{A \cup B}$ | $\overline{A}$ | $\overline{B}$ | $\overline{A} \cap \overline{B}$ |
|---|---|---|---|---|---|---|
| 1 | 1 | 1 | 0 | 0 | 0 | 0 |
| 1 | 0 | 1 | 0 | 0 | 1 | 0 |
| 0 | 1 | 1 | 0 | 1 | 0 | 0 |
| 0 | 0 | 0 | 1 | 1 | 1 | 1 |

**17. a)** $x \in \overline{A \cap B \cap C} \equiv x \notin A \cap B \cap C \equiv x \notin A \lor x \notin B \lor x \notin C \equiv x \in \overline{A} \lor x \in \overline{B} \lor x \in \overline{C} \equiv x \in \overline{A} \cup \overline{B} \cup \overline{C}$

**b)**

| $A$ | $B$ | $C$ | $A \cap B \cap C$ | $\overline{A \cap B \cap C}$ | $\overline{A}$ | $\overline{B}$ | $\overline{C}$ | $\overline{A} \cup \overline{B} \cup \overline{C}$ |
|---|---|---|---|---|---|---|---|---|
| 1 | 1 | 1 | 1 | 0 | 0 | 0 | 0 | 0 |
| 1 | 1 | 0 | 0 | 1 | 0 | 0 | 1 | 1 |
| 1 | 0 | 1 | 0 | 1 | 0 | 1 | 0 | 1 |
| 1 | 0 | 0 | 0 | 1 | 0 | 1 | 1 | 1 |
| 0 | 1 | 1 | 0 | 1 | 1 | 0 | 0 | 1 |
| 0 | 1 | 0 | 0 | 1 | 1 | 0 | 1 | 1 |
| 0 | 0 | 1 | 0 | 1 | 1 | 1 | 0 | 1 |
| 0 | 0 | 0 | 0 | 1 | 1 | 1 | 1 | 1 |

**19. a)** Both sides equal $\{x \mid x \in A \wedge x \notin B\}$. **b)** $A = A \cap U = A \cap (B \cup \overline{B}) = (A \cap B) \cup (A \cap \overline{B})$ **21.** $x \in A \cup (B \cup C) \equiv (x \in A) \vee (x \in (B \cup C)) \equiv (x \in A) \vee (x \in B \vee x \in C) \equiv (x \in A \vee x \in B) \vee (x \in C) \equiv x \in (A \cup B) \cup C$ **23.** $x \in A \cup (B \cap C) \equiv (x \in A) \vee (x \in (B \cap C)) \equiv (x \in A) \vee (x \in B \wedge x \in C) \equiv (x \in A \vee x \in B) \wedge (x \in A \vee x \in C) \equiv x \in (A \cup B) \cap (A \cup C)$ **25. a)** $\{4,6\}$ **b)** $\{0,1,2,3,4,5,6,7,8,9,10\}$ **c)** $\{4, 5, 6, 8, 10\}$ **d)** $\{0,2,4, 5,6,7,8,9,10\}$ **27. a)** The double-shaded portion is the desired set.

**b)** The desired set is the entire shaded portion.

**c)** The desired set is the entire shaded portion.

**29. a)** $B \subseteq A$ **b)** $A \subseteq B$ **c)** $A \cap B = \emptyset$ **d)** Nothing, because this is always true **e)** $A = B$ **31.** $A \subseteq B \equiv \forall x (x \in A \rightarrow x \in B) \equiv \forall x (x \notin B \rightarrow x \notin A) \equiv \forall x (x \in \overline{B} \rightarrow x \in \overline{A}) \equiv \overline{B} \subseteq \overline{A}$ **33.** The set of students who are computer science majors but not mathematics majors or who are mathematics majors but not computer science majors **35.** An element is in $(A \cup B) - (A \cap B)$ if it is in the union of $A$ and $B$ but not in the intersection of $A$ and $B$, which means that it is in either $A$ or $B$ but not in both $A$ and $B$. This is exactly what it means for an element to belong to $A \oplus B$. **37. a)** $A \oplus A = (A - A) \cup (A - A) = \emptyset \cup \emptyset = \emptyset$ **b)** $A \oplus \emptyset = (A - \emptyset) \cup (\emptyset - A) = A \cup \emptyset = A$ **c)** $A \oplus U = (A - U) \cup (U - A) = \emptyset \cup \overline{A} = \overline{A}$ **d)** $A \oplus \overline{A} = (A - \overline{A}) \cup (\overline{A} - A) = A \cup \overline{A} = U$ **39.** $B = \emptyset$ **41.** Yes **43.** Yes **45.** If $A \cup B$ were finite, then it would have $n$ elements for some natural number $n$. But $A$ already has more than $n$ elements, because it is infinite, and $A \cup B$ has all the elements that $A$ has, so $A \cup B$ has more than $n$ elements. This contradiction shows that $A \cup B$ must be infinite. **47. a)** $\{1, 2, 3, \ldots, n\}$ **b)** $\{1\}$ **49. a)** $A_n$ **b)** $\{0, 1\}$ **51. a)** $\mathbf{Z}$, $\{-1, 0, 1\}$ **b)** $\mathbf{Z} - \{0\}$, $\emptyset$ **c)** $\mathbf{R}$, $[-1, 1]$ **d)** $[1, \infty)$, $\emptyset$ **53. a)** $\{1, 2, 3, 4, 7, 8, 9, 10\}$ **b)** $\{2, 4, 5, 6, 7\}$ **c)** $\{1, 10\}$ **55.** The bit in the $i$th position of the bit string of the difference of two sets is 1 if the $i$th bit of the first string is 1 and the $i$th bit of the second string is 0, and is 0 otherwise. **57. a)** 11 1110 0000 0000 0000 0000 0000 $\vee$ 01 1100 1000 0000 0100 0101 0000 = 11 1110 1000 0000 0100 0101 0000, representing $\{a, b, c, d, e, g, p, t, v\}$

**b)** 11 1110 0000 0000 0000 0000 0000 $\wedge$ 01 1100 1000 0000 0100 0101 0000 = 01 1100 0000 0000 0000 0000 0000, representing $\{b, c, d\}$ **c)** (11 1110 0000 0000 0000 0000 0000 $\vee$ 00 0110 0110 0001 1000 0110 0110) $\wedge$ (01 1100 1000 0000 0100 0101 0000 $\vee$ 00 1010 0010 0000 1000 0010 0111) = 11 1110 0110 0001 1000 0110 0110 $\wedge$ 01 1110 1010 0000 1100 0111 0111 = 01 1110 0010 0000 1000 0110 0110, representing $\{b, c, d, e, i, o, t, u, x, y\}$ **d)** 11 1110 0000 0000 0000 0000 0000 $\vee$ 01 1100 1000 0000 0100 0101 0000 $\vee$ 00 1010 0010 0000 1000 0010 0111 $\vee$ 00 0110 0110 0001 1000 0110 0110 = 11 1110 1110 0001 1100 0111 0111, representing $\{a,b,c,d,e,g,h,i,n,o,p,t,u,v,x,y,z\}$ **59. a)** $\{1, 2, 3, \{1, 2, 3\}\}$ **b)** $\{\emptyset\}$ **c)** $\{\emptyset, \{\emptyset\}\}$ **d)** $\{\emptyset, \{\emptyset\}, \{\emptyset, \{\emptyset\}\}\}$ **61. a)** $\{3 \cdot a, 3 \cdot b, 1 \cdot c, 4 \cdot d\}$ **b)** $\{2 \cdot a, 2 \cdot b\}$ **c)** $\{1 \cdot a, 1 \cdot c\}$ **d)** $\{1 \cdot b, 4 \cdot d\}$ **e)** $\{5 \cdot a, 5 \cdot b, 1 \cdot c, 4 \cdot d\}$ **63.** $\overline{F} = \{0.4 \text{ Alice}, 0.1 \text{ Brian}, 0.6 \text{ Fred}, 0.9 \text{ Oscar}, 0.5 \text{ Rita}\}$, $\overline{R} = \{0.6 \text{ Alice}, 0.2 \text{ Brian}, 0.8 \text{ Fred}, 0.1 \text{ Oscar}, 0.3 \text{ Rita}\}$ **65.** $\{0.4 \text{ Alice}, 0.8 \text{ Brian}, 0.2 \text{ Fred}, 0.1 \text{ Oscar}, 0.5 \text{ Rita}\}$

## Section 2.3

**1. a)** $f(0)$ is not defined. **b)** $f(x)$ is not defined for $x < 0$. **c)** $f(x)$ is not well-defined because there are two distinct values assigned to each $x$. **3. a)** Not a function **b)** A function **c)** Not a function **5. a)** Domain the set of bit strings; range the set of integers **b)** Domain the set of bit strings; range the set of even nonnegative integers **c)** Domain the set of bit strings; range the set of nonnegative integers not exceeding 7 **d)** Domain the set of positive integers; range the set of squares of positive integers $= \{1, 4, 9, 16, \ldots\}$ **7. a)** Domain $\mathbf{Z}^+ \times \mathbf{Z}^+$; range $\mathbf{Z}^+$ **b)** Domain $\mathbf{Z}^+$; range $\{0, 1, 2, 3, 4, 5, 6, 7, 8, 9\}$ **c)** Domain the set of bit strings; range $\mathbf{N}$ **d)** Domain the set of bit strings; range $\mathbf{N}$ **9. a)** 1 **b)** 0 **c)** 0 **d)** $-1$ **e)** 3 **f)** $-1$ **g)** 2 **h)** 1 **11.** Only the function in part (a) **13.** Only the functions in parts (a) and (d) **15. a)** Onto **b)** Not onto **c)** Onto **d)** Not onto **e)** Onto **17. a)** Depends on whether teachers share offices **b)** One-to-one assuming only one teacher per bus **c)** Most likely not one-to-one, especially if salary is set by a collective bargaining agreement **d)** One-to-one **19.** Answers will vary. **a)** Set of offices at the school; probably not onto **b)** Set of buses going on the trip; onto, assuming every bus gets a teacher chaperone **c)** Set of real numbers; not onto **d)** Set of strings of nine digits with hyphens after third and fifth digits; not onto **21. a)** The function $f(x)$ with $f(x) = 3x + 1$ when $x \geq 0$ and $f(x) = -3x + 2$ when $x < 0$ **b)** $f(x) = |x| + 1$ **c)** The function $f(x)$ with $f(x) = 2x + 1$ when $x \geq 0$ and $f(x) = -2x$ when $x < 0$ **d)** $f(x) = x^2 + 1$ **23. a)** Yes **b)** No **c)** Yes **d)** No **25.** Suppose that $f$ is strictly decreasing. This means that $f(x) > f(y)$ whenever $x < y$. To show that $g$ is strictly increasing, suppose that $x < y$. Then $g(x) = 1/f(x) < 1/f(y) = g(y)$. Conversely, suppose that $g$ is strictly increasing. This means that $g(x) < g(y)$ whenever $x < y$. To show that $f$ is strictly decreasing, suppose that $x < y$. Then $f(x) = 1/g(x) > 1/g(y) = f(y)$. **27. a)** Let $f$ be a given strictly decreasing function from $\mathbf{R}$ to itself. If

$a < b$, then $f(a) > f(b)$; if $a > b$, then $f(a) < f(b)$. Thus if $a \neq b$, then $f(a) \neq f(b)$. **b)** Answers will vary; for example, $f(x) = 0$ for $x < 0$ and $f(x) = -x$ for $x \geq 0$. **29.** The function is not one-to-one, so it is not invertible. On the restricted domain, the function is the identity function on the nonnegative real numbers, $f(x) = x$, so it is its own inverse. **31. a)** $f(S) = \{0, 1, 3\}$ **b)** $f(S) = \{0, 1, 3, 5, 8\}$ **c)** $f(S) = \{0, 8, 16, 40\}$ **d)** $f(S) = \{1, 12, 33, 65\}$ **33. a)** Let $x$ and $y$ be distinct elements of $A$. Because $g$ is one-to-one, $g(x)$ and $g(y)$ are distinct elements of $B$. Because $f$ is one-to-one, $f(g(x)) = (f \circ g)(x)$ and $f(g(y)) = (f \circ g)(y)$ are distinct elements of $C$. Hence, $f \circ g$ is one-to-one. **b)** Let $y \in C$. Because $f$ is onto, $y = f(b)$ for some $b \in B$. Now because $g$ is onto, $b = g(x)$ for some $x \in A$. Hence, $y = f(b) = f(g(x)) = (f \circ g)(x)$. It follows that $f \circ g$ is onto. **35.** No. For example, suppose that $A = \{a\}$, $B = \{b, c\}$, and $C = \{d\}$. Let $g(a) = b$, $f(b) = d$, and $f(c) = d$. Then $f$ and $f \circ g$ are onto, but $g$ is not. **37.** $(f + g)(x) = x^2 + x + 3$, $(fg)(x) = x^3 + 2x^2 + x + 2$ **39.** $f$ is one-to-one because $f(x_1) = f(x_2) \rightarrow ax_1 + b = ax_2 + b \rightarrow ax_1 = ax_2 \rightarrow x_1 = x_2$. $f$ is onto because $f((y - b)/a) = y$. $f^{-1}(y) = (y - b)/a$. **41. a)** $A = B = \mathbf{R}$, $S = \{x \mid x > 0\}$, $T = \{x \mid x < 0\}$, $f(x) = x^2$ **b)** It suffices to show that $f(S) \cap f(T) \subseteq f(S \cap T)$. Let $y \in B$ be an element of $f(S) \cap f(T)$. Then $y \in f(S)$, so $y = f(x_1)$ for some $x_1 \in S$. Similarly, $y = f(x_2)$ for some $x_2 \in T$. Because $f$ is one-to-one, it follows that $x_1 = x_2$. Therefore $x_1 \in S \cap T$, so $y \in f(S \cap T)$. **43. a)** $\{x \mid 0 \leq x < 1\}$ **b)** $\{x \mid -1 \leq x < 2\}$ **c)** $\emptyset$ **45.** $\overline{f^{-1}(S)} = \{x \in A \mid f(x) \notin S\} = \overline{\{x \in A \mid f(x) \in S\}} = \overline{f^{-1}(S)}$ **47.** Let $x = \lfloor x \rfloor + \epsilon$, where $\epsilon$ is a real number with $0 \leq \epsilon < 1$. If $\epsilon < \frac{1}{2}$, then $\lfloor x \rfloor - 1 < x - \frac{1}{2} < \lfloor x \rfloor$, so $\lceil x - \frac{1}{2} \rceil = \lfloor x \rfloor$ and this is the integer closest to $x$. If $\epsilon > \frac{1}{2}$, then $\lfloor x \rfloor < x - \frac{1}{2} < \lfloor x \rfloor + 1$, so $\lceil x - \frac{1}{2} \rceil = \lfloor x \rfloor + 1$ and this is the integer closest to $x$. If $\epsilon = \frac{1}{2}$, then $\lceil x - \frac{1}{2} \rceil = \lfloor x \rfloor$, which is the smaller of the two integers that surround $x$ and are the same distance from $x$. **49.** Write the real number $x$ as $\lfloor x \rfloor + \epsilon$, where $\epsilon$ is a real number with $0 \leq \epsilon < 1$. Because $\epsilon = x - \lfloor x \rfloor$, it follows that $0 \leq -\lfloor x \rfloor < 1$. The first two inequalities, $x - 1 < \lfloor x \rfloor$ and $\lfloor x \rfloor \leq x$, follow directly. For the other two inequalities, write $x = \lceil x \rceil - \epsilon'$, where $0 \leq \epsilon' < 1$. Then $0 \leq \lceil x \rceil - x < 1$, and the desired inequality follows. **51. a)** If $x < n$, because $\lfloor x \rfloor \leq x$, it follows that $\lfloor x \rfloor < n$. Suppose that $x \geq n$. By the definition of the floor function, it follows that $\lfloor x \rfloor \geq n$. This means that if $\lfloor x \rfloor < n$, then $x < n$. **b)** If $n < x$, then because $x \leq \lceil x \rceil$, it follows that $n \leq \lceil x \rceil$. Suppose that $n \geq x$. By the definition of the ceiling function, it follows that $\lceil x \rceil \leq n$. This means that if $n < \lceil x \rceil$, then $n < x$. **53.** If $n$ is even, then $n = 2k$ for some integer $k$. Thus, $\lfloor n/2 \rfloor = \lfloor k \rfloor = k = n/2$. If $n$ is odd, then $n = 2k + 1$ for some integer $k$. Thus, $\lfloor n/2 \rfloor = \lfloor k + \frac{1}{2} \rfloor = k = (n - 1)/2$. **55.** Assume that $x \geq 0$. The left-hand side is $\lceil -x \rceil$ and the right-hand side is $-\lfloor x \rfloor$. If $x$ is an integer, then both sides equal $-x$. Otherwise, let $x = n + \epsilon$, where $n$ is a natural number and $\epsilon$ is a real number with $0 \leq \epsilon < 1$. Then $\lceil -x \rceil = \lceil -n - \epsilon \rceil = -n$ and $-\lfloor x \rfloor = -\lfloor n + \epsilon \rfloor = -n$ also. When $x < 0$, the equation also holds because it can

be obtained by substituting $-x$ for $x$. **57.** $\lceil b \rceil - \lfloor a \rfloor - 1$ **59. a)** 1 **b)** 3 **c)** 126 **d)** 3600 **61. a)** 100 **b)** 256 **c)** 1030 **d)** 30,200

**63.**

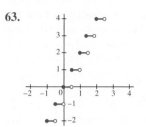

**65.**

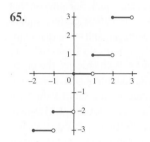

**67. a)** **b)**

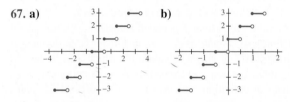

**c)** **d)**

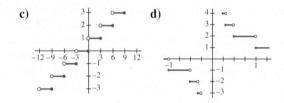

**e)** **f)**

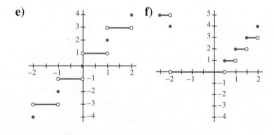

**g)** See part (a). **69.** $f^{-1}(y) = (y - 1)^{1/3}$ **71. a)** $f_{A \cap B}(x) = 1 \leftrightarrow x \in A \cap B \leftrightarrow x \in A$ and $x \in B \leftrightarrow f_A(x) = 1$ and $f_B(x) = 1 \leftrightarrow f_A(x) f_B(x) = 1$ **b)** $f_{A \cup B}(x) = 1 \leftrightarrow x \in A \cup B \leftrightarrow x \in A$ or $x \in B \leftrightarrow f_A(x) = 1$ or $f_B(x) = 1 \leftrightarrow f_A(x) + f_B(x) - f_A(x) f_B(x) = 1$ **c)** $f_{\overline{A}}(x) = 1 \leftrightarrow x \in \overline{A} \leftrightarrow x \notin A \leftrightarrow f_A(x) = 0 \leftrightarrow 1 - f_A(x) = 1$ **d)** $f_{A \oplus B}(x) = 1 \leftrightarrow x \in A \oplus B \leftrightarrow (x \in A$ and $x \notin B)$ or $(x \notin A$ and $x \in B) \leftrightarrow f_A(x) + f_B(x) - 2 f_A(x) f_B(x) = 1$ **73. a)** True; because $\lfloor x \rfloor$ is already an integer, $\lceil \lfloor x \rfloor \rceil = \lfloor x \rfloor$. **b)** False; $x = \frac{1}{2}$ is a counterexample. **c)** True; if $x$ or $y$ is an integer, then by property 4b in Table 1, the difference is 0. If neither $x$ nor $y$ is an integer, then $x = n + \epsilon$ and $y = m + \delta$, where $n$ and $m$ are integers and $\epsilon$ and $\delta$ are positive real numbers less than 1. Then $m + n < x + y < m + n + 2$, so $\lceil x + y \rceil$ is either $m + n + 1$ or $m + n + 2$. Therefore, the given expression is either $(n + 1) + (m + 1) - (m + n + 1) = 1$ or $(n + 1) + (m + 1) - (m + n + 2) = 0$, as desired.  **d)** False; $x = \frac{1}{4}$ and $y = 3$ is a counterexample.  **e)** False; $x = \frac{1}{2}$ is a counterexample.    **75. a)** If $x$ is a positive integer, then the two sides are equal. So suppose that $x = n^2 + m + \epsilon$, where $n^2$ is the largest perfect square less than $x$, $m$ is a nonnegative integer, and $0 < \epsilon \le 1$. Then both $\sqrt{x}$ and $\sqrt{\lfloor x \rfloor} = \sqrt{n^2 + m}$ are between $n$ and $n + 1$, so both sides equal $n$.  **b)** If $x$ is a positive integer, then the two sides are equal. So suppose that $x = n^2 - m - \epsilon$, where $n^2$ is the smallest perfect square greater than $x$, $m$ is a nonnegative integer, and $\epsilon$ is a real number with $0 < \epsilon \le 1$. Then both $\sqrt{x}$ and $\sqrt{\lceil x \rceil} = \sqrt{n^2 - m}$ are between $n - 1$ and $n$. Therefore, both sides of the equation equal $n$.  **77. a)** Domain is $\mathbf{Z}$; codomain is $\mathbf{R}$; domain of definition is the set of nonzero integers; the set of values for which $f$ is undefined is $\{0\}$; not a total function.  **b)** Domain is $\mathbf{Z}$; codomain is $\mathbf{Z}$; domain of definition is $\mathbf{Z}$; set of values for which $f$ is undefined is $\emptyset$; total function.  **c)** Domain is $\mathbf{Z} \times \mathbf{Z}$; codomain is $\mathbf{Q}$; domain of definition is $\mathbf{Z} \times (\mathbf{Z} - \{0\})$; set of values for which $f$ is undefined is $\mathbf{Z} \times \{0\}$; not a total function.  **d)** Domain is $\mathbf{Z} \times \mathbf{Z}$; codomain is $\mathbf{Z}$; domain of definition is $\mathbf{Z} \times \mathbf{Z}$; set of values for which $f$ is undefined is $\emptyset$; total function.  **e)** Domain is $\mathbf{Z} \times \mathbf{Z}$; codomain is $\mathbf{Z}$; domain of definitions is $\{(m, n) \mid m > n\}$; set of values for which $f$ is undefined is $\{(m, n) \mid m \le n\}$; not a total function.  **79. a)** By definition, to say that $S$ has cardinality $m$ is to say that $S$ has exactly $m$ distinct elements. Therefore we can assign the first object to 1, the second to 2, and so on. This provides the one-to-one correspondence.  **b)** By part (a), there is a bijection $f$ from $S$ to $\{1, 2, \ldots, m\}$ and a bijection $g$ from $T$ to $\{1, 2, \ldots, m\}$. Then the composition $g^{-1} \circ f$ is the desired bijection from $S$ to $T$.

## Section 2.4

**1. a)** 3  **b)** $-1$  **c)** 787  **d)** 2639    **3. a)** $a_0 = 2$, $a_1 = 3$, $a_2 = 5$, $a_3 = 9$    **b)** $a_0 = 1$, $a_1 = 4$, $a_2 = 27$, $a_3 = 256$  **c)** $a_0 = 0$, $a_1 = 0$, $a_2 = 1$, $a_3 = 1$  **d)** $a_0 = 0$, $a_1 = 1$, $a_2 = 2$, $a_3 = 3$    **5. a)** 2, 5, 8, 11, 14, 17, 20, 23, 26, 29  **b)** 1, 1, 1, 2, 2, 2, 3, 3, 3, 4  **c)** 1, 1, 3, 3, 5, 5, 7, 7, 9, 9  **d)** $-1$, $-2$, $-2$, 8, 88, 656, 4912, 40064, 362368, 3627776  **e)** 3, 6, 12, 24, 48, 96, 192, 384, 768, 1536  **f)** 2, 4, 6, 10, 16, 26, 42, 68, 110, 178  **g)** 1, 2, 2, 3, 3, 3, 3, 4, 4, 4  **h)** 3, 3, 5, 4, 4, 3, 5, 5, 4, 3    **7.** Each term could be twice the previous term; the $n$th term could be obtained from the previous term by adding $n - 1$; the terms could be the positive integers that are not multiples of 3; there are infinitely many other possibilities.    **9. a)** 2, 12, 72, 432, 2592  **b)** 2, 4, 16, 256, 65,536 **c)** 1, 2, 5, 11, 26  **d)** 1, 1, 6, 27, 204  **e)** 1, 2, 0, 1, 3    **11. a)** 6, 17, 49, 143, 421    **b)** $49 = 5 \cdot 17 - 6 \cdot 6$, $143 = 5 \cdot 49 - 6 \cdot 17$, $421 = 5 \cdot 143 - 6 \cdot 49$    **c)** $5a_{n-1} - 6a_{n-2} = 5(2^{n-1} + 5 \cdot$

$3^{n-1}) - 6(2^{n-2} + 5 \cdot 3^{n-2}) = 2^{n-2}(10 - 6) + 3^{n-2}(75 - 30) = 2^{n-2} \cdot 4 + 3^{n-2} \cdot 9 \cdot 5 = 2^n + 3^n \cdot 5 = a_n$    **13. a)** Yes  **b)** No  **c)** No  **d)** Yes  **e)** Yes  **f)** Yes **g)** No  **h)** No    **15. a)** $a_{n-1} + 2a_{n-2} + 2n - 9 = -(n - 1) + 2 + 2[-(n - 2) + 2] + 2n - 9 = -n + 2 = a_n$  **b)** $a_{n-1} + 2a_{n-2} + 2n - 9 = 5(-1)^{n-1} - (n - 1) + 2 + 2[5(-1)^{n-2} - (n - 2) + 2] + 2n - 9 = 5(-1)^{n-2}(-1 + 2) - n + 2 = a_n$  **c)** $a_{n-1} + 2a_{n-2} + 2n - 9 = 3(-1)^{n-1} + 2^{n-1} - (n-1) + 2 + 2[3(-1)^{n-2} + 2^{n-2} - (n - 2) + 2] + 2n - 9 = 3(-1)^{n-2}(-1 + 2) + 2^{n-2}(2 + 2) - n + 2 = a_n$  **d)** $a_{n-1} + 2a_{n-2} + 2n - 9 = 7 \cdot 2^{n-1} - (n - 1) + 2 + 2[7 \cdot 2^{n-2} - (n - 2) + 2] + 2n - 9 = 2^{n-2}(7 \cdot 2 + 2 \cdot 7) - n + 2 = a_n$    **17. a)** $a_n = 2 \cdot 3^n$  **b)** $a_n = 2n + 3$  **c)** $a_n = 1 + n(n + 1)/2$  **d)** $a_n = n^2 + 4n + 4$  **e)** $a_n = 1$  **f)** $a_n = (3^{n+1} - 1)/2$  **g)** $a_n = 5n!$  **h)** $a_n = 2^n n!$    **19. a)** $a_n = 3a_{n-1}$  **b)** 5,904,900    **21. a)** $a_n = n + a_{n-1}$, $a_0 = 0$  **b)** $a_{12} = 78$  **c)** $a_n = n(n + 1)/2$    **23.** $B(k) = [1 + (0.07/12)]B(k - 1) - 100$, with $B(0) = 5000$    **25. a)** One 1 and one 0, followed by two 1s and two 0s, followed by three 1s and three 0s, and so on; 1, 1, 1  **b)** The positive integers are listed in increasing order with each even positive integer listed twice; 9, 10, 10.  **c)** The terms in odd-numbered locations are the successive powers of 2; the terms in even-numbered locations are all 0; 32, 0, 64.  **d)** $a_n = 3 \cdot 2^{n-1}$; 384, 768, 1536  **e)** $a_n = 15 - 7(n - 1) = 22 - 7n$; $-34$, $-41$, $-48$  **f)** $a_n = (n^2 + n + 4)/2$; 57, 68, 80  **g)** $a_n = 2n^3$; 1024, 1458, 2000  **h)** $a_n = n! + 1$; 362881, 3628801, 39916801    **27.** Among the integers $1, 2, \ldots, a_n$, where $a_n$ is the $n$th positive integer not a perfect square, the nonsquares are $a_1, a_2, \ldots, a_n$ and the squares are $1^2, 2^2, \ldots, k^2$, where $k$ is the integer with $k^2 < n + k < (k + 1)^2$. Consequently, $a_n = n + k$, where $k^2 < a_n < (k + 1)^2$. To find $k$, first note that $k^2 < n + k < (k + 1)^2$, so $k^2 + 1 \le n + k \le (k + 1)^2 - 1$. Hence, $(k - \frac{1}{2})^2 + \frac{3}{4} = k^2 - k + 1 \le n \le k^2 + k = (k + \frac{1}{2})^2 - \frac{1}{4}$. It follows that $k - \frac{1}{2} < \sqrt{n} < k + \frac{1}{2}$, so $k = \{\sqrt{n}\}$ and $a_n = n + k = n + \{\sqrt{n}\}$.  **29. a)** 20  **b)** 11  **c)** 30  **d)** 511    **31. a)** 1533  **b)** 510  **c)** 4923  **d)** 9842    **33. a)** 21  **b)** 78  **c)** 18  **d)** 18    **35.** $\sum_{j=1}^{n}(a_j - a_{j-1}) = a_n - a_0$    **37. a)** $n^2$  **b)** $n(n + 1)/2$    **39.** 15150    **41.** $\frac{n(n+1)(2n+1)}{3} + \frac{n(n+1)}{2} + (n + 1)(m - (n + 1)^2 + 1)$, where $n = \lfloor \sqrt{m} \rfloor - 1$    **43. a)** 0  **b)** 1680  **c)** 1  **d)** 1024    **45.** 34

## Section 2.5

**1. a)** Countably infinite, $-1, -2, -3, -4, \ldots$  **b)** Countably infinite, $0, 2, -2, 4, -4, \ldots$  **c)** Countably infinite, $99, 98, 97, \ldots$  **d)** Uncountable  **e)** Finite  **f)** Countably infinite, $0, 7, -7, 14, -14, \ldots$    **3. a)** Countable: match $n$ with the string of $n$ 1s.  **b)** Countable. To find a correspondence, follow the path in Example 4, but omit fractions in the top three rows (as well as continuing to omit fractions not in lowest terms).  **c)** Uncountable  **d)** Uncountable    **5.** Suppose $m$ new guests arrive at the fully occupied hotel. Move the guest in Room $n$ to Room $m + n$ for $n = 1, 2, 3, \ldots$; then the new guests can occupy rooms 1 to $m$.    **7.** For $n = 1, 2, 3, \ldots$, put

having $q$ iterate only from $i$ to $j$, rather than from $1$ to $k$.
**43.** $n(n + 1)(n + 2)/6$  **45.** $A((BC)D)$

## Supplementary Exercises

**1. a) procedure** *last max*$(a_1, \ldots, a_n$: integers)
$\quad max := a_1$
$\quad last := 1$
$\quad i := 2$
$\quad$**while** $i \le n$
$\quad\quad$**if** $a_i \ge max$ **then**
$\quad\quad\quad max := a_i$
$\quad\quad\quad last := i$
$\quad\quad i := i + 1$
$\quad$**return** *last*

**b)** $2n - 1 = O(n)$ comparisons

**3. a) procedure** *pair zeros*$(b_1 b_2 \ldots b_n$: bit string, $n \ge 2$)
$\quad x := b_1$
$\quad y := b_2$
$\quad k := 2$
$\quad$**while** $k < n$ and $(x \ne 0$ or $y \ne 0)$
$\quad\quad k := k + 1$
$\quad\quad x := y$
$\quad\quad y := b_k$
$\quad$**if** $x = 0$ and $y = 0$ **then** print "YES"
$\quad$**else** print "NO"

**b)** $O(n)$

**5. a)** and **b)**
$\quad$**procedure** *smallest and largest*$(a_1, a_2, \ldots, a_n$: integers)
$\quad min := a_1$
$\quad max := a_1$
$\quad$**for** $i := 2$ **to** $n$
$\quad\quad$**if** $a_i < min$ **then** $min := a_i$
$\quad\quad$**if** $a_i > max$ **then** $max := a_i$
$\quad$\{*min* is the smallest integer among the input, and *max* is the largest\}

**c)** $2n - 2$

**7.** Before any comparisons are done, there is a possibility that each element could be the maximum and a possibility that it could be the minimum. This means that there are $2n$ different possibilities, and $2n - 2$ of them have to be eliminated through comparisons of elements, because we need to find the unique maximum and the unique minimum. We classify comparisons of two elements as "virgin" or "nonvirgin," depending on whether or not both elements being compared have been in any previous comparison. A virgin comparison eliminates the possibility that the larger one is the minimum and that the smaller one is the maximum; thus each virgin comparison eliminates two possibilities, but it clearly cannot do more. A nonvirgin comparison must be between two elements that are still in the running to be the maximum or two elements that are still in the running to be the minimum, and at least one of these elements must *not* be in the running for

the other category. For example, we might be comparing $x$ and $y$, where all we know is that $x$ has been eliminated as the minimum. If we find that $x > y$ in this case, then only one possibility has been ruled out—we now know that $y$ is not the maximum. Thus in the worst case, a nonvirgin comparison eliminates only one possibility. (The cases of other nonvirgin comparisons are similar.) Now there are at most $\lfloor n/2 \rfloor$ comparisons of elements that have not been compared before, each removing two possibilities; they remove $2\lfloor n/2 \rfloor$ possibilities altogether. Therefore we need $2n - 2 - 2\lfloor n/2 \rfloor$ more comparisons that, as we have argued, can remove only one possibility each, in order to find the answers in the worst case, because $2n - 2$ possibilities have to be eliminated. This gives us a total of $2n - 2 - 2\lfloor n/2 \rfloor + \lfloor n/2 \rfloor$ comparisons in all. But $2n - 2 - 2\lfloor n/2 \rfloor + \lfloor n/2 \rfloor = 2n - 2 - \lfloor n/2 \rfloor = 2n - 2 + \lceil -n/2 \rceil = \lceil 2n - n/2 \rceil - 2 = \lceil 3n/2 \rceil - 2$, as desired.
**9.** The following algorithm has worst-case complexity $O(n^4)$.
**procedure** *equal sums*$(a_1, a_2, \ldots, a_n)$
**for** $i := 1$ **to** $n$
$\quad$**for** $j := i + 1$ **to** $n$ \{since we want $i < j$\}
$\quad\quad$**for** $k := 1$ **to** $n$
$\quad\quad\quad$**for** $l := k + 1$ **to** $n$ \{since we want $k < l$\}
$\quad\quad\quad\quad$**if** $a_i + a_j = a_k + a_l$ and $(i, j) \ne (k, l)$
$\quad\quad\quad\quad\quad$**then** output these pairs
**11.** At end of first pass: 3, 1, 4, 5, 2, 6; at end of second pass: 1, 3, 2, 4, 5, 6; at end of third pass: 1, 2, 3, 4, 5, 6; fourth pass finds nothing to exchange and algorithm terminates   **13.** There are possibly as many as $n$ passes through the list, and each pass uses $O(n)$ comparisons. Thus there are $O(n^2)$ comparisons in all.   **15.** Because $\log n < n$, we have $(n \log n + n^2)^3 \le (n^2 + n^2)^3 \le (2n^2)^3 = 8n^6$ for all $n > 0$. This proves that $(n \log n + n^2)^3$ is $O(n^6)$, with witnesses $C = 8$ and $k = 0$.   **17.** $O(x^2 2^x)$   **19.** Note that $\frac{n!}{2^n} = \frac{n}{2} \cdot \frac{n-1}{2} \cdots \frac{3}{2} \cdot \frac{2}{2} \cdot \frac{1}{2} > \frac{n}{2} \cdot 1 \cdot 1 \cdots 1 \cdot \frac{1}{2} = \frac{n}{4}$.   **21.** All of these functions are of the same order.   **23.** $2^{107}$   **25.** $(\log n)^2$, $2^{\sqrt{\log_2 n}}$, $n(\log n)^{1001}$, $n^{1.0001}$, $1.0001^n$, $n^n$   **27.** For example, $f(n) = n^{2\lfloor n/2 \rfloor + 1}$ and $g(n) = n^{2\lceil n/2 \rceil}$
**29. a)**
$\quad$**procedure** *brute*$(a_1, a_2, \ldots, a_n$ : integers)
$\quad\quad$**for** $i := 1$ **to** $n - 1$
$\quad\quad\quad$**for** $j := i + 1$ **to** $n$
$\quad\quad\quad\quad$**for** $k := 1$ **to** $n$
$\quad\quad\quad\quad\quad$**if** $a_i + a_j = a_k$ **then return true else return false**
**b)** $O(n^3)$
**31.** For $m_1$: $w_1$ and $w_2$; for $m_2$: $w_1$ and $w_3$; for $m_3$: $w_2$ and $w_3$; for $w_1$: $m_1$ and $m_2$; for $w_2$: $m_1$ and $m_3$; for $w_3$: $m_2$ and $m_3$   **33.** A matching in which each woman is assigned her valid partner ranking highest on her preference list is female optimal; a matching in which each man is assigned his valid partner ranking lowest on his preference list is male pessimal.   **35. a)** Modify the preamble to Exercise 60 in Section 3.1 so that there are $s$ men $m_1, m_2, \ldots, m_s$ and $t$ women $w_1, w_2, \ldots, w_t$. A matching will contain $\min(s, t)$ marriages. The definition of "stable marriage" is the same, with the understanding that each person prefers any mate to being unmatched. **b)** Create $|s - t|$ fictitious people (men or women,

whichever is in shorter supply) so that the number of men and the number of women become the same, and put these fictitious people at the bottom of everyone's preference lists. **c)** This follows immediately from Exercise 63 in Section 3.1. **37.** 5; 15   **39.** The first situation in Exercise 37   **41. a)** For each subset $S$ of $\{1, 2, \ldots, n\}$, compute $\sum_{j \in S} w_j$. Keep track of the subset giving the largest such sum that is less than or equal to $W$, and return that subset as the output of the algorithm. **b)** The food pack and the portable stove   **43. a)** The makespan is always at least as large as the load on the processor assigned to do the lengthiest job, which must be at least $\max_{j=1,2,\ldots,n} t_j$. Therefore the minimum makespan satisfies this inequality. **b)** The total amount of time the processors need to spend working on the jobs (the total load) is $\sum_{j=1}^{n} t_j$. Therefore the average load per processor is $\frac{1}{p} \sum_{j=1}^{n} t_j$. The maximum load cannot be any smaller than the average, so the minimum makespan is always at least this large.   **45.** Processor 1: jobs 1, 4; processor 2: job 2; processor 3: jobs 3, 5

# CHAPTER 4

## Section 4.1

**1. a)** Yes **b)** No **c)** Yes **d)** No   **3.** Suppose that $a \mid b$. Then there exists an integer $k$ such that $ka = b$. Because $a(ck) = bc$ it follows that $a \mid bc$.   **5.** If $a \mid b$ and $b \mid a$, there are integers $c$ and $d$ such that $b = ac$ and $a = bd$. Hence, $a = acd$. Because $a \neq 0$ it follows that $cd = 1$. Thus either $c = d = 1$ or $c = d = -1$. Hence, either $a = b$ or $a = -b$.   **7.** Because $ac \mid bc$ there is an integer $k$ such that $ack = bc$. Hence, $ak = b$, so $a \mid b$.   **9. a)** 2, 5 **b)** $-11$, 10 **c)** 34, 7 **d)** 77, 0 **e)** 0, 0 **f)** 0, 3 **g)** $-1$, 2 **h)** 4, 0   **11. a)** 7:00 **b)** 8:00 **c)** 10:00   **13. a)** 10 **b)** 8 **c)** 0 **d)** 9 **e)** 6 **f)** 11   **15.** If $a \bmod m = b \bmod m$, then $a$ and $b$ have the same remainder when divided by $m$. Hence, $a = q_1 m + r$ and $b = q_2 m + r$, where $0 \le r < m$. It follows that $a - b = (q_1 - q_2)m$, so $m \mid (a - b)$. It follows that $a \equiv b \pmod{m}$.   **17.** There is some $b$ with $(b - 1)k < n \le bk$. Hence, $(b - 1)k \le n - 1 < bk$. Divide by $k$ to obtain $b - 1 < n/k \le b$ and $b - 1 \le (n - 1)/k < b$. Hence, $\lceil n/k \rceil = b$ and $\lfloor (n - 1)/k \rfloor = b - 1$.   **19.** $x \bmod m$ if $x \bmod m \le \lceil m/2 \rceil$ and $(x \bmod m) - m$ if $x \bmod m > \lceil m/2 \rceil$   **21. a)** 1 **b)** 2 **c)** 3 **d)** 9   **23. a)** 1, 109 **b)** 40, 89 **c)** $-31$, 222 **d)** $-21$, 38259   **25. a)** $-15$ **b)** $-7$ **c)** 140   **27.** $-1, -26, -51, -76, 24, 49, 74, 99$   **29. a)** No **b)** No **c)** Yes **d)** No   **31. a)** 13 **a)** 6   **33. a)** 9 **b)** 4 **c)** 25 **d)** 0   **35.** Let $m = tn$. Because $a \equiv b \pmod{m}$ there exists an integer $s$ such that $a = b + sm$. Hence, $a = b + (st)n$, so $a \equiv b \pmod{n}$.   **37. a)** Let $m = c = 2, a = 0$, and $b = 1$. Then $0 = ac \equiv bc = 2 \pmod 2$, but $0 = a \not\equiv b = 1 \pmod 2$. **b)** Let $m = 5, a = b = 3, c = 1$, and $d = 6$. Then $3 \equiv 3 \pmod 5$ and $1 \equiv 6 \pmod 5$, but $3^1 = 3 \not\equiv 4 \equiv 729 = 3^6 \pmod 5$.   **39.** By Exercise 38 the sum of two squares must be either $0 + 0 = 0, 0 + 1 = 1$, or $1 + 1 = 2$, modulo 4, never 3, and therefore not of the form $4k + 3$.   **41.** Because $a \equiv b \pmod m$, there exists an

integer $s$ such that $a = b + sm$, so $a - b = sm$. Then $a^k - b^k = (a - b)(a^{k-1} + a^{k-2}b + \cdots + ab^{k-2} + b^{k-1})$, $k \ge 2$, is also a multiple of $m$. It follows that $a^k \equiv b^k \pmod m$.   **43.** To prove closure, note that $a \cdot_m b = (a \cdot b) \bmod m$, which by definition is an element of $\mathbf{Z}_m$. Multiplication is associative because $(a \cdot_m b) \cdot_m c$ and $a \cdot_m (b \cdot_m c)$ both equal $(a \cdot b \cdot c) \bmod m$ and multiplication of integers is associative. Similarly, multiplication in $\mathbf{Z}_m$ is commutative because multiplication in $\mathbf{Z}$ is commutative, and 1 is the multiplicative identity for $\mathbf{Z}_m$ because 1 is the multiplicative identity for $\mathbf{Z}$.   **45.** $0 +_5 0 = 0, 0 +_5 1 = 1, 0 +_5 2 = 2, 0 +_5 3 = 3, 0 +_5 4 = 4; 1 +_5 1 = 2, 1 +_5 2 = 3, 1 +_5 3 = 4, 1 +_5 4 = 0; 2 +_5 2 = 4, 2 +_5 3 = 0, 2 +_5 4 = 1; 3 +_5 3 = 1, 3 +_5 4 = 2; 4 +_4 4 = 3$ and $0 \cdot_5 0 = 0, 0 \cdot_5 1 = 0, 0 \cdot_5 2 = 0, 0 \cdot_5 3 = 0, 0 \cdot_5 4 = 0; 1 \cdot_5 1 = 1, 1 \cdot_5 2 = 2, 1 \cdot_5 3 = 3, 1 \cdot_5 4 = 4; 2 \cdot_5 2 = 4, 2 \cdot_5 3 = 1, 2 \cdot_5 4 = 3; 3 \cdot_5 3 = 4, 3 \cdot_5 4 = 2; 4 \cdot_5 4 = 1$   **47.** $f$ is onto but not one-to-one (unless $d = 1$); $g$ is neither.

## Section 4.2

**1. a)** 1110 0111 **b)** 1 0001 1011 0100 **c)** 1 0111 11010110 1100   **3. a)** 31 **b)** 513 **c)** 341 **d)** 26,896   **5. a)** 1 0111 1010 **b)** 11 1000 0100 **c)** 1 0001 0011 **d)** 101 0000 1111   **7. a)** 1000 0000 1110 **b)** 1 0011 0101 1010 1011 **c)** 10101011 1011 1010 **d)** 1101 1110 1111 1010 11001110 1101   **9.** 1010 1011 1100 1101 1110 1111   **11.** $(B7B)_{16}$   **13.** Adding up to three leading 0s if necessary, write the binary expansion as $(\ldots b_{23} b_{22} b_{21} b_{20} b_{13} b_{12} b_{11} b_{10} b_{03} b_{02} b_{01} b_{00})_2$. The value of this numeral is $b_{00} + 2b_{01} + 4b_{02} + 8b_{03} + 2^4 b_{10} + 2^5 b_{11} + 2^6 b_{12} + 2^7 b_{13} + 2^8 b_{20} + 2^9 b_{21} + 2^{10} b_{22} + 2^{11} b_{23} + \cdots$, which we can rewrite as $b_{00} + 2b_{01} + 4b_{02} + 8b_{03} + (b_{10} + 2b_{11} + 4b_{12} + 8b_{13}) \cdot 2^4 + (b_{20} + 2b_{21} + 4b_{22} + 8b_{23}) \cdot 2^8 + \cdots$. Now $(b_{i3} b_{i2} b_{i1} b_{i0})_2$ translates into the hexadecimal digit $h_i$. So our number is $h_0 + h_1 \cdot 2^4 + h_2 \cdot 2^8 + \cdots = h_0 + h_1 \cdot 16 + h_2 \cdot 16^2 + \cdots$, which is the hexadecimal expansion $(\ldots h_1 h_1 h_0)_{16}$.   **15** Adding up to two leading 0s if necessary, write the binary expansion as $(\ldots b_{22} b_{21} b_{20} b_{12} b_{11} b_{10} b_{02} b_{01} b_{00})_2$. The value of this numeral is $b_{00} + 2b_{01} + 4b_{02} + 2^3 b_{10} + 2^4 b_{11} + 2^5 b_{12} + 2^6 b_{20} + 2^7 b_{21} + 2^8 b_{22} + \cdots$, which we can rewrite as $b_{00} + 2b_{01} + 4b_{02} + (b_{10} + 2b_{11} + 4b_{12}) \cdot 2^3 + (b_{20} + 2b_{21} + 4b_{22}) \cdot 2^6 + \cdots$. Now $(b_{i2} b_{i1} b_{i0})_2$ translates into the octal digit $h_i$. So our number is $h_0 + h_1 \cdot 2^3 + h_2 \cdot 2^6 + \cdots = h_0 + h_1 \cdot 8 + h_2 \cdot 8^2 + \cdots$, which is the octal expansion $(\ldots h_1 h_1 h_0)_8$.   **17.** 1 1101 1100 1010 1101 0001, $1273)_8$   **19.** Convert the given octal numeral to binary, then convert from binary to hexadecimal using Example 7.   **21. a)** 1011 1110, 10 0001 0000 0001 **b)** 1 1010 1100, 1011 0000 0111 0011 **c)** 100 1001 1010, 101 0010 1001 0110 0000 **d)** 110 0000 0000, 1000 0000 0001 1111 1111   **23. a)** 1132, 144,305 **b)** 6273, 2,134,272 **c)** 2110, 1,107,667 **d)** 57,777, 237,326,216   **25.** 436   **27.** 27   **29.** The binary expansion of the integer is the unique such sum.   **31.** Let $a = (a_{n-1} a_{n-2} \ldots a_1 a_0)_{10}$. Then $a = 10^{n-1} a_{n-1} + 10^{n-2} a_{n-2} + \cdots + 10a_1 + a_0 \equiv a_{n-1} + a_{n-2} + \cdots + a_1 + a_0 \pmod 3$, because

$10^j \equiv 1 \pmod 3$) for all nonnegative integers $j$. It follows that $3 \mid a$ if and only if 3 divides the sum of the decimal digits of $a$.    **33.** Let $a = (a_{n-1}a_{n-2}\ldots a_1a_0)_2$. Then $a = a_0 + 2a_1 + 2^2a_2 + \cdots + 2^{n-1}a_{n-1} \equiv a_0 - a_1 + a_2 - a_3 + \cdots \pm a_{n-1} \pmod 3$. It follows that $a$ is divisible by 3 if and only if the sum of the binary digits in the even-numbered positions minus the sum of the binary digits in the odd-numbered positions is divisible by 3.    **35. a)** $-6$  **b)** 13  **c)** $-14$  **d)** 0    **37.** The one's complement of the sum is found by adding the one's complements of the two integers except that a carry in the leading bit is used as a carry to the last bit of the sum.    **39.** If $m \geq 0$, then the leading bit $a_{n-1}$ of the one's complement expansion of $m$ is 0 and the formula reads $m = \sum_{i=0}^{n-2} a_i 2^i$. This is correct because the right-hand side is the binary expansion of $m$. When $m$ is negative, the leading bit $a_{n-1}$ of the one's complement expansion of $m$ is 1. The remaining $n-1$ bits can be obtained by subtracting $-m$ from $111\ldots1$ (where there are $n-1$ 1s), because subtracting a bit from 1 is the same as complementing it. Hence, the bit string $a_{n-2}\ldots a_0$ is the binary expansion of $(2^{n-1} - 1) - (-m)$. Solving the equation $(2^{n-1} - 1) - (-m) = \sum_{i=0}^{n-2} a_i 2^i$ for $m$ gives the desired equation because $a_{n-1} = 1$.    **41. a)** $-7$  **b)** 13  **c)** $-15$  **d)** $-1$    **43.** To obtain the two's complement representation of the sum of two integers, add their two's complement representations (as binary integers are added) and ignore any carry out of the leftmost column. However, the answer is invalid if an overflow has occurred. This happens when the leftmost digits in the two's complement representation of the two terms agree and the leftmost digit of the answer differs.    **45.** If $m \geq 0$, then the leading bit $a_{n-1}$ is 0 and the formula reads $m = \sum_{i=0}^{n-2} a_i 2^i$. This is correct because the right-hand side is the binary expansion of $m$. If $m < 0$, its two's complement expansion has 1 as its leading bit and the remaining $n-1$ bits are the binary expansion of $2^{n-1} - (-m)$. This means that $(2^{n-1}) - (-m) = \sum_{i=0}^{n-2} a_i 2^i$. Solving for $m$ gives the desired equation because $a_{n-1} = 1$.    **47.** $4n$

**49. procedure** *Cantor*($x$: positive integer)
  $n := 1; f := 1$
  **while** $(n+1) \cdot f \leq x$
    $n := n + 1$
    $f := f \cdot n$
  $y := x$
  **while** $n > 0$
    $a_n := \lfloor y/f \rfloor$
    $y := y - a_n \cdot f$
    $f := f/n$
    $n := n - 1$
  $\{x = a_n n! + a_{n-1}(n-1)! + \cdots + a_1 1!\}$

**51.** First step: $c = 0, d = 0, s_0 = 1$; second step: $c = 0$, $d = 1, s_1 = 0$; third step: $c = 1, d = 1, s_2 = 0$; fourth step: $c = 1, d = 1, s_3 = 0$; fifth step: $c = 1, d = 1, s_4 = 1$; sixth step: $c = 1, s_5 = 1$

**53. procedure** *subtract*($a, b$: positive integers, $a > b$,
  $a = (a_{n-1}a_{n-2}\ldots a_1a_0)_2$,
  $b = (b_{n-1}b_{n-2}\ldots b_1b_0)_2$)
  $B := 0$ {$B$ is the borrow}
  **for** $j := 0$ **to** $n - 1$
    **if** $a_j \geq b_j + B$ **then**
      $s_j := a_j - b_j - B$
      $B := 0$
    **else**
      $s_j := a_j + 2 - b_j - B$
      $B := 1$
  $\{(s_{n-1}s_{n-2}\ldots s_1s_0)_2$ is the difference}

**55. procedure** *compare*($a, b$: positive integers,
  $a = (a_n a_{n-1}\ldots a_1a_0)_2$,
  $b = (b_n b_{n-1}\ldots b_1b_0)_2$)
  $k := n$
  **while** $a_k = b_k$ and $k > 0$
    $k := k - 1$
  **if** $a_k = b_k$ **then** print "$a$ equals $b$"
  **if** $a_k > b_k$ **then** print "$a$ is greater than $b$"
  **if** $a_k < b_k$ **then** print "$a$ is less than $b$"

**57.** $O(\log n)$    **59.** The only time-consuming part of the algorithm is the **while** loop, which is iterated $q$ times. The work done inside is a subtraction of integers no bigger than $a$, which has $\log a$ bits. The result now follows from Example 9.

## Section 4.3

**1.** $29, 71, 97$ prime; $21, 111, 143$ not prime    **3. a)** $2^3 \cdot 11$  **b)** $2 \cdot 3^2 \cdot 7$  **c)** $3^6$  **d)** $7 \cdot 11 \cdot 13$  **e)** $11 \cdot 101$  **f)** $2 \cdot 3^3 \cdot 5 \cdot 7 \cdot 13 \cdot 37$    **5.** $2^8 \cdot 3^4 \cdot 5^2 \cdot 7$

**7.**   **procedure** *primetester*($n$ : integer greater than 1)
    $isprime := $ **true**
    $d := 2$
    **while** $isprime$ and $d \leq \sqrt{n}$
      **if** $n$ **mod** $d = 0$ **then** $isprime := $ **false**
      **else** $d := d + 1$
    **return** $isprime$

**9.** Write $n = rs$, where $r > 1$ and $s > 1$. Then $2^n - 1 = 2^{rs} - 1 = (2^r)^s - 1 = (2^r - 1)((2^r)^{s-1} + (2^r)^{s-2} + (2^r)^{s-3} + \cdots + 1)$. The first factor is at least $2^2 - 1 = 3$ and the second factor is at least $2^2 + 1 = 5$. This provides a factoring of $2^n - 1$ into two factors greater than 1, so $2^n - 1$ is composite.    **11.** Suppose that $\log_2 3 = a/b$ where $a, b \in \mathbf{Z}^+$ and $b \neq 0$. Then $2^{a/b} = 3$, so $2^a = 3^b$. This violates the fundamental theorem of arithmetic. Hence, $\log_2 3$ is irrational.    **13.** 3, 5, and 7 are primes of the desired form.    **15.** 1, 7, 11, 13, 17, 19, 23, 29    **17. a)** Yes  **b)** No  **c)** Yes  **d)** Yes    **19.** Suppose that $n$ is not prime, so that $n = ab$, where $a$ and $b$ are integers greater than 1. Because $a > 1$, by the identity in the hint, $2^a - 1$ is a factor of $2^n - 1$ that is greater than 1, and the second factor in this identity is also greater than 1. Hence, $2^n - 1$ is not prime. **21. a)** 2 **b)** 4 **c)** 12 **23.** $\phi(p^k) = p^k - p^{k-1}$ **25. a)** $3^5 \cdot 5^3$ **b)** 1 **c)** $23^{17}$ **d)** $41 \cdot 43 \cdot 53$ **e)** 1 **f)** 1111 **27. a)** $2^{11} \cdot 3^7 \cdot 5^9 \cdot 7^3$ **b)** $2^9 \cdot 3^7 \cdot 5^5 \cdot 7^3 \cdot 11 \cdot 13 \cdot 17$ **c)** $23^{31}$ **d)** $41 \cdot 43 \cdot 53$ **e)** $2^{12}3^{13}5^{17}7^{21}$ **f)** Undefined **29.** gcd (92928, 123552) = 1056; lcm(92928, 123552) = 10,872,576; both products are 11,481,440,256. **31.** Because $\min(x, y) + \max(x, y) = x + y$, the exponent of $p_i$ in the prime factorization of $\gcd(a, b) \cdot \text{lcm}(a, b)$ is the sum of the exponents of $p_i$ in the prime factorizations of $a$ and $b$. **33. a)** 6 **b)** 3 **c)** 11 **d)** 3 **e)** 40 **f)** 12 **35.** 9 **37.** By Exercise 36 it follows that $\gcd(2^b - 1, (2^a - 1) \bmod (2^b - 1)) = \gcd(2^b - 1, 2^{a \bmod b} - 1)$. Because the exponents involved in the calculation are $b$ and $a \bmod b$, the same as the quantities involved in computing $\gcd(a, b)$, the steps used by the Euclidean algorithm to compute $\gcd(2^a - 1, 2^b - 1)$ run in parallel to those used to compute $\gcd(a, b)$ and show that $\gcd(2^a - 1, 2^b - 1) = 2^{\gcd(a,b)} - 1$. **39. a)** $1 = (-1) \cdot 10 + 1 \cdot 11$ **b)** $1 = 21 \cdot 21 + (-10) \cdot 44$ **c)** $12 = (-1) \cdot 36 + 48$ **d)** $1 = 13 \cdot 55 + (-21) \cdot 34$ **e)** $3 = 11 \cdot 213 + (-20) \cdot 117$ **f)** $223 = 1 \cdot 0 + 1 \cdot 223$ **g)** $1 = 37 \cdot 2347 + (-706) \cdot 123$ **h)** $2 = 1128 \cdot 3454 + (-835) \cdot 4666$ **i)** $1 = 2468 \cdot 9999 + (-2221) \cdot 11111$ **41.** $(-3) \cdot 26 + 1 \cdot 91 = 13$ **43.** $34 \cdot 144 + (-55) \cdot 89 = 1$

**45. procedure** *extended Euclidean*($a, b$: positive integers)
$x := a$
$y := b$
*oldolds* := 1
*olds* := 0
*oldoldt* := 0
*oldt* := 1
**while** $y \neq 0$
  $q := x \ \textbf{div} \ y$
  $r := x \ \textbf{mod} \ y$
  $x := y$
  $y := r$
  $s := oldolds - q \cdot olds$
  $t := oldoldt - q \cdot oldt$
  *oldolds* := *olds*
  *oldoldt* := *oldt*
  *olds* := $s$
  *oldt* := $t$
{$\gcd(a, b)$ is $x$, and $(oldolds)a + (oldoldt)b = x$}

**47. a)** $a_n = 1$ if $n$ is prime and $a_n = 0$ otherwise. **b)** $a_n$ is the smallest prime factor of $n$ with $a_1 = 1$. **c)** $a_n$ is the number of positive divisors of $n$. **d)** $a_n = 1$ if $n$ has no divisors that are perfect squares greater than 1 and $a_n = 0$ otherwise. **e)** $a_n$ is the largest prime less than or equal to $n$. **f)** $a_n$ is the product of the first $n - 1$ primes. **49.** Because every second integer is divisible by 2, the product is divisible by 2. Because every third integer is divisible by 3, the product is divisible by 3. Therefore the product has both 2 and 3 in its prime factorization and is therefore divisible by $3 \cdot 2 = 6$. **51.** $n = 1601$ is a counterexample. **53** Setting $k = a + b + 1$ will produce the composite number $a(a + b + 1) + b = a^2 + ab + a + b = (a + 1)(a + b)$.

**55.** Suppose that there are only finitely many primes of the form $4k + 3$, namely $q_1, q_2, \ldots, q_n$, where $q_1 = 3, q_2 = 7$, and so on. Let $Q = 4q_1q_2 \cdots q_n - 1$. Note that $Q$ is of the form $4k + 3$ (where $k = q_1q_2 \cdots q_n - 1$). If $Q$ is prime, then we have found a prime of the desired form different from all those listed. If $Q$ is not prime, then $Q$ has at least one prime factor not in the list $q_1, q_2, \ldots, q_n$, because the remainder when $Q$ is divided by $q_j$ is $q_j - 1$, and $q_j - 1 \neq 0$. Because all odd primes are either of the form $4k + 1$ or of the form $4k + 3$, and the product of primes of the form $4k + 1$ is also of this form (because $(4k + 1)(4m + 1) = 4(4km + k + m) + 1$), there must be a factor of $Q$ of the form $4k + 3$ different from the primes we listed. **57.** Given a positive integer $x$, we show that there is exactly one positive rational number $m/n$ (in lowest terms) such that $K(m/n) = x$. From the prime factorization of $x$, read off the $m$ and $n$ such that $K(m/n) = x$. The primes that occur to even powers are the primes that occur in the prime factorization of $m$, with the exponents being half the corresponding exponents in $x$; and the primes that occur to odd powers are the primes that occur in the prime factorization of $n$, with the exponents being half of one more than the exponents in $x$.

## Section 4.4

**1.** $15 \cdot 7 = 105 \equiv 1 \pmod{26}$ **3.** 7 **5. a)** 7 **b)** 52 **c)** 34 **d)** 73 **7.** Suppose that $b$ and $c$ are both inverses of $a$ modulo $m$. Then $ba \equiv 1 \pmod{m}$ and $ca \equiv 1 \pmod{m}$. Hence, $ba \equiv ca \pmod{m}$. Because $\gcd(a, m) = 1$ it follows by Theorem 7 in Section 4.3 that $b \equiv c \pmod{m}$. **9.** 8 **11. a)** 67 **b)** 88 **c)** 146 **13.** 3 and 6 **15.** Let $m' = m/\gcd(c, m)$. Because all the common factors of $m$ and $c$ are divided out of $m$ to obtain $m'$, it follows that $m'$ and $c$ are relatively prime. Because $m$ divides $ac - bc = (a - b)c$, it follows that $m'$ divides $(a - b)c$. By Lemma 3 in Section 4.3, we see that $m'$ divides $a - b$, so $a \equiv b \pmod{m'}$. **17.** Suppose that $x^2 \equiv 1 \pmod{p}$. Then $p$ divides $x^2 - 1 = (x + 1)(x - 1)$. By Lemma 2 it follows that $p \mid x + 1$ or $p \mid x - 1$, so $x \equiv -1 \pmod{p}$ or $x \equiv 1 \pmod{p}$. **19. a)** Suppose that $ia \equiv ja \pmod{p}$, where $1 \leq i < j < p$. Then $p$ divides $ja - ia = a(j - i)$. By Theorem 1, because $a$ is not divisible by $p$, $p$ divides $j - i$, which is impossible because $j - i$ is a positive integer less than $p$. **b)** By part (a), because no two of $a, 2a, \ldots, (p - 1)a$ are congruent modulo $p$, each must be congruent to a different number from 1 to $p - 1$. It follows that $a \cdot 2a \cdot 3a \cdots \cdot (p - 1) \cdot a \equiv 1 \cdot 2 \cdot 3 \cdots \cdot (p - 1) \pmod{p}$. It follows that $(p - 1)! \cdot a^{p-1} \equiv p - 1 \pmod{p}$. **c)** By Wilson's theorem and part (b), if $p$ does not divide $a$, it follows that $(-1) \cdot a^{p-1} \equiv -1 \pmod{p}$. Hence, $a^{p-1} \equiv 1 \pmod{p}$. **d)** If $p \mid a$, then $p \mid a^p$. Hence, $a^p \equiv a \equiv 0 \pmod{p}$. If $p$ does not divide $a$, then $a^{p-1} \equiv a \pmod{p}$, by part (c). Multiplying both sides of this congruence by $a$ gives $a^p \equiv a \pmod{p}$. **21.** All integers of the form $323 + 330k$, where $k$ is an integer **23.** All integers of the form $53 + 60k$, where $k$ is an integer

**25. procedure** *chinese*($m_1, m_2, \ldots, m_n$ : relatively
        prime positive integers ; $a_1, a_2, \ldots, a_n$ : integers)
   $m := 1$
   **for** $k := 1$ **to** $n$
     $m := m \cdot m_k$
   **for** $k := 1$ **to** $n$
     $M_k := m/m_k$
     $y_k := M_k^{-1} \bmod m_k$
   $x := 0$
   **for** $k := 1$ **to** $n$
     $x := x + a_k M_k y_k$
   **while** $x \geq m$
     $x := x - m$
   **return** $x$ {the smallest solution to the system
     $\{x \equiv a_k \pmod{m_k}, k = 1, 2, \ldots, n \}$}

**27.** All integers of the form $16 + 252k$, where $k$ is an integer **29.** Suppose that $p$ is a prime appearing in the prime factorization of $m_1 m_2 \cdots m_n$. Because the $m_i$s are relatively prime, $p$ is a factor of exactly one of the $m_i$s, say $m_j$. Because $m_j$ divides $a - b$, it follows that $a - b$ has the factor $p$ in its prime factorization to a power at least as large as the power to which it appears in the prime factorization of $m_j$. It follows that $m_1 m_2 \cdots m_n$ divides $a - b$, so $a \equiv b \pmod{m_1 m_2 \cdots m_n}$. **31.** $x \equiv 1 \pmod 6$ **33.** 7 **35.** $a^{p-2} \cdot a = a \cdot a^{p-2} = a^{p-1} \equiv 1 \pmod p$ **37. a)** By Fermat's little theorem, we have $2^{10} \equiv 1 \pmod{11}$. Hence, $2^{340} = (2^{10})^{34} \equiv 1^{34} = 1 \pmod{11}$. **b)** Because $32 \equiv 1 \pmod{31}$, it follows that $2^{340} = (2^5)^{68} = 32^{68} \equiv 1^{68} = 1 \pmod{31}$. **c)** Because 11 and 31 are relatively prime, and $11 \cdot 31 = 341$, it follows by parts (a) and (b) and Exercise 29 that $2^{340} \equiv 1 \pmod{341}$. **39. a)** 3, 4, 8 **b)** 983 **41.** Suppose that $q$ is an odd prime with $q \mid 2^p - 1$. By Fermat's little theorem, $q \mid 2^{q-1} - 1$. From Exercise 37 in Section 4.3, $\gcd(2^p - 1, 2^{q-1} - 1) = 2^{\gcd(p, q-1)} - 1$. Because $q$ is a common divisor of $2^p - 1$ and $2^{q-1} - 1$, $\gcd(2^p - 1, 2^{q-1} - 1) > 1$. Hence, $\gcd(p, q-1) = p$, because the only other possibility, namely, $\gcd(p, q-1) = 1$, gives us $\gcd(2^p - 1, 2^{q-1} - 1) = 1$. Hence, $p \mid q - 1$, and therefore there is a positive integer $m$ such that $q - 1 = mp$. Because $q$ is odd, $m$ must be even, say, $m = 2k$, and so every prime divisor of $2^p - 1$ is of the form $2kp + 1$. Furthermore, the product of numbers of this form is also of this form. Therefore, all divisors of $2^p - 1$ are of this form. **43.** $M_{11}$ is not prime; $M_{17}$ is prime. **45.** First, $2047 = 23 \cdot 89$ is composite. Write $2047 - 1 = 2046 = 2 \cdot 1023$, so $s = 1$ and $t = 1023$ in the definition. Then $2^{1023} = (2^{11})^{93} = 2048^{93} \equiv 1^{93} = 1 \pmod{2047}$, as desired. **47.** We must show that $b^{2820} \equiv 1 \pmod{2821}$ for all $b$ relatively prime to 2821. Note that $2821 = 7 \cdot 13 \cdot 31$, and if $\gcd(b, 2821) = 1$, then $\gcd(b, 7) = \gcd(b, 13) = \gcd(b, 31) = 1$. Using Fermat's little theorem we find that $b^6 \equiv 1 \pmod 7$, $b^{12} \equiv 1 \pmod{13}$, and $b^{30} \equiv 1 \pmod{31}$. It follows that $b^{2820} \equiv (b^6)^{470} \equiv 1 \pmod 7$, $b^{2820} \equiv (b^{12})^{235} \equiv 1 \pmod{13}$, and $b^{2820} \equiv (b^{30})^{94} \equiv 1 \pmod{31}$. By Exercise 29 (or the Chinese remainder theorem) it follows that $b^{2820} \equiv 1 \pmod{2821}$, as desired. **49. a)** If we multiply out this expression, we get

$n = 1296m^3 + 396m^2 + 36m + 1$. Clearly $6m \mid n - 1$, $12m \mid n - 1$, and $18m \mid n - 1$. Therefore, the conditions of Exercise 48 are met, and we conclude that $n$ is a Carmichael number. **b)** Letting $m = 51$ gives $n = 172{,}947{,}529$. **51.** $0 = (0, 0)$, $1 = (1, 1)$, $2 = (2, 2)$, $3 = (0, 3)$, $4 = (1, 4)$, $5 = (2, 0)$, $6 = (0, 1)$, $7 = (1, 2)$, $8 = (2, 3)$, $9 = (0, 4)$, $10 = (1, 0)$, $11 = (2, 1)$, $12 = (0, 2)$, $13 = (1, 3)$, $14 = (2, 4)$ **53.** We have $m_1 = 99$, $m_2 = 98$, $m_3 = 97$, and $m_4 = 95$, so $m = 99 \cdot 98 \cdot 97 \cdot 95 = 89{,}403{,}930$. We find that $M_1 = m/m_1 = 903{,}070$, $M_2 = m/m_2 = 912{,}285$, $M_3 = m/m_3 = 921{,}690$, and $M_4 = m/m_4 = 941{,}094$. Using the Euclidean algorithm, we compute that $y_1 = 37$, $y_2 = 33$, $y_3 = 24$, and $y_4 = 4$ are inverses of $M_k$ modulo $m_k$ for $k = 1, 2, 3, 4$, respectively. It follows that the solution is $65 \cdot 903{,}070 \cdot 37 + 2 \cdot 912{,}285 \cdot 33 + 51 \cdot 921{,}690 \cdot 24 + 10 \cdot 941{,}094 \cdot 4 = 3{,}397{,}886{,}480 \equiv 537{,}140 \pmod{89{,}403{,}930}$. **55.** $\log_2 5 = 16$, $\log_2 6 = 14$ **57.** $\log_3 1 = 0$, $\log_3 2 = 14$, $\log_3 3 = 1$, $\log_3 4 = 12$, $\log_3 5 = 5$, $\log_3 6 = 15$, $\log_3 7 = 11$, $\log_3 8 = 10$, $\log_3 9 = 2$, $\log_3 10 = 3$, $\log_3 11 = 7$, $\log_3 12 = 13$, $\log_3 13 = 4$, $\log_3 14 = 9$, $\log_3 15 = 6$, $\log_3 16 = 8$ **59.** Assume that $s$ is a solution of $x^2 \equiv a \pmod p$. Then because $(-s)^2 = s^2$, $-s$ is also a solution. Furthermore, $s \not\equiv -s \pmod p$. Otherwise, $p \mid 2s$, which implies that $p \mid s$, and this implies, using the original assumption, that $p \mid a$, which is a contradiction. Furthermore, if $s$ and $t$ are incongruent solutions modulo $p$, then because $s^2 \equiv t^2 \pmod p$, $p \mid s^2 - t^2$. This implies that $p \mid (s + t)(s - t)$, and by Lemma 3 in Section 4.3, $p \mid s - t$ or $p \mid s + t$, so $s \equiv t \pmod p$ or $s \equiv -t \pmod p$. Hence, there are at most two solutions. **61.** The value of $\left(\frac{a}{p}\right)$ depends only on whether $a$ is a quadratic residue modulo $p$, that is, whether $x^2 \equiv a \pmod p$ has a solution. Because this depends only on the equivalence class of $a$ modulo $p$, it follows that $\left(\frac{a}{p}\right) = \left(\frac{b}{p}\right)$ if $a \equiv b \pmod p$. **63.** By Exercise 62, $\left(\frac{a}{p}\right)\left(\frac{b}{p}\right) = a^{(p-1)/2} b^{(p-1)/2} = (ab)^{(p-1)/2} \equiv \left(\frac{ab}{p}\right) \pmod p$. **65.** $x \equiv 8, 13, 22$, or $27 \pmod{35}$ **67.** Compute $r^e \bmod p$ for $e = 0, 1, 2, \ldots, p - 2$ until we get the answer $a$. Worst case and average case time complexity are $O(p \log p)$.

## Section 4.5

**1.** 91, 57, 21, 5 **3. a)** 7, 19, 7, 7, 18, 0 **b)** Take the next available space **mod** 31. **5.** 1, 5, 4, 1, 5, 4, 1, 5, 4, ... **7.** 2, 6, 7, 10, 8, 2, 6, 7, 10, 8, ... **9.** 2357, 5554, 8469, 7239, 4031, 2489, 1951, 8064 **11.** 2, 1, 1, 1, ... **13.** Only string (d) **15.** 4 **17.** Correctly, of course **19. a)** Not valid **b)** Valid **c)** Valid **d)** Not valid **21. a)** No **b)** 5 **c)** 7 **d)** 8 **23.** Transposition errors involving the last digit **25. a)** Yes **b)** No **c)** Yes **d)** No **27.** Transposition errors will be detected if and only if the transposed digits are an odd number of positions apart and do not differ by 5. **29. a)** Valid **b)** Not valid **c)** Valid **d)** Valid **31.** Yes, as long as the two digits do not differ by 7 **33. a)** Not valid **b)** Valid **c)** Valid **d)** Not valid **35.** The given congruence is equivalent to $3d_1 + 4d_2 + 5d_3 + 6d_4 + 7d_5 + 8d_6 + 9d_7 + 10d_8 \equiv 0 \pmod{11}$. Transposing adjacent digits $x$ and $y$ (with $x$ on the left) causes the left-hand side to increase by $x - y$. Because $x \not\equiv y \pmod{11}$, the congruence will no longer hold. Therefore errors of this type are always detected.

## Section 4.6

**1. a)** GR QRW SDVV JR **b)** QB ABG CNFF TB **c)** QX UXM AHJJ ZX **3. a)** KOHQV MCIF GHSD **b)** RVBXP TJPZ NBZX **c)** DBYNE PHRM FYZA **5. a)** SURRENDER NOW **b)** BE MY FRIEND **c)** TIME FOR FUN **7.** TO SLEEP PERCHANCE TO DREAM **9.** ANY SUFFI-CIENTLY ADVANCED TECHNOLOGY IS INDISTIN-GUISHABLE FROM MAGIC **11.** $p = 7c + 13 \bmod 26$ **13.** $a = 18$, $b = 5$ **15.** BEWARE OF MARTIANS **17.** Presumably something like an affine cipher **19.** HURRICANE **21.** The length of the key may well be the greatest common divisor of the distances between the starts of the repeated string (or a factor of the gcd). **23.** Suppose we know both $n = pq$ and $(p-1)(q-1)$. To find $p$ and $q$, first note that $(p-1)(q-1) = pq - p - q + 1 = n - (p+q) + 1$. From this we can find $s = p + q$. Because $q = s - p$, we have $n = p(s - p)$. Hence, $p^2 - ps + n = 0$. We now can use the quadratic formula to find $p$. Once we have found $p$, we can find $q$ because $q = n/p$. **25.** 2545 2757 1211 **27.** SILVER **29.** Alice sends $5^8 \bmod 23 = 16$ to Bob. Bob sends $5^5 \bmod 23 = 20$ to Alice. Alice computes $20^8 \bmod 23 = 6$ and Bob computes $16^5 \bmod 23 = 6$. The shared key is 6. **31.** 2186 2087 1279 1251 0326 0816 1948 **33.** Alice can decrypt the first part of Cathy's message to learn the key, and Bob can decrypt the second part of Cathy's message, which Alice forwarded to him, to learn the key. No one else besides Cathy can learn the key, because all of these communications use secure private keys.

## Supplementary Exercises

**1.** The actual number of miles driven is $46518 + 100000k$ for some natural number $k$. **3.** 5, 22, $-12$, $-29$ **5.** Because $ac \equiv bc \pmod{m}$ there is an integer $k$ such that $ac = bc + km$. Hence, $a - b = km/c$. Because $a - b$ is an integer, $c \mid km$. Letting $d = \gcd(m, c)$, write $c = de$. Because no factor of $e$ divides $m/d$, it follows that $d \mid m$ and $e \mid k$. Thus $a - b = (k/e)(m/d)$, where $k/e \in \mathbf{Z}$ and $m/d \in \mathbf{Z}$. Therefore $a \equiv b \pmod{m/d}$. **7.** Proof of the contrapositive: If $n$ is odd, then $n = 2k + 1$ for some integer $k$. Therefore $n^2 + 1 = (2k + 1)^2 + 1 = 4k^2 + 4k + 2 \equiv 2 \pmod{4}$. But perfect squares of even numbers are congruent to 0 modulo 4 (because $(2m)^2 = 4m^2$), and perfect squares of odd numbers are congruent to 1 or 3 modulo 4, so $n^2 + 1$ is not a perfect square. **9.** $n$ is divisible by 8 if and only if the binary expansion of $n$ ends with 000. **11.** We assume that someone has chosen a positive integer less than $2^n$, which we are to guess. We ask the person to write the number in binary, using leading 0s if necessary to make it $n$ bits long. We then ask "Is the first bit a 1?", "Is the second bit a 1?", "Is the third bit a 1?", and so

on. After we know the answers to these $n$ questions, we will know the number, because we will know its binary expansion. **13.** $(a_n a_{n-1} \ldots a_1 a_0)_{10} = \sum_{k=0}^{n} 10^k a_k \equiv \sum_{k=0}^{n} a_k \pmod{9}$ because $10^k \equiv 1 \pmod{9}$ for every nonnegative integer $k$. **15.** Because for all $k \leq n$, when $Q_n$ is divided by $k$ the remainder will be 1, it follows that no prime number less than or equal to $n$ is a factor of $Q_n$. Thus by the fundamental theorem of arithmetic, $Q_n$ must have a prime factor greater than $n$. **17.** Take $a = 10$ and $b = 1$ in Dirichlet's theorem. **19.** Every number greater than 11 can be written as either $8 + 2n$ or $9 + 2n$ for some $n \geq 2$. **21.** Assume that every even integer greater than 2 is the sum of two primes, and let $n$ be an integer greater than 5. If $n$ is odd, write $n = 3 + (n - 3)$ and decompose $n - 3 = p + q$ into the sum of two primes; if $n$ is even, then write $n = 2 + (n - 2)$ and decompose $n - 2 = p + q$ into the sum of two primes. For the converse, assume that every integer greater than 5 is the sum of three primes, and let $n$ be an even integer greater than 2. Write $n + 2$ as the sum of three primes, one of which is necessarily 2, so $n + 2 = 2 + p + q$, whence $n = p + q$. **23.** Recall that a nonconstant polynomial can take on the same value only a finite number of times. Thus $f$ can take on the values 0 and $\pm 1$ only finitely many times, so if there is not some $y$ such that $f(y)$ is composite, then there must be some $x_0$ such that $\pm f(x_0)$ is prime, say $p$. Look at $f(x_0 + kp)$. When we plug $x_0 + kp$ in for $x$ in the polynomial and multiply it out, every term will contain a factor of $p$ except for the terms that form $f(x_0)$. Therefore $f(x_0 + kp) = f(x_0) + mp = (m \pm 1)p$ for some integer $m$. As $k$ varies, this value can be 0, $p$, or $-p$ only finitely many times; therefore it must be a composite number for some values of $k$. **25.** 1 **27.** 1 **29.** If not, then suppose that $q_1, q_2, \ldots, q_n$ are all the primes of the form $6k + 5$. Let $Q = 6q_1 q_2 \cdots q_n - 1$. Note that $Q$ is of the form $6k + 5$, where $k = q_1 q_2 \cdots q_n - 1$. Let $Q = p_1 p_2 \cdots p_t$ be the prime factorization of $Q$. No $p_i$ is 2, 3, or any $q_j$, because the remainder when $Q$ is divided by 2 is 1, by 3 is 2, and by $q_j$ is $q_j - 1$. All odd primes other than 3 are of the form $6k + 1$ or $6k + 5$, and the product of primes of the form $6k + 1$ is also of this form. Therefore at least one of the $p_i$'s must be of the form $6k + 5$, a contradiction. **31.** The product of numbers of the form $4k + 1$ is of the form $4k + 1$, but numbers of this form might have numbers not of this form as their only prime factors. For example, $49 = 4 \cdot 12 + 1$, but the prime factorization of 49 is $7 \cdot 7 = (4 \cdot 1 + 3)(4 \cdot 1 + 3)$. **33. a)** Not mutually relatively prime **b)** Mutually relatively prime **c)** Mutually relatively prime **d)** Mutually relatively prime **35** 1 **37.** $x \equiv 28 \pmod{30}$ **39.** By the Chinese remainder theorem, it suffices to show that $n^9 - n \equiv 0 \pmod{2}$, $n^9 - n \equiv 0 \pmod{3}$, and $n^9 - n \equiv 0 \pmod{5}$. Each in turn follows from applying Fermat's little theorem. **41.** By Fermat's little theorem, $p^{q-1} \equiv 1 \pmod{q}$ and clearly $q^{p-1} \equiv 0 \pmod{q}$. Therefore $p^{q-1} + q^{p-1} \equiv 1 + 0 = 1 \pmod{q}$. Similarly, $p^{q-1} + q^{p-1} \equiv 1 \pmod{p}$. It follows from the Chinese remainder theorem that $p^{q-1} + q^{p-1} \equiv 1 \pmod{pq}$. **43.** If $a_i$ is changed from $x$ to $y$, then the change in the left-hand side of the congruence is either $y - x$ or $3(y - x)$, modulo 10, neither of which can be 0 because 1 and

3 are relatively prime to 10. Therefore the sum can no longer be 0 modulo 10. **45.** Working modulo 10, solve for $d_9$. The check digit for 11100002 is 5. **47.** PLEASE SEND MONEY **49. a)** QAL HUVEM AT WVESGB **b)** QXB EVZZL ZEVZZRFS

# CHAPTER 5

## Section 5.1

**1.** Let $P(n)$ be the statement that the train stops at station $n$. *Basis step:* We are told that $P(1)$ is true. *Inductive step:* We are told that $P(n)$ implies $P(n + 1)$ for each $n \geq 1$. Therefore by the principle of mathematical induction, $P(n)$ is true for all positive integers $n$. **3. a)** $1^2 = 1 \cdot 2 \cdot 3/6$ **b)** Both sides of $P(1)$ shown in part (a) equal 1. **c)** $1^2 + 2^2 + \cdots + k^2 = k(k + 1)(2k + 1)/6$ **d)** For each $k \geq 1$ that $P(k)$ implies $P(k + 1)$; in other words, that assuming the inductive hypothesis [see part (c)] we can show $1^2 + 2^2 + \cdots + k^2 + (k + 1)^2 = (k + 1)(k + 2)(2k + 3)/6$ **e)** $(1^2 + 2^2 + \cdots + k^2) + (k + 1)^2 = [k(k + 1)(2k + 1)/6] + (k + 1)^2 = [(k + 1)/6][k(2k + 1) + 6(k + 1)] = [(k + 1)/6](2k^2 + 7k + 6) = [(k + 1)/6](k + 2)(2k + 3) = (k + 1)(k + 2)(2k + 3)/6$ **f)** We have completed both the basis step and the inductive step, so by the principle of mathematical induction, the statement is true for every positive integer $n$. **5.** Let $P(n)$ be "$1^2 + 3^2 + \cdots + (2n + 1)^2 = (n + 1)(2n + 1)(2n + 3)/3$." *Basis step:* $P(0)$ is true because $1^2 = 1 = (0 + 1)(2 \cdot 0 + 1)(2 \cdot 0 + 3)/3$. *Inductive step:* Assume that $P(k)$ is true. Then $1^2 + 3^2 + \cdots + (2k + 1)^2 + [2(k + 1) + 1]^2 = (k + 1)(2k + 1)(2k + 3)/3 + (2k + 3)^2 = (2k + 3)[(k + 1)(2k + 1)/3 + (2k + 3)] = (2k + 3)(2k^2 + 9k + 10)/3 = (2k + 3)(2k + 5)(k + 2)/3 = [(k + 1) + 1][2(k + 1) + 1][2(k + 1) + 3]/3$. **7.** Let $P(n)$ be "$\sum_{j=0}^{n} 3 \cdot 5^j = 3(5^{n+1} - 1)/4$." *Basis step:* $P(0)$ is true because $\sum_{j=0}^{0} 3 \cdot 5^j = 3 = 3(5^1 - 1)/4$. *Inductive step:* Assume that $\sum_{j=0}^{k} 3 \cdot 5^j = 3(5^{k+1} - 1)/4$. Then $\sum_{j=0}^{k+1} 3 \cdot 5^j = (\sum_{j=0}^{k} 3 \cdot 5^j) + 3 \cdot 5^{k+1} = 3(5^{k+1} - 1)/4 + 3 \cdot 5^{k+1} = 3(5^{k+1} + 4 \cdot 5^{k+1} - 1)/4 = 3(5^{k+2} - 1)/4$. **9. a)** $2 + 4 + 6 + \cdots + 2n = n(n + 1)$ **b)** *Basis step:* $2 = 1 \cdot (1 + 1)$ is true. *Inductive step:* Assume that $2 + 4 + 6 + \cdots + 2k = k(k + 1)$. Then $(2 + 4 + 6 + \cdots + 2k) + 2(k + 1) = k(k + 1) + 2(k + 1) = (k + 1)(k + 2)$. **11. a)** $\sum_{j=1}^{n} 1/2^j = (2^n - 1)/2^n$ **b)** *Basis step:* $P(1)$ is true because $\frac{1}{2} = (2^1 - 1)/2^1$. *Inductive step:* Assume that $\sum_{j=1}^{k} 1/2^j = (2^k - 1)/2^k$. Then $\sum_{j=1}^{k+1} \frac{1}{2^j} = (\sum_{j=1}^{k} \frac{1}{2^j}) + \frac{1}{2^{k+1}} = \frac{2^k - 1}{2^k} + \frac{1}{2^{k+1}} = \frac{2^{k+1} - 2 + 1}{2^{k+1}} = \frac{2^{k+1} - 1}{2^{k+1}}$. **13.** Let $P(n)$ be "$1^2 - 2^2 + 3^2 - \cdots + (-1)^{n-1}n^2 = (-1)^{n-1}n(n + 1)/2$." *Basis step:* $P(1)$ is true because $1^2 = 1 = (-1)^0 1^2$. *Inductive step:* Assume that $P(k)$ is true. Then $1^2 - 2^2 + 3^2 - \cdots + (-1)^{k-1}k^2 + (-1)^k(k + 1)^2 = (-1)^{k-1}k(k + 1)/2 + (-1)^k(k + 1)^2 = (-1)^k(k + 1)[-k/2 + (k + 1)] = (-1)^k(k + 1)[(k/2) + 1] = (-1)^k(k + 1)(k + 2)/2$. **15.** Let $P(n)$ be "$1 \cdot 2 + 2 \cdot 3 + \cdots + n(n + 1) = n(n + 1)(n + 2)/3$." *Basis step:* $P(1)$ is true because

$1 \cdot 2 = 2 = 1(1 + 1)(1 + 2)/3$. *Inductive step:* Assume that $P(k)$ is true. Then $1 \cdot 2 + 2 \cdot 3 + \cdots + k(k + 1) + (k + 1)(k + 2) = [k(k + 1)(k + 2)/3] + (k + 1)(k + 2) = (k + 1)(k + 2)[(k/3) + 1] = (k + 1)(k + 2)(k + 3)/3$. **17.** Let $P(n)$ be the statement that $1^4 + 2^4 + 3^4 + \cdots + n^4 = n(n + 1)(2n + 1)(3n^2 + 3n - 1)/30$. $P(1)$ is true because $1 \cdot 2 \cdot 3 \cdot 5/30 = 1$. Assume that $P(k)$ is true. Then $(1^4 + 2^4 + 3^4 + \cdots + k^4) + (k + 1)^4 = k(k + 1)(2k + 1)(3k^2 + 3k - 1)/30 + (k + 1)^4 = [(k + 1)/30][k(2k + 1)(3k^2 + 3k - 1) + 30(k + 1)^3] = [(k + 1)/30](6k^4 + 39k^3 + 91k^2 + 89k + 30) = [(k + 1)/30](k + 2)(2k + 3)[3(k + 1)^2 + 3(k + 1) - 1]$. This demonstrates that $P(k + 1)$ is true. **19. a)** $1 + \frac{1}{4} < 2 - \frac{1}{2}$ **b)** This is true because 5/4 is less than 6/4. **c)** $1 + \frac{1}{4} + \cdots + \frac{1}{k^2} < 2 - \frac{1}{k}$ **d)** For each $k \geq 2$ that $P(k)$ implies $P(k + 1)$; in other words, we want to show that assuming the inductive hypothesis [see part (c)] we can show $1 + \frac{1}{4} + \cdots + \frac{1}{k^2} + \frac{1}{(k+1)^2} < 2 - \frac{1}{k+1}$ **e)** $1 + \frac{1}{4} + \cdots + \frac{1}{k^2} + \frac{1}{(k+1)^2} < 2 - \frac{1}{k} + \frac{1}{(k+1)^2} = 2 - [\frac{1}{k} - \frac{1}{(k+1)^2}] = 2 - [\frac{k^2 + 2k + 1 - k}{k(k+1)^2}] = 2 - \frac{k^2 + k}{k(k+1)^2} - \frac{1}{k(k+1)^2} = 2 - \frac{1}{k+1} - \frac{1}{k(k+1)^2} < 2 - \frac{1}{k+1}$ **f)** We have completed both the basis step and the inductive step, so by the principle of mathematical induction, the statement is true for every integer $n$ greater than 1. **21.** Let $P(n)$ be "$2^n > n^2$." *Basis step:* $P(5)$ is true because $2^5 = 32 > 25 = 5^2$. *Inductive step:* Assume that $P(k)$ is true, that is, $2^k > k^2$. Then $2^{k+1} = 2 \cdot 2^k > k^2 + k^2 > k^2 + 4k \geq k^2 + 2k + 1 = (k + 1)^2$ because $k > 4$. **23.** By inspection we find that the inequality $2n + 3 \leq 2^n$ does not hold for $n = 0, 1, 2, 3$. Let $P(n)$ be the proposition that this inequality holds for the positive integer $n$. $P(4)$, the basis case, is true because $2 \cdot 4 + 3 = 11 \leq 16 = 2^4$. For the inductive step assume that $P(k)$ is true. Then, by the inductive hypothesis, $2(k + 1) + 3 = (2k + 3) + 2 < 2^k + 2$. But because $k \geq 1$, $2^k + 2 \leq 2^k + 2^k = 2^{k+1}$. This shows that $P(k + 1)$ is true. **25.** Let $P(n)$ be "$1 + nh \leq (1 + h)^n, h > -1$." *Basis step:* $P(0)$ is true because $1 + 0 \cdot h = 1 \leq 1 = (1 + h)^0$. *Inductive step:* Assume $1 + kh \leq (1 + h)^k$. Then because $(1 + h) > 0$, $(1 + h)^{k+1} = (1 + h)(1 + h)^k \geq (1 + h)(1 + kh) = 1 + (k + 1)h + kh^2 \geq 1 + (k + 1)h$. **27.** Let $P(n)$ be "$1/\sqrt{1} + 1/\sqrt{2} + 1/\sqrt{3} + \cdots + 1/\sqrt{n} > 2(\sqrt{n + 1} - 1)$." *Basis step:* $P(1)$ is true because $1 > 2(\sqrt{2} - 1)$. *Inductive step:* Assume that $P(k)$ is true. Then $1 + 1/\sqrt{2} + \cdots + 1/\sqrt{k} + 1/\sqrt{k + 1} > 2(\sqrt{k + 1} - 1) + 1/\sqrt{k + 1}$. If we show that $2(\sqrt{k + 1} - 1) + 1/\sqrt{k + 1} > 2(\sqrt{k + 2} - 1)$, it follows that $P(k + 1)$ is true. This inequality is equivalent to $2(\sqrt{k + 2} - \sqrt{k + 1}) < 1/\sqrt{k + 1}$, which is equivalent to $2(\sqrt{k + 2} - \sqrt{k + 1})(\sqrt{k + 2} + \sqrt{k + 1}) < \sqrt{k + 1}/\sqrt{k + 1} + \sqrt{k + 2}/\sqrt{k + 1}$. This is equivalent to $2 < 1 + \sqrt{k + 2}/\sqrt{k + 1}$, which is clearly true. **29.** Let $P(n)$ be "$H_{2^n} \leq 1 + n$." *Basis step:* $P(0)$ is true because $H_{2^0} = H_1 = 1 \leq 1 + 0$. *Inductive step:* Assume that $H_{2^k} \leq 1 + k$. Then $H_{2^{k+1}} = H_{2^k} + \sum_{j=2^k+1}^{2^{k+1}} \frac{1}{j} \leq 1 + k + 2^k(\frac{1}{2^{k+1}}) < 1 + k + 1 = 1 + (k + 1)$. **31.** *Basis step:* $1^2 + 1 = 2$ is divisible by 2. *Inductive step:* Assume the inductive hypothesis, that $k^2 + k$ is divisible by 2. Then $(k + 1)^2 + (k + 1) = k^2 + 2k + 1 + k + 1 = (k^2 + k) + 2(k + 1)$, the sum of a multiple of 2 (by the inductive hypothesis) and a multiple of 2 (by definition), hence, divisible by 2. **33.** Let $P(n)$ be "$n^5 - n$ is divisible by 5." *Basis step:* $P(0)$ is true because $0^5 - 0 = 0$ is divisible by 5. *Inductive step:* Assume that $P(k)$ is true, that is, $k^5 - 5$ is divisible by 5. Then $(k+1)^5 - (k+1) = (k^5 + 5k^4 + 10k^3 + 10k^2 + 5k + 1) - (k+1) = (k^5 - k) + 5(k^4 + 2k^3 + 2k^2 + k)$ is also divisible by 5, because both terms in this sum are divisible by 5. **35.** Let $P(n)$ be the proposition that $(2n - 1)^2 - 1$ is divisible by 8. The basis case $P(1)$ is true because $8 \mid 0$. Now assume that $P(k)$ is true. Because $[(2(k + 1) - 1]^2 - 1 = [(2k - 1)^2 - 1] + 8k$, $P(k+1)$ is true because both terms on the right-hand side are divisible by 8. This shows that $P(n)$ is true for all positive integers $n$, so $m^2 - 1$ is divisible by 8 whenever $m$ is an odd positive integer. **37.** *Basis step:* $11^{1+1} + 12^{2\cdot 1 - 1} = 121 + 12 = 133$ *Inductive step:* Assume the inductive hypothesis, that $11^{n+1} + 12^{2n-1}$ is divisible by 133. Then $11^{(n+1)+1} + 12^{2(n+1)-1} = 11 \cdot 11^{n+1} + 144 \cdot 12^{2n-1} = 11 \cdot 11^{n+1} + (11 + 133) \cdot 12^{2n-1} = 11(11^{n+1} + 12^{2n-1}) + 133 \cdot 12^{2n-1}$. The expression in parentheses is divisible by 133 by the inductive hypothesis, and obviously the second term is divisible by 133, so the entire quantity is divisible by 133, as desired. **39.** *Basis step:* $A_1 \subseteq B_1$ tautologically implies that $\bigcap_{j=1}^1 A_j \subseteq \bigcap_{j=1}^1 B_j$. *Inductive step:* Assume the inductive hypothesis that if $A_j \subseteq B_j$ for $j = 1, 2, \ldots, k$, then $\bigcap_{j=1}^k A_j \subseteq \bigcap_{j=1}^k B_j$. We want to show that if $A_j \subseteq B_j$ for $j = 1, 2, \ldots, k+1$, then $\bigcap_{j=1}^{k+1} A_j \subseteq \bigcap_{j=1}^{k+1} B_j$. Let $x$ be an arbitrary element of $\bigcap_{j=1}^{k+1} A_j = \left(\bigcap_{j=1}^k A_j\right) \cap A_{k+1}$. Because $x \in \bigcap_{j=1}^k A_j$, we know by the inductive hypothesis that $x \in \bigcap_{j=1}^k B_j$; because $x \in A_{k+1}$, we know from the given fact that $A_{k+1} \subseteq B_{k+1}$ that $x \in B_{k+1}$. Therefore, $x \in \left(\bigcap_{j=1}^k B_j\right) \cap B_{k+1} = \bigcap_{j=1}^{k+1} B_j$. **41.** Let $P(n)$ be "$(A_1 \cup A_2 \cup \cdots \cup A_n) \cap B = (A_1 \cap B) \cup (A_2 \cap B) \cup \cdots \cup (A_n \cap B)$." *Basis step:* $P(1)$ is trivially true. *Inductive step:* Assume that $P(k)$ is true. Then $(A_1 \cup A_2 \cup \cdots \cup A_k \cup A_{k+1}) \cap B = [(A_1 \cup A_2 \cup \cdots \cup A_k) \cup A_{k+1}] \cap B = [(A_1 \cup A_2 \cup \cdots \cup A_k) \cap B] \cup (A_{k+1} \cap B) = [(A_1 \cap B) \cup (A_2 \cap B) \cup \cdots \cup (A_k \cap B)] \cup (A_{k+1} \cap B) = (A_1 \cap B) \cup (A_2 \cap B) \cup \cdots \cup (A_k \cap B) \cup (A_{k+1} \cap B)$. **43.** Let $P(n)$ be "$\overline{\bigcup_{k=1}^n A_k} = \bigcap_{k=1}^n \overline{A_k}$." *Basis step:* $P(1)$ is trivially true. *Inductive step:* Assume that $P(k)$ is true. Then $\overline{\bigcup_{j=1}^{k+1} A_j} = \overline{\left(\bigcup_{j=1}^k A_j\right) \cup A_{k+1}} = \overline{\left(\bigcup_{j=1}^k A_j\right)} \cap \overline{A_{k+1}} = \left(\bigcap_{j=1}^k \overline{A_j}\right) \cap \overline{A_{k+1}} = \bigcap_{j=1}^{k+1} \overline{A_j}$. **45.** Let $P(n)$ be the statement that a set with $n$ elements has $n(n - 1)/2$ two-element subsets. $P(2)$, the basis case, is true, because a set with two elements has one subset with two elements—namely, itself—and $2(2 - 1)/2 = 1$. Now assume that $P(k)$ is true. Let $S$ be a set with $k + 1$ elements. Choose an element $a$ in $S$ and let $T = S - \{a\}$. A two-element subset of $S$ either contains $a$ or does not. Those subsets not containing $a$ are the subsets of $T$ with two elements; by the inductive hypothesis there are $k(k - 1)/2$ of these. There are $k$ subsets of $S$ with two elements that contain $a$, because such a subset contains $a$ and one of the $k$ elements in $T$. Hence, there are $k(k-1)/2 + k = (k+1)k/2$ two-element subsets of $S$. This

completes the inductive proof. **47.** Reorder the locations if necessary so that $x_1 \leq x_2 \leq x_3 \leq \cdots \leq x_d$. Place the first tower at position $t_1 = x_1 + 1$. Assume tower $k$ has been placed at position $t_k$. Then place tower $k + 1$ at position $t_{k+1} = x + 1$, where $x$ is the smallest $x_i$ greater than $t_k + 1$. **49.** The two sets do not overlap if $n + 1 = 2$. In fact, the conditional statement $P(1) \to P(2)$ is false. **51.** The mistake is in applying the inductive hypothesis to look at $\max(x - 1, y - 1)$, because even though $x$ and $y$ are positive integers, $x - 1$ and $y - 1$ need not be (one or both could be 0). **53.** For the basis step $(n = 2)$ the first person cuts the cake into two portions that she thinks are each $1/2$ of the cake, and the second person chooses the portion he thinks is at least $1/2$ of the cake (at least one of the pieces must satisfy that condition). For the inductive step, suppose there are $k + 1$ people. By the inductive hypothesis, we can suppose that the first $k$ people have divided the cake among themselves so that each person is satisfied that he got at least a fraction $1/k$ of the cake. Each of them now cuts his or her piece into $k+1$ pieces of equal size. The last person gets to choose one piece from each of the first $k$ people's portions. After this is done, each of the first $k$ people is satisfied that she still has $(1/k)(k/(k + 1)) = 1/(k + 1)$ of the cake. To see that the last person is satisfied, suppose that he thought that the $i$th person $(1 \leq i \leq k)$ had a portion $p_i$ of the cake, where $\sum_{i=1}^k p_i = 1$. By choosing what he thinks is the largest piece from each person, he is satisfied that he has at least $\sum_{i=1}^k p_i/(k+1) = (1/(k+1)) \sum_{i=1}^k p_i = 1/(k+1)$ of the cake. **55.** We use the notation $(i, j)$ to mean the square in row $i$ and column $j$ and use induction on $i + j$ to show that every square can be reached by the knight. *Basis step:* There are six base cases, for the cases when $i + j \leq 2$. The knight is already at $(0, 0)$ to start, so the empty sequence of moves reaches that square. To reach $(1, 0)$, the knight moves $(0, 0) \to (2, 1) \to (0, 2) \to (1, 0)$. Similarly, to reach $(0, 1)$, the knight moves $(0, 0) \to (1, 2) \to (2, 0) \to (0, 1)$. Note that the knight has reached $(2, 0)$ and $(0, 2)$ in the process. For the last basis step there is $(0, 0) \to (1, 2) \to (2, 0) \to (0, 1) \to (2, 2) \to (0, 3) \to (1, 1)$. *Inductive step:* Assume the inductive hypothesis, that the knight can reach any square $(i, j)$ for which $i + j = k$, where $k$ is an integer greater than 1. We must show how the knight can reach each square $(i, j)$ when $i + j = k + 1$. Because $k + 1 \geq 3$, at least one of $i$ and $j$ is at least 2. If $i \geq 2$, then by the inductive hypothesis, there is a sequence of moves ending at $(i - 2, j + 1)$, because $i - 2 + j + 1 = i + j - 1 = k$; from there it is just one step to $(i, j)$; similarly, if $j \geq 2$. **57.** *Basis step:* The base cases $n = 0$ and $n = 1$ are true because the derivative of $x^0$ is 0 and the derivative of $x^1 = x$ is 1. *Inductive step:* Using the product rule, the inductive hypothesis, and the basis step shows that $\frac{d}{dx}x^{k+1} = \frac{d}{dx}(x \cdot x^k) = x \cdot \frac{d}{dx}x^k + x^k \frac{d}{dx}x = x \cdot kx^{k-1} + x^k \cdot 1 = kx^k + x^k = (k+1)x^k$. **59.** *Basis step:* For $k = 0$, $1 \equiv 1 \pmod{m}$. *Inductive step:* Suppose that $a \equiv b \pmod{m}$ and $a^k \equiv b^k \pmod{m}$; we must show that $a^{k+1} \equiv b^{k+1} \pmod{m}$. By Theorem 5 from Section 4.1, $a \cdot a^k \equiv b \cdot b^k \pmod{m}$, which by definition says that $a^{k+1} \equiv b^{k+1}$ (mod $m$).   **61.** Let $P(n)$ be "$[(p_1 \to p_2) \land (p_2 \to p_3) \land \cdots \land (p_{n-1} \to p_n)] \to [(p_1 \land \cdots \land p_{n-1}) \to p_n]$." *Basis step:* $P(2)$ is true because $(p_1 \to p_2) \to (p_1 \to p_2)$ is a tautology. *Inductive step:* Assume $P(k)$ is true. To show $[(p_1 \to p_2) \land \cdots \land (p_{k-1} \to p_k) \land (p_k \to p_{k+1})] \to [(p_1 \land \cdots \land p_{k-1} \land p_k) \to p_{k+1}]$ is a tautology, assume that the hypothesis of this conditional statement is true. Because both the hypothesis and $P(k)$ are true, it follows that $(p_1 \land \cdots \land p_{k-1}) \to p_k$ is true. Because this is true, and because $p_k \to p_{k+1}$ is true (it is part of the assumption) it follows by hypothetical syllogism that $(p_1 \land \cdots \land p_{k-1}) \to p_{k+1}$ is true. The weaker statement $(p_1 \land \cdots \land p_{k-1} \land p_k) \to p_{k+1}$ follows from this.   **63.** We will first prove the result when $n$ is a power of 2, that is, if $n = 2^k, k = 1, 2, \ldots$. Let $P(k)$ be the statement $A \geq G$, where $A$ and $G$ are the arithmetic and geometric means, respectively, of a set of $n = 2^k$ positive real numbers. *Basis step:* $k = 1$ and $n = 2^1 = 2$. Note that $(\sqrt{a_1} - \sqrt{a_2})^2 \geq 0$. Expanding this shows that $a_1 - 2\sqrt{a_1 a_2} + a_2 \geq 0$, that is, $(a_1 + a_2)/2 \geq (a_1 a_2)^{1/2}$. *Inductive step:* Assume that $P(k)$ is true, with $n = 2^k$. We will show that $P(k+1)$ is true. We have $2^{k+1} = 2n$. Now $(a_1 + a_2 + \cdots + a_{2n})/(2n) = [(a_1 + a_2 + \cdots + a_n)/n + (a_{n+1} + a_{n+2} + \cdots + a_{2n})/n]/2$ and similarly $(a_1 a_2 \cdots a_{2n})^{1/(2n)} = [(a_1 \cdots a_n)^{1/n}(a_{n+1} \cdots a_{2n})^{1/n}]^{1/2}$. To simplify the notation, let $A(x, y, \ldots)$ and $G(x, y, \ldots)$ denote the arithmetic mean and geometric mean of $x, y, \ldots$, respectively. Also, if $x \leq x', y \leq y'$, and so on, then $A(x, y, \ldots) \leq A(x', y', \ldots)$ and $G(x, y, \ldots) \leq G(x', y', \ldots)$. Hence, $A(a_1, \ldots, a_{2n}) = A(A(a_1, \ldots, a_n), A(a_{n+1}, \ldots, a_{2n})) \geq A(G(a_1, \ldots, a_n), G(a_{n+1}, \ldots, a_{2n})) \geq G(G(a_1, \ldots, a_n), G(a_{n+1}, \ldots, a_{2n})) = G(a_1, \ldots, a_{2n})$. This finishes the proof for powers of 2. Now if $n$ is not a power of 2, let $m$ be the next higher power of 2, and let $a_{n+1}, \ldots, a_m$ all equal $A(a_1, \ldots, a_n) = \bar{a}$. Then we have $[(a_1 a_2 \cdots a_n)\bar{a}^{m-n}]^{1/m} \leq A(a_1, \ldots, a_m)$, because $m$ is a power of 2. Because $A(a_1, \ldots, a_m) = \bar{a}$, it follows that $(a_1 \cdots a_n)^{1/m} \bar{a}^{1-n/m} \leq \bar{a}^{n/m}$. Raising both sides to the $(m/n)$th power gives $G(a_1, \ldots, a_n) \leq A(a_1, \ldots, a_n)$.   **65.** *Basis step:* For $n = 1$, the left-hand side is just $\frac{1}{1}$, which is 1. For $n = 2$, there are three nonempty subsets $\{1\}, \{2\}$, and $\{1, 2\}$, so the left-hand side is $\frac{1}{1} + \frac{1}{2} + \frac{1}{1 \cdot 2} = 2$. *Inductive step:* Assume that the statement is true for $k$. The set of the first $k + 1$ positive integers has many nonempty subsets, but they fall into three categories: a nonempty subset of the first $k$ positive integers together with $k + 1$, a nonempty subset of the first $k$ positive integers, or just $\{k + 1\}$. By the inductive hypothesis, the sum of the first category is $k$. For the second category, we can factor out $1/(k + 1)$ from each term of the sum and what remains is just $k$ by the inductive hypothesis, so this part of the sum is $k/(k + 1)$. Finally, the third category simply yields $1/(k + 1)$. Hence, the entire summation is $k + k/(k + 1) + 1/(k + 1) = k + 1$.   **67.** *Basis step:* If $A_1 \subseteq A_2$, then $A_1$ satisfies the condition of being a subset of each set in the collection; otherwise $A_2 \subseteq A_1$, so $A_2$ satisfies the condition. *Inductive step:* Assume the inductive hypothesis, that the conditional statement is true for $k$ sets,

and suppose we are given $k + 1$ sets that satisfy the given conditions. By the inductive hypothesis, there must be a set $A_i$ for some $i \leq k$ such that $A_i \subseteq A_j$ for $1 \leq j \leq k$. If $A_i \subseteq A_{k+1}$, then we are done. Otherwise, we know that $A_{k+1} \subseteq A_i$, and this tells us that $A_{k+1}$ satisfies the condition of being a subset of $A_j$ for $1 \leq j \leq k + 1$.   **69.** $G(1) = 0$, $G(2) = 1$, $G(3) = 3$, $G(4) = 4$   **71.** To show that $2n - 4$ calls are sufficient to exchange all the gossip, select persons 1, 2, 3, and 4 to be the central committee. Every person outside the central committee calls one person on the central committee. At this point the central committee members *as a group* know all the scandals. They then exchange information among themselves by making the calls 1-2, 3-4, 1-3, and 2-4 in that order. At this point, *every* central committee member knows all the scandals. Finally, again every person outside the central committee calls one person on the central committee, at which point everyone knows all the scandals. [The total number of calls is $(n - 4) + 4 + (n - 4) = 2n - 4$.] That this cannot be done with fewer than $2n - 4$ calls is much harder to prove; see Sandra M. Hedetniemi, Stephen T. Hedetniemi, and Arthur L. Liestman, "A survey of gossiping and broadcasting in communication networks," *Networks* **18** (1988), no. 4, 319–349, for details.   **73.** We prove this by mathematical induction. The basis step ($n = 2$) is true tautologically. For $n = 3$, suppose that the intervals are $(a, b), (c, d)$, and $(e, f)$, where without loss of generality we can assume that $a \leq c \leq e$. Because $(a, b) \cap (e, f) \neq \emptyset$, we must have $e < b$; for a similar reason, $e < d$. It follows that the number halfway between $e$ and the smaller of $b$ and $d$ is common to all three intervals. Now for the inductive step, assume that whenever we have $k$ intervals that have pairwise nonempty intersections then there is a point common to all the intervals, and suppose that we are given intervals $I_1, I_2, \ldots, I_{k+1}$ that have pairwise nonempty intersections. For each $i$ from 1 to $k$, let $J_i = I_i \cap I_{k+1}$. We claim that the collection $J_1, J_2, \ldots, J_k$ satisfies the inductive hypothesis, that is, that $J_{i_1} \cap J_{i_2} \neq \emptyset$ for each choice of subscripts $i_1$ and $i_2$. This follows from the $n = 3$ case proved above, using the sets $I_{i_1}, I_{i_2}$, and $I_{k+1}$. We can now invoke the inductive hypothesis to conclude that there is a number common to all of the sets $J_i$ for $i = 1, 2, \ldots, k$, which perforce is in the intersection of all the sets $I_i$ for $i = 1, 2, \ldots, k + 1$.   **75.** Pair up the people. Have the people stand at mutually distinct small distances from their partners but far away from everyone else. Then each person throws a pie at his or her partner, so everyone gets hit.

**77.**

**79.** Let $P(n)$ be the statement that every $2^n \times 2^n \times 2^n$ checkerboard with a $1 \times 1 \times 1$ cube removed can be covered by tiles that are $2 \times 2 \times 2$ cubes each with a $1 \times 1 \times 1$ cube removed. The basis step, $P(1)$, holds because one tile coincides with the solid to be tiled. Now assume that $P(k)$ holds. Now consider a $2^{k+1} \times 2^{k+1} \times 2^{k+1}$ cube with a $1 \times 1 \times 1$ cube removed. Split this object into eight pieces using planes parallel to its faces and running through its center. The missing $1 \times 1 \times 1$ piece occurs in one of these eight pieces. Now position one tile with its center at the center of the large object so that the missing $1 \times 1 \times 1$ cube lies in the octant in which the large object is missing a $1 \times 1 \times 1$ cube. This creates eight $2^k \times 2^k \times 2^k$ cubes, each missing a $1 \times 1 \times 1$ cube. By the inductive hypothesis we can fill each of these eight objects with tiles. Putting these tilings together produces the desired tiling.

**81.**

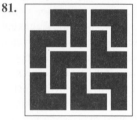

**83.** Let $Q(n)$ be $P(n+b-1)$. The statement that $P(n)$ is true for $n = b, b+1, b+2, \ldots$ is the same as the statement that $Q(m)$ is true for all positive integers $m$. We are given that $P(b)$ is true [i.e., that $Q(1)$ is true], and that $P(k) \to P(k+1)$ for all $k \geq b$ [i.e., that $Q(m) \to Q(m+1)$ for all positive integers $m$]. Therefore, by the principle of mathematical induction, $Q(m)$ is true for all positive integers $m$.

## Section 5.2

**1.** *Basis step:* We are told we can run one mile, so $P(1)$ is true. *Inductive step:* Assume the inductive hypothesis, that we can run any number of miles from 1 to $k$. We must show that we can run $k + 1$ miles. If $k = 1$, then we are already told that we can run two miles. If $k > 1$, then the inductive hypothesis tells us that we can run $k - 1$ miles, so we can run $(k - 1) + 2 = k + 1$ miles. **3. a)** $P(8)$ is true, because we can form 8 cents of postage with one 3-cent stamp and one 5-cent stamp. $P(9)$ is true, because we can form 9 cents of postage with three 3-cent stamps. $P(10)$ is true, because we can form 10 cents of postage with two 5-cent stamps. **b)** The statement that using just 3-cent and 5-cent stamps we can form $j$ cents postage for all $j$ with $8 \leq j \leq k$, where we assume that $k \geq 10$ **c)** Assuming the inductive hypothesis, we can form $k + 1$ cents postage using just 3-cent and 5-cent stamps **d)** Because $k \geq 10$, we know that $P(k-2)$ is true, that is, that we can form $k-2$ cents of postage. Put one more 3-cent stamp on the envelope, and we have formed $k + 1$ cents of postage. **e)** We have completed both the basis step and the inductive step, so by the principle of strong induction, the statement is true for every integer $n$ greater than or equal to 8. **5. a)** 4, 8, 11, 12, 15, 16, 19, 20, 22, 23, 24, 26, 27, 28, and all values greater than or equal to 30 **b)** Let $P(n)$ be the statement that

we can form $n$ cents of postage using just 4-cent and 11-cent stamps. We want to prove that $P(n)$ is true for all $n \geq 30$. For the basis step, $30 = 11 + 11 + 4 + 4$. Assume that we can form $k$ cents of postage (the inductive hypothesis); we will show how to form $k + 1$ cents of postage. If the $k$ cents included an 11-cent stamp, then replace it by three 4-cent stamps. Otherwise, $k$ cents was formed from just 4-cent stamps. Because $k \geq 30$, there must be at least eight 4-cent stamps involved. Replace eight 4-cent stamps by three 11-cent stamps, and we have formed $k + 1$ cents in postage. **c)** $P(n)$ is the same as in part (b). To prove that $P(n)$ is true for all $n \geq 30$, we check for the basis step that $30 = 11 + 11 + 4 + 4$, $31 = 11 + 4 + 4 + 4 + 4 + 4$, $32 = 4 + 4 + 4 + 4 + 4 + 4 + 4 + 4$, and $33 = 11 + 11 + 11$. For the inductive step, assume the inductive hypothesis, that $P(j)$ is true for all $j$ with $30 \leq j \leq k$, where $k$ is an arbitrary integer greater than or equal to 33. We want to show that $P(k + 1)$ is true. Because $k - 3 \geq 30$, we know that $P(k - 3)$ is true, that is, that we can form $k - 3$ cents of postage. Put one more 4-cent stamp on the envelope, and we have formed $k + 1$ cents of postage. In this proof, our inductive hypothesis was that $P(j)$ was true for all values of $j$ between 30 and $k$ inclusive, rather than just that $P(30)$ was true. **7.** We can form all amounts except \$1 and \$3. Let $P(n)$ be the statement that we can form $n$ dollars using just 2-dollar and 5-dollar bills. We want to prove that $P(n)$ is true for all $n \geq 5$. (It is clear that \$1 and \$3 cannot be formed and that \$2 and \$4 can be formed.) For the basis step, note that $5 = 5$ and $6 = 2 + 2 + 2$. Assume the inductive hypothesis, that $P(j)$ is true for all $j$ with $5 \leq j \leq k$, where $k$ is an arbitrary integer greater than or equal to 6. We want to show that $P(k + 1)$ is true. Because $k - 1 \geq 5$, we know that $P(k - 1)$ is true, that is, that we can form $k - 1$ dollars. Add another 2-dollar bill, and we have formed $k + 1$ dollars. **9.** Let $P(n)$ be the statement that there is no positive integer $b$ such that $\sqrt{2} = n/b$. *Basis step:* $P(1)$ is true because $\sqrt{2} > 1 \geq 1/b$ for all positive integers $b$. *Inductive step:* Assume that $P(j)$ is true for all $j \leq k$, where $k$ is an arbitrary positive integer; we prove that $P(k+1)$ is true by contradiction. Assume that $\sqrt{2} = (k+1)/b$ for some positive integer $b$. Then $2b^2 = (k + 1)^2$, so $(k + 1)^2$ is even, and hence, $k + 1$ is even. So write $k + 1 = 2t$ for some positive integer $t$, whence $2b^2 = 4t^2$ and $b^2 = 2t^2$. By the same reasoning as before, $b$ is even, so $b = 2s$ for some positive integer $s$. Then $\sqrt{2} = (k + 1)/b = (2t)/(2s) = t/s$. But $t \leq k$, so this contradicts the inductive hypothesis, and our proof of the inductive step is complete. **11.** *Basis step:* There are four base cases. If $n = 1 = 4 \cdot 0 + 1$, then clearly the second player wins. If there are two, three, or four matches ($n = 4 \cdot 0 + 2, n = 4 \cdot 0 + 3$, or $n = 4 \cdot 1$), then the first player can win by removing all but one match. *Inductive step:* Assume the strong inductive hypothesis, that in games with $k$ or fewer matches, the first player can win if $k \equiv 0, 2$, or $3 \pmod 4$ and the second player can win if $k \equiv 1 \pmod 4$. Suppose we have a game with $k + 1$ matches, with $k \geq 4$. If $k + 1 \equiv 0 \pmod 4$, then the first player can remove three matches, leaving $k - 2$ matches for the other player. Because $k - 2 \equiv 1 \pmod 4$, by the inductive hypothesis, this is a game that the second player at that point (who is the first player in our game) can win. Similarly, if $k + 1 \equiv 2 \pmod 4$, then the first player can remove one match; and if $k + 1 \equiv 3 \pmod 4$, then the first player can remove two matches. Finally, if $k + 1 \equiv 1 \pmod 4$, then the first player must leave $k$, $k - 1$, or $k - 2$ matches for the other player. Because $k \equiv 0 \pmod 4$, $k - 1 \equiv 3 \pmod 4$, and $k - 2 \equiv 2 \pmod 4$, by the inductive hypothesis, this is a game that the first player at that point (who is the second player in our game) can win.   **13.** Let $P(n)$ be the statement that exactly $n - 1$ moves are required to assemble a puzzle with $n$ pieces. Now $P(1)$ is trivially true. Assume that $P(j)$ is true for all $j \leq k$, and consider a puzzle with $k + 1$ pieces. The final move must be the joining of two blocks, of size $j$ and $k + 1 - j$ for some integer $j$ with $1 \leq j \leq k$. By the inductive hypothesis, it required $j - 1$ moves to construct the one block, and $k + 1 - j - 1 = k - j$ moves to construct the other. Therefore, $1 + (j - 1) + (k - j) = k$ moves are required in all, so $P(k + 1)$ is true.   **15.** Let the Chomp board have $n$ rows and $n$ columns. We claim that the first player can win the game by making the first move to leave just the top row and leftmost column. Let $P(n)$ be the statement that if a player has presented his opponent with a Chomp configuration consisting of just $n$ cookies in the top row and $n$ cookies in the leftmost column, then he can win the game. We will prove $\forall n\, P(n)$ by strong induction. We know that $P(1)$ is true, because the opponent is forced to take the poisoned cookie at his first turn. Fix $k \geq 1$ and assume that $P(j)$ is true for all $j \leq k$. We claim that $P(k + 1)$ is true. It is the opponent's turn to move. If she picks the poisoned cookie, then the game is over and she loses. Otherwise, assume she picks the cookie in the top row in column $j$, or the cookie in the left column in row $j$, for some $j$ with $2 \leq j \leq k + 1$. The first player now picks the cookie in the left column in row $j$, or the cookie in the top row in column $j$, respectively. This leaves the position covered by $P(j - 1)$ for his opponent, so by the inductive hypothesis, he can win.   **17.** Let $P(n)$ be the statement that if a simple polygon with $n$ sides is triangulated, then at least two of the triangles in the triangulation have two sides that border the exterior of the polygon. We will prove $\forall n \geq 4\, P(n)$. The statement is clearly true for $n = 4$, because there is only one diagonal, leaving two triangles with the desired property. Fix $k \geq 4$ and assume that $P(j)$ is true for all $j$ with $4 \leq j \leq k$. Consider a polygon with $k + 1$ sides, and some triangulation of it. Pick one of the diagonals in this triangulation. First suppose that this diagonal divides the polygon into one triangle and one polygon with $k$ sides. Then the triangle has two sides that border the exterior. Furthermore, the $k$-gon has, by the inductive hypothesis, two triangles that have two sides that border the exterior of that $k$-gon, and only one of these triangles can fail to be a triangle that has two sides that border the exterior of the original polygon. The only other case is that this diagonal divides the polygon into two polygons with $j$ sides and $k + 3 - j$ sides for some $j$ with $4 \leq j \leq k - 1$. By the inductive hypothesis, each of these two polygons has two triangles that have two sides that border their exterior, and in each case only one of these triangles can fail to be a trian-

gle that has two sides that border the exterior of the original polygon.   **19.** Let $P(n)$ be the statement that the area of a simple polygon with $n$ sides and vertices all at lattice points is given by $I(P) + B(P)/2 - 1$. We will prove $P(n)$ for all $n \geq 3$. We begin with an additivity lemma: If $P$ is a simple polygon with all vertices at lattice points, divided into polygons $P_1$ and $P_2$ by a diagonal, then $I(P) + B(P)/2 - 1 = [I(P_1) + B(P_1)/2 - 1] + [I(P_2) + B(P_2)/2 - 1]$. To prove this, suppose there are $k$ lattice points on the diagonal, not counting its endpoints. Then $I(P) = I(P_1) + I(P_2) + k$ and $B(P) = B(P_1) + B(P_2) - 2k - 2$; and the result follows by simple algebra. What this says in particular is that if Pick's formula gives the correct area for $P_1$ and $P_2$, then it must give the correct formula for $P$, whose area is the sum of the areas for $P_1$ and $P_2$; and similarly if Pick's formula gives the correct area for $P$ and one of the $P_i$'s, then it must give the correct formula for the other $P_i$. Next we prove the theorem for rectangles whose sides are parallel to the coordinate axes. Such a rectangle necessarily has vertices at $(a, b)$, $(a, c)$, $(d, b)$, and $(d, c)$, where $a, b, c,$ and $d$ are integers with $b < c$ and $a < d$. Its area is $(c - b)(d - a)$. Also, $B = 2(c - b + d - a)$ and $I = (c - b - 1)(d - a - 1) = (c - b)(d - a) - (c - b) - (d - a) + 1$. Therefore, $I + B/2 - 1 = (c - b)(d - a) - (c - b) - (d - a) + 1 + (c - b + d - a) - 1 = (c - b)(d - a)$, which is the desired area. Next consider a right triangle whose legs are parallel to the coordinate axes. This triangle is half a rectangle of the type just considered, for which Pick's formula holds, so by the additivity lemma, it holds for the triangle as well. (The values of $B$ and $I$ are the same for each of the two triangles, so if Pick's formula gave an answer that was either too small or too large, then it would give a correspondingly wrong answer for the rectangle.) For the next step, consider an arbitrary triangle with vertices at lattice points that is not of the type already considered. Embed it in as small a rectangle as possible. There are several possible ways this can happen, but in any case (and adding one more edge in one case), the rectangle will have been partitioned into the given triangle and two or three right triangles with sides parallel to the coordinate axes. Again by the additivity lemma, we are guaranteed that Pick's formula gives the correct area for the given triangle. This completes the proof of $P(3)$, the basis step in our strong induction proof. For the inductive step, given an arbitrary polygon, use Lemma 1 in the text to split it into two polygons. Then by the additivity lemma above and the inductive hypothesis, we know that Pick's formula gives the correct area for this polygon.   **21. a)** In the left figure $\angle abp$ is smallest, but $\overline{bp}$ is not an interior diagonal. **b)** In the right figure $\overline{bd}$ is not an interior diagonal. **c)** In the right figure $\overline{bd}$ is not an interior diagonal. **23. a)** When we try to prove the inductive step and find a triangle in each subpolygon with at least two sides bordering the exterior, it may happen in each case that the triangle we are guaranteed in fact borders the diagonal (which is part of the boundary of that polygon). This leaves us with no triangles guaranteed to touch the boundary of the *original* polygon. **b)** We proved the stronger statement $\forall n \geq 4\, T(n)$ in Exercise 17.   **25. a)** The inductive step here allows us to conclude that

$P(3)$, $P(5)$, ... are all true, but we can conclude nothing about $P(2)$, $P(4)$, .... **b)** $P(n)$ is true for all positive integers $n$, using strong induction. **c)** The inductive step here enables us to conclude that $P(2)$, $P(4)$, $P(8)$, $P(16)$, ...are all true, but we can conclude nothing about $P(n)$ when $n$ is not a power of 2. **d)** This is mathematical induction; we can conclude that $P(n)$ is true for all positive integers $n$. **27.** Suppose, for a proof by contradiction, that there is some positive integer $n$ such that $P(n)$ is not true. Let $m$ be the smallest positive integer greater than $n$ for which $P(m)$ *is* true; we know that such an $m$ exists because $P(m)$ is true for infinitely many values of $m$. But we know that $P(m) \rightarrow P(m-1)$, so $P(m-1)$ is also true. Thus, $m-1$ cannot be greater than $n$, so $m-1=n$ and $P(n)$ is in fact true. This contradiction shows that $P(n)$ is true for all $n$. **29.** The error is in going from the base case $n=0$ to the next case, $n=1$; we cannot write 1 as the sum of two smaller natural numbers. **31.** Assume that the well-ordering property holds. Suppose that $P(1)$ is true and that the conditional statement $[P(1) \wedge P(2) \wedge \cdots \wedge P(n)] \rightarrow P(n+1)$ is true for every positive integer $n$. Let $S$ be the set of positive integers $n$ for which $P(n)$ is false. We will show $S = \emptyset$. Assume that $S \neq \emptyset$. Then by the well-ordering property there is a least integer $m$ in $S$. We know that $m$ cannot be 1 because $P(1)$ is true. Because $n=m$ is the least integer such that $P(n)$ is false, $P(1)$, $P(2)$, ..., $P(m-1)$ are true, and $m-1 \geq 1$. Because $[P(1) \wedge P(2) \wedge \cdots \wedge P(m-1)] \rightarrow P(m)$ is true, it follows that $P(m)$ must also be true, which is a contradiction. Hence, $S = \emptyset$. **33.** In each case, give a proof by contradiction based on a "smallest counterexample," that is, values of $n$ and $k$ such that $P(n, k)$ is not true and $n$ and $k$ are smallest in some sense. **a)** Choose a counterexample with $n+k$ as small as possible. We cannot have $n=1$ and $k=1$, because we are given that $P(1, 1)$ is true. Therefore, either $n>1$ or $k>1$. In the former case, by our choice of counterexample, we know that $P(n-1, k)$ is true. But the inductive step then forces $P(n, k)$ to be true, a contradiction. The latter case is similar. So our supposition that there is a counterexample mest be wrong, and $P(n, k)$ is true in all cases. **b)** Choose a counterexample with $n$ as small as possible. We cannot have $n=1$, because we are given that $P(1, k)$ is true for all $k$. Therefore, $n>1$. By our choice of counterexample, we know that $P(n-1, k)$ is true. But the inductive step then forces $P(n, k)$ to be true, a contradiction. **c)** Choose a counterexample with $k$ as small as possible. We cannot have $k=1$, because we are given that $P(n, 1)$ is true for all $n$. Therefore, $k>1$. By our choice of counterexample, we know that $P(n, k-1)$ is true. But the inductive step then forces $P(n, k)$ to be true, a contradiction. **35.** Let $P(n)$ be the statement that if $x_1, x_2, \ldots, x_n$ are $n$ distinct real numbers, then $n-1$ multiplications are used to find the product of these numbers no matter how parentheses are inserted in the product. We will prove that $P(n)$ is true using strong induction. The basis case $P(1)$ is true because $1-1=0$ multiplications are required to find the product of $x_1$, a product with only one factor. Suppose that $P(k)$ is true for $1 \leq k \leq n$. The last multiplication used to find the product of the $n+1$ distinct real numbers $x_1, x_2, \ldots, x_n, x_{n+1}$ is a multiplication

of the product of the first $k$ of these numbers for some $k$ and the product of the last $n+1-k$ of them. By the inductive hypothesis, $k-1$ multiplications are used to find the product of $k$ of the numbers, no matter how parentheses were inserted in the product of these numbers, and $n-k$ multiplications are used to find the product of the other $n+1-k$ of them, no matter how parentheses were inserted in the product of these numbers. Because one more multiplication is required to find the product of all $n+1$ numbers, the total number of multiplications used equals $(k-1) + (n-k) + 1 = n$. Hence, $P(n+1)$ is true. **37.** Assume that $a = dq+r = dq'+r'$ with $0 \leq r < d$ and $0 \leq r' < d$. Then $d(q-q') = r'-r$. It follows that $d$ divides $r'-r$. Because $-d < r'-r < d$, we have $r'-r = 0$. Hence, $r' = r$. It follows that $q = q'$. **39.** This is a paradox caused by self-reference. The answer is clearly "no." There are a finite number of English words, so only a finite number of strings of 15 words or fewer; therefore, only a finite number of positive integers can be so described, not all of them. **41.** Suppose that the well-ordering property were false. Let $S$ be a nonempty set of nonnegative integers that has no least element. Let $P(n)$ be the statement "$i \notin S$ for $i = 0, 1, \ldots, n$." $P(0)$ is true because if $0 \in S$ then $S$ has a least element, namely, 0. Now suppose that $P(n)$ is true. Thus, $0 \notin S$, $1 \notin S$, ..., $n \notin S$. Clearly, $n+1$ cannot be in $S$, for if it were, it would be its least element. Thus $P(n+1)$ is true. So by the principle of mathematical induction, $n \notin S$ for all nonnegative integers $n$. Thus, $S = \emptyset$, a contradiction. **43.** Strong induction implies the principle of mathematical induction, for if one has shown that $P(k) \rightarrow P(k+1)$ is true, then one has also shown that $[P(1) \wedge \cdots \wedge P(k)] \rightarrow P(k+1)$ is true. By Exercise 41, the principle of mathematical induction implies the well-ordering property. Therefore by assuming strong induction as an axiom, we can prove the well-ordering property.

## Section 5.3

**1. a)** $f(1) = 3$, $f(2) = 5$, $f(3) = 7$, $f(4) = 9$ **b)** $f(1) = 3$, $f(2) = 9$, $f(3) = 27$, $f(4) = 81$ **c)** $f(1) = 2$, $f(2) = 4$, $f(3) = 16$, $f(4) = 65{,}536$ **d)** $f(1) = 3$, $f(2) = 13$, $f(3) = 183$, $f(4) = 33{,}673$ **3. a)** $f(2) = -1$, $f(3) = 5$, $f(4) = 2$, $f(5) = 17$ **b)** $f(2) = -4$, $f(3) = 32$, $f(4) = -4096$, $f(5) = 536{,}870{,}912$ **c)** $f(2) = 8$, $f(3) = 176$, $f(4) = 92{,}672$, $f(5) = 25{,}764$, $174$, $848$ **d)** $f(2) = -\frac{1}{2}$, $f(3) = -4$, $f(4) = \frac{1}{8}$, $f(5) = -32$ **5. a)** Not valid **b)** $f(n) = 1 - n$. *Basis step:* $f(0) = 1 = 1 - 0$. *Inductive step:* if $f(k) = 1 - k$, then $f(k+1) = f(k) - 1 = 1 - k - 1 = 1 - (k+1)$. **c)** $f(n) = 4 - n$ if $n > 0$, and $f(0) = 2$. *Basis step:* $f(0) = 2$ and $f(1) = 3 = 4 - 1$. *Inductive step* (with $k \geq 1$): $f(k+1) = f(k) - 1 = (4-k) - 1 = 4 - (k+1)$. **d)** $f(n) = 2^{\lfloor (n+1)/2 \rfloor}$. *Basis step:* $f(0) = 1 = 2^{\lfloor (0+1)/2 \rfloor}$ and $f(1) = 2 = 2^{\lfloor (1+1)/2 \rfloor}$. *Inductive step* (with $k \geq 1$): $f(k+1) = 2f(k-1) = 2 \cdot 2^{\lfloor k/2 \rfloor} = 2^{\lfloor k/2 \rfloor + 1} = 2^{\lfloor ((k+1)+1)/2 \rfloor}$. **e)** $f(n) = 3^n$. *Basis step:* Trivial. *Inductive step:* For odd $n$, $f(n) = 3f(n-1) = 3 \cdot 3^{n-1} = 3^n$; and for even $n > 1$, $f(n) = 9f(n-2) = 9 \cdot 3^{n-2} = 3^n$. **7.** There

erties divide the plane into $k^2 - k + 2 + 2k = (k^2 + 2k + 1) - (k + 1) + 2 = (k + 1)^2 - (k + 1) + 2$ regions. **51.** Suppose $\sqrt{2}$ were rational. Then $\sqrt{2} = a/b$, where $a$ and $b$ are positive integers. It follows that the set $S = \{n\sqrt{2} \mid n \in \mathbf{N}\} \cap \mathbf{N}$ is a nonempty set of positive integers, because $b\sqrt{2} = a$ belongs to $S$. Let $t$ be the least element of $S$, which exists by the well-ordering property. Then $t = s\sqrt{2}$ for some integer $s$. We have $t - s = s\sqrt{2} - s = s(\sqrt{2} - 1)$, so $t - s$ is a positive integer because $\sqrt{2} > 1$. Hence, $t - s$ belongs to $S$. This is a contradiction because $t - s = s\sqrt{2} - s < s$. Hence, $\sqrt{2}$ is irrational.     **53. a)** Let $d = \gcd(a_1, a_2, \ldots, a_n)$. Then $d$ is a divisor of each $a_i$ and so must be a divisor of $\gcd(a_{n-1}, a_n)$. Hence, $d$ is a common divisor of $a_1, a_2, \ldots, a_{n-2}$, and $\gcd(a_{n-1}, a_n)$. To show that it is the greatest common divisor of these numbers, suppose that $c$ is a common divisor of them. Then $c$ is a divisor of $a_i$ for $i = 1, 2, \ldots, n - 2$ and a divisor of $\gcd(a_{n-1}, a_n)$, so it is a divisor of $a_{n-1}$ and $a_n$. Hence, $c$ is a common divisor of $a_1, a_2, \ldots, a_{n-1}$, and $a_n$. Hence, it is a divisor of $d$, the greatest common divisor of $a_1, a_2, \ldots, a_n$. It follows that $d$ is the greatest common divisor, as claimed. **b)** If $n = 2$, apply the Euclidean algorithm. Otherwise, apply the Euclidean algorithm to $a_{n-1}$ and $a_n$, obtaining $d = \gcd(a_{n-1}, a_n)$, and then apply the algorithm recursively to $a_1, a_2, \ldots, a_{n-2}, d$. **55.** $f(n) = n^2$. Let $P(n)$ be "$f(n) = n^2$." *Basis step:* $P(1)$ is true because $f(1) = 1 = 1^2$, which follows from the definition of $f$. *Inductive step:* Assume $f(n) = n^2$. Then $f(n + 1) = f((n+1) - 1) + 2(n+1) - 1 = f(n) + 2n + 1 = n^2 + 2n + 1 = (n + 1)^2$.     **57. a)** $\lambda$, 0, 1, 00, 01, 11, 000, 001, 011, 111, 0000, 0001, 0011, 0111, 1111, 00000, 00001, 00011, 00111, 01111, 11111   **b)** $S = \{\alpha\beta \mid \alpha$ is a string of $m$ 0s and $\beta$ is a string of $n$ 1s, $m \geq 0, n \geq 0\}$ **59.** Apply the first recursive step to $\lambda$ to get $() \in B$. Apply the second recursive step to this string to get $()() \in B$. Apply the first recursive step to this string to get $(()()) \in B$. By Exercise 62, $(())$ is not in $B$ because the number of left parentheses does not equal the number of right parentheses. **61.** $\lambda$, (), (()), ()()    **63. a)** 0  **b)** $-2$  **c)** 2  **d)** 0

**65.**
```
procedure generate(n: nonnegative integer)
if n is odd then
    S := S(n − 1) {the S constructed by generate(n − 1)}
    T := T(n − 1) {the T constructed by generate(n − 1)}
else if n = 0 then
    S := ∅
    T := {λ}
else
    S′ := S(n − 2) {the S constructed by generate(n − 2)}
    T′ := T(n − 2) {the T constructed by generate(n − 2)}
    T := T′ ∪ {(x)|x ∈ T′ ∪ S′ ∧ length(x) = n − 2}
    S := S′ ∪ {xy|x ∈ T′ ∧ y ∈ T′ ∪ S′ ∧ length(xy) = n}
{T ∪ S is the set of balanced strings of length at most n}
```
**67.** If $x \leq y$ initially, then $x := y$ is not executed, so $x \leq y$ is a true final assertion. If $x > y$ initially, then $x := y$ is executed, so $x \leq y$ is again a true final assertion.
**69. procedure** *zerocount*($a_1, a_2, \ldots, a_n$: list of integers)
    **if** $n = 1$ **then**

**if** $a_1 = 0$ **then return** 1
**else return** 0
**else**
  **if** $a_n = 0$ **then return** *zerocount*$(a_1, a_2, \ldots, a_{n-1}) + 1$
  **else return** *zerocount*$(a_1, a_2, \ldots, a_{n-1})$
**71.** We will prove that $a(n)$ is a natural number and $a(n) \leq n$. This is true for the base case $n = 0$ because $a(0) = 0$. Now assume that $a(n - 1)$ is a natural number and $a(n - 1) \leq n - 1$. Then $a(a(n - 1))$ is $a$ applied to a natural number less than or equal to $n - 1$. Hence, $a(a(n - 1))$ is also a natural number minus than or equal to $n - 1$. Therefore, $n - a(a(n - 1))$ is $n$ minus some natural number less than or equal to $n - 1$, which is a natural number less than or equal to $n$.     **73.** From Exercise 72, $a(n) = \lfloor (n + 1)\mu \rfloor$ and $a(n - 1) = \lfloor n\mu \rfloor$. Because $\mu < 1$, these two values are equal or they differ by 1. First suppose that $\mu n - \lfloor \mu n \rfloor < 1 - \mu$. This is equivalent to $\mu(n+1) < 1 + \lfloor \mu n \rfloor$. If this is true, then $\lfloor \mu(n + 1) \rfloor = \lfloor \mu n \rfloor$. On the other hand, if $\mu n - \lfloor \mu n \rfloor \geq 1 - \mu$, then $\mu(n + 1) \geq 1 + \lfloor \mu n \rfloor$, so $\lfloor \mu(n + 1) \rfloor = \lfloor \mu n \rfloor + 1$, as desired.     **75.** $f(0) = 1$, $m(0) = 0$; $f(1) = 1$, $m(1) = 0$; $f(2) = 2$, $m(2) = 1$; $f(3) = 2$, $m(3) = 2$; $f(4) = 3$, $m(4) = 2$; $f(5) = 3$, $m(5) = 3$; $f(6) = 4$, $m(6) = 4$; $f(7) = 5$, $m(7) = 4$; $f(8) = 5$, $m(8) = 5$; $f(9) = 6$, $m(9) = 6$     **77.** The last occurrence of $n$ is in the position for which the total number of 1s, 2s, $\ldots$, $n$s all together is that position number. But because $a_k$ is the number of occurrences of $k$, this is just $\sum_{k=1}^{n} a_k$, as desired. Because $f(n)$ is the sum of the first $n$ terms of the sequence, $f(f(n))$ is the sum of the first $f(n)$ terms of the sequence. But because $f(n)$ is the last term whose value is $n$, this means that the sum is the sum of all terms of the sequence whose value is at most $n$. Because there are $a_k$ terms of the sequence whose value is $k$, this sum is $\sum_{k=1}^{n} k \cdot a_k$, as desired

# CHAPTER 6

## Section 6.1

**1. a)** 5850   **b)** 343   **3. a)** $4^{10}$   **b)** $5^{10}$   **5.** 42   **7.** $26^3$ **9.** 676   **11.** $2^8$   **13.** $n + 1$ (counting the empty string) **15.** 475,255 (counting the empty string)   **17.** 1,321,368,961 **19. a)** 729   **b)** 256   **c)** 1024   **d)** 64   **21. a)** Seven: 56, 63, 70, 77, 84, 91, 98   **b)** Five: 55, 66, 77, 88, 99 **c)** One: 77   **23. a)** 128   **b)** 450   **c)** 9   **d)** 675   **e)** 450 **f)** 450   **g)** 225   **h)** 75   **25. a)** 990   **b)** 500   **c)** 27   **27.** $3^{50}$ **29.** 52,457,600   **31.** 20,077,200   **33. a)** 37,822,859,361 **b)** 8,204,716,800   **c)** 40,159,050, 880   **d)** 12,113,640,000 **e)** 171,004,205,215   **f)** 72,043,541,640   **g)** 6,230,721,635 **h)** 223,149,655   **35. a)** 0 **b)** 120 **c)** 720 **d)** 2520   **37. a)** 2 if $n = 1$, 2 if $n = 2$, 0 if $n \geq 3$   **b)** $2^{n-2}$ for $n > 1$; 1 if $n = 1$   **c)** $2(n - 1)$   **39.** $(n + 1)^m$   **41.** If $n$ is even, $2^{n/2}$; if $n$ is odd, $2^{(n+1)/2}$   **43. a)** 175   **b)** 248   **c)** 232   **d)** 84 **45.** 60   **47. a)** 240   **b)** 480   **c)** 360   **49.** 352   **51.** 147 **53.** 33   **55. a)** 9,920,671,339,261,325,541,376 $\approx$ 9.9 $\times$ $10^{21}$   **b)** 6,641,514,961,387,068,437,760 $\approx$ 6.6 $\times$ $10^{21}$   **c)** About 314,000 years   **57.** $54(64^{65536} - 1)/63$

**59.** 7,104,000,000,000 **61.** $16^{10} + 16^{26} + 16^{58}$
**63.** 666,667 **65.** 18 **67.** 17 **69.** 22 **71.** Let $P(m)$ be
the sum rule for $m$ tasks. For the basis case take $m = 2$. This
is just the sum rule for two tasks. Now assume that $P(m)$ is
true. Consider $m + 1$ tasks, $T_1, T_2, \ldots, T_m, T_{m+1}$, which can
be done in $n_1, n_2, \ldots, n_m, n_{m+1}$ ways, respectively, such that
no two of these tasks can be done at the same time. To do one
of these tasks, we can either do one of the first $m$ of these or
do task $T_{m+1}$. By the sum rule for two tasks, the number of
ways to do this is the sum of the number of ways to do one of
the first $m$ tasks, plus $n_{m+1}$. By the inductive hypothesis, this
is $n_1 + n_2 + \cdots + n_m + n_{m+1}$, as desired. **73.** $n(n-3)/2$

## Section 6.2

**1.** Because there are six classes, but only five weekdays, the
pigeonhole principle shows that at least two classes must be
held on the same day. **3. a)** 3 **b)** 14 **5.** Because there are
four possible remainders when an integer is divided by 4,
the pigeonhole principle implies that given five integers, at
least two have the same remainder. **7.** Let $a, a + 1, \ldots,$
$a + n - 1$ be the integers in the sequence. The integers
$(a + i) \bmod n, i = 0, 1, 2, \ldots, n - 1$, are distinct, because
$0 < (a + j) - (a + k) < n$ whenever $0 \le k < j \le n-1$. Because there are $n$ possible values for $(a + i) \bmod n$ and there
are $n$ different integers in the set, each of these values is taken
on exactly once. It follows that there is exactly one integer in
the sequence that is divisible by $n$. **9.** 4951 **11.** The midpoint of the segment joining the points $(a, b, c)$ and $(d, e, f)$
is $((a+d)/2, (b+e)/2, (c+f)/2)$. It has integer coefficients
if and only if $a$ and $d$ have the same parity, $b$ and $e$ have the
same parity, and $c$ and $f$ have the same parity. Because there
are eight possible triples of parity [such as $(even, odd, even)$],
by the pigeonhole principle at least two of the nine points have
the same triple of parities. The midpoint of the segment joining two such points has integer coefficients. **13. a)** Group
the first eight positive integers into four subsets of two integers each so that the integers of each subset add up to 9: {1, 8},
{2, 7}, {3, 6}, and {4, 5}. If five integers are selected from the
first eight positive integers, by the pigeonhole principle at least
two of them come from the same subset. Two such integers
have a sum of 9, as desired. **b)** No. Take {1, 2, 3, 4}, for example. **15.** 4 **17.** 21,251 **19. a)** If there were fewer than 9
freshmen, fewer than 9 sophomores, and fewer than 9 juniors
in the class, there would be no more than 8 with each of these
three class standings, for a total of at most 24 students, contradicting the fact that there are 25 students in the class. **b)** If
there were fewer than 3 freshmen, fewer than 19 sophomores,
and fewer than 5 juniors, then there would be at most 2 freshmen, at most 18 sophomores, and at most 4 juniors, for a total
of at most 24 students. This contradicts the fact that there are
25 students in the class. **21.** 4, 3, 2, 1, 8, 7, 6, 5, 12, 11,
10, 9, 16, 15, 14, 13 **23.** Number the seats around the table
from 1 to 50, and think of seat 50 as being adjacent to seat 1.
There are 25 seats with odd numbers and 25 seats with even
numbers. If no more than 12 boys occupied the odd-numbered

seats, then at least 13 boys would occupy the even-numbered
seats, and vice versa. Without loss of generality, assume that
at least 13 boys occupy the 25 odd-numbered seats. Then at
least two of those boys must be in consecutive odd-numbered
seats, and the person sitting between them will have boys as
both of his or her neighbors.
**25. procedure** $long(a_1, \ldots, a_n$: positive integers)
    {first find longest increasing subsequence}
    $max := 0; set := 00\ldots00$ {$n$ bits}
    **for** $i := 1$ **to** $2^n$
      $last := 0; count := 0, OK :=$ **true**
      **for** $j := 1$ **to** $n$
        **if** $set(j) = 1$ **then**
          **if** $a_j > last$ **then** $last := a_j$
          $count := count + 1$
        **else** $OK :=$ **false**
      **if** $count > max$ **then**
        $max := count$
        $best := set$
      $set := set + 1$ (binary addition)
    {$max$ is length and $best$ indicates the sequence}
    {repeat for decreasing subsequence with only
        changes being $a_j < last$ instead of $a_j > last$
        and $last := \infty$ instead of $last := 0$}
**27.** By symmetry we need prove only the first statement. Let
$A$ be one of the people. Either $A$ has at least four friends, or $A$
has at least six enemies among the other nine people (because
$3 + 5 < 9$). Suppose, in the first case, that $B, C, D$, and $E$
are all $A$'s friends. If any two of these are friends with each
other, then we have found three mutual friends. Otherwise
$\{B, C, D, E\}$ is a set of four mutual enemies. In the second
case, let $\{B, C, D, E, F, G\}$ be a set of enemies of $A$. By
Example 11, among $B, C, D, E, F$, and $G$ there are either
three mutual friends or three mutual enemies, who form, with
$A$, a set of four mutual enemies. **29.** We need to show two
things: that if we have a group of $n$ people, then among them
we must find either a pair of friends or a subset of $n$ of them
all of whom are mutual enemies; and that there exists a group
of $n - 1$ people for which this is not possible. For the first
statement, if there is any pair of friends, then the condition is
satisfied, and if not, then every pair of people are enemies, so
the second condition is satisfied. For the second statement, if
we have a group of $n - 1$ people all of whom are enemies of
each other, then there is neither a pair of friends nor a subset
of $n$ of them all of whom are mutual enemies. **31.** There
are 6,432,816 possibilities for the three initials and a birthday.
So, by the generalized pigeonhole principle, there are at least
$\lceil 37,000,000/6,432,816 \rceil = 6$ people who share the same
initials and birthday. **33.** Because $800,001 > 200,000$, the
pigeonhole principle guarantees that there are at least two
Parisians with the same number of hairs on their heads. The
generalized pigeonhole principle guarantees that there are at
least $\lceil 800,001/200,000 \rceil = 5$ Parisians with the same number of hairs on their heads. **35.** 18 **37.** Because there are
six computers, the number of other computers a computer is
connected to is an integer between 0 and 5, inclusive. However, 0 and 5 cannot both occur. To see this, note that if some

computer is connected to no others, then no computer is connected to all five others, and if some computer is connected to all five others, then no computer is connected to no others. Hence, by the pigeonhole principle, because there are at most five possibilities for the number of computers a computer is connected to, there are at least two computers in the set of six connected to the same number of others. **39.** Label the computers $C_1$ through $C_{100}$, and label the printers $P_1$ through $P_{20}$. If we connect $C_k$ to $P_k$ for $k = 1, 2, \ldots, 20$ and connect each of the computers $C_{21}$ through $C_{100}$ to *all* the printers, then we have used a total of $20 + 80 \cdot 20 = 1620$ cables. Clearly this is sufficient, because if computers $C_1$ through $C_{20}$ need printers, then they can use the printers with the same subscripts, and if any computers with higher subscripts need a printer instead of one or more of these, then they can use the printers that are not being used, because they are connected to all the printers. Now we must show that 1619 cables is not enough. Because there are 1619 cables and 20 printers, the average number of computers per printer is $1619/20$, which is less than 81. Therefore some printer must be connected to fewer than 81 computers. That means it is connected to 80 or fewer computers, so there are 20 computers that are not connected to it. If those 20 computers all needed a printer simultaneously, then they would be out of luck, because they are connected to at most the 19 other printers. **41.** Let $a_i$ be the number of matches completed by hour $i$. Then $1 \le a_1 < a_2 < \cdots < a_{75} \le 125$. Also $25 \le a_1 + 24 < a_2 + 24 < \cdots < a_{75} + 24 \le 149$. There are 150 numbers $a_1, \ldots, a_{75}, a_1 + 24, \ldots, a_{75} + 24$. By the pigeonhole principle, at least two are equal. Because all the $a_i$s are distinct and all the $(a_i + 24)$s are distinct, it follows that $a_i = a_j + 24$ for some $i > j$. Thus, in the period from the $(j + 1)$st to the $i$th hour, there are exactly 24 matches. **43.** Use the generalized pigeonhole principle, placing the $|S|$ objects $f(s)$ for $s \in S$ in $|T|$ boxes, one for each element of $T$. **45.** Let $d_j$ be $jx - N(jx)$, where $N(jx)$ is the integer closest to $jx$ for $1 \le j \le n$. Each $d_j$ is an irrational number between $-1/2$ and $1/2$. We will assume that $n$ is even; the case where $n$ is odd is messier. Consider the $n$ intervals $\{x \mid j/n < x < (j + 1)/n\}, \{x \mid -(j + 1)/n < x < -j/n\}$ for $j = 0, 1, \ldots, (n/2) - 1$. If $d_j$ belongs to the interval $\{x \mid 0 < x < 1/n\}$ or to the interval $\{x \mid -1/n < x < 0\}$ for some $j$, we are done. If not, because there are $n - 2$ intervals and $n$ numbers $d_j$, the pigeonhole principle tells us that there is an interval $\{x \mid (k - 1)/n < x < k/n\}$ containing $d_r$ and $d_s$ with $r < s$. The proof can be finished by showing that $(s - r)x$ is within $1/n$ of its nearest integer. **47. a)** Assume that $i_k \le n$ for all $k$. Then by the generalized pigeonhole principle, at least $\lceil (n^2 + 1)/n \rceil = n + 1$ of the numbers $i_1, i_2, \ldots, i_{n^2+1}$ are equal. **b)** If $a_{k_j} < a_{k_{j+1}}$, then the subsequence consisting of $a_{k_j}$ followed by the increasing subsequence of length $i_{k_{j+1}}$ starting at $a_{k_{j+1}}$ contradicts the fact that $i_{k_j} = i_{k_{j+1}}$. Hence, $a_{k_j} > a_{k_{j+1}}$. **c)** If there is no increasing subsequence of length greater than $n$, then parts (a) and (b) apply. Therefore, we have $a_{k_{n+1}} > a_{k_n} > \cdots > a_{k_2} > a_{k_1}$, a decreasing sequence of length $n + 1$.

## Section 6.3

**1.** $abc$, $acb$, $bac$, $bca$, $cab$, $cba$ **3.** 720 **5. a)** 120 **b)** 720 **c)** 8 **d)** 6720 **e)** 40,320 **f)** 3,628,800 **7.** 15,120 **9.** 1320 **11. a)** 210 **b)** 386 **c)** 848 **d)** 252 **13.** $2(n!)^2$ **15.** 65,780 **17.** $2^{100} - 5051$ **19. a)** 1024 **b)** 45 **c)** 176 **d)** 252 **21. a)** 120 **b)** 24 **c)** 120 **d)** 24 **e)** 6 **f)** 0 **23.** 609,638,400 **25. a)** 94,109,400 **b)** 941,094 **c)** 3,764,376 **d)** 90,345,024 **e)** 114,072 **f)** 2328 **g)** 24 **h)** 79,727,040 **i)** 3,764,376 **j)** 109,440 **27. a)** 12,650 **b)** 303,600 **29. a)** 37,927 **b)** 18,915 **31. a)** 122,523,030 **b)** 72,930,375 **c)** 223,149,655 **d)** 100,626,625 **33.** 54,600 **35.** 45 **37.** 912 **39.** 11,232,000 **41.** $n!/(r(n - r)!)$ **43.** 13 **45.** 873

## Section 6.4

**1.** $x^4 + 4x^3 y + 6x^2 y^2 + 4xy^3 + y^4$ **3.** $x^6 + 6x^5 y + 15x^4 y^2 + 20x^3 y^3 + 15x^2 y^4 + 6xy^5 + y^6$ **5.** 101 **7.** $-2^{10} \binom{19}{9} = -94,595,072$ **9.** $-2^{101} 3^{99} \binom{200}{99}$ **11.** $(-1)^{(200-k)/3} \binom{100}{(200-k)/3}$ if $k \equiv 2 \pmod 3$ and $-100 \le k \le 200$; 0 otherwise **13.** 1 9 36 84 126 126 84 36 9 1 **15.** The sum of *all* the positive numbers $\binom{n}{k}$, as $k$ runs from 0 to $n$, is $2^n$, so each one of them is no bigger than this sum. **17.** $\binom{n}{k} = \frac{n(n-1)(n-2)\cdots(n-k+1)}{k(k-1)(k-2)\cdots 2} \le \frac{n \cdot n \cdots n}{2 \cdot 2 \cdots 2} = n^k/2^{k-1}$ **19.** $\binom{n}{k-1} + \binom{n}{k} = \frac{n!}{(k-1)!(n-k+1)!} + \frac{n!}{k!(n-k)!} = \frac{n!}{k!(n-k+1)!} \cdot [k + (n - k + 1)] = \frac{(n+1)!}{k!(n+1-k)!} = \binom{n+1}{k}$ **21. a)** We show that each side counts the number of ways to choose from a set with $n$ elements a subset with $k$ elements and a distinguished element of that set. For the left-hand side, first choose the $k$-set (this can be done in $\binom{n}{k}$ ways) and then choose one of the $k$ elements in this subset to be the distinguished element (this can be done in $k$ ways). For the right-hand side, first choose the distinguished element out of the entire $n$-set (this can be done in $n$ ways), and then choose the remaining $k - 1$ elements of the subset from the remaining $n - 1$ elements of the set (this can be done in $\binom{n-1}{k-1}$ ways). **b)** $k\binom{n}{k} = k \cdot \frac{n!}{k!(n-k)!} = \frac{n \cdot (n-1)!}{(k-1)!(n-k)!} = n\binom{n-1}{k-1}$ **23.** $\binom{n+1}{k} = \frac{(n+1)!}{k!(n+1-k)!} = \frac{(n+1)}{k} \frac{n!}{(k-1)![n-(k-1)]!} = (n + 1) \binom{n}{k-1}/k$. This identity together with $\binom{n}{0} = 1$ gives a recursive definition. **25.** $\binom{2n}{n+1} + \binom{2n}{n} = \binom{2n+1}{n+1} = \frac{1}{2}\left[\binom{2n+1}{n+1} + \binom{2n+1}{n+1}\right] = \frac{1}{2}\left[\binom{2n+1}{n+1} + \binom{2n+1}{n}\right] = \frac{1}{2}\binom{2n+2}{n+1}$ **27. a)** $\binom{n+r+1}{r}$ counts the number of ways to choose a sequence of $r$ 0s and $n + 1$ 1s by choosing the positions of the 0s. Alternately, suppose that the $(j + 1)$st term is the last term equal to 1, so that $n \le j \le n+r$. Once we have determined where the last 1 is, we decide where the 0s are to be placed in the $j$ spaces before the last 1. There are $n$ 1s and $j - n$ 0s in this range. By the sum rule it follows that there are $\sum_{j=n}^{n+r} \binom{j}{j-n} = \sum_{k=0}^{r} \binom{n+k}{k}$ ways to do this. **b)** Let $P(r)$ be the statement to be proved. The basis step is the equation $\binom{n}{0} = \binom{n+1}{0}$, which is just $1 = 1$. Assume that $P(r)$ is true. Then $\sum_{k=0}^{r+1} \binom{n+k}{k} = \sum_{k=0}^{r} \binom{n+k}{k} + \binom{n+r+1}{r+1} = \binom{n+r+1}{r} + \binom{n+r+1}{r+1} = \binom{n+r+2}{r+1}$, using the inductive hypothesis and Pascal's identity. **29.** We can choose the leader first in $n$ different ways. We can then choose the rest of the committee in $2^{n-1}$ ways. Hence, there are $n2^{n-1}$ ways to choose the committee and its leader. Meanwhile, the number of ways to select a committee with $k$ people is $\binom{n}{k}$. Once we have chosen a committee with $k$ people, there are $k$ ways to choose its leader. Hence, there are $\sum_{k=1}^{n} k\binom{n}{k}$ ways to choose the committee and its leader. Hence, $\sum_{k=1}^{n} k\binom{n}{k} = n2^{n-1}$. **31.** Let the set have $n$ elements. From Corollary 2 we have $\binom{n}{0} - \binom{n}{1} + \binom{n}{2} - \cdots + (-1)^n\binom{n}{n} = 0$. It follows that $\binom{n}{0} + \binom{n}{2} + \binom{n}{4} + \cdots = \binom{n}{1} + \binom{n}{3} + \binom{n}{5} + \cdots$. The left-hand side gives the number of subsets with an even number of elements, and the right-hand side gives the number of subsets with an odd number of elements. **33. a)** A path of the desired type consists of $m$ moves to the right and $n$ moves up. Each such path can be represented by a bit string of length $m + n$ with $m$ 0s and $n$ 1s, where a 0 represents a move to the right and a 1 a move up. **b)** The number of bit strings of length $m + n$ containing exactly $n$ 1s equals $\binom{m+n}{n} = \binom{m+n}{m}$ because such a string is determined by specifying the positions of the $n$ 1s or by specifying the positions of the $m$ 0s. **35.** By Exercise 33 the number of paths of length $n$ of the type described in that exercise equals $2^n$, the number of bit strings of length $n$. On the other hand, a path of length $n$ of the type described in Exercise 33 must end at a point that has $n$ as the sum of its coordinates, say $(n - k, k)$ for some $k$ between 0 and $n$, inclusive. By Exercise 33, the number of such paths ending at $(n - k, k)$ equals $\binom{n-k+k}{k} = \binom{n}{k}$. Hence, $\sum_{k=0}^{n} \binom{n}{k} = 2^n$. **37.** By Exercise 33 the number of paths from $(0, 0)$ to $(n + 1, r)$ of the type described in that exercise equals $\binom{n+r+1}{r}$. But such a path starts by going $j$ steps vertically for some $j$ with $0 \le j \le r$. The number of these paths beginning with $j$ vertical steps equals the number of paths of the type described in Exercise 33 that go from $(1, j)$ to $(n + 1, r)$. This is the same as the number of such paths that go from $(0, 0)$ to $(n, r - j)$, which by Exercise 33 equals $\binom{n+r-j}{r-j}$. Because $\sum_{j=0}^{r} \binom{n+r-j}{r-j} = \sum_{k=0}^{r} \binom{n+k}{k}$, it follows that $\sum_{k=1}^{r} \binom{n+k}{k} = \binom{n+r-1}{r}$. **39. a)** $\binom{n+1}{2}$ **b)** $\binom{n+2}{3}$ **c)** $\binom{2n-2}{n-1}$ **d)** $\binom{2n-2}{\lfloor(n-1)/2\rfloor}$ **e)** Largest odd entry in $n$th row of Pascal's triangle **f)** $\binom{3n-3}{n-1}$

## Section 6.5

**1.** 243 **3.** $26^6$ **5.** 125 **7.** 35 **9. a)** 1716 **b)** 50,388 **c)** 2,629,575 **d)** 330 **11.** 9 **13.** 4,504,501 **15. a)** 10,626 **b)** 1,365 **c)** 11,649 **d)** 106 **17.** 2,520 **19.** 302,702,400 **21.** 3003 **23.** 7,484,400 **25.** 30,492 **27.** $C(59, 50)$ **29.** 35 **31.** 83,160 **33.** 63 **35.** 19,635 **37.** 210 **39.** 27,720 **41.** $52!/(7!^5 17!)$ **43.** Approximately $6.5 \times 10^{32}$ **45. a)** $C(k + n - 1, n)$ **b)** $(k + n - 1)!/(k - 1)!$ **47.** There are $C(n, n_1)$ ways to choose $n_1$ objects for the first box. Once these objects are chosen, there are $C(n - n_1, n_2)$ ways to choose objects for the second box. Similarly, there are $C(n - n_1 - n_2, n_3)$ ways to choose objects for the third box. Continue in this way until there is

$C(n - n_1 - n_2 - \cdots - n_{k-1}, n_k) = C(n_k, n_k) = 1$ way to choose the objects for the last box (because $n_1 + n_2 + \cdots + n_k = n$). By the product rule, the number of ways to make the entire assignment is $C(n, n_1)C(n - n_1, n_2)C(n - n_1 - n_2, n_3) \cdots C(n - n_1 - n_2 - \cdots - n_{k-1}, n_k)$, which equals $n!/(n_1!n_2!\cdots n_k!)$, as straightforward simplification shows. **49. a)** Because $x_1 \le x_2 \le \cdots \le x_r$, it follows that $x_1 + 0 < x_2 + 1 < \cdots < x_r + r - 1$. The inequalities are strict because $x_j + j - 1 < x_{j+1} + j$ as long as $x_j \le x_{j+1}$. Because $1 \le x_j \le n + r - 1$, this sequence is made up of $r$ distinct elements from $T$. **b)** Suppose that $1 \le x_1 < x_2 < \cdots < x_r \le n + r - 1$. Let $y_k = x_k - (k - 1)$. Then it is not hard to see that $y_k \le y_{k+1}$ for $k = 1, 2, \ldots, r - 1$ and that $1 \le y_k \le n$ for $k = 1, 2, \ldots r$. It follows that $\{y_1, y_2, \ldots, y_r\}$ is an $r$-combination with repetitions allowed of $S$. **c)** From parts (a) and (b) it follows that there is a one-to-one correspondence of $r$-combinations with repetitions allowed of $S$ and $r$-combinations of $T$, a set with $n + r - 1$ elements. We conclude that there are $C(n + r - 1, r)$ $r$-combinations with repetitions allowed of $S$. **51.** 65 **53.** 65 **55.** 2 **57.** 3 **59. a)** 150 **b)** 25 **c)** 6 **d)** 2 **61.** 90,720 **63.** The terms in the expansion are of the form $x_1^{n_1} x_2^{n_2} \cdots x_m^{n_m}$, where $n_1 + n_2 + \cdots + n_m = n$. Such a term arises from choosing the $x_1$ in $n_1$ factors, the $x_2$ in $n_2$ factors, $\ldots$, and the $x_m$ in $n_m$ factors. This can be done in $C(n; n_1, n_2, \ldots, n_m)$ ways, because a choice is a permutation of $n_1$ labels "1," $n_2$ labels "2," $\ldots$, and $n_m$ labels "m." **65.** 2520

## Section 6.6

**1.** 14532, 15432, 21345, 23451, 23514, 31452, 31542, 43521, 45213, 45321 **3.** AAA1, AAA2, AAB1, AAB2, AAC1, AAC2, ABA1, ABA2, ABB1, ABB2, ABC1, ABC2, ACA1, ACA2, ACB1, ACB2, ACC1, ACC2, BAA1, BAA2, BAB1, BAB2, BAC1, BAC2, BBA1, BBA2, BBB1, BBB2, BBC1, BBC2, BCA1, BCA2, BCB1, BCB2, BCC1, BCC2, CAA1, CAA2, CAB1, CAB2, CAC1, CAC2, CBA1, CBA2, CBB1, CBB2, CBC1, CBC2, CCA1, CCA2, CCB1, CCB2, CCC1, CCC2 **5. a)** 2134 **b)** 54132 **c)** 12534 **d)** 45312 ) 7. 1234, 1243, 1324, 1342, 1423, 1432, 2134, 2143, 2314, 2341, 2413, 2431, 3124, 3142, 3214, 3241, 3412, 3421, 4123, 4132, 4213, 4231, 4312, 4321 **9.** {1, 2, 3}, {1, 2, 4}, {1, 2, 5}, {1, 3, 4}, {1, 3, 5}, {1, 4, 5}, {2, 3, 4}, {2, 3, 5}, {2, 4, 5}, {3, 4, 5} **11.** The bit string representing the next larger $r$-combination must differ from the bit string representing the original one in position $i$ because positions $i + 1, \ldots, r$ are occupied by the largest possible numbers. Also $a_i + 1$ is the smallest possible number we can put in position $i$ if we want a combination greater than the original one. Then $a_i + 2, \ldots, a_i + r - i + 1$ are the smallest allowable numbers for positions $i + 1$ to $r$. Thus, we have produced the next $r$-combination. **13.** 123, 132, 213, 231, 312, 321, 124, 142, 214, 241, 412, 421, 125, 152, 215, 251, 512, 521, 134, 143, 314, 341, 413, 431, 135, 153, 315, 351, 513, 531, 145, 154, 415, 451, 514, 541, 234, 243, 324, 342, 423, 432,

235, 253, 325, 352, 523, 532, 245, 254, 425, 452, 524, 542, 345, 354, 435, 453, 534, 543 **15.** We will show that it is a bijection by showing that it has an inverse. Given a positive integer less than $n!$, let $a_1, a_2, \ldots, a_{n-1}$ be its Cantor digits. Put $n$ in position $n - a_{n-1}$; then clearly, $a_{n-1}$ is the number of integers less than $n$ that follow $n$ in the permutation. Then put $n - 1$ in free position $(n - 1) - a_{n-2}$, where we have numbered the free positions $1, 2, \ldots, n - 1$ (excluding the position that $n$ is already in). Continue until 1 is placed in the only free position left. Because we have constructed an inverse, the correspondence is a bijection.

**17. procedure** *Cantor permutation*($n, i$: integers with
$n \geq 1$ and $0 \leq i < n!$)
$x := n$
**for** $j := 1$ **to** $n$
$\quad p_j := 0$
**for** $k := 1$ **to** $n - 1$
$\quad c := \lfloor x/(n-k)! \rfloor; x := x - c(n-k)!; h := n$
$\quad$ **while** $p_h \neq 0$
$\quad\quad h := h - 1$
$\quad$ **for** $j := 1$ **to** $c$
$\quad\quad h := h - 1$
$\quad\quad$ **while** $p_h \neq 0$
$\quad\quad\quad h := h - 1$
$\quad p_h := n - k + 1$
$h := 1$
**while** $p_h \neq 0$
$\quad h := h + 1$
$p_h := 1$
$\{p_1 p_2 \ldots p_n$ is the permutation corresponding
to $i\}$

## Supplementary Exercises

**1. a)** 151,200 **b)** 1,000,000 **c)** 210 **d)** 5005 **3.** $3^{100}$
**5.** 24,600 **7. a)** 4060 **b)** 2688 **c)** 25,009,600 **9. a)** 192
**b)** 301 **c)** 300 **d)** 300 **11.** 639 **13.** The maximum possible sum is 240, and the minimum possible sum is 15. So the number of possible sums is 226. Because there are 252 subsets with five elements of a set with 10 elements, by the pigeonhole principle it follows that at least two have the same sum. **15. a)** 50 **b)** 50 **c)** 14 **d)** 17 **17.** Let $a_1, a_2, \ldots, a_m$ be the integers, and let $d_i = \sum_{j=1}^{i} a_j$. If $d_i \equiv 0$ (mod $m$) for some $i$, we are done. Otherwise $d_1 \bmod m$, $d_2 \bmod m, \ldots, d_m \bmod m$ are $m$ integers with values in $\{1, 2, \ldots, m - 1\}$. By the pigeonhole principle $d_k = d_l$ for some $1 \leq k < l \leq m$. Then $\sum_{j=k+1}^{l} a_j = d_l - d_k \equiv 0$ (mod $m$). **19.** The decimal expansion of the rational number $a/b$ can be obtained by division of $b$ into $a$, where $a$ is written with a decimal point and an arbitrarily long string of 0s following it. The basic step is finding the next digit of the quotient, namely, $\lfloor r/b \rfloor$, where $r$ is the remainder with the next digit of the dividend brought down. The current remainder is obtained from the previous remainder by subtracting $b$ times the previous digit of the quotient. Eventually the dividend has nothing but 0s to bring down. Furthermore, there are only

$b$ possible remainders. Thus, at some point, by the pigeonhole principle, we will have the same situation as had previously arisen. From that point onward, the calculation must follow the same pattern. In particular, the quotient will repeat. **21. a)** 125,970 **b)** 20 **c)** 141,120,525 **d)** 141,120,505 **e)** 177,100 **f)** 141,078,021 **23. a)** 10 **b)** 8 **c)** 7 **25.** $3^n$
**27.** $C(n + 2, r + 1) = C(n + 1, r + 1) + C(n + 1, r) = 2C(n + 1, r + 1) - C(n + 1, r + 1) + C(n + 1, r) = 2C(n + 1, r + 1) - (C(n, r + 1) + C(n, r)) + (C(n, r) + C(n, r - 1)) = 2C(n + 1, r + 1) - C(n + 1, r + 1) + C(n, r - 1)$
**29.** Substitute $x = 1$ and $y = 3$ into the binomial theorem.
**31.** Both sides count the number of ways to choose a subset of three distinct numbers $\{i, j, k\}$ with $i < j < k$ from $\{1, 2, \ldots, n\}$. **33.** $C(n + 1, 5)$ **35.** 3,491,888,400 **37.** $5^{24}$
**39. a)** 45 **b)** 57 **c)** 12 **41. a)** 386 **b)** 56 **43.** 0 if $n < m$;
$C(n - 1, n - m)$ if $n \geq m$ **45. a)** 15,625 **b)** 202 **c)** 210
**d)** 10 **47. a)** 3 **b)** 11 **c)** 6 **d)** 10 **49.** There are two possibilities: three people seated at one table with everyone else sitting alone, which can be done in $2C(n, 3)$ ways (choose the three people and seat them in one of two arrangements), or two groups of two people seated together with everyone else sitting alone, which can be done in $3C(n, 4)$ ways (choose four people and then choose one of the three ways to pair them up). Both $2C(n, 3) + 3C(n, 4)$ and $(3n - 1)C(n, 3)/4$ equal $n^4/8 - 5n^3/12 + 3n^2/8 - n/12$. **51.** The number of permutations of $2n$ objects of $n$ different types, two of each type, is $(2n)!/2^n$. Because this must be an integer, the denominator must divide the numerator. **53.** CCGGUCCGAAAG
**55. procedure** *next permutation*($n$: positive integer,
$\quad a_1, a_2, \ldots, a_r$: positive integers not exceeding
$\quad n$ with $a_1 a_2 \ldots a_r \neq nn \ldots n$)
$i := r$
**while** $a_i = n$
$\quad a_i := 1$
$\quad i := i - 1$
$a_i := a_i + 1$
$\{a_1 a_2 \ldots a_r$ is the next permutation in lexicographic
order$\}$
**57.** We must show that if there are $R(m, n - 1) + R(m - 1, n)$ people at a party, then there must be at least $m$ mutual friends or $n$ mutual enemies. Consider one person; let's call him Jerry. Then there are $R(m - 1, n) + R(m, n - 1) - 1$ other people at the party, and by the pigeonhole principle there must be at least $R(m - 1, n)$ friends of Jerry or $R(m, n - 1)$ enemies of Jerry among these people. First let's suppose there are $R(m - 1, n)$ friends of Jerry. By the definition of $R$, among these people we are guaranteed to find either $m - 1$ mutual friends or $n$ mutual enemies. In the former case, these $m - 1$ mutual friends together with Jerry are a set of $m$ mutual friends; and in the latter case, we have the desired set of $n$ mutual enemies. The other situation is similar: Suppose there are $R(m, n - 1)$ enemies of Jerry; we are guaranteed to find among them either $m$ mutual friends or $n - 1$ mutual enemies. In the former case, we have the desired set of $m$ mutual friends, and in the latter case, these $n - 1$ mutual enemies together with Jerry are a set of $n$ mutual enemies.

# CHAPTER 7

## Section 7.1

**1.** $1/13$  **3.** $1/2$  **5.** $1/2$  **7.** $1/64$  **9.** $47/52$  **11.** $1/C(52, 5)$
**13.** $1 - [C(48, 5)/C(52, 5)]$  **15.** $C(13, 2)C(4, 2)C(4, 2)$
$C(44, 1)/C(52, 5)$  **17.** $10{,}240/C(52, 5)$  **19.** $1{,}302{,}540/$
$C(52, 5)$  **21.** $1/64$  **23.** $8/25$  **25. a)** $1/\ C(50, 6) =$
$1/15{,}890{,}700$  **b)** $1/C(52, 6) = 1/20{,}358{,}520$
**c)** $1/C(56, 6) = 1/32{,}468{,}436$  **d)** $1/C(60, 6) = 1/$
$50{,}063{,}860$  **27. a)** $139{,}128/319{,}865$ **b)** $212{,}667/511{,}313$
**c)** $151{,}340/386{,}529$ **d)** $163{,}647/446{,}276$  **29.** $1/C(100, 8)$
**31.** $3/100$  **33. a)** $1/7{,}880{,}400$  **b)** $1/8{,}000{,}000$
**35. a)** $9/19$  **b)** $81/361$  **c)** $1/19$  **d)** $1{,}889{,}568/2{,}476{,}099$
**e)** $48/361$  **37.** Three dice  **39.** The door the contestant
chooses is chosen at random without knowing where the
prize is, but the door chosen by the host is not chosen at
random, because he always avoids opening the door with the
prize. This makes any argument based on symmetry invalid.
**41. a)** $671/1296$  **b)** $1 - 35^{24}/36^{24}$; no  **c)** The former

## Section 7.2

**1.** $p(T) = 1/4$, $p(H) = 3/4$  **3.** $p(1) = p(3) = p(5) =$
$p(6) = 1/16$; $p(2) = p(4) = 3/8$  **5.** $9/49$  **7. a)** $1/2$
**b)** $1/2$ **c)** $1/3$ **d)** $1/4$ **e)** $1/4$  **9. a)** $1/26!$ **b)** $1/26$ **c)** $1/2$
**d)** $1/26$ **e)** $1/650$ **f)** $1/15{,}600$  **11.** Clearly, $p(E \cup F) \geq$
$p(E) = 0.7$. Also, $p(E \cup F) \leq 1$. If we apply Theorem 2
from Section 7.1, we can rewrite this as $p(E) + p(F) -$
$p(E \cap F) \leq 1$, or $0.7 + 0.5 - p(E \cap F) \leq 1$. Solving for $p(E \cap F)$ gives $p(E \cap F) \geq 0.2$.  **13.** Because
$p(E \cup F) = p(E) + p(F) - p(E \cap F)$ and $p(E \cup F) \leq 1$,
it follows that $1 \geq p(E) + p(F) - p(E \cap F)$. From this
inequality we conclude that $p(E) + p(F) \leq 1 + p(E \cap F)$.
**15.** We will use mathematical induction to prove that the inequality holds for $n \geq 2$. Let $P(n)$ be the statement that
$p(\bigcup_{j=1}^{n} E_j) \leq \sum_{j=1}^{n} p(E_j)$. *Basis step:* $P(2)$ is true because $p(E_1 \cup E_2) = p(E_1) + p(E_2) - p(E_1 \cap E_2) \leq$
$p(E_1) + p(E_2)$. *Inductive step:* Assume that $P(k)$ is true. Using the basis case and the inductive hypothesis, it follows that
$p(\bigcup_{j=1}^{k+1} E_j) \leq p(\bigcup_{j=1}^{k} E_j) + p(E_{k+1}) \leq \sum_{j=1}^{k+1} p(E_j)$.
This shows that $P(k+1)$ is true, completing the proof by math-
ematical induction.  **17.** Because $E \cup \overline{E}$ is the entire sample
space $S$, the event $F$ can be split into two disjoint events:
$F = S \cap F = (E \cup \overline{E}) \cap F = (E \cap F) \cup (\overline{E} \cap F)$, using the
distributive law. Therefore, $p(F) = p((E \cap F) \cup (\overline{E} \cap F)) =$
$p(E \cap F) + p(\overline{E} \cap F)$, because these two events are disjoint. Subtracting $p(E \cap F)$ from both sides, using the fact
that $p(E \cap F) = p(E) \cdot p(F)$ (the hypothesis that $E$
and $F$ are independent), and factoring, we have $p(F)[1-
p(E)] = p(\overline{E} \cap F)$. Because $1 - p(E) = p(\overline{E})$, this
says that $p(\overline{E} \cap F) = p(\overline{E}) \cdot p(F)$, as desired.  **19. a)** $1/12$
**b)** $1 - \frac{11}{12} \cdot \frac{10}{12} \cdots \cdots \frac{13-n}{12}$ **c)** $5$  **21.** $614$  **23.** $1/4$  **25.** $3/8$
**27. a)** Not independent  **b)** Not independent  **c)** Not inde-
pendent  **29.** $3/16$  **31. a)** $1/32 = 0.03125$  **b)** $0.49^5 \approx$

$0.02825$ **c)** $0.03795012$   **33. a)** $5/8$ **b)** $0.627649$ **c)** $0.6431$
**35. a)** $p^n$   **b)** $1 - p^n$   **c)** $p^n + n \cdot p^{n-1} \cdot (1 - p)$  **d)** $1 - [p^n + n \cdot p^{n-1} \cdot (1 - p)]$   **37.** $p(\bigcup_{i=1}^{\infty} E_i)$ is
the sum of $p(s)$ for each outcome $s$ in $\bigcup_{i=1}^{\infty} E_i$. Because
the $E_i$s are pairwise disjoint, this is the sum of the probabilities of all the outcomes in any of the $E_i$s, which is what
$\sum_{i=1}^{\infty} p(E_i)$ is. (We can rearrange the summands and still get
the same answer because this series converges absolutely.)
**39. a)** $\overline{E} = \bigcup_{j=1}^{\binom{m}{k}} F_j$, so the given inequality now follows
from Boole's Inequality (Exercise 15).  **b)** The probability that
a particular player not in the $j$th set beats all $k$ of the players
in the $j$th set is $(1/2)^k = 2^{-k}$. Therefore, the probability
that this player does not do so is $1 - 2^{-k}$, so the probability
that all $m - k$ of the players not in the $j$th set are unable to
boast of a perfect record against everyone in the $j$th set is
$(1 - 2^{-k})^{m-k}$. That is precisely $p(F_j)$.  **c)** The first inequality
follows immediately, because all the summands are the same
and there are $\binom{m}{k}$ of them. If this probability is less than 1,
then it must be possible that $\overline{E}$ fails, i.e., that $E$ happens. So
there is a tournament that meets the conditions of the problem
as long as the second inequality holds.  **d)** $m \geq 21$ for $k = 2$,
and $m \geq 91$ for $k = 3$
**41.**   **procedure** *probabilistic prime*$(n, k)$
    *composite* := **false**
    $i := 0$
    **while** *composite* = **false** and $i < k$
      $i := i + 1$
      choose $b$ uniformly at random with $1 < b < n$
      apply Miller's test to base $b$
      **if** $n$ fails the test **then** *composite* := **true**
    **if** *composite* = **true then** print ("composite")
    **else** print ("probably prime")

## Section 7.3

NOTE: In the answers for Section 7.3, all probabilities given in decimal form are rounded to three decimal
places.  **1.** $3/5$  **3.** $3/4$  **5.** $0.481$  **7. a)** $0.999$ **b)** $0.324$
**9. a)** $0.740$   **b)** $0.260$   **c)** $0.002$   **d)** $0.998$  **11.** $0.724$
**13.** $3/17$  **15. a)** $1/3$  **b)** $p(M = j \mid W = k) = 1$
if $i$, $j$, and $k$ are distinct; $p(M = j \mid W = k) = 0$
if $j = k$ or $j = i$; $p(M = j \mid W = k) = 1/2$
if $i = k$ and $j \neq i$  **c)** $2/3$  **d)** You should change
doors, because you now have a 2/3 chance to win by switching.  **17.** The definition of conditional probability tells us
that $p(F_j \mid E) = p(E \cap F_j)/p(E)$. For the numerator,
again using the definition of conditional probability, we have
$p(E \cap F_j) = p(E \mid F_j)p(F_j)$, as desired. For the denominator, we show that $p(E) = \sum_{i=1}^{n} p(E \mid F_i)p(F_i)$. The events
$E \cap F_i$ partition the event $E$; that is, $(E \cap F_{i_1}) \cap (E \cap F_{i_2}) = \emptyset$
when $i_1 \neq i_2$ (because the $F_i$'s are mutually exclusive), and
$\bigcup_{i=1}^{n}(E \cap F_{i_1}) = E$ (because the $\bigcup_{i=1}^{n} F_i = S$). Therefore,
$p(E) = \sum_{i=1}^{n} p(E \cap F_i) = \sum_{i=1}^{n} p(E \mid F_i)p(F_i)$.  **19.** No
**21.** Yes  **23.** By Bayes' theorem, $p(S \mid E_1 \cap E_2) = p(E_1 \cap
E_2 \mid S)p(S)/[p(E_1 \cap E_2 \mid S)p(S) + p(E_1 \cap E_2 \mid \overline{S})p(\overline{S})]$.

**c)** $a_n = 3^n - 3 \cdot 2^n$  **d)** $a_n = (-2)^n$ for $n \geq 2$, $a_1 = -3$, $a_0 = 2$  **e)** $a_n = (-2)^n + n!$  **f)** $a_n = (-3)^n + n! \cdot 2^n$ for $n \geq 2$, $a_0 = 1$, $a_1 = -2$  **g)** $a_n = 0$ if $n$ is odd and $a_n = n!/(n/2)!$ if $n$ is even  **49. a)** $a_n = 6a_{n-1} + 8^{n-1}$ for $n \geq 1$, $a_0 = 1$  **b)** The general solution of the associated linear homogeneous recurrence relation is $a_n^{(h)} = \alpha 6^n$. A particular solution is $a_n^{(p)} = \frac{1}{2} \cdot 8^n$. Hence, the general solution is $a_n = \alpha 6^n + \frac{1}{2} \cdot 8^n$. Using the initial condition, it follows that $\alpha = \frac{1}{2}$. Hence, $a_n = (6^n + 8^n)/2$.  **c)** Let $G(x) = \sum_{k=0}^{\infty} a_k x^k$. Using the recurrence relation for $\{a_k\}$, it can be shown that $G(x) - 6xG(x) = (1-7x)/(1-8x)$. Hence, $G(x) = (1-7x)/[(1-6x)(1-8x)]$. Using partial fractions, it follows that $G(x) = (1/2)/(1-6x) + (1/2)/(1-8x)$. With the help of Table 1, it follows that $a_n = (6^n + 8^n)/2$.  **51.** $\frac{1}{1-x} \cdot \frac{1}{1-x^2} \cdot \frac{1}{1-x^3} \cdots$  **53.** $(1+x)(1+x)^2(1+x)^3 \cdots$  **55.** The generating functions obtained in Exercises 52 and 53 are equal because $(1+x)(1+x^2)(1+x^3) \cdots = \frac{1-x^2}{1-x} \cdot \frac{1-x^4}{1-x^2} \cdot \frac{1-x^6}{1-x^3} \cdots = \frac{1}{1-x} \cdot \frac{1}{1-x^3} \cdot \frac{1}{1-x^5} \cdots$.  **57. a)** $G_X(1) = \sum_{k=0}^{\infty} p(X=k) \cdot 1^k = \sum_{k=0}^{\infty} P(X=k) = 1$  **b)** $G_X'(1) = \frac{d}{dx} \sum_{k=0}^{\infty} p(X=k) \cdot x^k |_{x=1} = \sum_{k=0}^{\infty} p(X=k) \cdot k \cdot x^{k-1} |_{x=1} = \sum_{k=0}^{\infty} p(X=k) \cdot k = E(X)$  **c)** $G_X''(1) = \frac{d^2}{dx^2} \sum_{k=0}^{\infty} p(X=k) \cdot x^k |_{x=1} = \sum_{k=0}^{\infty} p(X=k) \cdot k(k-1) \cdot x^{k-2} |_{x=1} = \sum_{k=0}^{\infty} p(X=k) \cdot (k^2-k) = V(X) + E(X)^2 - E(X)$. Combining this with part (b) gives the desired results.  **59. a)** $G(x) = p^m/(1-qx)^m$  **b)** $V(x) = mq/p^2$

## Section 8.5

**1. a)** 30 **b)** 29 **c)** 24 **d)** 18  **3.** 1%  **5. a)** 300 **b)** 150 **c)** 175 **d)** 100  **7.** 492  **9.** 974  **11.** 55  **13.** 248  **15.** 50,138  **17.** 234  **19.** $|A_1 \cup A_2 \cup A_3 \cup A_4 \cup A_5| = |A_1| + |A_2| + |A_3| + |A_4| + |A_5| - |A_1 \cap A_2| - |A_1 \cap A_3| - |A_1 \cap A_4| - |A_1 \cap A_5| - |A_2 \cap A_3| - |A_2 \cap A_4| - |A_2 \cap A_5| - |A_3 \cap A_4| - |A_3 \cap A_5| - |A_4 \cap A_5| + |A_1 \cap A_2 \cap A_3| + |A_1 \cap A_2 \cap A_4| + |A_1 \cap A_2 \cap A_5| + |A_1 \cap A_3 \cap A_4| + |A_1 \cap A_3 \cap A_5| + |A_1 \cap A_4 \cap A_5| + |A_2 \cap A_3 \cap A_4| + |A_2 \cap A_3 \cap A_5| + |A_2 \cap A_4 \cap A_5| + |A_3 \cap A_4 \cap A_5| - |A_1 \cap A_2 \cap A_3 \cap A_4| - |A_1 \cap A_2 \cap A_3 \cap A_5| - |A_1 \cap A_2 \cap A_4 \cap A_5| - |A_1 \cap A_3 \cap A_4 \cap A_5| - |A_2 \cap A_3 \cap A_4 \cap A_5| + |A_1 \cap A_2 \cap A_3 \cap A_4 \cap A_5|$  **21.** $|A_1 \cup A_2 \cup A_3 \cup A_4 \cup A_5 \cup A_6| = |A_1| + |A_2| + |A_3| + |A_4| + |A_5| + |A_6| - |A_1 \cap A_2| - |A_1 \cap A_3| - |A_1 \cap A_4| - |A_1 \cap A_5| - |A_1 \cap A_6| - |A_2 \cap A_3| - |A_2 \cap A_4| - |A_2 \cap A_5| - |A_2 \cap A_6| - |A_3 \cap A_4| - |A_3 \cap A_5| - |A_3 \cap A_6| - |A_4 \cap A_5| - |A_4 \cap A_6| - |A_5 \cap A_6|$  **23.** $p(E_1 \cup E_2 \cup E_3) = p(E_1) + p(E_2) + p(E_3) - p(E_1 \cap E_2) - p(E_1 \cap E_3) - p(E_2 \cap E_3) + p(E_1 \cap E_2 \cap E_3)$  **25.** 4972/71,295  **27.** $p(E_1 \cup E_2 \cup E_3 \cup E_4 \cup E_5) = p(E_1) + p(E_2) + p(E_3) + p(E_4) + p(E_5) - p(E_1 \cap E_2) - p(E_1 \cap E_3) - p(E_1 \cap E_4) - p(E_1 \cap E_5) - p(E_2 \cap E_3) - p(E_2 \cap E_4) - p(E_2 \cap E_5) - p(E_3 \cap E_4) - p(E_3 \cap E_5) - p(E_4 \cap E_5) + p(E_1 \cap E_2 \cap E_3) + p(E_1 \cap E_2 \cap E_4) + p(E_1 \cap E_2 \cap E_5) + p(E_1 \cap E_3 \cap E_4) + p(E_1 \cap E_3 \cap E_5) + p(E_1 \cap E_4 \cap E_5) + p(E_2 \cap E_3 \cap E_4) + P(E_2 \cap E_3 \cap E_5) + p(E_2 \cap E_4 \cap E_5) + p(E_3 \cap E_4 \cap E_5)$  **29.** $p\left(\bigcup_{i=1}^{n} E_i\right) = \sum_{1 \leq i \leq n} p(E_i) - \sum_{1 \leq i < j \leq n} p(E_i \cap E_j) + \sum_{1 \leq i < j < k \leq n} p(E_i \cap E_j \cap E_k) - \cdots + (-1)^{n+1} p\left(\bigcap_{i=1}^{n} E_i\right)$

## Section 8.6

**1.** 75  **3.** 6  **5.** 46  **7.** 9875  **9.** 540  **11.** 2100  **13.** 1854  **15. a)** $D_{100}/100!$  **b)** $100 D_{99}/100!$  **c)** $C(100,2)/100!$  **d)** 0  **e)** 1/100!  **17.** 2,170,680  **19.** By Exercise 18 we have $D_n - nD_{n-1} = -[D_{n-1} - (n-1)D_{n-2}]$. Iterating, we have $D_n - nD_{n-1} = -[D_{n-1}-(n-1)D_{n-2}] = -[-(D_{n-2} - (n-2)D_{n-3})] = D_{n-2} - (n-2)D_{n-3} = \cdots = (-1)^n (D_2 - 2D_1) = (-1)^n$ because $D_2 = 1$ and $D_1 = 0$.  **21.** When $n$ is odd  **23.** $\phi(n) = n - \sum_{i=1}^{m} \frac{n}{p_i} + \sum_{1 \leq i < j \leq m} \frac{n}{p_i p_j} - \cdots \pm \frac{n}{p_1 p_2 \cdots p_m} = n \prod_{i=1}^{m} \left(a - \frac{1}{p_i}\right)$  **25.** 4  **27.** There are $n^m$ functions from a set with $m$ elements to a set with $n$ elements, $C(n, 1)(n-1)^m$ functions from a set with $m$ elements to a set with $n$ elements that miss exactly one element, $C(n, 2)(n-2)^m$ functions from a set with $m$ elements to a set with $n$ elements that miss exactly two elements, and so on, with $C(n, n-1) \cdot 1^m$ functions from a set with $m$ elements to a set with $n$ elements that miss exactly $n-1$ elements. Hence, by the principle of inclusion–exclusion, there are $n^m - C(n, 1)(n-1)^m + C(n, 2)(n-2)^m - \cdots + (-1)^{n-1} C(n, n-1) \cdot 1^m$ onto functions.

## Supplementary Exercises

**1. a)** $A_n = 4A_{n-1}$  **b)** $A_1 = 40$  **c)** $A_n = 10 \cdot 4^n$  **3. a)** $M_n = M_{n-1} + 160,000$  **b)** $M_1 = 186,000$  **c)** $M_n = 160,000n + 26,000$  **d)** $T_n = T_{n-1} + 160,000n + 26,000$  **e)** $T_n = 80,000n^2 + 106,000n$  **5. a)** $a_n = a_{n-2} + a_{n-3}$  **b)** $a_1 = 0$, $a_2 = 1$, $a_3 = 1$  **c)** $a_{12} = 12$  **7. a)** 2  **b)** 5  **c)** 8  **d)** 16  **9.** $a_n = 2^n$  **11.** $a_n = 2 + 4n/3 + n^2/2 + n^3/6$  **13.** $a_n = a_{n-2} + a_{n-3}$  **15. a)** Under the given conditions, one longest common subsequence clearly ends at the last term in each sequence, so $a_m = b_n = c_p$. Furthermore, a longest common subsequence of what is left of the $a$-sequence and the $b$-sequence after those last terms are deleted has to form the beginning of a longest common subsequence of the original sequences.  **b)** If $c_p \neq a_m$, then the longest common subsequence's appearance in the $a$-sequence must terminate before the end; therefore the $c$-sequence must be a longest common subsequence of $a_1, a_2, \ldots, a_{m-1}$ and $b_1, b_2, \ldots, b_n$. The other half is similar.

**17.** **procedure** *howlong*$(a_1, \ldots, a_m, b_1, \ldots, b_n$: sequences)
  **for** $i := 1$ **to** $m$
    $L(i, 0) := 0$
  **for** $j := 1$ **to** $n$
    $L(0, j) := 0$
  **for** $i := 1$ **to** $m$
    **for** $j := 1$ **to** $n$
      **if** $a_i = b_j$ **then** $L(i, j) := L(i-1, j-1) + 1$
      **else** $L(i, j) := \max(L(i, j-1), L(i-1, j))$
  **return** $L(m, n)$

**19.** $f(n) = (4n^2 - 1)/3$   **21.** $O(n^4)$   **23.** $O(n)$   **25.** Using just two comparisons, the algorithm is able to narrow the search for $m$ down to the first half or the second half of the original sequence. Since the length of the sequence is cut in half each time, only about $2 \log_2 n$ comparisons are needed in all.   **27. a)** $18n + 18$   **b)** $18$   **c)** $0$   **29.** $\Delta(a_n b_n) = a_{n+1} b_{n+1} - a_n b_n = a_{n+1}(b_{n+1} - b_n) + b_n(a_{n+1} - a_n) = a_{n+1} \Delta b_n + b_n \Delta a_n$   **31. a)** Let $G(x) = \sum_{n=0}^{\infty} a_n x^n$. Then $G'(x) = \sum_{n=1}^{\infty} n a_n x^{n-1} = \sum_{n=0}^{\infty} (n+1) a_{n+1} x^n$. Therefore, $G'(x) - G(x) = \sum_{n=0}^{\infty} [(n+1)a_{n+1} - a_n] x^n = \sum_{n=0}^{\infty} x^n/n! = e^x$, as desired. That $G(0) = a_0 = 1$ is given.   **b)** We have $[e^{-x} G(x)]' = e^{-x} G'(x) - e^{-x} G(x) = e^{-x}[G'(x) - G(x)] = e^{-x} \cdot e^x = 1$. Hence, $e^{-x} G(x) = x + c$, where $c$ is a constant. Consequently, $G(x) = xe^x + ce^x$. Because $G(0) = 1$, it follows that $c = 1$.   **c)** We have $G(x) = \sum_{n=0}^{\infty} x^{n+1}/n! + \sum_{n=0}^{\infty} x^n/n! = \sum_{n=1}^{\infty} x^n/(n-1)! + \sum_{n=0}^{\infty} x^n/n!$. Therefore, $a_n = 1/(n-1)! + 1/n!$ for all $n \geq 1$, and $a_0 = 1$.   **33.** 7   **35.** 110   **37.** 0   **39. a)** 19   **b)** 65   **c)** 122   **d)** 167   **e)** 168   **41.** $D_{n-1}/(n-1)!$   **43.** 11/32

# CHAPTER 9

## Section 9.1

**1. a)** $\{(0, 0), (1, 1), (2, 2), (3, 3)\}$   **b)** $\{(1, 3), (2, 2), (3, 1), (4, 0)\}$   **c)** $\{(1, 0), (2, 0), (2, 1), (3, 0), (3, 1), (3, 2), (4, 0), (4, 1), (4, 2), (4, 3)\}$   **d)** $\{(1, 0), (1, 1), (1, 2), (1, 3), (2, 0), (2, 2), (3, 0), (3, 3), (4, 0)\}$   **e)** $\{(0, 1), (1, 0), (1, 1), (1, 2), (1, 3), (2, 1), (2, 3), (3, 1), (3, 2), (4, 1), (4, 3)\}$   **f)** $\{(1, 2), (2, 1), (2, 2)\}$   **3. a)** Transitive   **b)** Reflexive, symmetric, transitive   **c)** Symmetric   **d)** Antisymmetric   **e)** Reflexive, symmetric, antisymmetric, transitive   **f)** None of these properties   **5. a)** Reflexive, transitive   **b)** Symmetric   **c)** Symmetric   **d)** Symmetric   **7. a)** Symmetric   **b)** Symmetric, transitive   **c)** Symmetric   **d)** Reflexive, symmetric, transitive   **e)** Reflexive, transitive   **f)** Reflexive, symmetric, transitive   **g)** Antisymmetric   **h)** Antisymmetric, transitive   **9.** Each of the three properties is vacuously satisfied.   **11.** (c), (d), (f)   **13. a)** Not irreflexive   **b)** Not irreflexive   **c)** Not irreflexive   **d)** Not irreflexive   **15.** Yes, for instance $\{(1, 1)\}$ on $\{1, 2\}$   **17.** $(a, b) \in R$ if and only if $a$ is taller than $b$   **19.** (a)   **21.** None   **23.** $\forall a \forall b \, [(a, b) \in R \to (b, a) \notin R]$   **25.** $2^{mn}$   **27. a)** $\{(a, b) \mid b \text{ divides } a\}$   **b)** $\{(a, b) \mid a \text{ does not divide } b\}$   **29.** The graph of $f^{-1}$   **31. a)** $\{(a, b) \mid a \text{ is required to read or has read } b\}$   **b)** $\{(a, b) \mid a \text{ is required to read and has read } b\}$   **c)** $\{(a, b) \mid \text{either } a \text{ is required to read } b \text{ but has not read it or } a \text{ has read } b \text{ but is not required to}\}$   **d)** $\{(a, b) \mid a \text{ is required to read } b \text{ but has not read it}\}$   **e)** $\{(a, b) \mid a \text{ has read } b \text{ but is not required to}\}$   **33.** $S \circ R = \{(a, b) \mid a \text{ is a parent of } b \text{ and } b \text{ has a sibling}\}$, $R \circ S = \{(a, b) \mid a \text{ is an aunt}$

or uncle of $b\}$   **35. a)** $\mathbf{R}^2$   **b)** $R_6$   **c)** $R_3$   **d)** $R_3$   **e)** $\emptyset$   **f)** $R_1$   **g)** $R_4$   **h)** $R_4$   **37. a)** $R_1$   **b)** $R_2$   **c)** $R_3$   **d)** $\mathbf{R}^2$   **e)** $R_3$   **f)** $\mathbf{R}^2$   **g)** $\mathbf{R}^2$   **h)** $\mathbf{R}^2$   **39.** $b$ got his or her doctorate under someone who got his or her doctorate under $a$; there is a sequence of $n + 1$ people, starting with $a$ and ending with $b$, such that each is the advisor of the next person in the sequence   **41. a)** $\{(a, b) \mid a - b \equiv 0, 3, 4, 6, , 8, \text{ or } 9 \pmod{12}\}$   **b)** $\{(a, b) \mid a \equiv b \pmod{12}\}$   **c)** $\{(a, b) \mid a - b \equiv 3, 6, \text{ or } 9 \pmod{12}\}$   **d)** $\{(a, b) \mid a - b \equiv 4 \text{ or } 8 \pmod{12}\}$   **e)** $\{(a, b) \mid a - b \equiv 3, 4, 6, 8, \text{ or } 9 \pmod{12}\}$   **43.** 8   **45. a)** 65,536   **b)** 32,768   **47. a)** $2^{n(n+1)/2}$   **b)** $2^n 3^{n(n-1)/2}$   **c)** $3^{n(n-1)/2}$   **d)** $2^{n(n-1)}$   **e)** $2^{n(n-1)/2}$   **f)** $2^{n^2} - 2 \cdot 2^{n(n-1)}$   **49.** There may be no such $b$.   **51.** If $R$ is symmetric and $(a, b) \in R$, then $(b, a) \in R$, so $(a, b) \in R^{-1}$. Hence, $R \subseteq R^{-1}$. Similarly, $R^{-1} \subseteq R$. So $R = R^{-1}$. Conversely, if $R = R^{-1}$ and $(a, b) \in R$, then $(a, b) \in R^{-1}$, so $(b, a) \in R$. Thus $R$ is symmetric.   **53.** $R$ is reflexive if and only if $(a, a) \in R$ for all $a \in A$ if and only if $(a, a) \in R^{-1}$ [because $(a, a) \in R$ if and only if $(a, a) \in R^{-1}$] if and only if $R^{-1}$ is reflexive.   **55.** Use mathematical induction. The result is trivial for $n = 1$. Assume $R^n$ is reflexive and transitive. By Theorem 1, $R^{n+1} \subseteq R$. To see that $R \subseteq R^{n+1} = R^n \circ R$, let $(a, b) \in R$. By the inductive hypothesis, $R^n = R$ and hence, is reflexive. Thus $(b, b) \in R^n$. Therefore $(a, b) \in R^{n+1}$.   **57.** Use mathematical induction. The result is trivial for $n = 1$. Assume $R^n$ is reflexive. Then $(a, a) \in R^n$ for all $a \in A$ and $(a, a) \in R$. Thus $(a, a) \in R^n \circ R = R^{n+1}$ for all $a \in A$.   **59.** No, for instance, take $R = \{(1, 2), (2, 1)\}$.

## Section 9.2

**1.** $\{(1, 2, 3), (1, 2, 4), (1, 3, 4), (2, 3, 4)\}$   **3.** (Nadir, 122, 34, Detroit, 08:10), (Acme, 221, 22, Denver, 08:17), (Acme, 122, 33, Anchorage, 08:22), (Acme, 323, 34, Honolulu 08:30), (Nadir, 199, 13, Detroit, 08:47), (Acme, 222, 22, Denver, 09:10), (Nadir, 322, 34, Detroit, 09:44)   **5.** Airline and flight number, airline and departure time   **7. a)** Yes **b)** No **c)** No   **9. a)** Social Security number **b)** There are no two people with the same name who happen to have the same street address. **c)** There are no two people with the same name living together.   **11.** (Nadir, 122, 34, Detroit, 08 : 10), (Nadir, 199, 13, Detroit, 08 : 47), (Nadir, 322, 34, Detroit, 09 : 44)   **13.** (Nadir, 122, 34, Detroit, 08 : 10), (Nadir, 199, 13, Detroit, 08 : 47), (Nadir, 322, 34, Detroit, 09 : 44), (Acme, 221, 22, Denver, 08 : 17), (Acme, 222, 22, Denver, 09 : 10)   **15.** $P_{3,5,6}$

**17.**

| Airline | Destination |
|---------|-------------|
| Nadir | Detroit |
| Acme | Denver |
| Acme | Anchorage |
| Acme | Honolulu |

**19.**

| Supplier | Part_ number | Project | Quantity | Color_ code |
|---|---|---|---|---|
| 23 | 1092 | 1 | 2 | 2 |
| 23 | 1101 | 3 | 1 | 1 |
| 23 | 9048 | 4 | 12 | 2 |
| 31 | 4975 | 3 | 6 | 2 |
| 31 | 3477 | 2 | 25 | 2 |
| 32 | 6984 | 4 | 10 | 1 |
| 32 | 9191 | 2 | 80 | 4 |
| 33 | 1001 | 1 | 14 | 8 |

**21.** Both sides of this equation pick out the subset of $R$ consisting of those $n$-tuples satisfying both conditions $C_1$ and $C_2$.
**23.** Both sides of this equation pick out the set of $n$-tuples that are in $R$, are in $S$, and satisfy condition $C$.  **25.** Both sides of this equation pick out the $m$-tuples consisting of $i_1$th, $i_2$th, ..., $i_m$th components of $n$-tuples in either $R$ or $S$.
**27.** Let $R = \{(a, b)\}$ and $S = \{(a, c)\}$, $n = 2, m = 1$, and $i_1 = 1$; $P_1(R - S) = \{(a)\}$, but $P_1(R) - P_1(S) = \emptyset$.
**29. a)** $J_2$ followed by $P_{1,3}$ **b)** (23, 1), (23, 3), (31, 3), (32, 4)
**31.** There is no primary key.

## Section 9.3

**1. a)** $\begin{bmatrix} 1 & 1 & 1 \\ 0 & 0 & 0 \\ 0 & 0 & 0 \end{bmatrix}$ **b)** $\begin{bmatrix} 0 & 1 & 0 \\ 1 & 1 & 0 \\ 0 & 0 & 1 \end{bmatrix}$
**c)** $\begin{bmatrix} 1 & 1 & 1 \\ 0 & 1 & 1 \\ 0 & 0 & 1 \end{bmatrix}$ **d)** $\begin{bmatrix} 0 & 0 & 1 \\ 0 & 0 & 0 \\ 1 & 0 & 0 \end{bmatrix}$

**3. a)** (1, 1), (1, 3), (2, 2), (3, 1), (3, 3) **b)** (1, 2), (2, 2), (3, 2) **c)** (1, 1), (1, 2), (1, 3), (2, 1), (2, 3), (3, 1), (3, 2), (3, 3)  **5.** The relation is irreflexive if and only if the main diagonal of the matrix contains only 0s.  **7. a)** Reflexive, symmetric, transitive **b)** Antisymmetric, transitive **c)** Symmetric
**9. a)** 4950 **b)** 9900 **c)** 99 **d)** 100 **e)** 1  **11.** Change each 0 to a 1 and each 1 to a 0.

**13. a)** $\begin{bmatrix} 0 & 1 & 1 \\ 1 & 1 & 0 \\ 1 & 0 & 1 \end{bmatrix}$ **b)** $\begin{bmatrix} 1 & 0 & 0 \\ 0 & 0 & 1 \\ 0 & 1 & 0 \end{bmatrix}$ **c)** $\begin{bmatrix} 1 & 1 & 1 \\ 1 & 1 & 1 \\ 1 & 1 & 1 \end{bmatrix}$

**15. a)** $\begin{bmatrix} 0 & 0 & 1 \\ 1 & 1 & 0 \\ 0 & 1 & 1 \end{bmatrix}$ **b)** $\begin{bmatrix} 1 & 1 & 0 \\ 0 & 1 & 1 \\ 1 & 1 & 1 \end{bmatrix}$ **c)** $\begin{bmatrix} 0 & 1 & 1 \\ 1 & 1 & 1 \\ 1 & 1 & 1 \end{bmatrix}$

**17.** $n^2 - k$

**19. a)** 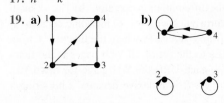 **b)**

**21.**
For simplicity we have indicated pairs of edges between the same two vertices in opposite directions by using a double arrowhead, rather than drawing two separate lines.

 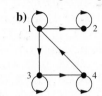 

**23.** $\{(a, b), (a, c), (b, c), (c, b)\}$  **25.** $(a, c), (b, a), (c, d), (d, b)$  **27.** $\{(a, a), (a, b), (a, c), (b, a), (b, b), (b, c), (c, a), (c, b), (d, d)\}$  **29.** The relation is asymmetric if and only if the directed graph has no loops and no closed paths of length 2.  **31.** Exercise 23: irreflexive. Exercise 24: reflexive, antisymmetric, transitive. Exercise 25: irreflexive, antisymmetric.  **33.** Reverse the direction on every edge in the digraph for $R$.  **35.** Proof by mathematical induction. *Basis step:* Trivial for $n = 1$. *Inductive step:* Assume true for $k$. Because $R^{k+1} = R^k \circ R$, its matrix is $\mathbf{M}_R \odot \mathbf{M}_{R^k}$. By the inductive hypothesis this is $\mathbf{M}_R \odot \mathbf{M}_R^{[k]} = \mathbf{M}_R^{[k+1]}$.

## Section 9.4

**1. a)** $\{(0, 0), (0, 1), (1, 1), (1, 2), (2, 0), (2, 2), (3, 0), (3, 3)\}$
**b)** $\{(0, 1), (0, 2), (0, 3), (1, 0), (1, 1), (1, 2), (2, 0), (2, 1), (2, 2), (3, 0)\}$  **3.** $\{(a, b) \mid a$ divides $b$ or $b$ divides $a\}$

**5.** **7.**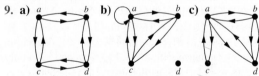

**9. a)** **b)** **c)**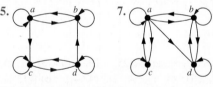

**11. a)** **b)** **c)**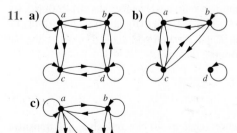

**13.** The symmetric closure of $R$ is $R \cup R^{-1}$. $\mathbf{M}_{R \cup R^{-1}} = \mathbf{M}_R \vee \mathbf{M}_{R^{-1}} = \mathbf{M}_R \vee \mathbf{M}_R^t$.  **15.** Only when $R$ is irreflexive, in which case it is its own closure.   **17.** $a, a, a, a; a, b, e, a;$ $a, d, e, a; b, c, c, b; b, e, a, b; c, b, c, c; c, c, c, b, c; c, c, c, c, c; d,$ $e, a, d; d, e, e, d; e, a, b, e; e, a, d, e; e, d, e, e; e, e, d, e; e, e,$ $e, e$   **19. a)** $\{(1, 1), (1, 5), (2, 3), (3, 1), (3, 2), (3, 3), (3, 4),$ $(4, 1), (4, 5), (5, 3), (5, 4)\}$   **b)** $\{(1, 1), (1, 2), (1, 3), (1, 4),$ $(2, 1), (2, 5), (3, 1), (3, 3), (3, 4), (3, 5), (4, 1), (4, 2), (4, 3),$ $(4, 4), (5, 1), (5, 3), (5, 5)\}$   **c)** $\{(1, 1), (1, 3), (1, 4), (1, 5),$ $(2, 1), (2, 2), (2, 3), (2, 4), (3, 1), (3, 2), (3, 3), (3, 4), (3, 5),$ $(4, 1), (4, 3), (4, 4), (4, 5), (5, 1), (5, 2), (5, 3), (5, 4), (5, 5)\}$ **d)** $\{(1, 1), (1, 2), (1, 3), (1, 4), (1, 5), (2, 1), (2, 3), (2, 4),$ $(2, 5), (3, 1), (3, 2), (3, 3), (3, 4), (3, 5), (4, 1), (4, 2), (4, 3),$ $(4, 4), (4, 5), (5, 1), (5, 2), (5, 3), (5, 4), (5, 5)\}$   **e)** $\{(1, 1),$ $(1, 2), (1, 3), (1, 4), (1, 5), (2, 1), (2, 2), (2, 3), (2, 4), (2, 5),$ $(3, 1), (3, 2), (3, 3), (3, 4), (3, 5), (4, 1), (4, 2), (4, 3), (4, 4),$ $(4, 5), (5, 1), (5, 2), (5, 3), (5, 4), (5, 5)\}$   **f)** $\{(1, 1), (1, 2),$ $(1, 3), (1, 4), (1, 5), (2, 1), (2, 2), (2, 3), (2, 4), (2, 5), (3, 1),$ $(3, 2), (3, 3), (3, 4), (3, 5), (4, 1), (4, 2), (4, 3), (4, 4), (4, 5),$ $(5, 1), (5, 2), (5, 3), (5, 4), (5, 5)\}$   **21. a)** If there is a student $c$ who shares a class with $a$ and a class with $b$   **b)** If there are two students $c$ and $d$ such that $a$ and $c$ share a class, $c$ and $d$ share a class, and $d$ and $b$ share a class   **c)** If there is a sequence $s_0, \ldots, s_n$ of students with $n \geq 1$ such that $s_0 = a$, $s_n = b$, and for each $i = 1, 2, \ldots, n$, $s_i$ and $s_{i-1}$ share a class   **23.** The result follows from $(R^*)^{-1} = \left(\bigcup_{n=1}^{\infty} R^n\right)^{-1} = \bigcup_{n=1}^{\infty} (R^n)^{-1} = \bigcup_{n=1}^{\infty} R^n = R^*$.

**25. a)** $\begin{bmatrix} 1 & 1 & 1 & 1 \\ 1 & 1 & 1 & 1 \\ 1 & 1 & 1 & 1 \\ 1 & 1 & 1 & 1 \end{bmatrix}$   **b)** $\begin{bmatrix} 0 & 0 & 0 & 0 \\ 1 & 0 & 1 & 1 \\ 1 & 0 & 1 & 1 \\ 1 & 0 & 1 & 1 \end{bmatrix}$

**c)** $\begin{bmatrix} 0 & 1 & 1 & 1 \\ 0 & 0 & 1 & 1 \\ 0 & 0 & 0 & 1 \\ 0 & 0 & 0 & 0 \end{bmatrix}$   **d)** $\begin{bmatrix} 1 & 1 & 1 & 1 \\ 1 & 1 & 1 & 1 \\ 1 & 1 & 1 & 1 \\ 1 & 1 & 1 & 1 \end{bmatrix}$

**27.** Answers same as for Exercise 25.   **29. a)** $\{(1, 1), (1, 2),$ $(1, 4), (2, 2), (3, 3), (4, 1), (4, 2), (4, 4)\}$   **b)** $\{(1, 1),$ $(1, 2), (1, 4), (2, 1), (2, 2), (2, 4), (3, 3), (4, 1), (4, 2),$ $(4, 4)\}$   **c)** $\{(1, 1), (1, 2), (1, 4), (2, 1), (2, 2), (2, 4), (3, 3),$ $(4, 1), (4, 2), (4, 4)\}$   **31.** Algorithm 1: $O(n^{3.8})$; Algorithm 2: $O(n^3)$   **33.** Initialize with $\mathbf{A} := \mathbf{M}_R \vee \mathbf{I}_n$ and loop only for $i := 2$ to $n - 1$.   **35. a)** Because $R$ is reflexive, every relation containing it must also be reflexive.   **b)** Both $\{(0, 0),$ $(0, 1), (0, 2), (1, 1), (2, 2)\}$ and $\{(0, 0), (0, 1), (1, 0), (1, 1),$ $(2, 2)\}$ contain $R$ and have an odd number of elements, but neither is a subset of the other.

## Section 9.5

**1. a)** Equivalence relation   **b)** Not reflexive, not transitive **c)** Equivalence relation   **d)** Not transitive   **e)** Not symmetric, not transitive   **3. a)** Equivalence relation   **b)** Not transitive **c)** Not reflexive, not symmetric, not transitive   **d)** Equivalence relation   **e)** Not reflexive, not transitive   **5.** Many answers are possible. (1) Two buildings are equivalent if they were opened during the same year; an equivalence class consists of the set of buildings opened in a given year (as long as there was at least one building opened that year). (2) Two buildings are equivalent if they have the same number of stories; the equivalence classes are the set of 1-story buildings, the set of 2-story buildings, and so on (one class for each $n$ for which there is at least one $n$-story building). (3) Every building in which you have a class is equivalent to every building in which you have a class (including itself), and every building in which you don't have a class is equivalent to every building in which you don't have a class (including itself); there are two equivalence classes—the set of buildings in which you have a class and the set of buildings in which you don't have a class (assuming these are nonempty).   **7.** The statement "$p$ is equivalent to $q$" means that $p$ and $q$ have the same entries in their truth tables. $R$ is reflexive, because $p$ has the same truth table as $p$. $R$ is symmetric, for if $p$ and $q$ have the same truth table, then $q$ and $p$ have the same truth table. If $p$ and $q$ have the same entries in their truth tables and $q$ and $r$ have the same entries in their truth tables, then $p$ and $r$ also do, so $R$ is transitive. The equivalence class of $\mathbf{T}$ is the set of all tautologies; the equivalence class of $\mathbf{F}$ is the set of all contradictions. **9. a)** $(x, x) \in R$ because $f(x) = f(x)$. Hence, $R$ is reflexive. $(x, y) \in R$ if and only if $f(x) = f(y)$, which holds if and only if $f(y) = f(x)$ if and only if $(y, x) \in R$. Hence, $R$ is symmetric. If $(x, y) \in R$ and $(y, z) \in R$, then $f(x) = f(y)$ and $f(y) = f(z)$. Hence, $f(x) = f(z)$. Thus, $(x, z) \in R$. It follows that $R$ is transitive.   **b)** The sets $f^{-1}(b)$ for $b$ in the range of $f$   **11.** Let $x$ be a bit string of length 3 or more. Because $x$ agrees with itself in the first three bits, $(x, x) \in R$. Hence, $R$ is reflexive. Suppose that $(x, y) \in R$. Then $x$ and $y$ agree in the first three bits. Hence, $y$ and $x$ agree in the first three bits. Thus, $(y, x) \in R$. If $(x, y)$ and $(y, z)$ are in $R$, then $x$ and $y$ agree in the first three bits, as do $y$ and $z$. Hence, $x$ and $z$ agree in the first three bits. Hence, $(x, z) \in R$. It follows that $R$ is transitive.   **13.** This follows from Exercise 9, where $f$ is the function that takes a bit string of length 3 or more to the ordered pair with its first bit as the first component and the third bit as its second component.   **15.** For reflexivity, $((a, b), (a, b)) \in R$ because $a + b = b + a$. For symmetry, if $((a, b), (c, d)) \in R$, then $a + d = b + c$, so $c + b = d + a$, so $((c, d), (a, b)) \in R$. For transitivity, if $((a, b), (c, d)) \in R$ and $((c, d), (e, f)) \in R$, then $a + d = b + c$ and $c + e = d + f$, so $a + d + c + e = b + c + d + f$, so $a + e = b + f$, so $((a, b), (e, f)) \in R$. An easier solution is to note that by algebra, the given condition is the same as the condition that $f((a, b)) = f((c, d))$, where $f((x, y)) = x - y$; therefore by Exercise 9 this is an equivalence relation.   **17. a)** This follows from Exercise 9, where the function $f$ from the set of differentiable functions (from $\mathbf{R}$ to $\mathbf{R}$) to the set of functions (from $\mathbf{R}$ to $\mathbf{R}$) is the differentiation operator.   **b)** The set of all functions of the form $g(x) = x^2 + C$ for some constant $C$ **19.** This follows from Exercise 9, where the function $f$ from the set of all URLs to the set of all Web pages is the function that assigns to each URL the Web page for that URL. **21.** No   **23.** No   **25.** $R$ is reflexive because a bit string $s$

has the same number of 1s as itself. $R$ is symmetric because $s$ and $t$ having the same number of 1s implies that $t$ and $s$ do. $R$ is transitive because $s$ and $t$ having the same number of 1s, and $t$ and $u$ having the same number of 1s implies that $s$ and $u$ have the same number of 1s. **27. a)** The sets of people of the same age **b)** The sets of people with the same two parents **29.** The set of all bit strings with exactly two 1s. **31. a)** The set of all bit strings of length 3 **b)** The set of all bit strings of length 4 that end with a 1 **c)** The set of all bit strings of length 5 that end 11 **d)** The set of all bit strings of length 8 that end 10101 **33.** Each of the 15 bit strings of length less than four is in an equivalence class by itself: $[\lambda]_{R_4} = \{\lambda\}$, $[0]_{R_4} = \{0\}$, $[1]_{R_4} = \{1\}$, $[00]_{R_4} = \{00\}$, $[01]_{R_4} = \{01\}$, ..., $[111]_{R_4} = \{111\}$. The remaining 16 equivalence classes are determined by the bit strings of length 4: $[0000]_{R_4} = \{0000, 00000, 00001, 000000, 000001, 000010, 000011, 0000000, \ldots\}$, $[0001]_{R_4} = \{0001, 00010, 00011, 000100, 000101, 000110, 000111, 0001000, \ldots\}$, ..., $[1111]_{R_4} = \{1111, 11110, 11111, 111100, 111101, 111110, 111111, 1111000, \ldots\}$ **35. a)** $[2]_5 = \{i \mid i \equiv 2 \pmod 5\} = \{\ldots, -8, -3, 2, 7, 12, \ldots\}$ **b)** $[3]_5 = \{i \mid i \equiv 3 \pmod 5\} = \{\ldots, -7, -2, 3, 8, 13, \ldots\}$ **c)** $[6]_5 = \{i \mid i \equiv 6 \pmod 5\} = \{\ldots, -9, -4, 1, 6, 11, \ldots\}$ **d)** $[-3]_5 = \{i \mid i \equiv -3 \pmod 5\} = \{\ldots, -8, -3, 2, 7, 12, \ldots\}$ **37.** $\{6n + k \mid n \in \mathbf{Z}\}$ for $k \in \{0, 1, 2, 3, 4, 5\}$ **39. a)** $[(1, 2)] = \{(a, b) \mid a - b = -1\} = \{(1, 2), (3, 4), (4, 5), (5, 6), \ldots\}$ **b)** Each equivalence class can be interpreted as an integer (negative, positive, or zero); specifically, $[(a, b)]$ can be interpreted as $a - b$. **41. a)** No **b)** Yes **c)** Yes **d)** No **43.** (a), (c), (e) **45.** (b), (d), (e) **47. a)** $\{(0, 0), (1, 1), (1, 2), (2, 1), (2, 2), (3, 3), (3, 4), (3, 5), (4, 3), (4, 4), (4, 5), (5, 3), (5, 4), (5, 5)\}$ **b)** $\{(0, 0), (0, 1), (1, 0), (1, 1), (2, 2), (2, 3), (3, 2), (3, 3), (4, 4), (4, 5), (5, 4), (5, 5)\}$ **c)** $\{(0, 0), (0, 1), (0, 2), (1, 0), (1, 1), (1, 2), (2, 0), (2, 1), (2, 2), (3, 3), (3, 4), (3, 5), (4, 3), (4, 4), (4, 5), (5, 3), (5, 4), (5, 5)\}$ **d)** $\{(0, 0), (1, 1), (2, 2), (3, 3), (4, 4), (5, 5)\}$ **49.** $[0]_6 \subseteq [0]_3$, $[1]_6 \subseteq [1]_3$, $[2]_6 \subseteq [2]_3$, $[3]_6 \subseteq [0]_3$, $[4]_6 \subseteq [1]_3$, $[5]_6 \subseteq [2]_3$ **51.** Let $A$ be a set in the first partition. Pick a particular element $x$ of $A$. The set of all bit strings of length 16 that agree with $x$ on the last four bits is one of the sets in the second partition, and clearly every string in $A$ is in that set. **53.** We claim that each equivalence class $[x]_{R_{31}}$ is a subset of the equivalence class $[x]_{R_8}$. To show this, choose an arbitrary element $y \in [x]_{R_{31}}$. Then $y$ is equivalent to $x$ under $R_{31}$, so either $y = x$ or $y$ and $x$ are each at least 31 characters long and agree on their first 31 characters. Because strings that are at least 31 characters long and agree on their first 31 characters perforce are at least 8 characters long and agree on their first 8 characters, we know that either $y = x$ or $y$ and $x$ are each at least 8 characters long and agree on their first 8 characters. This means that $y$ is equivalent to $x$ under $R_8$, so $y \in [x]_{R_8}$. **55.** $\{(a, a), (a, b), (a, c), (b, a), (b, b), (b, c), (c, a), (c, b), (c, c), (d, d), (d, e), (e, d), (e, e)\}$ **57. a)** $\mathbf{Z}$ **b)** $\{n + \frac{1}{2} \mid n \in \mathbf{Z}\}$ **59. a)** $R$ is reflexive because any coloring can be obtained from itself via a 360-degree rotation. To see that $R$ is symmetric and transitive, use the fact that each rotation is the composition of

two reflections and conversely the composition of two reflections is a rotation. Hence, $(C_1, C_2)$ belongs to $R$ if and only if $C_2$ can be obtained from $C_1$ by a composition of reflections. So if $(C_1, C_2)$ belongs to $R$, so does $(C_2, C_1)$ because the inverse of the composition of reflections is also a composition of reflections (in the opposite order). Hence, $R$ is symmetric. To see that $R$ is transitive, suppose $(C_1, C_2)$ and $(C_2, C_3)$ belong to $R$. Taking the composition of the reflections in each case yields a composition of reflections, showing that $(C_1, C_3)$ belongs to $R$. **b)** We express colorings with sequences of length four, with $r$ and $b$ denoting red and blue, respectively. We list letters denoting the colors of the upper left square, upper right square, lower left square, and lower right square, in that order. The equivalence classes are: $\{rrrr\}$, $\{bbbb\}$, $\{rrrb, rrbr, rbrr, brrr\}$, $\{bbbr, bbrb, brbb, rbbb\}$, $\{rbbr, brrb\}$, $\{rrbb, brbr, bbrr, rbrb\}$. **61.** 5 **63.** Yes **65.** $R$ **67.** First form the reflexive closure of $R$, then form the symmetric closure of the reflexive closure, and finally form the transitive closure of the symmetric closure of the reflexive closure. **69.** $p(0) = 1$, $p(1) = 1$, $p(2) = 2$, $p(3) = 5$, $p(4) = 15$, $p(5) = 52$, $p(6) = 203$, $p(7) = 877$, $p(8) = 4140$, $p(9) = 21147$, $p(10) = 115975$

## Section 9.6

**1. a)** Is a partial ordering **b)** Not antisymmetric, not transitive **c)** Is a partial ordering **d)** Is a partial ordering **e)** Not antisymmetric, not transitive **3. a)** No **b)** No **c)** Yes **5. a)** Yes **b)** No **c)** Yes **d)** No **7. a)** No **b)** Yes **c)** No **9.** No **11.** Yes **13. a)** $\{(0, 0), (1, 0), (1, 1), (2, 0), (2, 1), (2, 2)\}$ **b)** $(\mathbf{Z}, \leq)$ **c)** $(P(\mathbf{Z}), \subseteq)$ **d)** $(\mathbf{Z}^+, \text{"is a multiple of"})$ **15. a)** $\{0\}$ and $\{1\}$, for instance **b)** 4 and 6, for instance **17. a)** $(1, 1, 2) < (1, 2, 1)$ **b)** $(0, 1, 2, 3) < (0, 1, 3, 2)$ **c)** $(0, 1, 1, 1, 0) < (1, 0, 1, 0, 1)$ **19.** $0 < 0001 < 001 < 01 < 010 < 0101 < 011 < 11$

**21.**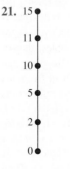

**23. a)** 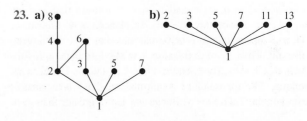 **b)**

**c)**

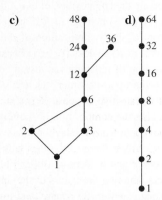

**25.** $(a, b), (a, c), (a, d), (b, c), (b, d), (a, a), (b, b), (c, c),$ $(d, d)$ **27.** $(a, a), (a, g), (a, d), (a, e), (a, f), (b, b), (b, g),$ $(b, d), (b, e), (b, f), (c, c), (c, g), (c, d), (c, e), (c, f), (g, d),$ $(g, e), (g, f), (g, g), (d, d), (e, e), (f, f)$ **29.** $(\emptyset, \{a\}),$ $(\emptyset, \{b\}), (\emptyset, \{c\}), (\{a\}, \{a, b\}), (\{a\}, \{a, c\}), (\{b\}, \{a, b\}),$ $(\{b\}, \{b, c\}), (\{c\}, \{a, c\}), (\{c\}, \{b, c\}), (\{a, b\}, \{a, b, c\}),$ $(\{a, c\}, \{a, b, c\})(\{b, c\}, \{a, b, c\})$ **31.** Let $(S, \preccurlyeq)$ be a finite poset. We will show that this poset is the reflexive transitive closure of its covering relation. Suppose that $(a, b)$ is in the reflexive transitive closure of the covering relation. Then $a = b$ or $a \prec b$, so $a \preccurlyeq b$, or else there is a sequence $a_1, a_2, \ldots, a_n$ such that $a \prec a_1 \prec a_2 \prec \cdots \prec a_n \prec b$, in which case again $a \preccurlyeq b$ by the transitivity of $\preccurlyeq$. Conversely, suppose that $a \prec b$. If $a = b$ then $(a, b)$ is in the reflexive transitive closure of the covering relation. If $a \prec b$ and there is no $z$ such that $a \prec z \prec b$, then $(a, b)$ is in the covering relation and therefore in its reflexive transitive closure. Otherwise, let $a \prec a_1 \prec a_2 \prec \cdots \prec a_n \prec b$ be a longest possible sequence of this form (which exists because the poset is finite). Then no intermediate elements can be inserted, so each pair $(a, a_1), (a_1, a_2), \ldots, (a_n, b)$ is in the covering relation, so again $(a, b)$ is in its reflexive transitive closure. **33. a)** 24, 45 **b)** 3, 5 **c)** No **d)** No **e)** 15, 45 **f)** 15 **g)** 15, 5, 3 **h)** 15 **35. a)** $\{1, 2\}, \{1, 3, 4\}, \{2, 3, 4\}$ **b)** $\{1\}, \{2\}, \{4\}$ **c)** No **d)** No **e)** $\{2, 4\}, \{2, 3, 4\}$ **f)** $\{2, 4\}$ **g)** $\{3, 4\}, \{4\}$ **h)** $\{3, 4\}$ **37.** Because $(a, b) \preccurlyeq (a, b)$, $\preccurlyeq$ is reflexive. If $(a_1, a_2) \preccurlyeq (b_1, b_2)$ and $(a_1, a_2) \neq (b_1, b_2)$, either $a_1 \prec b_1$, or $a_1 = b_1$ and $a_2 \prec b_2$. In either case, $(b_1, b_2)$ is not less than or equal to $(a_1, a_2)$. Hence, $\preccurlyeq$ is antisymmetric. Suppose that $(a_1, a_2) \prec (b_1, b_2) \prec (c_1, c_2)$. Then if $a_1 \prec b_1$ or $b_1 \prec c_1$, we have $a_1 \prec c_1$, so $(a_1, a_2) \prec (c_1, c_2)$, but if $a_1 = b_1 = c_1$, then $a_2 \prec b_2 \prec c_2$, which implies that $(a_1, a_2) \prec (c_1, c_2)$. Hence, $\preccurlyeq$ is transitive. **39.** Because $(s, t) \preccurlyeq (s, t)$, $\preccurlyeq$ is reflexive. If $(s, t) \preccurlyeq (u, v)$ and $(u, v) \preccurlyeq (s, t)$, then $s \preccurlyeq u \preccurlyeq s$ and $t \preccurlyeq v \preccurlyeq t$; hence, $s = u$ and $t = v$. Hence, $\preccurlyeq$ is antisymmetric. Suppose that $(s, t) \preccurlyeq (u, v) \preccurlyeq (w, x)$. Then $s \preccurlyeq u, t \preccurlyeq v, u \preccurlyeq w$, and $v \preccurlyeq x$. It follows that $s \preccurlyeq w$ and $t \preccurlyeq x$. Hence, $(s, t) \preccurlyeq (w, x)$. Hence, $\preccurlyeq$ is transitive. **41. a)** Suppose that $x$ is maximal and that $y$ is the largest element. Then $x \preccurlyeq y$. Because $x$ is not less than $y$, it follows that $x = y$. By Exercise 40(a) $y$ is unique. Hence, $x$ is unique. **b)** Suppose that $x$ is minimal and that $y$ is the smallest element. Then $x \succcurlyeq y$. Because $x$ is not greater than $y$, it

follows that $x = y$. By Exercise 40(b) $y$ is unique. Hence, $x$ is unique. **43. a)** Yes **b)** No **c)** Yes **45.** Use mathematical induction. Let $P(n)$ be "Every subset with $n$ elements from a lattice has a least upper bound and a greatest lower bound." *Basis step:* $P(1)$ is true because the least upper bound and greatest lower bound of $\{x\}$ are both $x$. *Inductive step:* Assume that $P(k)$ is true. Let $S$ be a set with $k + 1$ elements. Let $x \in S$ and $S' = S - \{x\}$. Because $S'$ has $k$ elements, by the inductive hypothesis, it has a least upper bound $y$ and a greatest lower bound $a$. Now because we are in a lattice, there are elements $z = \text{lub}(x, y)$ and $b = \text{glb}(x, a)$. We are done if we can show that $z$ is the least upper bound of $S$ and $b$ is the greatest lower bound of $S$. To show that $z$ is the least upper bound of $S$, first note that if $w \in S$, then $w = x$ or $w \in S'$. If $w = x$ then $w \preccurlyeq z$ because $z$ is the least upper bound of $x$ and $y$. If $w \in S'$, then $w \preccurlyeq z$ because $w \preccurlyeq y$, which is true because $y$ is the least upper bound of $S'$, and $y \preccurlyeq z$, which is true because $z = \text{lub}(x, y)$. To see that $z$ is the least upper bound of $S$, suppose that $u$ is an upper bound of $S$. Note that such an element $u$ must be an upper bound of $x$ and $y$, but because $z = \text{lub}(x, y)$, it follows that $z \preccurlyeq u$. We omit the similar argument that $b$ is the greatest lower bound of $S$. **47. a)** No **b)** Yes **c)** (*Proprietary, {Cheetah, Puma}*), (*Restricted, {Cheetah, Puma}*), (*Registered, {Cheetah, Puma}*), (*Proprietary, {Cheetah, Puma, Impala}*), (*Restricted, {Cheetah, Puma, Impala}*), (*Registered, {Cheetah, Puma, Impala}*) **d)** (*Non-proprietary, {Impala, Puma}*), (*Proprietary, {Impala, Puma}*), (*Restricted, {Impala, Puma}*), (*Nonproprietary, {Impala}*), (*Proprietary, {Impala}*), (*Restricted, {Impala}*), (*Nonproprietary, {Puma}*), (*Proprietary, {Puma}*), (*Restricted, {Puma}*), (*Nonproprietary, $\emptyset$*), (*Proprietary, $\emptyset$*), (*Restricted, $\emptyset$*) **49.** Let $\Pi$ be the set of all partitions of a set $S$ with $P_1 \preccurlyeq P_2$ if $P_1$ is a refinement of $P_2$, that is, if every set in $P_1$ is a subset of a set in $P_2$. First, we show that $(\Pi, \preccurlyeq)$ is a poset. Because $P \preccurlyeq P$ for every partition $P$, $\preccurlyeq$ is reflexive. Now suppose that $P_1 \preccurlyeq P_2$ and $P_2 \preccurlyeq P_1$. Let $T \in P_1$. Because $P_1 \preccurlyeq P_2$, there is a set $T' \in P_2$ such that $T \subseteq T'$. Because $P_2 \preccurlyeq P_1$ there is a set $T'' \in P_1$ such that $T' \subseteq T''$. It follows that $T \subseteq T''$. But because $P_1$ is a partition, $T = T''$, which implies that $T = T'$ because $T \subseteq T' \subseteq T''$. Thus, $T \in P_2$. By reversing the roles of $P_1$ and $P_2$ it follows that every set in $P_2$ is also in $P_1$. Hence, $P_1 = P_2$ and $\preccurlyeq$ is antisymmetric. Next, suppose that $P_1 \preccurlyeq P_2$ and $P_2 \preccurlyeq P_3$. Let $T \in P_1$. Then there is a set $T' \in P_2$ such that $T \subseteq T'$. Because $P_2 \preccurlyeq P_3$ there is a set $T'' \in P_3$ such that $T' \subseteq T''$. This means that $T \subseteq T''$. Hence, $P_1 \preccurlyeq P_3$. It follows that $\preccurlyeq$ is transitive. The greatest lower bound of the partitions $P_1$ and $P_2$ is the partition $P$ whose subsets are the nonempty sets of the form $T_1 \cap T_2$ where $T_1 \in P_1$ and $T_2 \in P_2$. We omit the justification of this statement here. The least upper bound of the partitions $P_1$ and $P_2$ is the partition that corresponds to the equivalence relation in which $x \in S$ is related to $y \in S$ if there is a sequence $x = x_0, x_1, x_2, \ldots, x_n = y$ for some nonnegative integer $n$ such that for each $i$ from 1 to $n$, $x_{i-1}$ and $x_i$ are in the same element of $P_1$ or of $P_2$. We omit the details that this is an equivalence relation and the details of the proof that this is

# Photo Credits

CHAPTER 9    **Page 604**: Courtesy Stephen Warshall;    **p. 623**: © Deutsches Museum;    **p. 636**: © The Royal Society.

CHAPTER 10    **Page 660**: © The Royal Society;    **p. 695**: Scientists and Inventors Portrait File Collection, Archives Center, National Museum of American History, Smithsonian Institution;    **p. 700**: © Master and Fellows of Trinity College, Cambridge;    **p. 701(top)**: © Rosemarie Dirac;    **p. 701(bottom)**: © Reverence to University History Photobase;    **p. 706**: Julius Petersen: *Metoder og Teorier. Edition no. 6*, Det Schoenbergske Forlag, Copenhagen 1912. Photo courtesy Bjarne Toft;    **p. 710**: Courtesy, Edsger W. Dijkstra;    **p. 723**: Courtesy, the Archive of Polish Mathematicians, at the Institute of Mathematics of the Polish Academy of Sciences;    **p. 728**: By permission of the London Mathematical Society.

CHAPTER 11    **Page 750**: © Master and Fellows of Trinity College, Cambridge;    **p. 763**: Courtesy, California State University, Santa Cruz;    **p. 782**: Courtesy, the Archive of Polish Mathematicians, at the Institute of Mathematics of the Polish Academy of Sciences;    **p. 798**: Courtesy, Robert Clay Prim;    **p. 800**: Courtesy Joseph B. Kruskal. Photo by Rachel Kruskal.

CHAPTER 12    **Page 812**: Courtesy MIT Museum;    **p. 830**: Courtesy Maurice Karnaugh;    **p. 837**: Courtesy Edward J. McCluskey;    **p. 839**: Courtesy the Quine Family.

CHAPTER 13    **Page 853**: © Donna Coveney/MIT;    **p. 854(top)**: Courtesy IBM, Almaden Research Center;    **p. 854(bottom)**: Courtesy Peter Naur;    **p. 867**: Photo from *I Have a Photographic Memory* by Paul Halmos (1987), American Mathematical Society;    **p. 872**: © Bettman/Corbis;    **p. 886**: © Science Photo Library/Photo Researchers, Inc.;    **p. 897**: © University Archives. Department of Rare Books and Special Collections. Princeton University Library.

APPENDIX 1    **Page A-4**: © Hulton-Deutsch Collection/Corbis.

# Index of Biographies

# Index

Notation
  big-*O*, 205, 232
  big-Omega (Ω), 214, 232
  big-Theta, 215
  big-Theta (Θ), 232
  dependency, 846
  for products
    well-formed formula in, 784
  infix, 779–782, 804
  little-*o*, 218
  Polish, 780, 804
  postfix, 779–782, 804, 858
  prefix, 779–782, 804
  product, 186
  reverse Polish, 781, 804, 858
  set builder, 116, 185
  summation, 162, 186
NOT gate, 21
Noun, 848
Noun phrase, 848
*Nova*, 107
NP, class of nondeterministic polynomial-time
    problems, 900
NP-complete problems, 227, 715, 830, 900
Null quantification, 56
Null set, 185
Null string, 849
Number(s)
  Bacon, 680
  Bell, 618
  cardinal, 121
  Carmichael, 283, 306
  Catalan, 507
  chromatic, 728, 737
    edge, 734
  crossing, 726
  computable, 886
  Cunningham, 262
  Erdős, 635, 680, 689
  Fibonacci, 347, 365–367, 771
    formula for, 517
    iterative algorithm for, 366
    rabbits and, 502–503
    recursive algorithms for, 365
  harmonic
    inequality of, 320–321
  independence, 741
  irrational, 85, 116
  large, law of, 459
  Lucas, 379, 525
  lucky, 570
  natural, 116
  pseudorandom, 288
  Ramsey, 404
  rational, 85, 116
  real, A-1–A-5
  Stirling, of the first kind, 431
    signless, 443
  Stirling, of the second kind, 430
  Ten Most Wanted, 262
  Ulam, 188
Number-theoretic functions, 892
Numbering plan, 387
Number theory, 237
  definition of, 237

Object, 118
Object(s)
  distinguishable, 428
    and distinguishable boxes, 428–429
    and indistinguishable boxes, 428–431

indistinguishable, 428
    and indistinguishable boxes, 428–431
  unlabeled, 428
Obligato game, 112
Octahedral die, 496
Octal expansions, 246, 306
Octal representation, 246, 306
Odd, 83
Odd pie fights, 325
Odlyzko, Andrew, 163
Odometer, 307
One's complement representations, 256
One-to-one (injective) function
  counting, 387
One-to-one correspondence, 144, 186
One-to-one function, 141, 143, 186
*On-Line Encyclopedia of Integer Sequences (OEIS)*,
    162
Only if, expressing conditional statement using, 7
Onto (surjective) function, 143, 186
  number of, 560–562, 566
Open interval, 117, 332
Open problems, 106, 263–264
Operands, well-formed formula of, 351
Operation(s)
  bit, 11, 110
  bitwise, 110
  set, 127
Operations
  on *n*-ary relations, 586–588
Operator(s)
  bitwise, 12
  logical, 109
  negation, 4
  logical, 109
  selection, 586
  well-formed formula of, 351
Opium, 475
Optimal algorithm, 230
Optimal for suitors, stable assignment, 343
Optimal solution, 198
Optimization problems, 198
OR, 18
Or
  exclusive, 5, 6
  inclusive, 5
Oracle of Bacon, 680
Order, 207
  of quantifiers, 58
Ordered *n*-tuple, 122
Ordered rooted tree, 749, 804, 806
Ordering
  dictionary, 435
  lexicographic, 356, 435, 620–622
  linear, 619
  partial, 618–629, 633
  quasi-ordering, 637
  total, 619, 633
Ordered pair
  defined using sets, 126
Ordinary generating function, 537
Ore's theorem, 701, 707
Ore, O., 701
Organizational tree, 750
OR gate, 21, 823, 843
Orientable graphs, 740
Orientation of undirected graph, 740
Out-degree of vertex, 654, 736
Output
  to an algorithm, 193

Output alphabet, 859
Outputs
  finite-state machines with, 859–863
  finite-state machines without, 865
Output string
  finite-state machine, 861

*P(n, r)*, 439
P, class of polynomial-time problems, 900
P=NP problem, 897
Pair, devil's, 678
Pairs, forbidden, 234
Pairwise relatively prime integers, 306
Palindrome(s), 202, 397, 857
  set of, 888
Paradigm
  Algorithmic, 224, 232
Paradox, 118, 185
  barber, 16
  Löb's, 112
  Russell's, 126
  St. Petersburg, 497
Parallel algorithms, 661
Parallel edges, 642
Parallel processing, 229, 661
  tree-connected, 751–752
Parentheses, balanced strings of, 382
Parent of vertex, 747, 803
Parent relation, 580
Parity
  same, 83
Parity check bit, 290
Parse tree, 852–854, 899
Parsing
  bottom-up, 853
  top-down, 853
Partial correctness, 372
Partial function, 152, 186, 889
  codomain of, 152
  domain of, 152
  domain of definition, 152
  undefined values, 152
Partially ordered set, 618
  antichain in, 637
  chain in, 637
  comparable elements in, 622, 633
  dense, 632
  dual of, 630
  greatest element of, 625, 634
  Hasse diagram of, 622–624, 634
  incomparable elements in, 622, 633
  least element of, 625, 634
  lower bound of, 625, 634
  maximal element of, 624, 634
  minimal element of, 624, 625, 634
  upper bound of, 625, 634
  well-founded, 632
Partial orderings, 618–629, 633
  compatible total ordering from, 634
Partition, 552
  of positive integer, 359, 431
  of set, 612–614, 633
  refinement of, 617
Partner
  valid, 234
Pascal's identity, 418–419, 439
Pascal's triangle, 419, 439
Pascal, Blaise, 282, 419, 445, 452
Passwords, 66, 391